International Handbook on Mega-Projects

Edited by

Hugo Priemus

Professor Emeritus of System Innovation and Spatial Development, Delft University of Technology, The Netherlands

Bert van Wee

Professor of Transport Policy, Delft University of Technology and Scientific Director, TRAIL Research School, The Netherlands

Edward Elgar
Cheltenham, UK • Northampton, MA, USA

Published by
Edward Elgar Publishing Limited
The Lypiatts
15 Lansdown Road
Cheltenham
Glos GL50 2JA
UK

Edward Elgar Publishing, Inc.
William Pratt House
9 Dewey Court
Northampton
Massachusetts 01060
USA

A catalogue record for this book
is available from the British Library

Library of Congress Control Number: 2013942223

This book is available electronically in the ElgarOnline.com Economics Subject Collection, E-ISBN 978 1 78100 230 8

FSC
www.fsc.org
MIX
Paper from
responsible sources
FSC® C013056

ISBN 978 1 78100 229 2 (cased)

Typeset by Servis Filmsetting Ltd, Stockport, Cheshire
Printed and bound in Great Britain by T.J. International Ltd, Padstow

Contents

Contributors

Jan Anne Annema (1961) is Assistant Professor of Transport Policy at Delft University of Technology since 2009. His research and educational activities concern mainly effectiveness and efficiency issues of transport policies. He focuses at the moment on three kinds of transport policies in particular: large infrastructure investments, innovative pricing policies and environmental policies. Jan Anne did a Masters in Chemistry at the University of Utrecht in 1987. In 2008 he defended his PhD at Delft University of Technology on the role of future research in transport policy. He worked for different Dutch research institutes related to the Ministry of Housing, Spatial Planning and the Environment and the Ministry of Transport.

Marian Bosch-Rekveldt is Assistant Professor of Project Management at Delft University of Technology. She holds an MSc in Mechanical Engineering (1999) and a PhD in Project Management (2011). Before starting her PhD research in 2006, she worked as a project engineer and project manager at a large organization for applied research. In 2011, she finished her PhD research titled 'Managing project complexity: a study into adapting early project phases to improve project performance in large engineering projects'. She is involved in teaching (BSc, MSc, DE graduate school and professional education) and research in the field of project management of (large) engineering projects.

Chantal C. Cantarelli is a Research Fellow at the BT Centre for Major Programme Management at Oxford University's Saïd Business School. The Centre's role is to understand how to best manage major programmes at a time when spending on infrastructure and mega-projects is the highest it has ever been as a share of world GDP. Chantal Cantarelli's research mainly focuses on project ownership and financing of major programmes. Prior to her research at Saïd Business School, she received her PhD from Delft University of Technology in 2011 on theoretical and empirical notions of cost overruns in transport infrastructure projects in the Netherlands and worldwide.

Kevin Dwarka is a Brooklyn-based urban planner specializing in transit-oriented development. For almost 15 years, he has served public and private sector clients in the United States and Israel. Kevin provides public agencies, developers, and law firms with expert land use guidance, cutting-edge economic analysis, and innovative approaches to public outreach. He has played a leading role in the regeneration of transit-oriented neighbourhoods as affordable, accessible, inclusive, and economically vibrant communities. Dwarka holds a PhD degree. Prior to forming his own planning consultancy in downtown Brooklyn, he held senior positions at Nelson/Nygaard Consulting Associates, New York City Transit and the Israel Union for Environmental Defense. Dwarka's research has been supported by the New Israel Fund, the National Endowment of Humanities, and Hebrew University. An Adjunct Professor at Baruch College's School of Public Affairs and at Yeshiva University, Dwarka teaches undergraduate and graduate seminars in land use, urban economic development, and environmental policy.

Eran Feitelson is a Professor at the Hebrew University of Jerusalem. A previous chair of the Department of Geography, he was for five years the head of the Federmann School of Public Policy and Government. Currently he is head of the newly established Advanced School for Environmental Studies. He holds an MA in Geography and Economics from the Hebrew University of Jerusalem and a PhD from the Johns Hopkins University, Baltimore. He has edited or co-edited three books, and published over 70 papers in refereed journals and edited volumes. In addition to his academic work Eran Feitelson has participated in several national planning teams and has been a member of many national committees. He has also served as chair of the Israeli Nature Reserves and National Parks Commission for ten years.

Bent Flyvbjerg is the first BT Professor and Founding Chair of Major Programme Management at Oxford University's Saïd Business School and Director of the university's BT Centre for Major Programme Management. He was twice a Visiting Fulbright Scholar to the USA, where he did research at UCLA, UC Berkeley, and Harvard. His books include *Megaprojects and Risk: An Anatomy of Ambition* and *Decision-Making on Mega-Projects*, co-authored with Nils Bruzelius and Werner Rothengatter (Cambridge University Press, 2003). His publications have been translated into 19 languages. Bent Flyvbjerg has served as advisor to the United Nations, the EU Commission, and to governments and companies around the world.

Mendel Giezen is Assistant Professor of Environmental Studies at the Copernicus Institute of Sustainable Development at Utrecht University. His specific focus in education is on sustainable urban development and transport. In his research he specifically looks at the role of uncertainty and complexity in decision-making and planning of transport and urban redevelopment projects. He holds an MSc in Comparative Political Science and an MSc in Metropolitan Studies from the University of Amsterdam. He also attained a PhD at the same university in the field of Urban Planning with research that was part of the OMEGA Centre for Mega-Projects in Transport and Development led by University College London.

Richard Gilbert is an independent consultant whose work focuses on transport and energy issues and urban governance. His main client during the past two decades has been the Paris-based Organisation for Economic Co-operation and Development. He has also worked for several governments in Europe and North America and several private-sector clients. He has authored or edited 14 books on a wide range of topics, the latest being *Transport Revolutions: Moving People and Freight Without Oil* (New Society, 2010), written with Anthony Perl. He is affiliated with the Cities Centre of the University of Toronto.

Carsten Greve is Professor of Public Management and Governance at the Department of Business and Politics, Copenhagen Business School. He is also Academic Director of the CBS Public-Private Platform. His main research areas are public management reform and market-based governance, including public-private partnerships, contracting out, and privatization. His recent books include *International Handbook on Public–Private Partnerships* (Edward Elgar, 2010), co-edited with Anthony Boardman and Graeme Hodge. Carsten Greve chairs a panel on PPPs at the International Research Society for Public Management's annual research conference together with Graeme Hodge. He is currently member of the strategic management group of an international research project on national sustainable transport planning (SUSTAIN) and an external faculty affiliate at Cornell University's Program in Infrastructure Policy.

Graeme Hodge is Professor of Law and Director of the Centre for Regulatory Studies at Monash University, Australia. His research interests cover public–private partnerships, privatization, and regulation. He has published 12 books and 100 papers across social and economic policy, management, public administration, and law. Graeme has worked with the OECD, European Commission, the United Nations, the Asian Development Bank, the Commonwealth Secretariat and Australian governments on matters of regulatory governance, public policy and PPPs in Australasia, Europe, Indonesia, Philippines, and China. He has also served as special adviser to several parliamentary committees and inquiries, and has worked in both the public and private sectors. His most recent book (edited with Carsten Greve) was *Rethinking Public–Private Partnerships: Strategies for Turbulent Times*, published by Routledge (2012).

Rob Konings is Senior Researcher at the faculty of Architecture and the Built Environment at Delft University of Technology. He is an economist with specialization in spatial and transport economics. His research is centred on freight transport with an emphasis on intermodal transport (barge and rail). One of his key interests in this area is the role of service network design and nodes in the performance of intermodal transport. He holds a PhD that deals with these issues in relation to barge transport. In recent years he has extended his research focus to sustainability issues regarding transport systems, including the analysis of innovations in transport systems.

Carl Koopmans is Research Director at SEO Economic Research in Amsterdam and Professor of Economics at VU University Amsterdam. He studied econometrics at Erasmus University, Rotterdam and received his PhD on informal labour at the University of Amsterdam. Previously he worked at SEO, WRR Netherlands Scientific Council for Government Policy, CPB Netherlands Bureau for Policy Analysis and KiM Netherlands Institute for Applied Transport Analysis. After research into labour, housing, and energy, he specialized in cost–benefit analysis and evidence-based policy. He has been a professor since 2003, first at the University of Amsterdam and then at VU University of Amsterdam.

Martijn Leijten is Assistant Professor of Organisation and Management at the faculty of Technology, Policy and Management of Delft University of Technology. His research activities and education concern policy-making in multi-actor systems and project and process management in construction and engineering, with a focus on complex infrastructure projects. He has a special interest in behavioural aspects of management and decision-making.

Donald R. Lessard is the Epoch Foundation Professor of International Management and Engineering Systems at the MIT Sloan School of Management. Lessard's research interests are on global strategic management and project management, with an emphasis on managing in the face of uncertainty and risk and in the energy sector. He has published extensively on these topics in academic and professional journals, and is co-author of *Strategic Management of Large Engineering Projects: Shaping Institutions, Risks, and Governance* (MIT Press 2001 with Roger Miller). Lessard earned his BA in Latin American Studies and his MBA and his PhD in business administration from Stanford University.

Cathy Macharis is Professor at the Vrije Universiteit Brussel and visiting Professor at the University of Gothenburg. Her research group MOBI – (Mobility, Logistics and Automotive Technology Research Centre) is an interdisciplinary group focusing on sustainable logistics, electric and hybrid vehicles, and travel behaviour. She has been involved in several regional, national, and European research projects dealing with topics such as the location of intermodal terminals, assessment of policy measures in the field of logistics and sustainable mobility, electric and hybrid vehicles. She has published several books and written more than 100 papers. She is the chairperson of Brussels Mobility Commission and of the Nectar Cluster on Logistics.

Roger Miller is Professor of Management at EMD, Ecole de Management in Aix-Marseille. He previously taught Project Management at Ecole Polytechnique in Montreal, Canada. He was also a Founding Partner of SECOR, a strategy-consulting firm. His work has focused on strategy and industry dynamics, public policies in science and technology, and project management. He was the director of two research mega-projects: IMEC (International program in the Management of Engineering and Construction) and MINE (Managing Innovation in the New Economy). The results of both programs were published extensively. Roger Miller holds a doctorate in Economics from Louvain University (Belgium), an MEng from Stanford, and an MBA from Columbia University.

Peter Nijkamp is Professor in Regional and Urban Economics and in Economic Geography at the VU University, Amsterdam. His main research interests cover quantitative plan evaluation, regional and urban modelling, multicriteria analysis, transport systems analysis, mathematical systems modelling, technological innovation, entrepreneurship, environmental and resource management, and sustainable development. In the past years he has focused on new quantitative methods for policy analysis and on spatial-behavioural analysis of economic agents. He is past president of the Netherlands Research Council (NWO). In 1996, he was awarded the most prestigious scientific prize in the Netherlands, the Spinoza Prize.

Hugo Priemus is Professor Emeritus of System Innovation and Spatial Development at Delft University of Technology. He was Professor of Housing at Delft University of Technology (1977–2003), Dean of the Faculties of Architecture (1979–83) and Technology, Policy and Management (2003–07). He was visiting professor in Leicester, Strasbourg and Glasgow and is Doctor Honoris Causa at Uppsala University, Sweden. He is Knight in the Order of the Netherlands Lion (1989), holds the Golden Medal of Delft University of Technology and the Dutch Hudig Medal (2010). He studied Architecture (Delft University of Technology) and Economics (Erasmus University, Rotterdam).

Piet Rietveld is a full Professor in Transport Economics at VU University, Amsterdam since 1990 and he became head of Department of Spatial Economics. He received the European Prize in Regional Science (EIB) in 2011. He is a member of the Royal Netherlands Academy of Arts and Sciences. His work focuses on economic impacts of infrastructure, social cost–benefit analysis, transport policy and planning, efficiency in transport, transport networks and evaluation of risk (traffic, floods). He studied econometrics at Erasmus University Rotterdam and received his PhD on multicriteria analysis in regional policy at VU University, Amsterdam. He worked at International Institution for Applied Systems Analysis (IIASA), Laxenburg (Austria) and at Universitas Kristen Satya Wacana (UKSW) (Indonesia).

Knut Samset is Professor of Project Management at the Faculty of Engineering Science and Technology, Norwegian University of Science and Technology. He is the director of the Concept Research Programme on Front-end Management of Large Investment Projects, and founding director and senior partner of Scanteam, an international consultancy based in Oslo. His academic background is in engineering and social science and he holds a PhD in Risk Management. He has extensive experience as advisor to national and international governmental and non-governmental organizations, and has written a number of books on project design, evaluation, and project risk. In his current position, he and his team is doing pioneering research into ways and means to ensure quality-at-entry of major projects upstream in order to improve return on investments downstream.

Matti Siemiatycki is Assistant Professor of Geography and Planning at the University of Toronto. His teaching and research focuses on the global experience of delivering large-scale infrastructure through public–private partnerships (PPPs). His published research examines major transit, highway, bridge and tunnel projects in Canada, the United States, India, Britain, Australia, and Spain.

Lóri Tavasszy is Principal Scientist at the research institute TNO in Delft and is part-time Professor in Freight and Logistics at the Delft University of Technology, where he obtained his PhD in 1996. His research includes freight and logistics models, long-term freight forecasts, innovative transport systems (city logistics, underground transport, multimodal transport) and cost–benefit analysis of major transport projects and public policies.

He has produced over 100 publications for international journals, books or conferences and holds regular lectures in the Netherlands and abroad.

Ernst ten Heuvelhof is Professor of Public Administration at the Faculty of Technology, Policy and Management of Delft University of Technology and at the Faculty of Social Sciences of Erasmus University Rotterdam. His research covers two areas: public administration, governance and process management, and liberalization, privatization, and deregulation of infrastructure-based utilities (e.g., energy, telecom and transport). He is one of the scientific directors of the research program Next Generation Infrastructures. He is a member of the Netherlands Institute of Government, the Dutch research school for Public Administration and Political Science, recognized by the Royal Netherlands Academy of Arts and Sciences.

Arjan van Binsbergen is Associate Professor at the Department of Transport & Planning of Delft University of Technology. Van Binsbergen studied Civil Engineering, with a specialization in traffic engineering, at TU Delft and received his PhD on the topic of freight distribution in urban areas. He worked as a researcher, assistant, and later associate professor in the fields of freight transport and logistics related to sustainability and urban areas. Previously he was member of the management team of the Netherlands research program Transition to Sustainable Mobility (Transumo), in which he was also involved in transition and implementation studies.

Ron van Duin is Assistant Professor Transport Policy at Delft University of Technology. His research and educational activities concern mainly logistics in multi-actor environments. He focuses on three kinds of logistics in particular: multimodal transport chains, city logistics and harbour logistics. Ron did a Masters in Econometrics at the Erasmus University Rotterdam in 1988. In 2012 he defended his PhD at Delft University of Technology on logistics concept development in multi-actor environments. He worked for VBF-Tubes, FEL-TNO, Opera (own company) and ISW-educational services. He is also director of the Institute of City Logistics.

Bert van Wee is Professor in Transport Policy at Delft University of Technology, Faculty of Technology, Policy and Management. In addition he is scientific director of the inter-university TRAIL research school. His main interests are in long-term developments in transport, large infrastructure projects, accessibility, environment, and safety, and in policy analysis.

Roger Vickerman is Professor of European Economics and Dean of the Brussels School of International Studies at the University of Kent. His research focuses on the relationship between transport (especially infrastructure), regional development and integration in the European Union. He is particularly known for his studies on major infrastructure projects, such as the Channel Tunnel and high-speed rail. He is the co-author of the textbook *Principles of Transport Economics* with Emile Quinet (Elgar, 2004), co-editor of *A Handbook of Transport Economics* with Andre de Palma, Robin Lindsey, and Emile Quinet (Elgar, 2011) and Editor in Chief of *Transport Policy*.

Acknowledgements

This book is the result of close cooperation with experts in the field who were able to outline the main topics and approaches within the area of decision-making on mega-projects. We are grateful for the following scientists who contributed in a double-blind procedure their critical reviews, which have often led to substantial improvement of the chapters:

Alex Anas (USA); Jan Anne Annema (Netherlands); David Banister (UK); Joseph Berechman (Israel/USA); Luca Bertolini (Netherlands); Alain Bonnafous (France); Michael Browne (UK); Hans de Bruijn (Netherlands); Kenneth J. Button (USA); Chantal Cantarelli (Netherlands); Marc Davidson (Netherlands); Harry Dimitriou (UK); Jonas Eliasson (Sweden); Rune Elvik (Norway); Bent Flyvbjerg (Denmark); Harry Geerlings (Netherlands); Karst Geurs (Netherlands); Mendel Giezen (Netherlands); Richard Gilbert (Canada); Hans van Ham (Netherlands); Arnold Heertje (Netherlands); Ernst ten Heuvelhof (Netherlands); Graeme Hodge (Australia); Martin de Jong (Netherlands); Mark Koetse (Netherlands); Carl Koopmans (Netherlands); Joop Koppenjan (Netherlands); Ekki Kreutzberger (Netherlands); Donald Lessard (France); Martijn Leijten (Netherlands); Cathy Macharis (Belgium); Peter Mackie (UK); Chris Nash (UK); Peter Nijkamp (Netherlands); James Odeck (Norway); Anthony Perl (Canada); Stef Proost (Belgium); Piet Rietveld (Netherlands); Kim Salling (Denmark); Knut Samset (Norway); Matti Siemiatycki (Canada); Eiichi Taniguichi (Japan); Barry Ubbels (Netherlands); Odette van de Riet (Netherlands); Didier van de Velde (Netherlands); Alexander Verbraeck (Netherlands); Martin Wachs (USA); Tom Worsley (UK).

1. Mega-projects: high ambitions, complex decision-making, different actors, multiple impacts

Hugo Priemus and Bert van Wee

1.1 INTRODUCTION

Most mega-projects are the result of public investment, which forms a large share of public budgets. This explains the high political profile of most mega-projects. Mega-projects are costly but – in most cases – they are also very useful, because they connect different cities, regions and parts of one or more countries, and they can be crucial for the accessibility of those areas.

In this *International Handbook*, 'mega-projects' are defined as large infrastructure projects for the transportation of people and/or goods. They could be main roads, conventional, high-speed or light rail projects, bridges, tunnels or combinations of any of these. We do not adopt a particular sum of investment as a minimum criterion to define a 'mega-project'. In general, the sum invested is at least several hundred million euros, but such an amount means different things in different countries. In any case, we consider mega-projects to be complex products that are the result of complex decision-making processes. The term 'mega-project' indicates both the decision-making process and the resulting infrastructure product.

Within the decision-making process on mega-projects, many stakeholders can be identified who want to play a role in developing or operating mega-projects. These stakeholders may be public, representing different levels of government – local, regional, national and international – as a result of which decision-making on mega-projects is mostly a case of multilevel governance. These stakeholders may also be private, opening up opportunities for public–private partnerships. That raises questions about who is going to gain from the realization of a mega-project, who will be the losers, to what extent these losses will be compensated, who will take on the risks in each stage of the decision-making process and who will decide what and when in the decision-making process.

Mega-projects may have a different meaning in different parts of the world. The infrastructure network of many developing countries is limited, so the added value of a mega-project may be high and a cost–benefit analysis may easily yield positive results. In developed countries, on the other hand, infrastructure networks could already be described as 'complete' and it is more difficult to design a mega-project that can really make a difference. But in these countries, too, there may be missing links (such as the bridge between Denmark and Sweden) or even missing networks (such as the absence of a high-speed rail network in European countries in the past). Mega-projects are often completely new constructions, but it is possible that the share of mega-projects that adapt or reconstruct existing traffic infrastructure will increase – to improve the safety of roads and tunnels, reduce harmful effects on the environment or harmonize the capacity of lines and nodes within a road or rail network.

In this *International Handbook on Mega-Projects*, the focus is not so much on the design, construction or characteristics of the mega-projects, but primarily on the decision-making processes behind them. When those processes are analysed and evaluated, it is crucial that we can determine whether a mega-project is a success or a failure, or perhaps a mixed bag with successes and failures. What are the general characteristics of decision-making processes relating to mega-projects, which are always complex, costly and are in operation over a long period of time?

The way we think about the decision-making processes relating to mega-projects has evolved over time. Nowadays there is much greater emphasis on flexibility, adaptability, uncertainties, resilience and option values. The tendency to split large infrastructure projects into smaller projects where possible is gaining ground, which is creating opportunities for adaptive process management and no-regret policy.

The interrelationship between the dynamics (and uncertainties) of a democratic society and decision-making on a mega-project is also becoming an increasingly relevant topic. Some traditional planners seem to consider the volatility of political governance in a democracy to be an impediment for an appropriate decision-making process on mega-projects, while others are aware of the conditions that a vital democracy places on such a decision-making process. This *International Handbook* presents the latest contributions on this topic of modern decision-making, which can affect mega-projects both positively and negatively.

Population growth is stagnating in many developed countries (in large parts of Europe for instance) and economic growth is more modest than it has been in the past. Partly due to these trends, car ownership and car use seem to be static or at least growth is slowing. Some modes of public transport are losing market share (bus, tram), while other modes are gaining ground (light rail, underground systems, high-speed trains). The role of intermodal transport, connecting origin and destination addresses with different modes, is becoming ever more widespread in the transportation of both people and goods. The increasing use of advanced information systems is facilitating the coordination of trips with different modes of transport with connections between those trips.

The idea of an *International Handbook on Mega-Projects* was initiated, not because there is a lack of publications on this issue, but actually because there is such an overwhelming range of publications, which makes it difficult to obtain a well-structured knowledge on mega-projects. This book presents the latest knowledge about the decision-making process relating to mega-projects, the relationships between public and private partners in this decision-making process, multi-actor analysis, the perspectives and pitfalls in determining the costs and benefits of a mega-project ex ante, and the wider impacts of mega-projects, including issues such as regional growth, energy transition and climate change.

This book focuses on transport infrastructure but some chapters are also relevant for other types of mega-projects or large engineering projects in general. There is a focus on the Western world: the advanced economies of North America, Europe and Australia, when we look at the reference projects in several contributions, but many chapters are also useful for other parts of the world, where large infrastructure projects are currently underway or will be developed in the coming years.

The book is divided into four parts:

Part I: Decision-making on mega-projects
Part II: Public–private partnership and multi-actor analysis
Part III: Cost–benefit analysis: ex ante evaluation of mega-projects
Part IV: Wider impacts: regional growth and sustainability

1.2 PART I: DECISION-MAKING ON MEGA-PROJECTS

Part I presents a number of contributions about the decision-making process behind mega-projects:

Chapter 2 (Samset) discusses how mega-projects can be defined in terms of their tactical and strategic performance. Quality-at-entry can help to ensure project performance and viability. The potential for improvement up-front is reviewed in terms of strategic alignment, reducing uncertainty and limiting the future cost of amendments. Up-front cost estimation is compared with the effect of cost management during implementation.

Some essential lessons and common pitfalls in mega-projects, which are associated with decisions in the earliest phases, are discussed.

Chapter 3 (Lessard and Miller) is about the shaping of large engineering projects. This category is broader than large infrastructure projects and includes power plants, electric grid extensions, extractive projects and large manufacturing plants. The authors observe that the seeds of success or failure are planted early. Different approaches to valuing projects are examined, with a special emphasis on the real options perspective. The chapter shows how uncertainty and risk evolve over the life of the process and how risks are engaged, shaped, assigned, contained and resolved.

Chapter 4 (Leijten) deals with real-world decision-making on mega-projects, seen from an actor perspective. The erratic and non-linear nature of mega-project decision-making processes causes frequent deviations from the anticipated development of the project. Two categories of explanations for these deviations are discussed: behavioural and cognitive issues that play a role in decision-making, and political and strategic issues that influence decision-making. A stronger focus on actors provides opportunities to optimise mega-projects.

Chapter 5 (Priemus, Bosch-Rekveldt and Giezen) focuses on long-term uncertainties and complexity. Central notions in this chapter are risk, redundancy and resilience. The underestimation of complexity in the early stages can create blind spots for particular uncertainties. Risks and uncertainties occur at different stages of the complex decision-making process. It is crucial that redundancy and resilience are stimulated and that real options are available. Flexibility and adaptability, particularly in early stages of the project, are crucial in decision-making on mega-projects.

Chapter 6 (ten Heuvelhof and Leijten) discusses New Public Management and new features of strategic behaviour. The introduction of New Public Management into the realization and operation of complex rail projects has resulted in a number of changes in the organization of these projects. The tendency is to split transport services, trains and infrastructure. However, design, construction, finance, maintenance and operation are coordinated more than in the past using contracts. Different kinds of strategic behaviour can be observed in the new interfaces.

1.3 PART II: PUBLIC–PRIVATE PARTNERSHIP AND MULTI-ACTOR ANALYSIS

Part II gives an overview of approaches and experiences with public–private partnerships to prepare, develop and operate mega-projects and relates to multi-actor analysis:

Chapter 7 (Siemiatycki) deals with successes and tensions in public–private partnerships. The chapter highlights how the use of public–private partnerships influences the types of mega-projects that are built, how meaningfully the community is engaged in project planning and approval, how cost overruns and delivery delays are managed, and the likelihood of tensions arising between the partners over the long term. Strategies are identified to improve the quality of cooperation between partners.

Chapter 8 (Dwarka and Feitelson) focuses on the private infrastructure finance and the political economy of urban light rail. The authors agree that since early 1985 the expansion in the involvement of the private sector in infrastructure finance has revolutionized the provision of public services. Through financial instruments like private finance initiatives (PFIs) and build/operate/transfer (BOT), governments and multinational corporations have accelerated the building of highways and rail networks. Today, the global infrastructure market is a massive business. This chapter argues that the focus of power in the urban infrastructure development process still resides with local government, despite the globalization and marketization of infrastructure.

Chapter 9 (Hodge and Greve) analyses public–private partnerships in the development and management of mega-projects. The authors specify five different families of public–private partnership:

- institutional cooperation for joint production and risk sharing;
- long-term infrastructure contracts, which emphasize tight specification of outputs in long-term legal contracts (such as PFI projects in the UK);
- public policy networks, which emphasize loose stakeholder relationships;
- civil society and community development;
- urban renewal and downtown economic development.

Conceptually, there is a continuum of options, ranging from public emphasis at one extreme to private emphasis at the other.

Chapter 10 (van Binsbergen, Konings, Tavasszy and van Duin) gives an overview of mega-projects in intermodal freight transport networks. Besides the traditional investment in seaports and inland transport infrastructure, new logistics service networks are developing to connect these terminals and infrastructures into new networks. The chapter describes several mega-projects, some realized, others not yet realized. It presents a framework of innovation adoption and identifies a number of success factors.

Chapter 11 (Macharis and Nijkamp) presents a methodology known as multi-actor multi-criteria analysis (MAMCA), which allows specifically for the inclusion of multiple stakeholders in the multi-criteria analysis. Macharis and Nijkamp apply their methodology to a mega-project case study on the Oosterweel Connection in Antwerp, Belgium. This project is the most controversial transport infrastructure project ever in the province of Flanders. The results of the case study demonstrate the real-world applicability of the method, and show that an objective stakeholder-based analysis is key when dealing with complex decision-making problems.

1.4 PART III: COST–BENEFIT ANALYSIS: EX ANTE EVALUATION OF MEGA-PROJECTS

Part III deals with cost–benefit analysis (CBA): the ex ante evaluation of mega-projects:

Chapter 12 (van Wee and Rietveld) presents a general overview of the strengths and weaknesses of CBA for the ex ante evaluation of mega-projects, including the challenges involved in improving the CBA tool. These challenges include changes in regional accessibility, the long-term impact, the wider economic impact and cross-border issues.

Chapter 13 (Annema) examines the empirical evidence on the use of CBA in decision-making on mega-projects. The main conclusion is that the connection between the results of CBA and investment in mega-projects is limited. The chapter identifies various barriers that explain why CBA has less impact on the decision-making process than expected. The author recommends the creation of a formal place for CBA in the interactive planning process and the use of CBA at an early stage in that process.

Chapter 14 (Koopmans and Rietveld) argues that the discount rate has a strong impact on the outcome of the ex ante evaluation of mega-projects. This is a crucial point, particularly in relation to climate change policy. The authors differentiate between the descriptive approach based on capital markets and the prescriptive approach based on sustainability and intergenerational equity. The chapter also raises the question of whether different impacts should be discounted at different rates. In different countries, different discount rates are used, which complicates the ex ante evaluation of cross-border mega-projects.

Chapter 15 (Cantarelli and Flyvbjerg) deals with project cost performance and lock-in. The chapter explains that the main problem occurs with inaccurate cost estimates and cost overruns. Four origins of lock-in are identified: sunk costs, the escalation of commitment, the need for justification and inflexibility. Improving accountability in infrastructure investment would be helpful. Forecasting methods could be improved by basing the forecasts on actual performance in a reference class of comparable projects.

Chapter 16 (van Wee) adds the ethical dimension to the ex ante evaluation of mega-projects. CBA is based on utilitarianism, an approach that can be challenged. Important factors to consider in an ethical approach of CBA are the distributive effects, the inclusion of specific accessibility indicators, an explicit check on the values and duties that are at stake, the welfare of the least advantaged people and the adoption of alternatives to utilitarianism. A checklist to include ethics in the ex ante evaluation of mega-projects is presented. The author concludes that CBA has several limitations when applied to the evaluation of transport infrastructure projects. CBA is not rejected, but in some cases a combination of CBA and MCA is recommended.

1.5 PART IV: WIDER IMPACTS: REGIONAL GROWTH AND SUSTAINABILITY

Part IV deals with wider impacts of mega-projects, in particular with regard to regional growth, energy transition and climate change:

Chapter 17 (Vickerman) presents an overview of the wider impacts of mega-projects. Often these wider impacts are cited as justification for a mega-project or as essential for the competitiveness of the city, region or country. Providing empirical evidence to substantiate such claims in a particular case has proved difficult. This chapter presents suggestions for ways to incorporate these wider impacts into appraisal practice.

Chapter 18 (Annema and Priemus) analyses changing issues on mega-projects to cope with climate change and energy transition. The chapter deals with the question of whether it is wise to take into account climate change and the expected energy transition from fossil-fuel-based vehicles to transport powered by renewable energy sources. If it is wise to do so, additional uncertainties will enter decision-making processes on mega-projects. The chapter proposes a pragmatic approach to dealing with these huge uncertainties.

Chapter 19 (Gilbert) relates infrastructure planning to a transport revolution such as the electrification of vehicles. This chapter is mainly concerned with various medium-term future scenarios for light-duty four-wheeled passenger vehicles (personal vehicles) and their implication for transport infrastructure. The author expects a transport revolution towards providing for a shift to electric motors and away from internal combustion engines. Two options are presented: one is the development of battery-powered vehicles; the other option is powering personal vehicles directly from the grid. The last option could be combined with an unfamiliar form of personal travel: personal rapid transit (PRT). The widespread deployment of PRT would constitute a major transport revolution and would have profound infrastructure implications.

PART I

DECISION-MAKING ON MEGA-PROJECTS

2. Strategic and tactical performance of mega-projects – between successful failures and inefficient successes

Knut Samset

2.1 WHAT IS MEANT BY SUCCESS?

Measuring success in mega-projects is not a simple and straightforward undertaking. This is because the term 'success', used as an indicator, is a highly complex and aggregated measure. One reason is that it may be interpreted differently by different individuals and institutions. Another, that it tends to be measured differently in different types of mega-projects, depending on the nature of their immediate outputs and long-term outcome. Also, different individuals tend to assess the success of the same mega-project differently depending on their preferences, values and to what degree they are affected by the project. And finally, the degree of success is time-dependent. For instance, Shenhar et al. (2001) offer a chronological sequence of events as a compound definition of project success: (1) meeting time, budget and other requirements, (2) impact on the customer, (3) benefit to the performing organization, and (4) preparing the future. The project's stakeholders do not necessarily share the same view of success. The project manager typically sees his or her job successfully accomplished when the project is on time, within budget and to specifications. The users will be concerned about the immediate effects of the project, and the investor or commissioner will typically be more concerned with the long-term economic viability.

Mega-projects are recognized as an important part of corporate and public life, but with varying reputation. The 'person on the street' will frequently be of the opinion that projects, and in particular mega-projects, are generally unsuccessful. This is reflected in the media where unsuccessful cases get more publicity than the successful ones. The number one criterion of failure in the media is cost overrun. Number two is delay in time. Even if the result is seen to be useful, there are often reports in the media of large public construction projects that have suffered huge cost or time overruns, such as Denver's $5 billion airport 200 per cent overspend (Szyliowicz and Goetz, 1995), or the UK's Scottish Parliament coming in '10 times over budget and more than three years late' (Tempest, 2004).

The user's view on success is frequently more significant. Pinto (2007) quotes from an Infoworld article describing, 'a US Army study of IT projects [that] found that 47% were delivered to the customer but not used; 29% were paid for but not delivered; 19% were abandoned or reworked; 3% were used with minor changes; and only 2% were used as delivered' (p. 7).

This is not to say that all mega-projects are managed badly – indeed, the management and governance of many mega-projects has made considerable improvements in recent years (see for example HM Treasury, 2007 for an upbeat report on the UK's Office of Government Commerce). After many decades with developments in the project management profession, there is more expertise now in delivering efficiently and successfully a well-defined pre-specified project within a well-defined constant environment. This has proved very valuable in certain circumstances. But the focus on project management has been much too narrow in the media and the public. Truly, a much wider view needs to be taken on the success and failure of projects. The initial choice of mega-project concept is of critical importance. This represents the one key decision of many made during the lifetime of a mega-project, which is likely to have the largest impact on long-term success or failure (Williams et al., 2009). Here, by 'the project concept' we mean much more than just the technical solution – it includes the entire business case, all of the various organizations involved, and the various mechanisms and arrangements involved in the inter-organizational relationships; see also Miller and Hobbs (2009).

Success as a generic term means to gain advantage, superiority, accomplishment, achievement or added value. Measuring success will have to look beyond the immediate outputs of the mega-project to assert the anticipated and wider impact in a longer-term perspective. A hospital will ultimately have to be assessed in terms of its health benefits. An industrial project might be judged essentially on financial terms, and an infrastructure project in term of its utility.

The assessment of success can be in absolute or in relative terms – that is, in relation to what was agreed versus what was realistically achievable. Ambition is expressed in terms of the mega-project's stipulated objectives. Its outcome is a direct measure of what has been actually achieved. Clearly, success measured in absolute terms may give a misleading conclusion if objectives are unrealistically ambitious. By measuring in relative terms, that is, in relation to what could reasonably be expected as compared with experiences in similar mega-projects – the same mega-project might possibly be considered a success.

More than two decades ago Pinto and Slevin (1988, p. 68) concluded that:

> the concept of mega-project success has remained ambiguously defined both in the project management literature and, indeed, often within the psyche of project managers. Until project management can arrive at a generally agreed upon determinant of success, our attempts to accurately monitor and anticipate project outcomes will be severely restricted.

Clearly, a successful mega-project is one that delivers its outputs and significantly contributes to the fulfilment of agreed objectives. Moreover, it should have only minor negative effects, its objectives should be consistent with needs and priorities in society, and it should be viable in the sense that the intended long-term benefits resulting from the mega-project are produced. These requirements were first formulated for US-funded international development projects by the United States Agency for International Development (USAID) in the 1960s, and subsequently endorsed by the United Nations (UN), the Organisation for Economic Co-operation and Development (OECD) and the European Commission (EC). They comprise five requirements or success factors that have to be fulfilled, that is, the mega-project's efficiency, effectiveness, relevance, impact and sustainability. These are tough requirements that go far beyond the issues that are usually covered by the media or indeed by many planners and decision-makers.

Efficiency measures are only the first signs and immediate indications of a mega-project's success in delivering its outputs, as there are many examples of mega-projects that score highly on efficiency but subsequently prove to be disastrous in terms of their effect and utility. There are also numerous mega-projects that failed to pass the efficiency test but still prove to be tremendously successful both in the short and long run (Morris, 1994). We are making the distinction here between what could be termed successful failures and inefficient successes.

2.2 ON STRATEGIC AND TACTICAL PERFORMANCE

In applying the success criteria above, we distinguish between the mega-projects' tactical and strategic performance. Success in tactical terms typically means meeting short-term performance targets, such as producing agreed outputs within budget and on time. These are essentially project management issues. Strategic performance, however, includes the broader and longer-term considerations of whether the mega-project would have a sustainable impact and remain relevant and effective over its lifespan. This is essentially a question of getting the business case right, or, in short, of choosing the most viable mega-project concept.

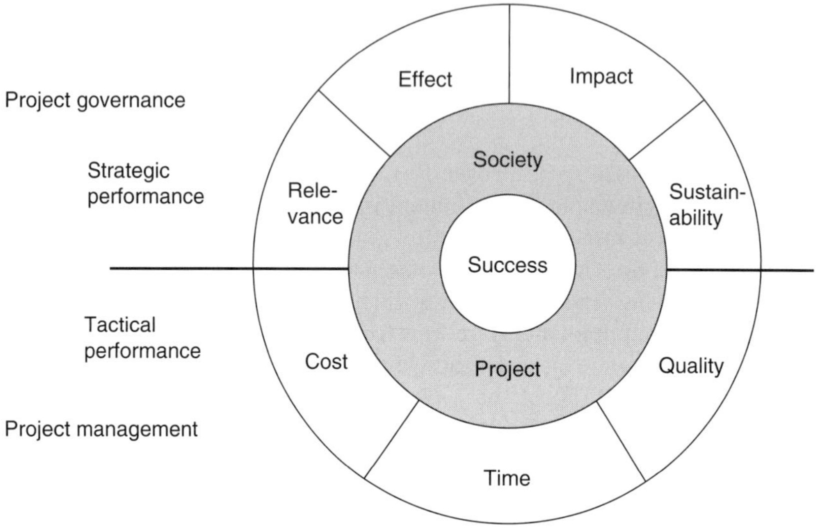

Figure 2.1 Successful mega-projects. Tactical performance is a question of delivering the project outputs as planned, while strategic performance is the worth or utility of the project as seen from a long-term perspective

This is illustrated in Figure 2.1. Tactical performance is a question of how the mega-project is implemented, that is, how inputs are converted into outputs. These are measures of its efficiency, here measured in terms of the cost, timing and quality of deliverables. Strategic performance is a question of how the mega-project performs after the outputs have been delivered. This will have to be monitored with the more compound measures mentioned above, which would cover the broader and longer-term perspectives. It would involve focusing on technology and management issues to a lesser degree, but more on societal and economic aspects.

One example of a project inefficient tactically but viable in strategic terms could be the University Hospital in Oslo, Norway (Samset, 2008). Due to emerging new technologies and added responsibilities, captured during the engineering phase after the budget was decided, it was completed in 2000, a year behind schedule and with considerable cost overrun, adverse newspaper reports and a public inquiry. No doubt, cost overrun was considerable in absolute terms, but in relative terms it was equivalent to only a few months' operational costs for the hospital, and therefore insignificant in a lifetime perspective. The overall conclusion after a few years of operation was that the University Hospital was a highly successful project; and it would perhaps be unfair to suggest that initial decisions should be able to capture problems at this level of precision.

More serious by far is when a mega-project fails in strategic terms, even if it successfully produces the intended outputs. Strategic failure means that the choice of concept turns out to be the wrong one: the wrong solution to the problem in hand, or a partial solution only, sometimes creating more new problems than it solves. In some cases the initial problem no longer exists once the project is completed. One such example is an on-shore torpedo battery built inside the rocks on the northern coast of Norway in 2004 (Samset, 2008). The facility is huge and complex, designed to accommodate as many as 150 military personnel for up to three months at a time. It was officially opened as planned and without cost overrun. A week later it was closed down by parliamentary decision. It was obvious to all involved that a potential enemy would not expose its ships to such an obvious risk; the concept had long since been overtaken by political, technological and military development. What was quite remarkable was that this project, which can only be characterized as strategic failure, got little attention in the media, possibly because it was a success in tactical terms.

2.3 FRONT-END ANALYSIS TO ENSURE PROJECT SUCCESS

Generally speaking, tactical considerations typically are restricted in time and perspective, such as the presumed ability to meet short-term performance targets and trade-offs to keep stakeholders on board, all likely to prove ephemeral when matched against the lifespan of most mega-projects. This includes the often proclaimed success of a mega-project simply because it has come in 'on cost and on time'. Strategic performance is the key issue, but strategic success will only emerge over time in the context of the mega-project having sustainable impact and remaining relevant and effective over its lifespan. Mega-projects that score highly on all the five success criteria mentioned above are those that perform successfully both tactically and strategically. Such mega-projects may be rare cases (Samset and Dowdeswell, 2008).

On the assumption that the choice of concept is vital for a successful mega-project, and considering the five success criteria mentioned above, the question now is to what extent information will be available to identify the best concept during the front-end phase of project definition. Obviously, the tactical performance of mega-projects is of less concern at the earliest project proposal stage. Strategic performance is the main issue. But to what extent is it possible to make a meaningful assessment of the proposal in relation to the above mentioned success measures? And not least, would the amount and types of information available early on be sufficient?

In order to assess the efficiency, the costs of a mega-project and the nature of its delivery are reasonably well understood at an early stage. But there is doubt as to whether cost estimates are realistic and the conditions of implementation will allow that outputs are produced as anticipated. Consequently, attempting to gauge efficiency may not be worthwhile in the front-end phase. Not least the complications facing planners and decision-makers in estimating realistic costs clearly indicate that the basis for rigorously evaluating efficiency is usually poor.

The same is true of effectiveness. Undoubtedly, the anticipated first-order effects are usually clearly known, their realization is time-dependent and relies on the fulfilment of other events outside the scope of the mega-project. Realistic forecasting may therefore be notoriously flawed.

Early estimates of impacts are even more difficult. Undoubtedly, experiential knowledge may be acquired by studying similar mega-projects. But we face conditions that are difficult to forecast and arguably require imagination and guesswork beyond our capabilities. However, the situation regarding assessing relevance differs. Common sense and user surveys, as well as knowledge of markets, laws and regulations permit us to form an early, accurate picture of whether an initiative is relevant. That we are also notoriously poor at this sort of early evaluation is not due to it being impossible, but rather to it not being done to a sufficient extent.

Forecasting future sustainability is also difficult. However, the question is closely related to whether the proposed mega-project is relevant. Moreover, early on, we have long been able to realistically analyse cash flows.

Consequently, the answer to the question above is that with modest effort, we can gain a good picture of whether a mega-project is relevant and sustainable. Extensive analyses of the other three criteria may not be worthwhile at an early stage. The good news, however, is that relevance and sustainability are precisely the attributes that determine whether a mega-project will be successful or not in the long term. Therefore, this may be a minimalistic answer to the question raised, or a quick-and-dirty approach to ex ante evaluation of project proposals, in which the benefits are great compared to the cost.

However, mega-projects are often designed without an adequate analysis of the key stakeholders' interests and needs. One example would be a sub-sea road tunnel that was built in order to link a community on a small island in Norway at the fringe of an archipelago with the largest island and thus get access by road to the mainland. The project was part of a vague overall strategy to promote economic development in remote areas, which was firmly rooted in a national policy to subsidize investment in local infrastructure with the aim to avoid depopulation of local communities. Important aspects pertaining to the relevance and sustainability of the investment were not properly assessed – such as its usefulness for local industry, and the users' ability and willingness to pay for the new infrastructure.

The mega-project was successful as seen in a project management perspective, being built on time and with costs considerably below budget estimates. However, because of the island's small population, it became apparent that the financial basis was inadequate and user toll was unacceptably high. Also, it was obvious that a road connection to the mainland was not decisive for the industry. The size of the investment, combined with low revenue from toll fees, made this seemingly successful mega-project a heavy burden for local district authorities.

An analysis of how to interpret 'regional development' in this case could have restricted the mega-project to meet the priorities of local industry and revealed that the real need was not for a road connection with the mainland, but for improved harbour facilities. In economic terms a much smaller project would therefore have been economically viable.

What happened was that the now easy access to the small island made it attractive for tourists. Real estate prices went up and in the years that followed most of the inhabitants sold out to tourists and moved to the main island, thus also dodging the high user fees for the tunnel. Industry suffered loss of employees and eventually closed. The local government was stuck with a huge debt from the investment and the loss of revenue from user fees. In order to solve the problem, user fees were now extended to include transport to all the islands in the archipelago. This stirred conflict and eventually led to a shift of local government.

In this case there was a range of wider impacts of the tunnel project for the entire local community, all negative in economic terms except for an increase in tourism during a short summer season. The problem was that the tunnel was not relevant in relation to the users' needs, and not sustainable in relation to the size of the population. Clearly, these problems could have been identified at a very early stage, and avoided.

2.4 DECISIONS THAT AFFECT TACTICAL AND STRATEGIC PERFORMANCE

Tactical Performance

What decision-makers are charged with here is the responsibility to secure efficient delivery of mega-project outputs in terms such as scope, quality, timing and budgetary compliance. The point of departure is the mega-project owner's specifications and requirements as well as the contractual obligations. The main challenge is to translate the specifications into a project design and implementation plan that is realistically achievable in view of uncertainties that might affect the undertaking. These tasks are clearly described, for instance by the Project Management Institute in its 'Body of Knowledge' (PMI, 2008). It would involve management of project integration, human resources, communication, procurement, design, planning, cost estimation, and risk. Although deficiencies in project management might have serious economic implications, the problems might still be marginal seen in a wider strategic perspective, as illustrated in the case of the national University Hospital in Norway discussed above. What remains noteworthy in much public service investment is the continuing high-profile emphasis on tactical dimensions. In the United Kingdom, for example, the private finance initiative (PFI) is becoming synonymous with the government mantra 'on time, on cost' as the dominant defining factor of success (Williams, 2008).

Strategic Performance

In order to succeed strategically, four of the five success criteria mentioned above need to be satisfied. The mega-project's intended effect should be useful (relevance), the effect should be achieved in time (effectiveness), there should be no major negative effects (impact) and the positive effects should be sustained (sustainability).

The task of ensuring that the mega-project is relevant would clearly require that its objectives are aligned with needs and priorities in society. This is often not the case, as illustrated by the road tunnel example above. The mega-project was a case of over-investment guided by the availability of public funds rather than by a scrutiny of local needs. The effect was the opposite to the intentions of the national policy.

The next challenge is to secure that the mega-project's objectives are realistically achievable and that the intended effect will be realized as planned (effectiveness). The question here is to what extent objectives will be fulfilled, given the resources available and the uncertainties facing the mega-project. There are a number of formal requirements that have to be satisfied in the strategic design of a project. Objectives should be consistent in the sense that they are logically linked, both sequentially and in parallel. They should also be realistic in probabilistic terms and essential risks should be identified and considered. Clearly, a mega-project with formally agreed objectives that are unrealistic will appear to be a failure when achievements are measured against these objectives. In the case of the road tunnel, the mega-project was guided by a number of unclear objectives pointing in different directions. In the local government there was no consensus regarding the mega-project's justification, what it was meant to achieve, and how.

Securing sustainability and avoiding adverse impacts would necessitate a thorough understanding of the complexity of the contextual situation in which the mega-project is implemented and operated. This includes its institutional setting, market demands and restrictions, stakeholder needs and priorities, technological and environmental opportunities and challenges. The task up-front is one of making comprehensive analyses, identifying stakeholders and facilitating communication and involvement. Such activities may delay decision-making, but experience strongly suggests that this is often worthwhile in order to avoid some of the strategic fallacies ahead. In the road tunnel case, there were several indications that the mega-project was not sustainable, the most obvious one being the size of investment, which was out of proportion to the small population of residents on the island.

One huge paradox in the front-end management of mega-projects is that many of these, even the largest public investment projects, originate as a single idea without systematic scrutiny or consultation. In addition, in too many cases, the initial idea will remain largely unchallenged and therefore survive and end up as the preferred concept – even in cases where it subsequently proved to be a strategic underperformer or failure. Improved front-end management is therefore likely to pay off if seen in a wider life cycle perspective (Miller and Lessard, 2001). There is much to be gained from improving quality-at-entry at the earliest stage of the process. This can be achieved by challenging the initial ideas and applying simple analyses, extracting and making use of previous experience from similar undertakings, and consulting and involving stakeholders.

2.5 QUALITY-AT-ENTRY AND QUALITY ASSURANCE UP-FRONT

According to Peter Morris (2011, p. 16):

> There is overwhelming evidence that the front-end of projects – the pre-sanction stage where the business case, project strategy, and technical options are progressively assessed, selected and developed – is the area where a project's future problems are often seeded and where opportunities for improving value lie. Managing the front-end is critical to project success. Yet although we have a relatively mature understanding of what managing projects in downstream

> delivery involves – once the project characteristics and targets have been set – we have not yet got a good generic understanding of what managing the front-end entails.

He further points to the irony that the importance of front-end management was highlighted as early as the 1970s when the Pentagon introduced a Milestone 0 – one before the then existing first Milestone – to confirm approval of the Mission Element Need Statement (the threat, capabilities to conduct the mission, and need, constraints, resources and schedule for doing so). It might have fallen under the radar in the years that followed, when the focus was essentially on project management.

Later, the importance of quality-at-entry, as measured by the quality of project identification, preparation and appraisal, has been emphasized in many studies. The World Bank (1996) gave a similar message in a study based on a review of 1125 of its projects that were evaluated between 1991 and 1994, concluding that projects with adequate or better identification, preparation and appraisal had an 80 per cent satisfaction rate, against 25 per cent for projects that were deficient in all these aspects, and that the quality of preparation and of appraisal had significantly more influence on satisfactory performance, than key country macroeconomic variables, external factors, or government considerations.

One of the prime goals of strategic planning is to attain structured and effective continuous management. The strategy will conduce decision-makers at various levels to pull in the same direction by providing a common long-term goal to keep in mind in making decisions. Research has shown that this is essential to attaining good results (van der Heijden, 1996). A survey conducted in the USA among about 600 project managers contributed to identifying which critical factors influence the level of achievement in projects. The conclusion was that planning the project was by far the most important factor. Problems that could have been avoided with a better project plan arose repeatedly during the entire project cycle (Pinto and Slevin, 1988).

An international project that drew on the experience of 60 large infrastructure programmes concluded that projects with great strategic depth, that is, an appreciable level and extent of strategic assessments that underlie a project, were more likely to be successful. A clear concurrence showed that the projects that attained the best results had allocated greater portions of their overall costs to their front-end phases. These cost allocations varied from 3 per cent for simple projects and as much as 35 per cent for complex projects. The costs in the front-end phase, before the decision was made to start, varied from \$15 to 500 million. The conclusion was that such costs were often justified and resulted in considerable cost reductions in the implementation phase, more socially acceptable projects and better risk management. The study also found that in particular, three aspects characterized the most successful projects: (1) the front-end phase had been long, that is, several years, (2) the concept had been revised several times, and (3) problem-solving was systematic and inclusive. Moreover, it was found that the use of risk analysis was vital and that there was a decided advantage in open debate on project planning (Miller and Lessard, 2001).

Typically, the less successful projects resulted from authoritative choices made by investors, public agencies or strong interest groups and were often carried out under time pressure. Little time was allocated to pre-project studies or to evaluation or appraisal of concepts. The original concept was maintained to save time, with insufficient emphasis on acquiring relevant information. Consequently, in many cases, projects had conflicting goals and were based on assumptions imposed by interest groups or the authorities.

Paradoxically, the greater portion of resources expended to ensure project success is not used up-front but during the implementation phase. Moreover, the greater part of the resources expended up-front is used to work out a relatively detailed strategic plan, while only a relatively smaller part of the resources are used in concept development, that is, to identify and test alternatives and delineate a strategic framework for the final project.

This is perhaps one of the principal problems in project activities in general. Early on, before the project is initiated, there is often too little attention given to fundamental questions concerning the concept itself. There are fine-tuned, resource-intensive precision instruments for controlling processes that do not detect whether the concept is sensible or not. In many cases, the methods are used to marginally improve concepts that should have been discarded and thereby contribute to upholding them. Projects with budgets in the billions are precision controlled in time spent, costs incurred and quality delivered, while the choice of concept itself is insufficiently considered.

This is due in part to the complexity of assessments, as they depend not only on knowing, but also on foreseeing. In the initial phase, uncertainty is greatest and the amount of reliable, factual information smallest. At that stage, there is not a great diversity of methods to apply, because information is scarce, qualitative and often judgemental. Consequently, it makes little sense to use precision instruments.

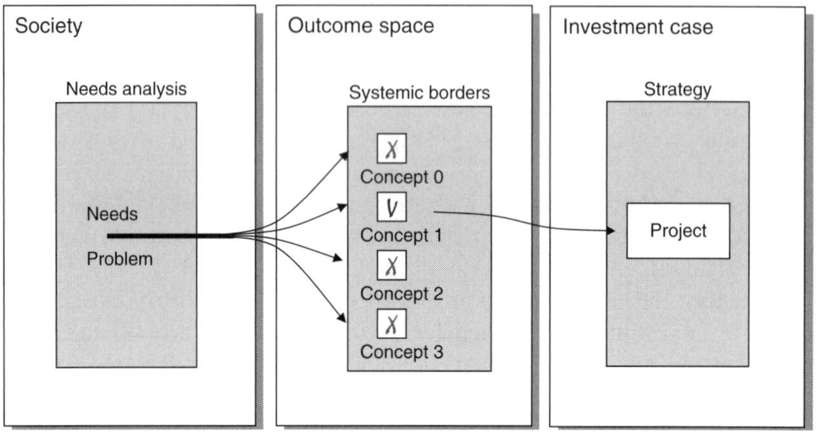

Figure 2.2 An investment case is implemented as a project after prior assessment of alternative concepts

2.6 IDENTIFYING ALTERNATIVE PROJECT CONCEPTS

A major challenge in the front-end phase is to identify one or several viable concepts and evaluate them. In the context of mega-projects, a 'concept' is a mental construction meant to help solve a problem or satisfy a need. Concepts should be generic in the sense that several concepts could be envisioned as alternative solutions to the same problem – all essentially different in the sense that they are not merely variants of one specific solution to the problem. This is illustrated in Figure 2.2, in which the investment case is distinguished from the mega-project. The investment case is an abstract construction or an instrument used by the commissioning party as a basis for appropriating funds, subsequently to be implemented in a mega-project.

The investment case is constructed as a cause–effect chain that originates in specific needs in society. These will be operationalized as goals in the strategy, and finally resolved in terms of the effects of the mega-project after it is implemented. The needs, goals and effects are expressions of the same phenomenon that would appear at three subsequent stages: up-front, during implementation and in the operational phase. The point of departure is an undesirable condition, here called the problem, which is the cause that gives rise to a need. To satisfy the need, there must be a positive change, here called the goal. If the goal is realized, an effect is achieved so that the undesirable condition ceases. The original problem is then solved.

Needs

Intervention is necessary to make the cause–effect chain process work. This is called the concept. It comprises the actions that enable realization of the goal. The choice of concept is then guided by the original problem and the expected effect. Needs, goals and effects may be defined at various levels. The less general the definitions of needs, the more it will provide guidance in the direction of specific types of solutions. That brings in the risk of the mega-project not being suitable to attaining the overriding goals. There are numerous examples of needs analyses identifying one particular technical solution as a need, and that goals and impact assessments being constrained to implementation of a given main concept.

What this means in practice is illustrated by the following example of the planning of a transport project in an urban area suffering congestion of its main streets (Næss, 2005). At the concept level, for example, the needs may concern reducing travel time between sectors of the urban area, prompting a more environmentally friendly transport mode distribution and furthering less travel-generating, car-dependent urban development patterns. The goals at this level must reflect these needs, and the effects of various solution concepts (and their relevant combinations must be assessed).

When a main concept, such as an urban tramway system, is chosen, demand analyses, goal setting and impact assessment will focus on ensuring that it is designed and implemented in the most socially acceptable manner. Needs and goals at this level may, for example, be concerned with attaining high passenger volumes, financially favourable and environmentally friendly routing, and with contributions (through the locations of stations) to urban development in targeted areas.

Whenever demand analyses, goal setting and impact assessment at the strategic level are skipped, and instead the project level is initiated within the framework of a given solution, the initiators' needs can easily be confused with those of the society. Hence, the wishes of special interests for financial gains, prestige or ideologically preferable solutions may take precedence over top-down political goals and the needs of broader social groups. Such constraint of planning at a premature stage is a commonplace weakness in the planning of large, public investment projects.

Problems

The assumed effect is influencing the choice of concept. But often the starting point is an undesired condition or a problem that initiates a search for a solution. In such cases, there are different aspects that need to be considered in determining a concept.

First, it is essential to focus on existing problems, not assumed, probable or future ones. Second, problems should not be expressed as absence of a particular solution. For example, if the problem concerns traffic congestion, stating it in terms of too few traffic lanes restricts the problem and points to just one solution. Expressing the problem in more general terms gives latitude for several alternative solutions, such as by routing some traffic on other streets or by using other means of transport. All are solutions to the overriding problem, which in this case deals with traffic flows.

This example underscores another aspect, namely that the concepts chosen should be dissimilar. Nonetheless, they would have to share common characteristics suited to solving the same problem. If that is not the case, they are merely variants of one set solution. Of course, the final choice of solution also needs to be assessed. But that should happen not at the concept level, but at the project level after the concept has been chosen.

We have no solid tradition for identifying truly alternative concepts as bases for designing projects. The reason is that it would stimulate creative thinking and thereby increase the chances of identifying the best concept. Experience suggests that this is worthwhile. At the same time, we know that innovative thinking is no guarantee that it will happen, so there is a need to assess several alternatives. Moreover, these alternatives ought to be assessed against the zero option to avoid ending up with something that turns out to be worse than what is existing.

There are no commonly agreed guidelines for a best practice for systematic identification and selection of unique and different solutions to a problem, what is termed here as concepts. Also, there are not a great many studies that offer a systematic inquiry into how this is done in practice, the range of alternative concepts that are identified, and which ones are chosen. One such study (Minken et al., 2009) that might offer some clues on the state of affairs in the Norwegian setting, concluded the following:

- The alternatives being considered were merely different technical solutions to the same problem rather than mutually exclusive concepts.
- The tendency was that the preferred technical solutions were used to guide the choice of concept rather than vice versa.
- The link between the choice of concept and the underlying societal need or problem was often not made explicit.
- The project-triggering need or problem would frequently be confused with other perceived needs or problems.

- The anticipated, desired effect of the project was often confused with various positive or negative anticipated side-effects.
- The zero option, or the low-investment alternative solution, was often not identified, formulated or considered in relation to the alternative concepts being analysed.

Experience also suggests that we tend to prefer incremental improvements of an inferior solution – rather than making fundamental change. Further, that there is an overwhelming inertia: once set in motion a project being implemented is almost impossible to stop. On the positive side there is much to suggest that the window of opportunities is usually larger than envisioned – and largely unexplored.

Outcome Space

The window of opportunities is exactly the same as what is termed the outcome space in Figure 2.2. It is delineated by the systemic borders that will define what can be identified as possible concepts. These borders would to a considerable degree translate into what would subsequently be the investment case's strategic frame for the mega-project. Laying out the systemic borders at an early stage is therefore much more essential than formulating objectives according to the SMART requirement that would eventually have to be done later, when the mega-project is implemented.

One challenge would be to apply different perspectives in the quest for sensible conceptual solutions, including (1) the retrospective, looking at trends in the past, (2) the normative, identifying the desirable and useful, (3) the explorative, using projections to identify what is possible, (4) the interdisciplinary, to identify opportunities, uncertainty and risk, and (5) the counterfactual, that take a second look at the zero option, which would usually be the lowest-cost alternative (Samset, 2010).

The problem of defining the outcome space to allow for alternative mutually exclusive concepts is illustrated in the following example. Proposals have long been made to build a tunnel for ships through a mountain between two fjords on the west coast of Norway. Ships then need not sail near a stretch of the coast where the sea is particularly rough when waves are large. The idea made sense in the old days when ships were small and stayed close to the coast where the sea is at its worst. The ships of today are larger and safer and can sail further out. Shipwrecks are things of the past.

Nonetheless, again and again proposals have been made by local authorities to build the tunnel with government funding. But they have repeatedly been turned down on the grounds that the concept of a tunnel was not feasible, the net benefit would be negative. Instead, two other projects were implemented by the government to improve safety at sea. The first charted a shipping lane further out from the problematical areas near land. The second initiated continuous monitoring and reporting of wind and wave conditions, directly accessible via the Internet.

Now the project originators proposed a larger tunnel that could accommodate even larger ships. However, this makes the concept even less suitable, because its logic remains unchanged. A larger tunnel will be even less relevant (because larger ships are less affected by the problem) and less profitable (because construction costs would be far greater). Moreover, safety already is greatly improved, with modern and safer vessels, new shipping lanes and wave warnings.

In this case, there is one problem (safety at sea) and five different concepts to solve it (safer ships, safer shipping lanes, wave warnings, small tunnel, large tunnel). The first three concepts have already been implemented. The last two are irrelevant and very expensive. In reality all concepts are possible within the common outcome space since they will all help improve safety at sea. However, if the outcome space is restricted by the size of investment the last two will have to be excluded. More so because they are both variants of the same concept, and because the first three have already by and large solved the initial problem.

2.7 ESTIMATING COSTS AND BENEFITS

In project management, cost is the management parameter that attracts the most attention during the front-end phase and implementation. In many projects, however, even large cost overruns have had little effect on long-term economic viability. Yet in other cases, cost overruns may comprise a death blow. Cost is eminently suitable as a management parameter, because it is expressed quantitatively with great precision and is continuously updated as a part of all transactions. Costs are suited to making participants accountable, to gauging progress and result attainment and to comparing expenses with income to assess economic viability over time.

The prime focus is on cost overruns related to budgets. Major cost overruns can be serious, not least because they may trigger prolonged conflicts between the responsible parties on who shall pay the bills or how costs shall be divided. But the relative size of costs involved in budget overruns is often only the tip of an iceberg. In many cases, the budget increase in the front-end phase, from the first cost estimate to the adopted budget, is much greater. An interesting observation is that in mega-projects in general, the initial cost estimate, almost without exception, is lower not higher than what eventually is decided as the final budget.

Flyvbjerg (2009) examines the various reasons behind the 'pervasive misinformation' that persistently troubles project estimation – not only technical explanations, such as inadequate data or lack of experience, but the main headings of optimism bias and strategic underestimation of costs. In the last of these, in many cases, underestimation of cost is done on purpose: underbidding might significantly improve the chance that the project is considered. Once 'on the list' it stands a better chance of being implemented. Decision-makers demonstrate a surprising degree of tolerance for what is accepted in terms of unrealistic estimates up-front without repercussion for the involved parties. This is so common that we talk not only of systematic underestimation but also of normalization of deviance (Pinto, 2006). Ultimately, this implies a culture where fundamental requirements regarding reliability and validity of information is neglected and decision-makers no longer see a reason to trust the figures presented. This means that inferior projects that should otherwise have been dismissed stand a better chance of being approved.

Underestimation therefore represents a considerable problem, particularly in public investment mega-projects. An inflation of the budget from the first estimate of 1000 per cent or more is not uncommon. Cost estimates typically develop as illustrated in Figure 2.3. The curve often ends up in a characteristic S shape. Cost estimates are low in the initial period when little information is available. With time, the information basis improves, and the first surprises come to light. In turn, that triggers greater focus on the effort, demands for greater openness and realistic estimates, often by independent appraisals, and the cost estimate rises rapidly to the level at which it should have been at the outset. Thereafter, there are minor modifications until the final budget is approved. The horizontal dashed line illustrates the development of cost in the front-end phase as it should have been had the process started with an estimate at a realistic level. The difference between the dashed and solid lines is called strategic underestimation.

Strategic underestimation is often of an entirely different order than the cost increases when the project is implemented, which might typically be in the range of 10–20 per cent. The problem is further compounded by overestimating benefits at an early stage, as depicted in Figure 2.4. The initial forecast is high, and may be scaled down during the front-end phase. After the mega-project is completed, benefits, for example, expressed in terms of sales figures or market demand, prove to be much less than expected. After a period the demand might increase and stabilize, and what could

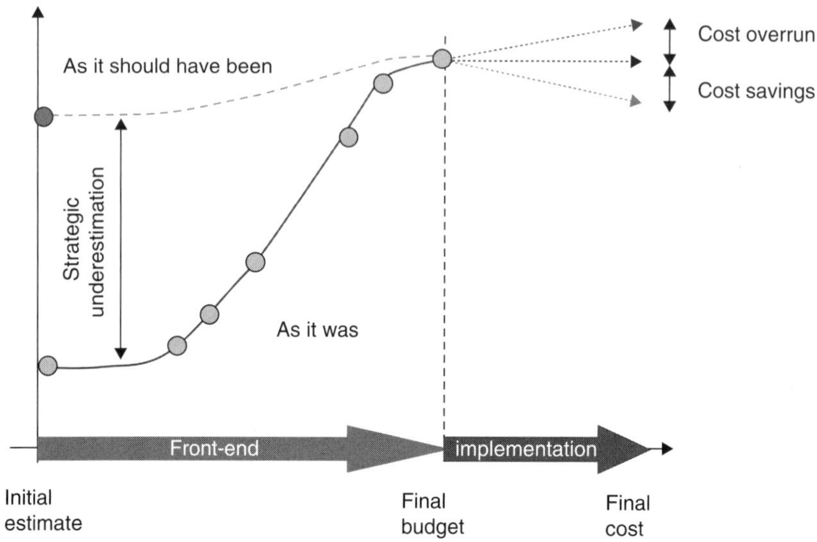

Source: Samset (2008).

Figure 2.3 *Underestimation of costs up-front is commonly more dramatic than cost overrun when the mega-project is implemented. The result might be that bad mega-projects are not dismissed at an early stage*

be termed strategic overestimation of benefits can be established, as indicated. Of course, since the benefit–cost ratio is commonly used as a decision criterion, the picture is particularly distorted in favour of the mega-project: a cost estimate half of what is realistic combined with an estimate of benefit that is double results in an anticipated benefit–cost ratio four times as high as it should be.

There is cause to believe that these sorts of bias, due either to errors or to more or less deliberate manipulation of information, are a prime reason why many poor mega-projects are chosen. In some cases, the bias is so large that further consideration of the mega-project would have been unthinkable had more realistic figures been presented in the first round.

In both types of estimation, the gap may be explained by two situations: systematic skewed estimation, which often is politically motivated; and errors that may be ascribed to flawed information and methods. It may be assumed that flawed information and methods may result in unsystematic errors, that is, errors in both directions. Whenever the estimates of several mega-projects systematically far exceed what turns out to be reality, there

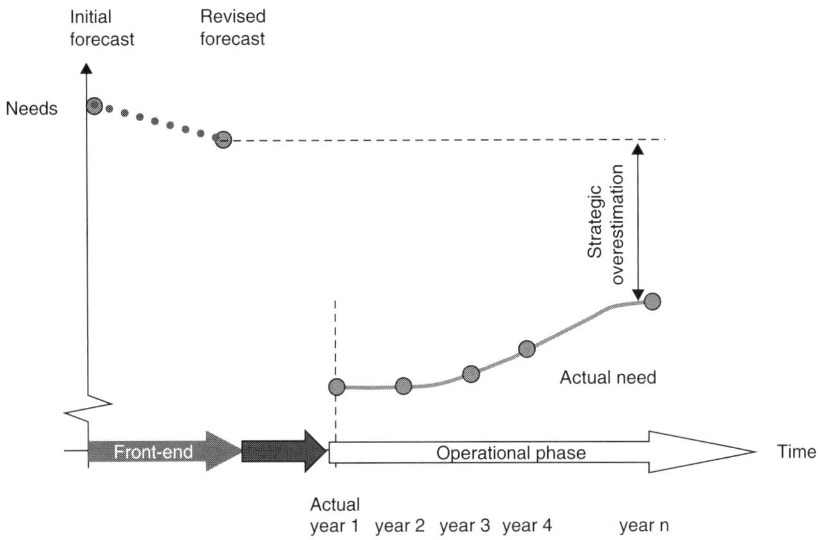

Source: Samset (2008).

Figure 2.4 Overestimation of benefits up-front is common. The realism of initial forecast can be verified only after the mega-project is completed

is reason to suspect an imbalance that can be put right only by an overriding requirement to make investigators and decision-makers more accountable. A further interesting observation is that cost overrun when a project is implemented may have considerable negative consequences for project managers – while it is unlikely that anyone will be made accountable for grave underestimation of costs up-front.

A disproportionate amount of research has focused on the problem of cost overruns in projects. The difference between budget and final cost is erroneously designated by some as strategic misrepresentation (Flyvbjerg et al., 2003). In light of the discussion above, this might rather be called tactical cost estimation. Here we may distinguish between two phenomena. Strategic underestimation in the front-end phase might influence the actual choice of project. Improving cost estimation in the front-end phase conceivably might be far more important than gaining control of cost overruns in implementation, as it may lead to fewer poor projects being chosen and thereby to increasing the overall benefit of investments.

2.8 ALIGNMENT OF OBJECTIVES, ANALYSIS AND DECISIONS

Quality-at-entry is essential to ensure successful strategic performance of mega-projects. This would involve a systematic review of underlying problems and needs, aligning needs with goals and anticipated effects, defining a realistic outcome space with corresponding delineating requirements, identifying and ranking the best alternative conceptual solutions to solve the initiating problem. Clearly, getting the alignment right is critical to the value of a mega-project. Turner (1993), for example, described the importance of the alignment of business strategy and portfolio, or programme, objectives. *The Gower Handbook of Project Management* has as its second chapter 'Implementing strategy through programmes of projects' (Jamieson and Morris, 2007). Morris (2009, p.44) points out that the UK Association of Project Managers' 'Body of Knowledge' now 'emphasises context, strategic imperative, commercial drivers, technology, the traditional control functions, and, not least, people'. This publication is concerned with how projects fit within their business/sponsor's context.

The front-end phase commences when the initial idea is conceived, and proceeds to generate information, consolidate stakeholders' views and positions and arrive at the final decision as to whether or not to finance the mega-project. To succeed in strategic terms, planners need to have a broad and long-term perspective to allow different concepts to be considered. However, this broader perspective requires planners to try to look deeper into the future; uncertainty is higher and conclusions more hypothetical and tentative, amplified by the fact that the front-end phase in mega-projects, particularly large public schemes, can extend over several years. Some authors emphasize the complexity and limitations we are up against. 'Projects are complex, ambiguous, confusing phenomena wherein the idea of a single, clear goal is at odds with the reality' (Linehan and Kavanagh, 2004). Engwall (2002) describes the establishment of the perfectly correct goal as a 'futile dream'.

Clearly, logical consistency and alignment of objectives with preferences are necessary but insufficient conditions for a rational choice. In addition, the logic needs to survive complex and unpredictable processes of subsequent analyses and negotiations, under influence of stakeholders with differing priorities, in order to end up as the final choice – preferably one that would answer to initial expectations.

Commonly, the logic behind a mega-project is strikingly simple. Still, it is often not discovered or laid out at the earliest stages of the decision-process – in some cases even neglected intentionally. Although we appreciate the rational decision model as an ideal, we are fully aware of the limitations facing planners and decision-makers in real life: time is limited, information is sparse. Analysis may be biased or inadequate. Alliances and pressures from individuals or groups of stakeholders may change. Information may be interpreted and used differently by different parties. The possibility for disinformation is considerable. Decisions may be affected more by political priorities than by rational analysis. In other words, we all live in a political reality that is not always rational or even reasonable and only to a limited degree predictable. What can be achieved by rational analysis and planning is accordingly limited.

This more complex type of decision-making is what we typically expect in a democratic society. In mega-projects, the front-end phase may last for many years and include several parliamentary election periods with changes of government. In such cases, the outcome of a decision process is difficult to foresee. This might seem to be an intractable problem. On the other hand, time-consuming processes permit ideas and decisions to mature, objectives to be aligned with policy and political preferences, stakeholders to be involved, the public to be informed, and so on. Democratic decisions take time.

The focus in this chapter is largely restricted to the idealized or rational view on how project planners should conceptualize projects and their delivery in order to achieve success. The ever-present political dynamics that arise between competing interests and explaining why such a rational approach to project management is not always followed is discussed in other chapters of this book.

A broad conclusion in this chapter is that starting with a well-formulated strategy may be an advantage, but is no guarantee of the best choice when the final decision is made. In some cases, the result may be entirely different from the initial choice. In other cases, the lengthy and unpredictable decision process may result in an optimal decision, even though the initial choice was entirely wrong.

The main concern here is to ensure successful strategic performance in the longer-term perspective. There is much evidence to suggest that measures to ensure quality-at-entry might be useful to that effect, but no guarantee. But there is also considerable evidence to conclude that if the quality-at-entry is inadequate, the chance of success will be severely restricted.

LITERATURE

Engwall, M. (2002), 'The futile dream of the perfect goal', in K. Sahil-Andersson and A. Soderholm (eds), *Beyond Project Management: New Perspectives on the Temporary–Permanent Dilemma*, Malmo: Copenhagen Business School Press, pp. 261–77.

Flyvbjerg, B. (2009), 'Optimism and misrepresentation in early project development', in T. Williams, K. Samset and K. Sunnevåg (eds), *Making Essential Choices with Scant Information*, Basingstoke: Palgrave Macmillan.
Flyvbjerg, B., N. Bruzelius and W. Rothengatter (2003), *Megaprojects and Risk: An Anatomy of Ambition*, Cambridge, UK: Cambridge University Press.
HM Treasury (2007), *Transforming Government Procurement*, London: HM Treasury, accessed 5 June 2013 at http://www.hm-treasury.gov.uk/d/government_procurement_pu147.pdf.
Jamieson, A. and P. Morris (2007), 'Implementing strategy through programmes of projects', in R. Turner (ed.), *The Gower Handbook on Project Management*, Aldershot: Gower Publishing Ltd.
Linehan, C. and D. Kavanagh (2004), 'From project ontologies to communities of virtue', paper presented at the 2nd International Workshop, 'Making Projects Critical', 13–14 December, University of Western England, UK.
Miller, R. and B. Hobbs (2009), 'The complexity of decision-making in large projects with multiple partners: be prepared to change', in T. Williams, K. Samset and K. Sunnevåg (eds), *Making Essential Choices with Scant Information*, Basingstoke: Palgrave Macmillan.
Miller, R. and D. Lessard (2001), *The Strategic Management of Large Engineering Projects: Shaping Institutions, Risks and Governance*, Cambridge, MA: MIT Press.
Minken, H., A. Strand, I. Jordanger and S. Malerud (2009), *Multi-criteria Decision Analysis in Major Public Investment Projects*, Concept Report No. 18 (in Norwegian), Trondheim: Norwegian University of Science and Technology.
Morris, P.W.G. (1994), *The Management of Projects*, London: Thomas Telford.
Morris, P. (2009), 'Implementing strategy through project management: the importance of managing the project front-end', in T. Williams, K. Samset and K. Sunnevåg (eds), *Making Essential Choices with Scant Information*, Basingstoke: Palgrave Macmillan.
Morris, P. (2011), 'A brief history of project management', in P. Morris, J.K. Pinto and J. Søderlund, *The Oxford Handbook on Project Management*, Oxford: Oxford University Press.
Næss, P. (2005), *Improved Design of Public Investment Projects. Up-front Appraisal of Needs, Objectives and Effects*, Concept Report No. 9 (in Norwegian), Trondheim: Norwegian University of Science and Technology.
Pinto, J. (2006), 'Organizational governance and project success: lessons from Boston's Big Dig', The Concept Symposium on Projects Governance, Trondheim: Norwegian University of Science and Technology, Fall.
Pinto, J. (2007), *Project Management: Achieving Competitive Advantage*, Upper Saddle River, NJ: Pearson Education Inc.
Pinto, J.K. and D.P. Slevin (1988), 'Project success: definition and measurement techniques', *Project Management Journal*, **XIX**(1), 67–71.
Project Management Institute (PMI) (2008), *A Guide to the Project Management Body of Knowledge*, Newtown Square, PA: Project Management Institute, USA.
Samset, K. (2008), 'How to overcome major weaknesses in mega-projects: the Norwegian approach', in H. Priemus, B. Flyvbjerg and B. van Wee (eds), *Decision-Making on Mega-Projects: Cost–Benefit Analysis, Planning and Innovation*, Cheltenham, UK and Northampton MA, USA: Edward Elgar, pp. 173–88.
Samset, K. (2010), *Early Project Appraisal: Making the Initial Choices*, Basingstoke: Palgrave Macmillan.
Samset, K. and B. Dowdeswell (2008), 'Concept planning: getting capital investment right', in B. Rechtel, S. Wright, N. Edwards, B. Dowdeswell and M. McKee, *Investing in Hospitals of the Future*, World Health Organization, on behalf of the European Observatory of Health Systems and Policies.
Shenhar, A.J., D. Dvir, O. Levy and A.C. Maltz (2001), 'Project success: a multidimensional strategic concept, long range planning', **34**(6), 699–725.
Szyliowicz, J. and A. Goetz (1995), 'Getting realistic about megaproject planning: the case of the new Denver International Airport', *Policy Sciences*, **28**(4), 347–67.

Tempest, M. (2004), 'Scottish parliament opens for business', guardian.co.uk, 7 September, accessed 5 June 2013 at http://www.guardian.co.uk/politics/2004/sep/07/scotland.devolution.
Turner, J.R. (1993), *The Handbook of Project-based Management*, Maidenhead: McGraw-Hill.
van der Heijden, K. (1996), *Scenarios: The Art of Strategic Conversation*, London: John Wiley & Sons.
Williams, T. (2008), 'Decisions made on scant information', in T. Williams, K. Samset and K. Sunnevåg (eds), *Making Essential Choices with Scant Information*, Basingstoke: Palgrave Macmillan.
Williams, T., K. Samset and K. Sunnevåg (eds) (2009), *Making Essential Choices with Scant Information: Front-End Decision-Making in Major Projects*, Basingstoke: Palgrave Macmillan.
World Bank (1996), *Evaluation Results 1994*, Washington DC: The International Bank of Reconstruction and Development.

3. The shaping of large engineering projects

*Donald R. Lessard and Roger Miller**

3.1 INTRODUCTION

Large engineering projects (LEPs) are games of ambition in which sponsors aim to build solutions to unmet needs. LEPs may involve the development of major engineering breakthroughs, pushing the engineering envelope of production systems through major capital investments, and/or developing new institutional constructs that allow diverse project actors and stakeholders to collaborate.[1] Sponsors of these large engineering projects often face a choice between taking few risks by limiting themselves to standardized solutions or to push for innovative configurations that provide more complete solutions while entailing more risk and complexity.

In this chapter we focus on an often overlooked aspect of LEPs – the 'fuzzy' front-end of opportunity and project shaping where the project concept, the projects sponsors and core team, and the engagement of various stakeholders co-evolve through the concerted efforts of a small number of players interacting with many emergent factors. Mega-projects are not simply selected. Instead, they are shaped over multiple episodes through strategic moves with risk resolution in mind. In 'one off' multi-party projects, these early stages include not only developing the project concept, but also the project coalition itself. In the case of LEPs led by established firms, such as oil and gas or electric power generation projects, these early stages are typically conducted by business development units rather than by the projects function within the firm.

The shaping of large engineering projects, including mega-projects, is the most important stage with the most flexibility to create a successful project or a failure. Despite this, it is possibly the least researched stage of project management. As noted by Morris (2009) this is in large part due to the execution focus of the projects management profession and literature.[2] Historical accounts of LEPs (McCullough, 1972; Hughes, 2000), in contrast, point to the important role of the sponsor in shaping a vision, attracting resources, garnering support and overcoming obstacles in the early stages. Morris and Hough's foundational study of mega-projects (1987) did point to factors that occurred in the early stages of projects as key to late delivery and cost overruns.

In 2001 we published a study (Miller and Lessard, 2001) that focused on the 'front-end' shaping of a large number of mega-projects. Soon after Flyvbjerg et al. (2003) published a study showing that many aspects of projects' ultimate performance were laid down during the early stages through the (over) promises and (mis) representations of project advocates. More recently, an increasing number of scholars have turned their attention to front-end issues. Priemus (2008, p. 106) argues and provides evidence that many later-stage problems are the result of 'defining the solution before the problem' in early stages. Williams et al. (2009) address various front-end aspects, but particularly those associated with the need to make decisions with scant information. Most recently, Merrow (2011), a leading authority on industrial projects, devotes a considerable proportion of his in-depth empirical analysis of mega-projects to front-end issues, building on our shaping perspective. This chapter builds on these ideas and links them to risk management and internal and external stakeholder management.

Front-end shaping is most important for mega-projects that are pioneering in either the technical or institutional domain, or both. Many mega-projects are pioneering in that they require significant departures from business as usual. LEPs include transport infrastructure mega-projects such as new roads, bridges, airports or integrated systems to meet growing traffic demand, power plants or grid expansions to ensure electric energy supply, as well as technology projects such as enterprise information systems to better manage resources, suppliers or client relations and so on. They also include extractive projects and large manufacturing plants.

The analysis of more than 100 large infrastructure, resource and information technology projects with which we have been associated over the last 20 years has led us to the conclusion that projects in general, and mega-projects in particular, are shaped.[3] Sponsors invest heavily in front-end planning to reduce major uncertainties and build coalitions to manage the commitment and risk ownership process. The seeds of success or failures are planted early.

In the next two sections of this chapter, we will examine the key attributes of large engineering projects and sketch the real nature of decision-making as we have observed it. Second, we will examine the varying approaches to valuing projects with a special emphasis on the options perspective. Third, we will propose a perspective of our own, which we call managing the process of commitment to gain flexibility in the front-end shaping period and governability during ramp-up and operations. Then, we will show how uncertainty and risk evolve over the life of this process and how risks are engaged, shaped, assigned, contained, and ultimately resolved. Finally, we will conclude by restating that successful projects, including mega-projects, are not simply selected but that they are shaped over multiple episodes through strategic moves with risk resolution in mind.

3.2 THE ATTRIBUTES OF LEPs

Simple projects take place in predictable environments. LEPs, including mega-projects, by contrast are complicated and complex ventures[4] that rapidly become difficult to manage because of the intertwined political, organizational, technical and institutional elements.[5] The main attributes of LEPs are the following:

1. The journey from the initial identification of the opportunity to engineering design, the construction sprint and ramp-up where revenues are generated can take more than ten years on average. Long lags between the need to make major commitments and outcomes are commonplace, and at times extend even longer. Front-end planning activities are spread over many years, yet the highly visible construction sprint takes only a few years. Substantial front-end shaping expenditures have to be incurred prior to committing. During the ramp-up period, market estimates are tested and the true worth of the project becomes apparent; sponsors may find that it is much lower than expected.
2. LEPs involve large, lumpy and irreversible financial commitments. Unlike R&D projects where a small allocation of effort can be used to test the waters, most LEPs have to be totally built prior to delivering services. Once built, assets are difficult to redeploy for other than the original purpose. Large engineering projects, including mega-projects, are thus high-stakes games characterized by substantial irreversible commitments and high probabilities of failure. Potential returns can be good but they are often truncated because of the myriad of interests involved and the potential for hold-up and re-contracting.
3. It is unusual for mega-projects to be directed by a single party who coordinates all communications, contracts and activities, and thus imparts a high level of coherence. Instead, LEPs involve multiple parties with differing ownership stakes and interests, each trying to exercise some leadership, impose requirements or suggest solutions. Sponsors have to act as orchestrators aiming at developing agreements. Bringing mega-projects to fruition thus requires the building of one or many coalitions of partners to frame the task and orient the constituencies and mobilize the resources required. Only

then can the conception, design and delivery of the mega-project proceed.

4. The dominant risks are broad and fall into the following categories: (a) demand and markets (b) the coalition of partners and sponsors (c) geo-political and institutional risks and (d) physical and technical challenges.[6] Foreseeable risks are often accompanied by the emergence of unplanned events in the course of project shaping, but these are gradually reduced as efforts are expended to control them. When external and internal conditions change radically, risks erupt and often combine to create turbulence; projects are thus subjected to high volatility. In the absence of institutional buttresses, turbulence and unexpected shocks can send a project into a degenerating crisis.
5. Each project has its set of interdependent issues. Decisions are rarely made in large-scale once-and-for-all planning efforts. Interdependent issues cannot be resolved all at once. Instead, issues form bundles of interlinked problems. Resolutions of key problems are often pre-conditions for proceeding to the resolution of other logically interlinked issues and problems. With the passage of time, previously resolved issues may re-emerge in different forms and become challenges that call for new efforts. Even issues for which formal agreements had been made must be re-opened as conditions and power shifts occur.

3.3 THE REALITY OF MEGA-PROJECT DECISION-MAKING

Not surprisingly, the task of shaping mega-projects before they can be engineered, built and ramped is a very messy process. The reality of decision-making in most mega-projects is often out of line with many of the assumptions of projection-based approaches.[7] Forecasting of revenues and costs into the future is possible for simple projects but difficult and nearly impossible for complex ones. Few are the mega-projects in which major choices are made in a few planning sessions.

Sponsors begin by making forecasts of revenues and costs but rapidly become aware that they must actively shape projects along multiple dimensions if they are to move ahead. Sponsors face strong uncertainties and must grapple with non-linear dynamics, emergent risks and renewed interdependencies. Sponsors thus do not sit idle, waiting for probabilities to materialize; they judge risks, imagine ways to cope, and work hard to shape outcomes. Sponsors divide the myriad of decisions necessary to commit into episodes containing the most salient sets of interdependent issues. This stylized process involves the unfolding of decision-making over the course of the shaping of the project rather than through a set of once-and-for-all decisions.

Sponsors with Competences

The active shaping of mega-projects requires sponsors with capabilities, deep pockets and the proper framing of issues. The prime competency is the ability to behave as a responsible owner who will analyse, fund and operate the project for the long term and live with the consequences of choices or omissions. Sponsors thus become experts in domains beyond engineering: (1) coalition building, (2) political relations and (3) public affairs.

Effective sponsors have the competencies to decide rapidly whether a mega-project's concept has value: they form task forces in which owner-operators join with lawyers, consultants and investment bankers to decide with diligence whether the idea is worth pursuing. Sponsors seek advice about market, technical and institutional-political uncertainties before they commit. Effective sponsors also have the *relational competencies* to engage in coalition-building and credible discussions with political authorities, bankers, multilateral agencies and other relevant parties.

Finally, effective sponsors have staying power when major downside risks materialize. Streams of revenues from the operations of a diversified portfolio of projects help sponsors adequately fund the development of front-end choices and the flexibility to react. In times of crisis sponsors can call on a network of partners and coalition members to help a mega-project survive.

The shaping of mega-projects is a costly, time-consuming business often beyond the reach of entrepreneurial firms. Planning expenditures range in the front-end from 2–3 per cent of the total cost for standard projects up to 30 per cent for highly complex ones. While many executives or politicians view shaping expenses as frivolous, effective clients view these as necessary.

Past experience in the shaping of mega-projects broadens the field of view. Experienced sponsors who have travelled across various rugged landscapes in the past know how to react in the face of strategic bifurcations, thresholds, interdependent opportunities and even idiosyncratic characteristics of mega-projects. These competencies will play a role in the development of options.

Division of Labour between the Sponsors and Experts

The entrepreneurial function in large engineering projects is shared between the leading sponsor, strategy consultants and systems engineering firms. Typically, the process starts with senior-level interactions between the leading sponsor and consultants to help define the competitive issues, innovation opportunities and broad project configuration. Once the interdependent strategy issues have been resolved, sponsors build teams with consultants to sketch out the architecture and outline the kinds of agreements that will ensure the project's viability. Sponsors then invite systems engineers with accumulated expertise to design, and articulate the novel solutions. Ideas are shared in generative debates and discussions.[8]

In order to ensure that projects can go forward, coalitions need to be built. Stakeholders demand that each project earns its right to exist. Challenges can erupt violently early or late. Sponsors have to meet the new expectations of legitimate parties as projects are introduced into the social fabric. Agreements that were thought to be firm are questioned and sometimes rejected. In some cases, projects are abandoned because no choice can be decided upon.

Consultants and systems engineers must stay significantly ahead of the sponsors that they are trying to advise. The means used by consulting experts to develop their competencies are: (1) learning by working with many leading sponsors who face significant challenges, (2) allying with technology suppliers and (3) accumulating past experience through knowledge management systems. Many strategy or engineering consultants fund research institutes to explore and build scenarios about the future evolution of the sectors they serve.

Multiple Shaping Episodes

Large engineering projects are certainly difficult technical tasks, but they are also political arenas that present complex decision challenges requiring versatile decision-making approaches. Grand decision-making sessions in which all options are considered rare. Instead, the shaping of a project is achieved by making interdependent and conditional choices over a series of episodes. Analysing many projects we noted that shaping occurs over six episodes, as shown in Table 3.1. Episodes constitute progressive problem-solving. Cycling back to earlier episodes is often necessary. The path taken during each episode depends on the extent of closure in the previous ones.[9]

Table 3.1 Episodes in the shaping of projects

	Shaping the Opportunity	Shaping the Project	Reshaping the Project	Engineering the Project	Sprinting to build the Project	Ramping up to Operations
Contextual conditions	Sponsor and experts shape key choices. Many degrees of freedom	Blocks of basic interdependent issues need resolution	As project gets 'real' fears and risks emerge and threaten	Period of stability as key choices are set	Linear world of project management	Irreversible lock-in with few degrees of freedom
Concept	Vision and sketches of key dimensions	Holistic solutions to interdependent issues in technology, markets and politics	Concept adapted to powerful players as they mobilize as project gets real	Multi-dimensional concept is clear and becomes a plan	Concept is fixed. Fast construction to achieve revenue generation	Concept is locked: market, technology and political agreements
Coalition	Credible sponsor recruits experts and key stakeholders	Roles defined: champion, experts, supporters and forbearers	Broad set of members and powerful stakeholders	Broad set of stakeholders gives licence to proceed	Coalition is fixed, buttressed by formal agreements	Coalition is fixed and callable resources are made available
Form of commitment	Verbal, informal but often public, but open to further shaping	Credible sponsor announces intentions	Agreement with powerful stakeholders	Detailed business plan	Sets of contracts and specifications	Final commitments. Ownership and financial structure
Process	Multiple iterations around vision	Sponsor, partners and stakeholders negotiate	Iteration to stress test concept and coalition	Formal contracts and partnership	Back to linear world	All relationships are stabilized
Closure	Memorandum of Agreement	Concrete frame agreement	Agreement working out consequences of real project	Detailed plans	Contracts	Stable contracts and irreversible choices

Shaping the opportunity

This episode lasts from a year to a few years as the sponsor and the experts develop the concept, build the coalition of partners and signal their readiness to act. The sponsor seeks to establish itself as a credible party that will allocate resources to start planning and debate on the appropriate ways and means of shaping and financing the idea. As the opportunity becomes public, new challenges and stakeholders emerge and the opportunity often has to be redefined to either include these interests or avoid obstacles.

Without a credible vision put forward by the leading sponsor, the project remains in an infancy trap. Typically, the sponsor allocates a few million dollars to explore and develop the concept. Engineering, financial and marketing feasibility studies are undertaken to understand risks. Closure is achieved after much iteration when various stakeholders have had their say and independent studies confirm the viability of the concept. A Memorandum of Agreement sketches out the agreements.

Shaping the project

The sponsor may decide to drop the project or instead embark on further iteration to refine the concept, solve the interdependent problems and solidify the coalition of partners. Typically sponsors will allocate large sums (even up to few dozen millions of dollars) to develop a complete solution.

Shaping the project involves the building of an investment scenario as well as the writing of a business case for investors. Discussions aim at building a coalition of partners to create strong ownership. Negotiations are held to ensure that eventual investments are protected against opportunistic behaviours by focusing on devices such as long-term contracts, frame agreements and so on.

Specialized partners join with the promise to contribute to overall value creation, often hoping to capture ‘more than their fair share’. The result is a seesaw between positive-sum collaboration and zero-sum gaming. Eventually, the balance becomes acceptable.

Reshaping the project

Once it becomes clear that the project is likely to go ahead, fears surface and affected interests mobilize. The sponsor regains the consent of affected parties by recognizing their rights, negotiating compensation and otherwise engaging in proactive strategies with communities. Gaining the right to build a mega-project often requires the leading sponsor to prove its good faith by incurring expenditures for cleaning up polluted sites, organizing referenda or building complementary facilities and so on. Sponsors may also need to set up economic development initiatives to demonstrate their credible commitments.

Unresolved issues that were skipped as the holistic proposal was developed now call for action. If parties are unable to forge agreements, they must wait for court, political or government decisions. The presence of public, social and environmental assessment frameworks and the engagement of relevant NGOs are extremely important here in helping to solve the dilemmas. Delays are the inevitable consequence of such formal assessments, but the public framework builds legitimacy and forces parties either to make trade-offs or to kill the project.

Engineering the project

The concept of the mega-project is now clear and the coalition of partners is firm. Commitment on a final package takes place when most major issues that have been identified are resolved, specific designs are produced and roles for execution are defined. In many mega-projects, sponsors may have spent up to a few hundred million dollars to gain consent, solve social and environmental issues and build agreements. Once a concept is selected front-end engineering starts. Even though the process from concept selection to engineering design is typically viewed as a waterfall, front-end engineering design often unearths new issues of a technical nature and/or among the various parties that requires a recycle to concept selection.

Sprinting to build the project

This episode, which is the focus of most formal tools for project management, usually takes place in a context of relative stability. The detailed design, procurement and construction sprint period should begin once full shaping has been achieved. In practice, time pressures often lead to an overlapping of these stages with the potential for recycle. The value of sprinting is that the economic value of the mega-project is highly geared to how quickly the revenues arrive given that major expenditures mount quickly and commitments are being made. The major constraint is the time required to adequately perform the various tasks along the critical path without incurring undue risk. Turbulence at this stage is usually lower, as most major issues have been resolved.

Ramping up to Operations

Once the mega-project is built, it enters into a ramp-up period. It is here that expectations about markets, technical functionality and social acceptability are tested. In extreme cases the 'teething problems' are so serious that the project is recycled into reshaping; if no adequate (re)definition is possible the mega-project dies. After a few years of ramp-up, the mega-project either performs satisfactorily or is deemed a white elephant.

3.4 METHODS OF ANALYSIS IN THE VALUATION OF MEGA-PROJECTS

When there are multiple owners and/or stakeholders, each with distinct objectives as is typical of mega-projects, there can be no single value criterion. Different stakeholders will capture different costs and benefits and will place different values on non-priced outcomes. This is the case for 'economic' mega-projects such as oil/gas and mineral extraction, and even more so for mega-projects that are designed to deliver multiple benefits, for example, dams with power, flood control, or agriculture benefits or transport mega-projects that deliver market 'values' but also change real estate values. In this section we will look at various ways to value mega-projects.

Projection-based Valuation

Mega-projects are often viewed as ventures that can be planned and specified in advance. In this view, mega-projects form a sequential unity. Each phase is a more detailed definition of the previous one. Quite often, this view is accompanied by the assumption that the passage of time does not appreciably change conditions. Forecasting of costs, revenues and other performance dimensions using models based on trends and accumulated data is a major part of front-end planning. Forecasting presupposes that there is a narrow range of possible futures that are waiting to be unveiled. However, some risks and opportunities are inherently non-forecastable.

Net present value (NPV) (and the closely related concept of internal rate of return – IRR; see Chapter 14) is the most widely used planning and evaluation technique. Though there are many variants, in essence NPV takes expected cash flows (revenues and costs) in each period and combines them into a single present value using a discount rate that reflects both the price of time and the price of risk. In the widely used capital asset pricing model (CAPM) formulation, the price of time is given by the risk-free rate. The risk premium is given by the market risk premium multiplied by the market sensitivity or beta of the mega-project in question.

Caveats to NPV techniques are well known. The biggest drawback in early planning stages is that it is difficult if not impossible to fully specify the distributions of various cash flow elements, and hence expectations, over the life of the mega-project. Further, discounting the cash flows at a single risk-adjusted discount rate is inappropriate given that risks are resolved differentially over time.

In the early stages of opportunity and mega-project shaping the focus should be on identifying the key variables that affect value and how these can be shaped, rather than seeking to pin down the probabilities of various scenarios. Projections of (the present value of) cash flows under specific scenarios can be used to test whether or not the mega-project could be valuable, and these in turn can be used to assess the threshold likelihood of the convergence of circumstances required to justify proceeding. Projection-based approaches are thus valid for simple projects, but they are inadequate for complex mega-projects facing high levels of complexity and uncertainty.

Decision Trees

Decision trees provide yet another avenue for modelling and valuing mega-projects, and would seem ideally suited since they allow for large numbers of future decision branches. However, in early planning stages the branches are more likely to be among scenarios involving many variables rather than single drivers. The 'present discounted values' of the mega-project under these alternative futures will be indicative at best since it is difficult to value payoffs that have both 'market-priced' and private risk drivers. While advanced decision-tree analysis can handle multiple drivers, including market-priced such as oil prices or disposable income as well as non-market drivers,[10] these valuation techniques will be most applicable in the 'engineering the mega-project' phase, after substantial commitments are made. Earlier stages typically involve multiple value drivers and perspectives, and require a great deal of judgement and art.

The Options Perspective to Evaluate Mega-projects

Methods in which mega-project cash flows are valued as a set of nested options on some underlying value driver or drivers would appear to fit large engineering projects much better. Mostly developed for the valuation of derivative financial instruments, the options approach is useful both as a metaphor for mega-projects and as a specific valuation method. The biggest difference between real options analysis (ROA) and decision trees, is that ROA formally incorporates the state-dependent pricing of risk, typically by adjusting the probabilities in the 'tree' so that the values can be discounted at risk-free rates.[11]

As metaphor, there is no question that options theories are appropriate. The shaping process we have just described is one of creating, managing (shaping, keeping warm, and so on), and exercising (or allowing to expire without exercise) a series of options. As a valuation technique, ROA for mega-projects requires pushing the modelling state of the art. Nonetheless, in large-scale extractive projects, which above all else are bets on the underlying price of oil or minerals, real options models have made substantial headway.

The difficulty with options value analysis for the type of large engineering projects we have studied is that each type of mega-project involves many options keyed not to one performance dimension such as a commodity price, but to a variety of drivers, some of which are not fully characterized and most are not actively traded in financial markets.

Take the example of the Canadian Confederation Bridge discussed in Miller and Lessard (2001). One element of uncertainty is traffic revenue, which depends both on political decisions and market forces. The market-force-based aspect could be modelled as a claim on the underlying economic activity. The cost of building the bridge, similarly, is driven in part by steel and concrete prices that might be modelled. However, the evolution of public perceptions of the legitimacy of a private sector firm receiving and assigning ongoing public 'subsidies' is a process that has no counterpart in financial markets, but nevertheless was a key element in the shaping of the mega-project. Similarly, the acceptance within a particular setting of institutional frameworks such as design–build–operate cannot be readily modelled.

While 'real options' are certainty part of the logic of mega-projects in the early stages, formal qualitative real options analyses keyed to one (or a few) underlying processes are unlikely to be applicable. Instead, more appropriate methods for analysis at this stage include discrete or Monte Carlo simulations with ad hoc valuation, or qualitative analysis across scenarios whereby the sponsor determines that the mega-project will be economic under various plausible scenarios, thus justifying moving forward.[12,13]

Even as a metaphor the options approach may have serious limits to the extent that it fosters an optimistic view of risks and promotes the illusion that sponsors do not need to commit, but can delay decisions to profit by long windows of opportunities. Sponsors cannot build mega-projects by postponing decisions: they must commit.

3.5 MANAGING THE COMMITMENT PROCESS

In this section, we present our approach that recognizes that mega-projects are shaped through iterative processes of searching for flexibility and governability while making decisions to commit when closure appears to be viable. To accommodate the various interests, the leading sponsor uses the front-end period to identify mutual-gain trajectories. Shaping may stretch the limits of sponsors' capabilities, but at the same time it offers substantial benefits that cannot be achieved with simpler projection-based approaches.

Infusing Flexibility and Governability

Mega-projects involve large commitments that are often irreversible. The real options approach proposes to deal with rigidities by searching for flexibility into the planning of projects. Sponsors thus hope to stay flexible in the face of futures that are often hard to predict or influence.

Flexibility

The search for flexibility may take many paths. Sponsors may design their mega-projects' technical, economic, commercial, organizational or political configurations in such ways as to be able to adapt to future environmental changes. Investing in information gathering may suggest delaying certain decisions or looking for growth opportunity with high volatility on specific dimensions.

In the search for flexibility, sponsors may agree to build mega-projects in stages, select an architecture that accepts varying inputs or remain ready to further share benefits with powerful stakeholders. Mega-projects can be decoupled into technical or economic modules and be built progressively. The sponsor may even select partners as a function of their ability to bring callable resources in case of emergency. The sponsor may be ready to share ownership with new partners in order to save the mega-project. Above all, the sponsor will retain the flexibility to drop the venture so as not to be dragged into committing to a non-viable mega-project.

There are limits to the search for flexibility. Mega-projects are not always divisible into modules; a bridge has to be built fully to be of use. Windows of opportunity may be short and require bold actions. Affected parties may become intolerant of delays and demand actions. Hesitations by sponsors may lead to deadlocks as affected parties refuse to wait.

Governability

Governability is a form of flexibility instilled though strategic thinking about the obligations or responsibilities that could be triggered should turbulence emerge. The goal is to embed self-correcting mechanisms to prevent catastrophic failures. Examples of emerging turbulence are: (1) failures of markets to materialize as planned (2) unexpected price changes that cut revenues or (3) bankruptcies of partners that manage specific risks.

Devices to impart governability are project-specific. Here are some illustrative examples. First the leading sponsor, its partners and the bankers agree in formal arrangements to respond when new conditions appear. Second, covenants and protocols specify in advance the terms of the obligations to respond. Third, the founding contract with the state sets in advance the conditions under which market price variations or other changes in mega-project conditions will allow the reopening of agreements or call for forbearance.

Opening and Closing of Episodes and Agreements

For each of the shaping episodes, sponsors form hypotheses about the extent of progress that can be achieved for each one of the many issues that need to be resolved. Bundles of interrelated issues must be solved together. This typically involves 'buying in' some stakeholders and 'buying off' others to elicit agreements, as illustrated in Figure 3.1.

In each episode, as sponsors shape mega-projects, the forces of criticisms, professional challenges and differences of opinion constrain efforts. Sponsors pursue flexibility while other parties want them to commit. By contrast, sponsors often yield to the temptations of making unreasonable

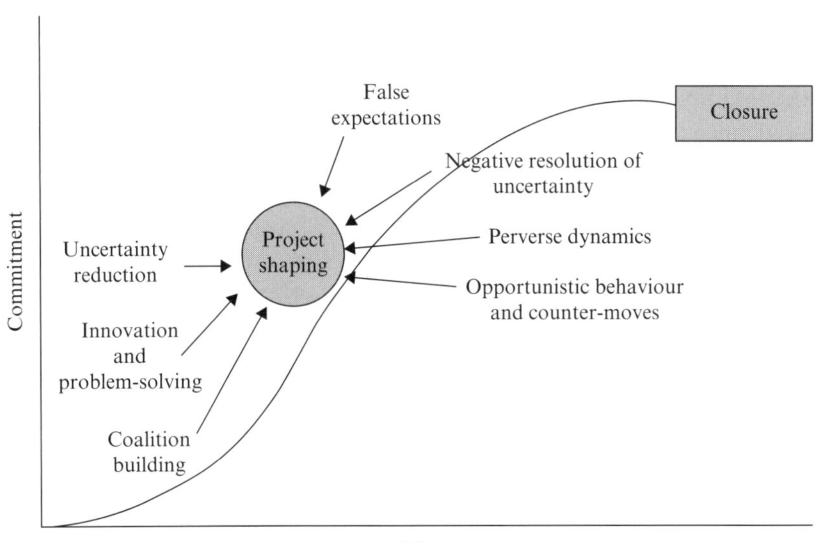

Figure 3.1 Shaping in the face of resistance

commitments. Excessive realism may lead to scepticism and the early rejection of good opportunities.

Efforts spent on each shaping episode eventually, often after numerous iterations, reach some form of *closure*. Closure may take the form of a decision to abandon the whole venture. Closure may also converge on temporary agreements on many dimensions, thus confirming that a major milestone has been achieved. At points of closure, sponsors and partners develop clear views of the many dimensions of mega-project performance with respect to: (1) political dimensions of the venture, (2) roles and responsibilities of the sponsor and partners, (3) financial structure, (4) physical design, and so on. As they commit, sponsors and partners lose some degrees of freedom, but progress by making decisions on interlinked sets of issues and gain a rich configuration.

Agreements signalling closure of a shaping episode will take many forms: treaties between nations, memorandums of understanding, business cases, negotiated outcomes, formal public commitments, sets of formal contracts, and so on. Closure may be too early, too late, too rigid, or too flexible.

3.6 RISK RESOLUTION PROCESSES

A parallel process of uncertainty resolution and, eventually, risk reduction accompanies the progressive process of shaping, closure and commitment that we have described. Mega-projects are options on opportunities that are not fully known and for which commitments must often be placed far in advance of the resolution of key uncertainties. During each stage risks may manifest themselves and possibly erupt into turbulence.

The classification of risks varies widely in the practice of mega-projects. In many cases, risks are classified according to the type of impact they have, that is, whether they impact schedule, cost, or health/safety/security/environment (HSSE). Further, the emphasis is often on specific events and their consequences rather than on the underlying (uncertain) drivers of these events and consequences, even though a few drivers underlie many outcomes.

In Miller and Lessard (2001), we classified risks in terms of the system in which they are generated: endogenous risk drivers that are generated within the mega-project, exogenous drivers that are generated in larger external systems, and 'interactive' risks that result from interactions between the two. This is illustrated in Figure 3.2 where we organize the four types of risk identified earlier from 'inside to outside' in four different levels.[14]

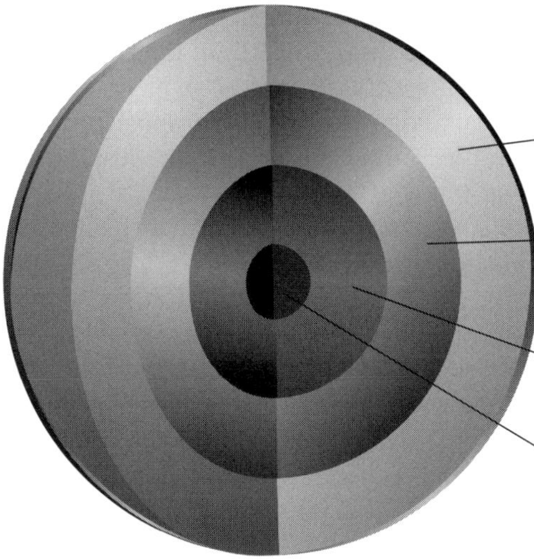

Figure 3.2 Risk drivers in mega-projects

In the earliest stage shaping the opportunity there is a great deal of ambiguity. As the mega-project is defined, risks and the underlying risk drivers are identified and understood, uncertainty is reduced through gaining information, and uncertainty is both created and resolved as the system of interacting interests is defined.

Risk resolution and commitment are inextricably linked across the various stages of mega-project shaping. At each stage, risks emerge or are better understood, either because the underlying uncertainties were not previously fully recognized or because the shaping process changes the drivers themselves. They then are engaged, structured, allocated and/or contained to the point that particular commitments are now possible, and the commitments themselves alter the endogenous drivers, risks and potential outcomes. Progress toward closure in each stage or episode also involves the reduction and even the closing out of some risks.

Market risks are apparent in all stages, but different aspects are addressed at different points. For projects that supply products into well-established commodity markets (e.g., oil/gas, mining and, possibly, electricity depending on the regulatory regime), the possible range of prices increases into the future, but typically less so than a random walk because of mean reversion. However, some mega-projects face uncertainty over the basis on which they will access these markets. This is an institutional (regulatory) risk that is resolved in the mega-project-shaping phase. In the case of an Algerian gas project, this resulted in a 'two-humped' distribution of prices going forward, with the two humps reflecting a 'favourable market access or not' decision early on, and the dispersion about the two humps reflecting the ongoing uncertainty of spot gas prices. For mega-projects that face specific demand, such as bridges or urban transport projects, projections can be made about traffic, but this uncertainty is substantially resolved only during the ramp-up phase. To the extent that the project's economics depend on regulatory actions to protect the project from competition, market risk is underpinned by the institutional risk.

Institutional risks, particularly for those mega-projects that require major regulatory changes and/or government support, come to a head in the shaping phase where they must be resolved or at least substantially reduced before the project can proceed. However, some types of public reaction only occur in the 'sprinting' phase as those who now begin to experience the physical impact of the project are mobilized. They also appear when institutional arrangements that are critical to the project turn out to be brittle. While this could also occur in the shaping phases, it often takes place later, often during ramp-up. The Orlyval Project cited in Miller and Lessard (2001) provides a case in point. It was premised on 'non-competition' from other forms of public transport, something that the authorities were unwilling or unable to deliver after the project was nearly complete and it was set to begin to charge for its services. Both of these reflect uncertainty regarding how institutions will evolve, often with some influence by the project sponsor or partners. A third category of institutional risk arises when project sponsors do not adequately understand the relevant institutions, which, as noted by Scott (2011, include normative 'how things are done' and cultural elements, as well as formal regulatory mechanisms. Orr and Scott (2008) present a series of vignettes showing that 'institutional exceptions' arising from this lack of knowledge arise over the life cycle of the mega-project.

The risks associated with the collaboration between partners pursuing distinct interests often emerge as the most complex and interesting in large engineering projects. These risks reflect the fundamental uncertainties of the project to the extent that these have the capacity to change the payoffs, incentives, and ultimately the capacity of different partners to withstand risks over the life cycle. They also reflect uncertainties regarding the financial strength of the sponsor or partners resulting from other exposures that they face. The failure or defection of one partner can place great stress on the sponsor and remaining partners and, absent prior agreement regarding how to bridge or 'wraparound' such cases, can threaten the governability of the mega-project.

Technical risks are explored initially as the opportunity is shaped, although in a number of cases they are strategically 'under-emphasized' as the sponsor seeks to engage partners and other stakeholders. They may be further explored and resolved during the shaping phase, especially if the choice of technology has implications for the engagement of key players, culminating in the concept selection that in turn enables closure regarding high-level engineering and procurement contracting. These risks are then further analysed and resolved during the engineering phase, and if they turn out to be greater than envisioned, may send the project back to the shaping phase, triggering rework not only in engineering design but also perhaps in external commitments and contracts. Finally, as the project ramps up, remaining uncertainties about the operability and reliability of the project technology are resolved, often with significant negative impacts on the project's economic and health, safety, security and environmental (HSSE) success. Epistemic elements of technical risk, such as uncertainty regarding subsurface characteristics in oil/gas or other geologically sensitive infrastructure projects are typically resolved to a significant extent through testing and characterization during defining the project stage but may not be fully resolved until substantial drilling or excavation activities take place during the 'sprinting' phase.[15] This process of sequential risk management is summarized in Table 3.2.

What makes mega-project risk management so challenging is the need to integrate these broad areas of risk – inside the project, among the partners, with key interests, and in the market and geo-political 'surround'. The purpose is to allocate the ownership of risks using multiple criteria (1) insight and influence over outcomes, (2) the capacity to bear the consequences of materialization, (3) the ability to integrate risks with the overriding value and safety objectives of the project sponsors. As a result, many if not most risks will require multiple responsible parties, since no single partner will dominate in all three respects.

Strategizing about risks is almost always beneficial, but at some point diminishing returns set in and the costs of acquiring additional information or gaining control over risks fall short of their value. The design of responses to risks must be judged on a cost–benefit basis. Aligning performance incentives is critical when particular parties to the mega-project have a significant degree of control over the economic value created by the project but do not have an incentive to maximize this overall value.

3.7 CONCLUSION: CREATING AND EXERCISING OPTIONS

The essence of mega-project leadership is to selectively commit as needed to move the project forward, but to delay costly and irreversible

Table 3.2 Emergence and resolution of risks over the shaping cycle

	Shaping the Opportunity	Shaping the Project	Engineering the Project	Sprinting to Build the Project	Ramping up to Operations
Market risks	Well characterized if serving an established market, only loosely known if market is to be created by project	Sharpened, some aspects may be resolved through contracting	Output in abeyance, supply emerge and are resolved by contract	Output market uncertainties 'in abeyance'. However, some supply market risks are resolved	Specific market uncertainties are resolved, general market uncertainties are updated
Institutional risks	Licence to operate, 'exclusivity' and market access surface as key uncertainties	Agreements with key parties and/or alignment of project with accepted norms reduce risks, though uncertainties remain	Multi-dimensional concept is clear and becomes a plan	As project becomes physical reality, new stakeholders are triggered and must be addressed	Accommodation, resolution within existing framework. Relationships become 'institutionalized'
Collaboration risks	Players, interests surface, many uncertainties reframe agreements	Give and take leads to increased trust or breakdown. Basis for collaboration resolved through frame agreement	Clarified in detailed business plan; strengths/ weaknesses and interest alignment revealed	Interface risks emerge and are resolved	Realigned, adapted to state of project
Technical risks	Characterized in most general terms, many possibilities	Concepts developed, feasibility explored, new technologies evaluated	Uncertainties reduced, specific risks accepted	Treated as part of management of change (MOC) process	Teething issues show up

commitments until dominant uncertainties are resolved. Much of the resolution of major risks takes place through the evolution of prices in markets. Most, however, results from project shaping as the main partners and stakeholders in the project wrestle to create a viable configuration that is mutually acceptable.

Our major point here is not to identify which methods are best suited to managing large engineering projects. Rather, it is to represent the iterative processes of exploration and commitment typical of these mega-projects. Our purpose is to inform both the management of such mega-projects in the future and the development of better models to support management decisions.

At each episode, particular risks and their underlying drivers are salient, some are resolved, and others deferred for future resolution. In early stages many uncertainties are recognized for the first time. During these stages, project sponsors sort out the basic concept and basis for collaboration, and determine what stakeholders support, accept or oppose the project. As agreements are reached among key partners and stakeholders, many of these initial uncertainties are resolved or at least substantially reduced. If not, the project does not move forward.

Successive decision-making episodes are needed to bring to an agreed-upon configuration. Simon (1976) refers to this as the shift from substantive to procedural rationality. Substantive rationality focuses on selecting the optimal option, while procedural rationality recognizes the unfolding of time, the presence of strong uncertainty and the need for collaboration. This distinction underpins our views regarding the limitations to formal quantitative valuation techniques in the early stages of a mega-project, in contrast with the later stages when substantive rationality takes hold.

In the early stages of shaping the project, uncertainties regarding technical options are first increased and then resolved through the search for alternatives offering flexibility and the extent to which they satisfy the concerns of the non-economic stakeholders. Often, if other similar concepts have been built and put into operation, uncertainty concerning costs enters the framing stage.

During later episodes, new uncertainties and risks are unveiled as the analysis goes from general concepts to specific designs, but quickly get resolved as designs are chosen, engineered and contracted for. At the close of this stage, the project design is largely committed, except for options that are explicitly built into.

Finally, in the operating stage, uncertainty reappears and risks to long-term operability come into play as the equipment and the organization erode though use and habituation. Some institutional risks may also increase as the sponsor's initial bargaining power erodes.[16] Market risks continue to the extent that the output is a commodity with volatile prizes, but the project's positioning in markets is typically resolved quite early in this stage.

NOTES

* We are grateful to Vivek Sakhrani, Ray Levitt, Dick Scott and two anonymous reviewers for their comments.

1. Two broad categories of engineering projects have been identified by Miller and Coté (2012). First 'systems breakthroughs' where the aim is to develop radically new engineering solutions to major industrial bottlenecks and eventually create new markets. Second, 'pushing the envelope' projects, which focus on complex infrastructure, industrial or information technology investments using existing knowledge and aiming at improving the performance of firms in mature sectors.
2. Levitt (2011) characterizes practice focused on execution as Project Management 1.0: 'This PM 1.0 style of project management assumes that planners can develop a detailed plan that will remain a valid baseline plan for the duration of even the most complex, decade-long project' (p. 197).
3. Over 60 of these projects are from the IMEC Project, led by Roger Miller at HEC Montreal in the late 1990s, which formed the basis for Miller and Lessard (2001). Another 20 were researched by Miller as part of the research that led to Miller and Coté (2012). Lessard independently researched more than 30 projects in the oil and gas domain as part of the MIT-BP Major Projects Research Programme that provided research support in the early stages of this project.
4. We refer to projects as complicated when they comprise many elements or activities, complex when they involve uncertainties and interdependencies that may result in extreme, often compounding outcomes. See Baccarini (1996) and Williams (2002).
5. One reviewer pointed us to research finding a very similar process of early-stage shaping in social-ecological projects (Olsson et al., 2006) that share many features with LEPs. Folke et al. (2005) provide a more comprehensive framing of the shaping and adaptive governance of social-ecological systems.
6. Miller and Lessard (2001, Chapter 3).
7. By projection-based decisions, we refer to decisions based on methods such as DCF/NPV (discounted cash flow/net present value) as well as many decision-tree models that focus on a single decision to engage in a project rather than engaging in a gradual shaping and commitment process.
8. Merrow (2011, Figure 8.4) traces the engagement of different experts and functions over the project life cycle.
9. For oil and gas projects, shaping the opportunity would correspond to access or pre-appraisal, shaping the project to appraise through early concept select, engineering the project to select and define, sprint to construction to execute, and ramping up to operate. We use the alternative stage labels to stress the shaping that takes place before the project enters the select stage. See Merrow (2011, Figure 2.1) for the terms used in different sectors.
10. See, for example, Laughton et al. (2008).
11. For an in-depth development of real options analysis, see Trigeorgis (1996).
12. Alessandri et al. (2004).
13. See Amram (2002, Chapter 7), for an illustration of combining market-priced and private risk in the evaluation of a staged option to expand.
14. In reality, some of these levels are intertwined. Global market risks (oil and other commodity prices, interest rates, the 'price' of risk) are nested within geo-political regimes that are subject to change. National and local institutions, in turn, are nested within

these geopolitical regimes and global markets. Local market prices, in turn, are nested in all three. The point here is to emphasize the difference between those classes of risk drivers that are mostly endogenous to the mega-project, those that are largely outside of the influence of project participants, and those that lie somewhere in between.

15. De Weck et al. (2012) model the resolution of subsurface uncertainty in oil/gas extraction through two different project stages, exploration (which would roughly equate to our shaping the project phase) and production (operating phase).
16. Vernon (1971) refers to this process as the obsolescing bargain. For a more recent discussion see Eden et al. (2005).

LITERATURE

Alessandri, T., D. Ford, D. Lander, K. Leggio and M. Taylor (2004), 'Managing risk and uncertainty in complex capital projects', *The Quarterly Review of Economics and Finance*, **44**(5), 751–67.

Amram, M. (2002), *Value Sweep: Mapping Corporate Growth Opportunities*, Boston, MA: Harvard Business School Press.

Baccarini, D. (1996), 'The concept of project complexity – a review', *International Journal of Project Management*, **14**(4), 201–4.

de Weck, O., L. Jijun and D. MacGowan (2012), 'Modelling epistemic subsurface reservoir uncertainty using a reverse Wiener jump-diffusion process', *Journal of Petroleum Science and Engineering*, **84/85**, 8–19.

Eden, L., S. Lenway and D. Schuler (2005), 'From the obsolescing bargain to the political bargaining model', in R. Grosse, *International Business and Government Relations in the 21st Century*, Cambridge, UK: Cambridge University Press, pp. 251–72.

Flyvbjerg, B., N. Bruzelius and W. Rothengatter (2003), *Megaprojects and Risk: An Anatomy of Ambition*, Cambridge, UK: Cambridge University Press.

Folke, C., T. Hahn, P. Olsson and J. Norberg (2005), 'Adaptive governance of social-ecological systems', *Annual Review of Environment and Resources*, **30**, 441–73.

Hughes, T.P. (2000), *Rescuing Prometheus*, New York: Vintage Books.

Laughton, D.G., R. Guerrero and D. Lessard (2008), 'Real asset valuation: a back-to-basics approach', *Journal of Applied Corporate Finance*, **20**(20), 46–65.

Levitt, R.E. (2011), 'Towards project management 2.0', *Engineering Project Organization Journal*, **1**(3), 197–210.

McCullough, D. (1972), *The Great Bridge: The Epic Story of the Building of the Brooklyn Bridge*, New York: Simon and Schuster.

Merrow, E.W. (2011), *Industrial Megaprojects: Concepts, Strategies and Practices for Success*, New York: John Wiley and Sons.

Miller, R. and M. Coté (2012), *Innovation Reinvented: Six Games that Drive Growth*, Toronto: University of Toronto Press.

Miller, R. and D. Lessard (2001), *The Strategic Management of Large Engineering Projects: Shaping Risks, Institutions and Governance*, Cambridge, MA: MIT Press.

Morris, P.W.G. (2009), 'Implementing strategy through project management: the importance of managing the project front-end', in T.M. Williams, K. Samset and K.J. Sunnevåg (eds), *Making Essential Choices with Scant Information*, Basingstoke and New York: Palgrave Macmillan.

Morris, P.W.G. and G.H. Hough (1987), *The Anatomy of Major Projects*, Chichester: John Wiley and Sons.

Olsson, P., L.H. Gunderson, S.R. Carpenter, P. Ryan, L. Lebel, C. Folke and C.S. Holling (2006), 'Shooting the rapids: navigating transitions to adaptive governance of social-ecological systems', *Ecology and Society*, **11**(1).

Orr, R.J. and W.R. Scott (2008), 'Institutional exceptions on global projects: a process model', *Journal of International Business Studies*, **39**(4), 562–88.

Priemus, H. (2008), 'How to improve the early stages of decision-making on mega-projects', in H. Priemus, B. Flyvbjerg and B. van Wee (eds), *Decision-making on Mega-projects: Cost–Benefit Analysis, Planning and Innovation*, Cheltenham, UK and Northampton, MA, USA: Edward Elgar.

Scott, W.R. (2011), 'The institutional environment of global projects', in W.R. Scott, R.J. Orr and R.E. Levitt (eds), *Global Projects: Institutional and Political Challenges*, New York: Cambridge University Press.

Simon, H. (1976), *Administrative Behavior: A study of Decision-making Processes in Administrative Organization*, New York: The Free Press.

Trigeorgis, L. (1996), *Real Options: Managerial Flexibility and Strategy in Resource Allocation*, Cambridge, MA: MIT Press.

Vernon, R. (1971), *Sovereignty at Bay: The Multinational Spread of U.S. Enterprises*, New York: Basic Books.

Williams, T.M. (2002), *Modelling Complex Projects*, Chichester: John Wiley and Sons.

Williams, T.M., K. Samset and K.J. Sunnavåg (eds) (2009), *Making Essential Choices with Scant Information*, Basingstoke and New York: Palgrave Macmillan.

4. Real-world decision-making on mega-projects: politics, bias and strategic behaviour

Martijn Leijten

4.1 INTRODUCTION

Decisions in which the responsible parties (often politicians) decide whether to build a mega-project are extremely difficult. Decision-makers are caught between interests, and they assess the value of projects based on disputable objectives and information that contains a high level of uncertainty. As will be demonstrated in Section 4.2, decision-making processes on mega-projects are often erratic and non-linear. Decision-makers often doubt the utility and necessity of such projects, and they sometimes approve large projects, only to regret them later.[1] Many initiatives have been proposed to improve these processes. Guidelines have been formulated, and techniques and instruments have been used to provide information that is intended to rationalize decisions. All of these measures are intended to make decisions on projects less complex and less controversial.

Several characteristics of the decision-making process, however, can seriously hamper such attempts. The objective of this chapter is to identify persistent causes of the problems associated with decision-making with regard to mega-projects. There is a long history of attempts to improve the reliability of information on which decisions about mega-projects are made (e.g., cost–benefit analyses). As observed in studies by Wachs (1989) and by Flyvbjerg and colleagues (2003) however, decisions regarding mega-projects involve more than the proper calculations of costs and benefits. The purpose of this chapter is therefore to identify additional causes of problematic decision-making as it occurs in reality, in addition to suggesting solutions to these problems. Two important categories of causes that are the subject of particular discussion – behavioural and cognitive deviations (Section 4.3) and politically and strategically fuelled deviations (Section 4.4) – require a course of action that goes beyond simply improving information for decision-making.

These deviations demonstrate that the process of making decisions regarding mega-projects is rarely a matter of simply weighing the pros and cons of the project in a neutral manner. These two categories of deviations do not fit within the framework of rational decision-making, as it has been known thus far. For this reason, Section 4.5 presents three suggestions: establishing a new source for rationality in decision-making on mega-projects, transforming the non-rationality in decision-making on mega-projects into an opportunity, and finding an alternative rationality for decision-making on mega-projects.

4.2 MEGA-PROJECTS: ERRATIC AND NON-LINEAR DECISION-MAKING

As discussed in this section, decision-making on mega-projects does not follow a simple and logical line from initiative to approval and implementation. Mega-projects are often policy initiatives in which the relationship between problem and solution is not clear. Moreover, they are developed within a world that is not static, but which develops rapidly, in part because of the project itself. The processes therefore tend to be erratic and partly unstructured, thus negating the possibility of a simple blueprint (cf. de Bruijn and Leijten, 2007; Miller and Lessard, 2008). This section explores several causes of erratic and non-linear decision-making.

Combining Problems and Solutions

Proper decision-making is difficult in the absence of clear problem formulation. A mega-project is a solution. In order to determine its legitimacy properly, however, decision-makers should be clear about which problem it is intended to solve (Priemus, 2010). Problem formulations and objectives are commonly dynamic however, and decision-makers are thus confronted with a dilemma. In order to make a proper deliberation and obtain a realistic view of potential private involvement – which is often an important condition for approving a project – the project should be properly defined, preferably with clear terms of reference from the outset. This is often considered the only proper way to plan a project. In practice, however, decision-making processes do not always follow a neat path in which, at some point, all technical requirements are clear, all budget programmes are available and all the desired private contributors have signed on at the same time.

Old ideas may be solutions to new problems, and a given project can appear suitable for solving problems that had previously not been considered. The idea for a project may have been brushed aside, only to become viable later, when new problems emerge. A potential hazard exists however, as some project ideas survive purely for political reasons. For example, politicians may wish to build such projects due to their value for highlighting political ability and decisiveness. This could be undesirable however, as such project ideas could edge out other policy initiatives that might be able to achieve the same or even better results with regard to solving the defined problem, possibly at a lower cost.

This does not mean that non-linear combinations of problems and solutions are always bad. In fact, they have major advantages. The functionality of a project may increase after approval, or even after realization. Moreover, societal progress (in general, as well as in the particular case of innovations) sometimes emerges in the form of newly developed solutions. In many cases, these solutions are for problems that people had been unaware of until after the solution had become available.

The spontaneous conception of ideas for mega-projects thus has advantages, although project advocates should follow three stages of justification in order to prevent opportunistic behaviour. First, they should identify the problem or challenge for which the proposed project offers a possible solution. Second, they should identify alternatives for solving the same problem. Finally, they should assess these alternatives according to important appraisal criteria that are established independently of the decision-making process for the proposed mega-project. This sequence of steps provides sufficient opportunity to assess projects according to multiple values, without being affected by personal interests. It requires careful problem definition. For example, imagine that a high-speed railway line is considered too expensive and therefore deemed unnecessary. Nevertheless, the line could provide additional railway capacity in an area where existing railway lines are choked, causing frequent delays. If the objective of the high-speed railway line is 'stretched' to include the provision of additional railway capacity in order to relieve the existing network, it might become a valid investment.

Emergent Developments and Other Dynamics

Throughout the planning, preparation and implementation of a project, issues may emerge that require changes or expansions to the project. Flanking policy may be necessary in order to generate a successful outcome. Even the fact that a new, high-profile project is forthcoming may motivate actors to embark on further projects. For example, the decision to build a high-speed railway line may motivate public actors to upgrade railway stations at which the future high-speed trains will stop. Such was the case with the reconstruction of railway stations in Antwerp, Rotterdam, Breda, Arnhem and other cities.

A project can also evoke its own dynamics within its environment. The prospect of new infrastructure that can offer a competitive service may motivate actors to become innovative as well. This is also known as the 'sailing ship effect', after the innovations that occurred in the market of sailing ships after the development of steamships. The Betuweroute freight railway line in the Netherlands was an example of such a project. When the project generated public upheaval and increased in costs, the providers of alternative means of transport (e.g., barge owners) gained an incentive to enhance the appeal of their own modes of transport. They appeared to be able to offer a service comparable to the Betuweroute, but at a lower cost (Roscam Abbing et al., 1999). This option had not been considered when the decision was made to build the Betuweroute. Other dynamics that are not related to innovations may occur as well. For example, the opening of the Channel Tunnel between France and Britain led to decreases in the price of ferry services across the Channel.

Decision-makers should therefore try to estimate the ways in which the project's environment will develop – not only around the project, but also because of the project. The developments in the price of ferry services on the Channel due to the opening of a competing modality may have been predictable. Other matters (e.g., the proliferation and growth of low-cost airlines with cross-Channel flights) however, were more difficult to foresee in a world in which these airlines did not yet exist. There is thus a chance that issues will be overlooked. Such insights, which often lead to post-decisional regret, generally occur with the luxury of hindsight and retrospective knowledge.

Non-routine Nature of Decision-making on Mega-projects

Large projects are unique, both in terms of their decision-making processes, as well as in their appearance. Rarely can an existing project simply be copied. Local circumstances always diverge, resulting in unproven applications (Korsten et al., 1996). In addition, the nature of technology often differs from that which decision-makers might expect. Although technology is often expected to be static and operate according to rules, Wynne (1988) describes it in terms of open-ended, technical-social (i.e., unruly) systems. There is little overall rationality for the local 'behaviour' of technology. Interaction with a new, unique environment may make technology behave differently than expected.

This creates dependencies on 'local' knowledge and technically specialized knowledge. In such cases, decision-makers (and perhaps planners, engineering designers and project managers) often cannot refer to experience – let alone to common experience – or use tacit knowledge. Many of them may go through such a process only once or twice during their careers. Even clients develop mega-projects only once during their lifetimes. Flyvbjerg observes that this problem is particularly prominent in contracting:

> Clients who decide to do major infrastructure – for instance, a city council deciding to build a new subway or toll road – do so relatively rarely, often only once, or never, in the lifetime of the individual city manager and council member. Learning is therefore impaired for clients, and if you do not know what your interests are, it is difficult to safeguard them. (Flyvbjerg, 2009, p. 361)

New decision-makers on a new mega-project are likely to make the same mistakes and encounter the same difficulties that their predecessors had encountered. It is therefore difficult to develop a routine or rely on heuristics, as described in Section 4.3.

Implications for Decision-making

The erratic and non-linear nature of decision-making processes regarding mega-projects can have several implications. They can be positive, as they could provide opportunities for optimization or render projects useful for purposes that had not been foreseen. On the other hand, they can also be negative, by creating major uncertainty in the process. The dynamics make decision-making analogous to shooting at a moving target. Premature approval is also a possibility, as when developments within the environment of a project could render it outdated or even obsolete. The non-routine nature of mega-projects even has the nasty characteristic of allowing mistakes to be made repeatedly, thus preventing any chance of improvement.

4.3 BEHAVIOURAL AND COGNITIVE ISSUES IN DECISION-MAKING ON MEGA-PROJECTS

As demonstrated in this section, the characteristics of mega-projects make decision-making on those projects a social science, at least in part. Behavioural and cognitive issues can play an important role within the situations of high uncertainty generated by the complex nature of mega-projects. This topic is explored in several respects involving the way in which the mind can deceive decision-makers in their pursuit of rational decisions. First, a characterization of the social aspects of decision-making is used to illustrate how the way in which the mind works in decision-making processes can undermine rationality. This is followed by a discussion of framing, which demonstrates that the way in which people perceive policy depends at least in part on the way it is presented to them. Subsequently, entrapment is discussed in terms of the reluctance of decision-makers to engage in any radical reconsideration of earlier decisions. The fourth topic involves the persistence of assumptions that take root in the minds of decision-makers and other people, even if they have been or can be invalidated by experts.

The Social Dimension of Decision-making

Prevalence and heuristics

There are two types of information: subjective and objective. Subjective information comes from sources related to a stakeholder, while objective information comes from unrelated parties. The most reliable information for decision-making is obviously objective, although even objective information can be used by stakeholders in order to serve their interests. For example, if there are various objective sources of information with diverging outcomes, stakeholders may select only information that is favourable to making their own point. The situation is further complicated by the fact that the distinction between subjective and objective information is often not so clear. What is presented as reality by one set of experts is often 'a social construct that can be deconstructed and reconstructed by other experts' (Flyvbjerg, 2003, p. 61).

The possible subjectivity of information does not apply solely to the sender of the information (e.g., through strategic behaviour in the provision of information). It can also apply to the receiver (e.g., in the interpretation or assessment of information). The way in which information is brought into decision-making processes depends strongly upon the actor who is interpreting it. People mirror the information that they receive through their own personal frames of reference, which are composed of values, including experiences, beliefs, organizational (or other) culture and personal preference. These frames of reference can create (whether consciously or unconsciously) general guidelines that are described in psychology and sociology as 'heuristics' (Kahneman et al., 1982). The impact of information in decision-making depends upon the comprehension, personal disposition and circumstances of the decision-maker. For example, politicians who know that they will be judged according to the way in which they deal with their budgets may be inclined to value information that enables them to maintain budgets higher than other information. They may also fend off information that could threaten the stability of their budgets, even though such information might concern important new insights. There is often little control to prevent such selection from producing unbalanced deliberations. The greatest problem for any subjective influence in information assessment, whether conscious or unconscious, is that it applies to strategically driven information provision by stakeholders, as well as to information that is assumed to be neutral (e.g., cost–benefit analyses produced by actors who are not involved in the decision-making process).

Satisficing

Even if it is possible to develop a routine for decision-making at all, the nature of the projects that require decision-making limits the extent to which decision-makers are able to follow such routines. This renders the pursuit of full rationality and optimization in the form of maximum utility impossible. Decision-makers therefore settle for outcomes that are considered good enough, rather than optimal. They also do this because the solution to be proposed must be acceptable to a variety of stakeholders (Miller and Hobbs, 2009; Williams and Samset, 2010). Such 'satisficing' behaviour (Simon, 1956, 1972) makes decision-making possible for projects that might otherwise become mired in endless procedures or those that might face too much opposition.

Satisficing has advantages and disadvantages. On the one hand, the success of a project may be measured by obtaining optimal satisfaction amongst stakeholders, in addition to success in terms of costs, revenues and other benefits. If a solution satisfices in order to generate wide support, the fact that it is sub-optimal may be acceptable. On the other hand, sub-optimization increases the likelihood that the project will become obsolete or too expensive for the functionality that it would provide. This raises the implication that there might have been a better alternative for a project that was built. Such implications can be subjective. Solutions and costs that are unacceptable to one party could still fit within the framework of another. Alternatively, sub-optimization may undermine discipline and caution in the decision-making process amongst those who do not support such a solution.

Risk as a social construct

Risks in a mega-project are usually quantified in risk analyses. Risk assessment nevertheless depends upon the personal disposition of the assessor. Risks can be approached as a social construct, just like reality. Different actors perceive risks differently (Slovic, 1987; Freudenburg, 1988; van Asperen, 1992; Wynne, 1992). For this reason, risks that are acceptable to one may be unacceptable to another. One person may be more averse to risk than another person is (Tversky and Kahneman, 1981). A risk-averse decision-maker may be less inclined to approve a complex mega-project costing several million euros than would a decision-maker who is less averse to risk.

Affect

The decision-making process is also influenced by affect, fear and sensitivity. This is a particularly important issue when considering the involvement of the public (i.e., citizens) in decision-making (Finucane et al., 2000). For example, citizens may fear health-related or other damage from projects, or they may oppose investments in means of transport that are associated with high pollution. In both cases, these fears are based on personal, ideological dispositions rather than technical or economic rationale. Decision-makers are often inclined to deal with such issues in a rational way (e.g., by acquiring additional technocratic information).[2] The nature of such information, however, does not correspond to the ideological nature of fears and sentiments. Technocracy aims to keep emotion out of decisions. Technocratic information is not intended to win the heart of the people.

One way of addressing this situation could involve making technocratic information a point of departure in negotiations with the affected citizens (e.g., by involving them in advance in decisions on which course of action should follow from which outcome of technocratic research). In this way, citizens have the opportunity to make themselves heard in project deliberations while decision-makers create commitment for the remainder of the decision-making process. Opponents who may wish to renege on agreements that have been made can be blamed for being unreliable. Such a process can therefore reinforce the position of the decision-maker.

Framing

The ways in which the actors involved in the decision-making process perceive information or a proposed policy also depend upon the way in which it is framed (i.e., the words that are used to describe it). For example, a shift of jobs from one region to another due to the construction of an infrastructure project could be presented as a 'drain of employment' from a certain region, although it can also be presented as 'balancing the labour market'. If the policy proposal is set in the latter frame, it is probably more likely to be endorsed than it would be if the former frame had been used, even though both frames may have applied to the same project and policy effect (Tversky and Kahneman, 1981; de Bruijn, 2011).

Why We Sometimes Pick the Wrong Projects and Continue Them

Adverse selection

Project advocates and parties that provide information on projects usually have more expert knowledge than do those who make decisions on those projects. This provides strategic power to the owners of information. As discussed in this section, they can select and frame the information they would like for the decision-maker to receive. They are also in a position to lie with numbers (Wachs, 1989). This can lead to problems in which the best project is not automatically selected when there are multiple projects to choose from. According to a study by Flyvbjerg (2007, 2009), nine out of ten projects overrun their budgets due to 'misrepresentation' of costs and benefits, such that the one that is selected is likely to be one about which lies have been presented as evidence. As argued by Flyvbjerg (2009), this transforms the decision-making process regarding large projects into a situation involving the 'survival of the unfittest'.

Entrapment

Projects that go wrong are rarely discontinued. A decision to approve a project may entail implicit approval for developments that occur later and for which decision-makers have no opportunity to make a new deliberation or which the decision-maker is reluctant to reconsider, due to the amount that has already been invested. In practice, projects for which high costs have been paid appear difficult to stop, even if continuing them will result in losses. Although the future costs may be much higher than the amount that would be lost by discontinuing the project before completion, decision-makers are reluctant to take such a radical step. Policy-makers thus become trapped in projects (cf. Brockner and Rubin, 1985; Staw, 1997; see also Chapter 15 by Cantarelli and Flyvbjerg in this book).

Several types of commitment can generate entrapment situations:

- *Entrapment due to financial commitment*: serious losses are difficult to communicate to the public, or the decision-maker has unrealistic hopes for future improvement. This situation resembles that of poker players who commit to their stakes in games that they are statistically unlikely to win.
- *Entrapment due to commitment to an effort or promise:* paradoxically, the most doubted decisions tend to generate the largest commitment. Former US Secretary of State Henry Kissinger described the pattern that decision-makers are reluctant to reconsider difficult decisions as follows: 'The alternative to the status quo is the prospect of repeating the whole anguishing process of arriving at decisions. This explains to some extent the curious phenomenon that decisions taken with enormous doubt and perhaps with a close division become practically sacrosanct, once accepted' (Kissinger, 1966, pp. 508–9). Given that decisions on mega-projects are often highly debated and doubted, and because of their highly contestable nature and the fact that they occur in an arena with a very critical

public, such decisions are perceived as achievements that must not be jeopardized. Decision-makers may be reluctant to give up on projects that they once endorsed, as doing so would invalidate their previous efforts and appear to damage their reliability. To give up would also be to acknowledge that the previous standpoint had been wrong, thus resulting in loss of face. For this reason, projects may be continued even though they should have been stopped in an early phase, despite all of the effort they may have cost.

- *Entrapment due to the persistence of an idea*: images of projects easily take root in the minds of decision-makers. Once a project has been suggested, it will not easily disappear as an idea until it is built. It is impossible to 'uninvent' an idea. The first ideas for a tunnel under the Channel were developed in the nineteenth century, when it was technically not feasible, and it continued to slumber in the common mindset until it was finally built in the late twentieth century. The Channel Tunnel was a project with exceptional iconic value, although many projects have comparable histories. Another example involves the Zuiderzeelijn, a proposed high-speed public transport connection between the western and northern regions of the Netherlands. Although the project has been abandoned by the Dutch central government for reasons of financial unfeasibility (Priemus and Leijten, 2005), the idea has not disappeared (as of 2013). It is now being treated as a project that the regional authorities would like to carry out on their own, in cooperation with a transport company.

Escalation of perceived value

Entrapment leads to an escalation of commitment, as more and more resources or effort are put into the project. In another phenomenon that is related to this escalation of commitment, decision-makers become inclined to continue (cf. Staw, 1997). Parallel to the escalation of commitment, an escalation of perceived value of prior investments can be observed. Decision-makers may thus consider a project 'theirs' and thus be reluctant to acknowledge that it might be a failure. For example, they may explain their commitment to a project by stating that, once it is finished, people will appreciate the project's functionality or beauty, and any delays and cost overruns suffered will become a minor issue. In many cases, they are right. Delays and overruns become 'sunk costs', while functionality and beauty last. This is obviously not how the deliberation was made at the start.

In some cases, however, this appreciation is valid, as the project indeed delivers more value than expected. The Sydney Opera House is probably the most famous example. It was a planning disaster. It was far too expensive, delivered late and with poor specifications for its actual purpose as an opera hall (Hall, 1982). Nevertheless, due to the iconic image of this complex for Sydney – and, indeed, for the whole of Australia – few people regret the reluctance of the decision-makers to discontinue its troublesome conception. Such retrospective rationalization of persistent project support, however, can also occur because of post-decisional dissonance in projects that have no clear benefits beyond the value that was defined in advance. Once the investment has been made, it is likely to be valued more highly than it was before (cf. Knox and Inkster, 1968).

Unsubstantiated Assumptions that Survive the Decision-making Process

The initiation of a mega-project is rarely based on extensive calculations of costs and benefits, as such calculations are made during later stages of the pre-decisional phase. Mega-projects may be conceived by people who have some stake in their realization. In this phase, their efforts are directed primarily towards gaining support from other actors. Quantifiable justification will come later, once the plan has made it to the political arena. At that point, however, unsubstantiated assumptions regarding the value of the project that were used in the conception of the idea and in order to generate support for it after its initiation may have tacitly taken root in the minds of the decision-makers.

Given that most modern countries are democracies rather than meritocracies (in which well-informed experts could invalidate unsubstantiated assumptions), such assumptions find their way into the decision-making process. In some cases, empirical research on the impact of real infrastructure projects has demonstrated effects that were not consistent with those that the decision-makers may have had in mind. For example, new infrastructure projects are expected to offer benefits for the economy as a whole, although their effects may be limited to a small area or they may have an absorption effect on other regions. Their distributive effects may even be contrary to the aims of the decision-makers. For example, the earliest high-speed railway projects in France and Japan were expected to divert economic activity away from Paris, Tokyo and other primate cities towards smaller cities that were further afield. In reality, however, some primate cities absorbed activity from the smaller cities that had been awarded high-speed railway stations. In addition, the economic benefits to the areas located near high-speed railway stations often proved to come at the expense of the even more peripheral regions surrounding the newly connected cities, which were in even greater need of economic improvement (cf. Bonnafous, 1987; Rietveld and Bruinsma, 1998). This deviance was first explained by Carroll (1978), who concluded that imagining an outcome makes it appear more likely.

The Westerschelde Tunnel in the southwestern part of the Netherlands was an infrastructure project that was conceived without official goals on economic distributive effects or traffic growth, but for which promising economic perspectives had nonetheless been drafted. The region in which the tunnel would be located would benefit economically from the improved accessibility. Such expectations and fears (for those who would be negatively affected) were widespread, particularly among businesses. An empirical study on the impact of this project, however, revealed that such effects were generally small (Meijers et al., 2012).

Without claiming that these examples indicate that the impact of large infrastructure projects is always limited, it can be said that their effects sometimes diverge strongly from unsubstantiated expectations (e.g., with regard to the beneficial effects of improved accessibility).

Implications for Decision-making

Cognitive dissonance can account for various divergences between expectations on projects and the reality that they ultimately produce. In addition to errors in the actual data, errors may occur in the assessment of data by decision-makers. Possible results of such errors include the selection of the wrong projects, the continuation of projects that should have been stopped and the selection of sub-optimal solutions. Whether a project is approved does not depend solely upon the quality of the project or of the information that is used to make a decision on it. It also depends upon the people making the decisions. This has clear disadvantages, as people's assessments are often far from rational. Nevertheless, it may also have an advantage. If a selected project turns out to be not as good as expected and it has not been stopped, people may develop milder perceptions of its value later, once the costs have sunk and grievances have been suffered. If a project is considered successful when stakeholders and users appreciate it, the poor conception may be more acceptable in hindsight. It is therefore important to distinguish between the success of a project and the success of its management, as noted by Munns and Bjeirmi (1996, p. 82), who consider 'inadequate basis for project' as a part of project management.

4.4 POLITICAL AND STRATEGIC ISSUES IN THE DECISION-MAKING ON MEGA-PROJECTS

Projects are conceived and developed in multi-actor settings. Interdependencies develop quickly within these networks of actors. Such interdependencies can enrich a project, as when public actors benefit from private innovative potential and specialist knowledge. On the other hand, they may also evoke some particularities that can affect decision-making efforts. This is particularly evident in political contexts, where decision-makers must deal with information that has strategic value, and in situations in which decision-makers attempt to find legitimacy of their own objectives, for example amongst private stakeholders. This section addresses such particularities, beginning with the role of information in rationalization attempts, continuing to the issue of ownership in a multi-actor context and arriving at typical features of private involvement in projects and their impact on decision-making.

Information and Rationalization in a Politicized Context

The role of figures in decision-making

Ex ante figures on costs and benefits have three roles in decision-making. First, they serve to determine the feasibility of a project to solve a defined problem. Second, they can be used to form a well-founded deliberation between policy alternatives. If various options are available, any uncertainty inherent in the calculations is likely to apply to all of the options, such that the uncertainty does not necessarily affect the results of such a deliberation. Third, these figures enhance the transparency of political decision-making. Politicians and other policy-makers need figures in order to support and objectify their policies.

Contrary to what one might expect from their exact appearance, figures do not always provide a straight path to rational decision-making, as Section 4.2 also showed. In the case of mega-projects, this is most applicable to forecasts (e.g., with regard to usage, revenues, impact on the environment or societal benefits). By definition, forecasts are never facts, because they concern future situations. This inevitably weakens their ability to support decisions on mega-projects. Although econometric models are becoming increasingly advanced, they are numerous, use different methods and often rest on assumptions that are difficult to see and test (cf. Bristow and Nellthorp, 2000; Weisbrod, 2008). Nevertheless, decision-makers often use figures in ways that are defined by their purpose instead of by their nature.

Moreover, figures are necessary in order to rationalize politics, even though politics cannot be expected to be fully rational. For example, differing valuations of nature preservation may distinguish a party that focuses on environmental awareness from other political parties. Moreover, the same figure can be interpreted differently by different people. Politics is not only about rationality, but also about ideologies. The role that figures play in rationality differs from the role that they play in terms of ideology. This does not mean that the ideological aspect to politics is bad for decision-making. Political variety and pluralism may also enrich the decision-making process, leading them towards a balance of public values. For example, diverging political viewpoints provide checks and balances. Decision-making processes regarding mega-projects thus involve a drive for rationality and a drive for ideology. There is tension between these two drives, with information as the nexus of their relationship.

Contestability and strategic value of information for decision-making

Figures have certain characteristics that easily make them deceptive. First, 'soft' figures automatically become 'hard'. For example, once figures on costs or revenues are produced, they will become an anchor point. From that point, all deviations will be compared to the original figures. By using these figures, public project owners also relinquish some of their strategic power. Potential private bidders now know how much money will become available, which could be important knowledge in a tender. For the well-being of the project, it could therefore be good for the public actor to lie about the numbers in order to pressure potential bidders. Such a strategy, however, is inconsistent with the values of a transparent government, and it would therefore not be defensible to the public.

Second, and following from the discussion above, information has strategic value. This certainly applies to figures, no matter how soft they may be. If figures are soft, and if there is room for interpretation, there is a potential for misuse in the actors' own interests. The objectives of actors can be supported with a specific set of data, which can be emphasized and ignored selectively.

Third, due to the high level of contestability of each possible policy and associated set of data, decision-making processes may turn into report wars. Each analysis is contestable in some respect, and it will therefore evoke counter-analyses with different outcomes. This may leave decision-makers in doubt, and they might request a new analysis that addresses all of the issues raised and that produces a coherent outcome. In its turn, however, the new analysis might evoke yet other counter-analyses, thus preventing the decision-makers from ever coming any closer to the rational decision that they aimed to achieve. The result is decision-making as a free-for-all and a vicious circle of generating and processing information (de Bruijn and Leijten, 2007).

Amongst other risks, the contestability of information provides opportunities for diverging into intuitive decision-making. In such cases, decision-makers no longer rely on the previously presumed objectifiability of information. Personal or common sets of beliefs and paradigms can become more dominant. This places the quality of decision-making in jeopardy, as policy becomes susceptible to wishful thinking and projects may be easily approved. As described by Flyvbjerg and colleagues, 'Politicians may have a "monument complex", engineers like to build things and local officials sometimes have the mentality of empire-builders' (Flyvbjerg et al., 2003, p. 46).

Due to the inherent uncertainty of forecasts, the strategic dimension of information is unavoidable, and thus contestability. Although it is possible to reduce uncertainty, it can never be removed completely. Instead of merely attempting to reduce this uncertainty further, thus creating an opportunity for strategic behaviour, decision-makers can also focus on eliminating such strategic behaviour by embarking on interactive rationality. Stakeholders should accept the uncertainty of their information and negotiate according to its validity instead of using it as absolute truth. To this end, information should be approached as a social construct rather than as a set of facts. With this negotiated knowledge, decision-makers are less inclined to aim for factual information than they are to seek consensus regarding the information that is to be used for decision-making (cf. de Bruijn and ten Heuvelhof, 2008).

Multiple and Dynamic Problem Ownership

Perceived problems that drive the development of a project are often shared by many people and organizations, but all against their own backgrounds and from within their own motives, rationality and wishes. Projects can have a wide variety of functions (e.g., transport service provider, economic enhancement instrument or job generator). To a certain extent, the objectives of others may coincide with the government's task to provide the means necessary for societal progress. Some public actors may therefore be inclined to adopt the problem perceptions of other parties. When problem perceptions that originally varied become aligned, deals can be made. This may enhance the viability and feasibility of the project, as multiple interests are met. The legitimacy of the project increases accordingly.

Nevertheless, the boundary between society's problems and entrepreneurial deficiencies is not always clear. For example, public actors who link their policies to the entrepreneurial targets of a private or otherwise entrepreneurial problem owner (e.g., a semi-public organization) may appear to become entrepreneurial problem owners themselves, possibly straying from their public tasks. The most important hazard is that the public actors will dance to the tune of the entrepreneurial actors. This could push them to make decisions that no longer possess full democratic legitimacy, given that the primary goals of entrepreneurial actors involve their own designated tasks, and not the common public interest. This can become a serious problem, as when private involvement is needed in order to finance the project. Knowing that the government has a stake in the same goal may discourage a private actor from actually contributing.

The Dutch central government's support for the Betuweroute freight railway line between the Port of Rotterdam and the German hinterland was conceived by two entrepreneurial branches of public organizations: the Rotterdam port authority (in order to strengthen the competitive position of the Port of Rotterdam and supported by large container-shipping companies) and the cargo branch of Dutch Railways (in order to promote freight transport by rail). The Cabinet endorsed the project, under the condition that private financial involvement would contribute to the total costs (see also Chapter 15 by Cantarelli and Flyvbjerg in this book). The legitimacy of public involvement could be related to various functions of the project that met public interests, including an investment in the competitive position of the economically important 'Mainport Rotterdam', investment in railway capacity on a busy route and a contribution to a shift from highly polluting road transport to more environmentally friendly railway transport. While the private involvement failed to materialize, the politicians involved approached political deadlines that required a 'yes' or 'no' with regard to the project. At that point, 'soft dependencies' may have developed. Government institutions had then included the project (and the functionality it was intended to provide) in their visions and long-term plans. In other words, the project had taken on a 'life'. In practice, therefore, few politicians would have the nerve to kill it (see also in Section 4.3 the subsection on entrapment). In the case of the Betuweroute, a 'yes' implied that the project would be built, and thus that funding would be made available. Private investors lost the incentive to invest their money. At that point, the Dutch government became the project's primary problem owner, as well as the sole financially responsible actor, despite the continued existence of the private interests of the initiators (Tweede Kamer der Staten-Generaal, 2004a).

Public actors can be dragged into a project based on entrepreneurial interests that may only partly comply with the common interest. Once the value of this contribution to the common interest can be reliably placed alongside the costs, interdependencies may have grown so strongly that the public actor is already trapped inside the project. In this situation, strong support from individual entrepreneurial interests could work against the common interest. Early government commitment to a project fuels such overvaluation of individual entrepreneurial interests.

Private Involvement as Problematic Project Legitimacy

Private involvement can improve decision-making on projects in at least four ways. First, it can improve the quality of proposals, thus making approval easier. Second, it provides an opportunity for the client to share risks. Third, as mentioned by Klijn and colleagues (2007), private involvement encourages governments to define clear performance requirements and introduce financial penalties for failure. These performance requirements can mark out the path to the formulation of valid project objectives. In this sense, private involvement can provide discipline to public decision-making, thereby leading to better projects. Fourth, as demonstrated in previous sections, decision-makers search for information in order to rationalize their deliberations, although inherent uncertainties may lead them to pursue such rationality in vain. Decision-makers may consider the willingness of private actors to take on the risk of a project as an alternative source of legitimacy for the project. After all, if it was a bad project that would only cost money, a company (chastened by the market) would not venture into the risk of investing in it (Flyvbjerg et al., 2003; Tweede Kamer der Staten-Generaal, 2004b, pp. 232–48).

It is necessary to mention several constraints to these assumptions. First, defining valid objectives in an early stage may not correspond to the non-linear features of decision-making on mega-projects, as described in Section 4.2. As an incentive to define objectives early, private involvement does indeed eliminate uncertainty and prevent the approval of poorly defined projects. Nevertheless, dynamics could also be valuable to projects. The adjustment of the terms of reference based on dynamics can be difficult when projects are tightly defined. Second, despite public–private partnership schemes, decision-makers are still apparently engaged in public–private partnership schemes that were not properly defined at the outset (see also Koppenjan, 2008, p. 202). Third, the early definition of valid objectives is problematic, in that it actually reduces the innovative potential that the private sector could offer, as it leaves less room for the private partner to realize new applications or higher efficiency (Koppenjan and Van Ham, 2002b, pp. 441–2, 454–5). It also makes the project organization less flexible for responding to emerging developments. Fourth, it could be unattractive for private parties to share their expertise in an early stage, in order for the project to become more valuable. If they do so, others might benefit from the information. This risk could lead potential private partners to hesitate or to provide innovative solutions late, after definition and approval (Tweede Kamer der Staten Generaal, 2004b, pp. 232–48). In such a case, decision-makers would then decide on a sub-optimal project.

The motives that private actors may have for participating may be quite different from those that public actors have. For example, a company may wish to apply a newly developed technology that needs a first application in order to prove its effectiveness. The company may accept a loss for such a purpose, thus leaving the public partner with an unprofitable project or a poorly functioning technical application. For example, in the case of the Dutch high-speed railway line between Amsterdam and the Belgian border, Dutch Railways bid far above the Transport Ministry's expectations for the operation contract, in order to prevent the introduction of competition into the market (Tweede Kamer der Staten Generaal, 2004c). After just over two years of service, however, the national government had to spend several hundred million euros in order to save the operator from bankruptcy.

In addition, private actors cannot be expected to take the same costs and benefits into account that public actors do. For example, nature preservation and the protection of citizens against nuisance are public values that are not automatically guarded by a private actor.

Relying on the willingness of private investors to participate poses several additional problems that often make private contribution troublesome, instead of meeting the expectations:

- Greater technical and social complexity strengthens the public owners' desire for private involvement, although it decreases the attractiveness of investing for private actors. If decision-makers wish to use private involvement to demonstrate the legitimacy of a project, therefore, they are not likely to achieve this in projects that are more complex (Koppenjan and Van Ham, 2002a). This would (perhaps wrongly) imply that only non-complex projects are legitimate.
- In order to benefit fully from the innovative powers of a private partner, such an actor should be involved early. Nevertheless, there are reasons for private actors to postpone their involvement until the capriciousness of political decision-making has toned down. At that point, the incentive for participating in risk-bearing may have faded (see Chapter 15 in this book by Cantarelli and Flyvbjerg).
- In some cases, expectations regarding the innovative potential resulting from private involvement, which could serve as a motive for approving a project, may be unrealistic. Private partners who bear financial risks in a project may be reluctant to accept the uncertainties involved in applying innovations (cf. the HSL-South project: Tweede Kamer der Staten-Generaal, 2004c).
- The success of a project often depends on flanking policy and investments. This may make private actors reluctant to participate before

they are fully certain that decision-makers will not cut back on such supporting investments (Künneke and Runhaar, 2002; Tweede Kamer der Staten Generaal, 2004b, pp. 232–48).

Implications for Decision-making

Political and strategic interests offer opportunities for mega-projects. For example, public decision-makers and private stakeholders can achieve mutual benefits if they manage to match public values with private business opportunities. This provides a firm basis for a project. At the same time, however, the political and strategic realities of the multi-actor environment in which mega-projects are developed undermine the rational decision-making process. Decision-making on mega-projects is a matter of politics, but the features of politics frustrate rational decision-making on mega-projects. The following are a few important factors related to political and strategic issues in decision-making on mega-projects:

- The greater the impact that key information has in a project, the greater will be its strategic value and the more likely it will be to be contested. The information that is most likely to make a difference in decision-making processes concerning mega-projects is thus the information that is most susceptible to strategic behaviour.
- Ownership can shift gradually and unwittingly. This needs not be problematic, as long as owners can oversee the implications for decision-making. This requires regular assessment of whether the ownership values of a project still correspond to the public values pursued by the owner.
- Public sector comparators can be used to reveal whether private involvement would have any actual benefits over public project development. Unfortunately, it cannot indicate the extent to which strategic behaviour would evolve in the project's decision-making processes. It is also incapable of identifying the true motives that private actors have for participating in a project and the extent to which this diverges from the public interest.

4.5 A DIFFERENT APPROACH TO RATIONALITY

The erratic and non-linear nature of decision-making on mega-projects and the high uncertainty associated with them requires views on problem definition, the formulation of objectives and the selection of alternatives that differ from those found in many other decision-making processes.

Because of these characteristics, and because of the high political stakes related to the projects, many of these processes are non-transparent, and the course of the process is difficult to control. These characteristics provide decision-makers with the opportunity to behave strategically or even mislead others.

Many decision-makers have the intention to objectify their decision-making behaviour by striving to achieve rational decision-making (i.e., assembling all available information and attempting to choose the best alternative). The nature of mega-projects (e.g., their uniqueness and the way they take on a life of their own), however, is a major handicap in this process. It is further complicated by the ways in which decision-makers behave in the face of uncertainty and within a complex multi-actor environment with proponents and opponents.

This demands a different approach to rationality. Four approaches are suggested here: an alternative method for gathering information to support decision-making, taking advantage of non-rational features, aiming for a different kind of rationality – interactive rationality – and putting uncertainty closer to the centre of project approval.

An Alternative Method of Gathering Information

An alternative rationality can be achieved with reference class forecasting. This is an idea for countering the 'planning fallacy' (Kahneman and Tversky 1979; Lovello and Kahneman, 2003). It has been proposed as a way to help obtain reliable cost and benefit data and, as such, it has been applied to the context of large projects by Flyvbjerg (2008). This method detaches data gathering to support decision-making processes from the strategic, political and cognitive issues discussed in this chapter. It provides a means for collective learning, in order to neutralize the effects of limited learning resulting from the non-routine nature of mega-project development.

In this method, forecasts are based on previous samples of comparable projects. The costs and benefits of previous projects are assumed to have predictive value for future projects. Users of this method thus benefit from the advantages of retrospective knowledge. Reference class forecasting facilitates collective learning, which should prevent reliance upon the unreachable ideal that each decision-maker should have previous experience with decision-making on projects. It is important to note that reference class forecasting does not predict the unexpected in a project. It merely aims to improve the reliability of forecasting data. Given the uniqueness of projects, it cannot predict the causes of overruns, the occurrence of unmanageability or similar matters. Another limitation has already been mentioned. The uniqueness of projects inevitably causes some variety in the reference class. Flyvbjerg also acknowledges that reference class forecasting is particularly valuable for situations in which potential inaccuracy is caused by optimism bias instead of by strategic misrepresentation. In the latter case, reliable forecasting is simply of no use (ibid., pp. 18–20).

Taking Advantage of Non-rationality

As suggested at several points in this chapter, the non-rational features of decision-making on mega-projects can also offer unforeseen opportunities for improving or enriching a project. For example, if a project has not been clearly defined, the goals of the project can be stretched in order to attract crucial stakeholders, or the scope can be broadened to add functionalities that provide the total package with clearer benefits than the narrow original project would have offered. Decision-makers can also seize opportunities to benefit from emergent developments in order to become more efficient or to increase the functionality of the project (cf. Geraldi, 2008; Koppenjan et al., 2011).

There are thus three desired points of departure for dealing with the erratic and non-linear nature of decision-making on mega-projects: (1) accept the non-linearity and erratic nature of the decision-making process, (2) try to take advantage of these characteristics by seizing unforeseen opportunities and (3) continue deliberating about whether the costs of keeping these processes under control might be higher than the benefits. The possibility of seizing opportunities enables planners and decision-makers to optimize the project. The non-linear and erratic nature of the process can therefore help decision-makers to make the best of a project. In this way, a function can be assigned to the non-rationality of the process.

An Alternative Rationality

Rationality is defined as the pursuit of an optimal decision in order to achieve a certain set of objectives. Rationality can be pursued by an individual decision-maker who assembles information in order to arrive at the best option. It can also be pursued by exchanging information and viewpoints with other actors. This interactive rationality can be achieved in two ways. First, decision-makers could include stakeholders in the formulation of objectives, under the condition that these stakeholders have demonstrated strong commitment to the process. It should also be clear which objectives are to serve public values and which are to serve the values of other stakeholders. Second, the uncertainty in the information that is used to support or rationalize decisions, along with the contestability of this information, could be addressed through negotiations between actors concerning the validity of the information that is to be used. The actors involved in such a process should include stakeholders who have contributed to the formulation of the objectives of the project, in addition to experts. In these complex, multi-actor decision-making processes, figures could be used for purposes such as providing input for negotiation (negotiated knowledge), instead of as a means of conviction or a weapon with which to win fights (cf. Lindblom and Cohen, 1979; Wildavsky, 1980).

Repositioning Uncertainty in Decision-making

Despite the availability of all these approaches, it is important to acknowledge the inherent and inevitable uncertainty involved with decision-making on mega-projects, as described in this chapter. Nevertheless, uncertainty is rarely a central topic in decision-making processes concerning such projects. It is often merely accepted as a peripheral condition, as no amount of effort could eliminate it completely. The fact that it cannot be eliminated does not mean that the uncertainty factor does not have to be considered. In addition to analysing whether suggested mega-projects can solve defined problems and selecting the best option from a set of alternatives, decision-makers could position uncertainty closer to the centre of the decision-making process. Relevant questions in this regard concern the nature of the uncertainties manifested in the deliberations and whether they can be accepted or be reduced to an acceptable level. If the uncertainty cannot be accepted or sufficiently reduced, a mega-project should be rejected, not because it would not do the job, but because of an excessive risk that it would become unmanageable.

4.6 CONCLUSIONS

The objective of this chapter is to demonstrate that the nature of mega-projects, particularly in cognitive and political/strategic terms, causes uncertainties that force decision-makers into a type of approach other than rational decision-making. For example, the wide variety of interests that are inevitably involved and the interdependencies between public and private actors introduce additional dimensions into deliberations, beyond the mere assessment of information and selecting the best available option according to this assessment. Many actors have no interest in rationality, and many particularities of human behaviour (on the part of the decision-maker, as well as on the part of information providers, private investors, citizens and other actors) can cause decision-makers to stray from it.

The alternative approaches that could help improve decision-making should focus more on interests and relationships rather than they do on technocratic input alone. This most certainly does not mean that technocratic input should be excluded. The analysis of proposals or alternatives could be improved, however, by placing it in the perspective of interests and interdependencies. The suggested approaches do not attempt to eliminate strategic behaviour or cognitive dissonance. Instead, they suggest a way in which to cope with these aspects and still arrive at acceptable outcomes. More specifically, they share the common feature of acknowledging that decision-making on mega-projects is a non-exact science.

NOTES

1. For example, see the outcome of the city council inquiry on the North/South metro line in Amsterdam: Rapport van de Enquêtecommissie Noord/Zuidlijn (2010).
2. For example, see the case of the reconstruction of the Grote Markt square in Groningen (Leijten, 2004).

LITERATURE

Bonnafous, A. (1987), 'The regional impact of the TGV', *Transportation*, **14**(2), 127–37.
Bristow, A.L. and J. Nellthorp (2000), 'Transport project appraisal in the European Union', *Transport Policy*, **7**(1), 51–60.
Brockner, J. and J.Z. Rubin (1985), *Entrapment in Escalating Conflicts*, New York: Springer.
Carroll, J.S. (1978), 'The effect of imagining an event on expectations for the event: an interpretation in terms of the availability heuristic', *Journal of Experimental Psychology*, **14**(1), 88–96.
de Bruijn, H. (2011), *Framing; Over de macht van taal in de politiek* [*Framing: On the Power of Language in Politics*], Amsterdam: Atlas.
de Bruijn, H. and M. Leijten (2007), 'Megaprojects and contested information', *Transportation Planning and Technology*, **30**(1), 49–69.
de Bruijn, H. and E. ten Heuvelhof (2008), *Management in Networks: On Multi-actor Decision Making*, Abingdon: Routledge.
Finucane, M.L., A. Alhakami, P. Slovic and S.M. Johnson (2000), 'The affect heuristic in judgments of risks and benefits', *Journal of Behavioral Decision Making*, **13**(1), 1–17.
Flyvbjerg, B. (2007), 'Policy and planning for large infrastructure projects: problems, causes, cures', *Environment and Planning B: Planning and Design*, **34**(4), 578–97.
Flyvbjerg, B. (2008), 'Curbing optimism bias and strategic misrepresentation in planning, reference class forecasting in practice', *European Planning Studies*, **16**(1), 3–21.
Flyvbjerg, B. (2009), 'Survival of the unfittest: why the worst infrastructure gets built – and what we can do about it', *Oxford Review of Economic Policy*, **25**(3), 344–67.
Flyvbjerg, B., N. Bruzelius and W. Rothengatter (2003), *Megaprojects and Risk: An Anatomy of Ambition*, Cambridge, UK: Cambridge University Press.

Freudenburg, W.R. (1988), 'Perceived risk, real risk: social science and the art of probabilistic risk assessment', *Science*, **242**(4875), 44–9.

Geraldi, J.G. (2008), 'The balance between order and chaos in multi-project firms: a conceptual model', *International Journal of Project Management*, **26**(4), 348–56.

Hall, P. (1982), *Great planning disasters*, Berkeley, CA: University of California Press.

Kahneman, D. and A. Tversky (1979), 'Intuitive prediction: biases and corrective procedures', *Management Science*, **12**, 313–27.

Kahneman, D., A. Tversky and P. Slovic (eds) (1982), *Judgment Under Uncertainty: Heuristics and Biases*, Cambridge, UK: Cambridge University Press.

Kissinger, H. (1966), 'Domestic structure and foreign policy', *Daedalus*, **95**(2), 503–29.

Klijn, E.-H., J. Edelenbos and M. Hughes (2007), 'Public–private partnerships: a two-headed reform: a comparison of PPP in England and the Netherlands', in C. Pollit, S. van Thiel and V. Homburg (eds), *New Public Management in Europe: Adaptations and Alternatives*, Basingstoke: Palgrave Macmillan

Knox, R.E. and J.A. Inkster (1968), 'Postdecision dissonance at post time', *Journal of Personality and Social Psychology*, **8**(4), 319–23.

Koppenjan, J. (2008), 'Public–private partnership and mega-projects', in H. Priemus, B. Flyvbjerg and B. van Wee, *Decision-making on Mega-projects: Cost–Benefit Analysis, Planning and Innovation*, Cheltenham, UK and Northampton, MA, USA: Edward Elgar, pp. 189–212.

Koppenjan, J. and H. van Ham (2002a), 'Tussenbalans: barrières en kansen voor publiek–private samenwerking bij transportinfrastructuur' [Intermezzo: barriers and opportunities for public–private partnerships in transport infrastructure], in H. van Ham and J. Koppenjan (eds), *Publiek–private samenwerking bij transportinfrastructuur: Wenkend of wijkend perspectief?* [*Public–Private Partnerships in Transport Infrastructure: Appealing or Appalling Perspective?*], Utrecht: Lemma, pp. 205–2.

Koppenjan, J. and H. van Ham (2002b), 'Patronen in de totstandkoming van publiek–private samenwerking bij transportinfrastructuur: een vergelijkende analyse' [Patterns in the realization of public–private partnerships in transport infrastructure: a comparative analysis], in H. van Ham and J. Koppenjan (eds), *Publiek-private samenwerking bij transportinfrastructuur: Wenkend of wijkend perspectief?* [*Public–Private Partnerships in Transport Infrastructure: Appealing or Appalling Perspective?*], Utrecht: Lemma, pp. 415–56.

Koppenjan, J., W. Veeneman, H. van der Voort, E. ten Heuvelhof and M. Leijten (2011), 'Competing management approaches in large engineering projects: Dutch RandstadRail project', *International Journal of Project Management*, **29**(6), 740–50.

Korsten, A.F.A., J.A. de Bruijn, P. de Jong and W.P.C. van Zanten (1996), 'Technisch-complexe projecten: een verkenning' [Technically complex projects: an exploration], in J.A. de Bruijn, P. de Jong, A.F.A. Korsten and W.P.C. van Zanten, *Grote projecten; Besluitvorming en management* [*Large Projects: Decision-making and Management*], Alphen aan den Rijn: Samsom H.D. Tjeenk Willink.

Künneke, R. and H. Runhaar (2002), 'Marktfalen, transactiekosten en opportunistisch gedrag als barrières voor publiek–private samenwerking: een economische benadering' [Market failure, transaction costs and opportunistic behaviour as barriers for public–private partnerships: an economic approach], in H. van Ham and J. Koppenjan (eds), *Publiek–private samenwerking bij transportinfrastructuur: wenkend of wijkend perspectief?* [*Public–Private Partnerships in Transport Infrastructure: Appealing or Appalling Perspective?*], Utrecht: Lemma, pp. 77–94.

Leijten, M. (2004), 'Grote Markt Groningen: down to earth', in H. de Bruijn, G.R. Teisman, J. Edelenbos and W. Veeneman, *Meervoudig ruimtegebruik en het management van meerstemmige processen* [*Multiple Land Use And Management Of Polyphonic Processes*], Utrecht: Lemma, pp. 203–22.

Lindblom, C.E. and D.K. Cohen (1979), *Usable Knowledge: Social Science and Social Problem Solving*, New Haven, CT: Yale University Press.

Lovello, D. and D. Kahneman (2003), 'Delusions of success: how optimism undermines executives' decisions', *Harvard Business Review*, 81(7), 56–63.

Meijers, E., J. Hoekstra, M. Leijten, E. Louw and M. Spaans (2012), 'Connecting the periphery, distributive effects of new infrastructure', *Journal of Transport Geography*, **22**(1), 187–98.

Miller, R. and B. Hobbs (2009), 'The complexity of decision-making in large projects with multiple partners: be prepared to change', in T. Williams, K. Samset and K. Sunnevåg (eds), *Making Essential Choices with Scant Information; Front-end Decision-making in Major Projects*, Basingstoke: Palgrave Macmillan.

Miller, R. and D.R. Lessard (2008), 'Evolving strategy: risk management and the shaping of mega-projects', in H. Priemus, B. Flyvbjerg and B. van Wee, *Decision-making on Mega-projects: Cost–Benefit Analysis, Planning and Innovation*, Cheltenham UK and Northampton, MA, USA: Edward Elgar pp. 145–72.

Munns, A.K. and B.F. Bjeirmi (1996), 'The role of project management in achieving project success', *International Journal of Project Management*, **14**(2), 81–7.

Priemus, H. (2010), 'Decision-making on mega-projects: drifting on political discontinuity and market dynamics', *European Journal of Transport Infrastructure Research*, **10**(1), 19–29.

Priemus, H. and M. Leijten (2005), 'The Dutch Zuider Zee railway: a giant with feet of clay', *Planning Practice and Research*, **20**(1), 59–67.

Rapport van de Enquêtecommissie Noord/Zuidlijn (2010), Den Haag: Sdu Uitgevers, accessed 8 June 2013 at http://www.amsterdam.nl/gemeente/gemeenteraad/enquetecommissie/enquetecommissie_0/.

Rietveld, P. and F. Bruinsma (1998), *Is Transport Infrastructure Effective? Transport Infrastructure and Accessibility: Impact on the Space Economy*, Berlin: Springer.

Roscam Abbing, M., A.A.J. Pols and M. Bierman (1999), 'Hoe spoort het water? Ontspoorde besluitvorming Betuwelijn: een analyse van genegeerde alternatieven' [How does water function as track? Derailed decision-making Betuwe Line: an investigation], Working Document, Delft: TU Delft/Amsterdam: SISWO.

Simon, H.A. (1956), 'Rational choice and the structure of the environment', *Psychological Review*, **63**(2), 129–38.

Simon, H.A. (1972), 'Theories of bounded rationality', in C.B. McGuire and R. Radner (eds), *Decision and Organizations*, Amsterdam: North-Holland Publishing Company.

Slovic, P. (1987), 'Perception of risk', *Science*, **236**(4799), 280–85.

Staw, B.M. (1997), 'The escalation of commitment: an update and appraisal', in Z. Shapira, *Organizational Decision Making*, Cambridge, UK: Cambridge University Press, pp. 191–215.

Tversky, A. and D. Kahneman (1981), 'The framing of decisions and the psychology of choice', *Science*, **211**(4481), 453–8.

Tweede Kamer der Staten-Generaal (2004a), *Reconstructie Betuweroute: De besluitvorming uitvergroot* [*Reconstruction Betuweroute: The Decision-making Enlarged*], The Hague: Sdu Uitgevers.

Tweede Kamer der Staten-Generaal (2004b), *Grote projecten: Inzichten en uitgangspunten: Achtergrondstudies* [*Large Projects: Insights and Basic Principles: Background Studies*], The Hague: Sdu Uitgevers.

Tweede Kamer der Staten-Generaal (2004c), *Reconstructie HSL-Zuid: De besluitvorming uitvergroot* [*Reconstruction HSL-South: The Decision-making Enlarged*], The Hague: Sdu Uitgevers.

van Asperen, G.M. (1992), 'Risico's een sociale constructie' [Risks: a social construction], in N.J.H. Huls (ed.), *Sturing in de risicomaatschappij* [*Steering in the Risk Society*], Zwolle: W. Tjeenk Willink, pp. 17–30.

Wachs, M. (1989), 'When planners lie with numbers', *Journal of the American Planning Association*, **55**(4), 476–80.

Weisbrod, G. (2008), 'Models to predict the economic development impact of transportation projects: historical experience and new applications', *Annals of Regional Science*, **42**(3), 519–43.

Wildavsky, A. (1980), *The Art and Craft of Policy Analysis*, Basingstoke: Macmillan.

Williams, T. and K. Samset (2010), 'Issues in front-end decision-making on projects', *Project Management Journal*, **41**(2), 38–49.

Wynne, B. (1988), 'Unruly technology: practical rules, impractical discourses and public understanding', *Social Studies of Science*, **18**(1), 147–67.

Wynne, B. (1992), 'Risico en reflexiviteit: van objectief naar onderhandelbaar risico' [Risk and reflexivity: from objective to negotiable risk], in N.J.H. Huls (ed.), *Sturing in de risicomaatschappij* [*Steering in the Risk Society*], Zwolle: W. Tjeenk Willink, pp. 93–114.

5. Dealing with the complexity, uncertainties and risk of mega-projects: redundancy, resilience and adaptivity

Hugo Priemus, Marian Bosch-Rekveldt and Mendel Giezen

5.1 INTRODUCTION

Projects can be defined in two ways: the 'temporary organization that is created for the purpose of delivering one or more products' and the 'product such as a piece of transport infrastructure which is the result of the process of preparation and implementation' (Murray, 2009, p. 3). Thus, a project can be defined as a process and as a product. In both definitions the ultimate goal of a project is to create value for the stakeholders, with the content of the term 'value' being different for the various stakeholders (Achterkamp and Vos, 2008). When we talk about mega-projects first of all we have the products in mind. When we talk about project management we think of the temporary organization and the process. This similarly applies to the project phases identified by Turner (2008, p. 14):

- proposal and initiation (concepts and feasibility);
- design and appraisal;
- execution and control;
- finalization and close-out.

The 'proposal and initiation' and 'design and appraisal' phases in a typical project life cycle are often called the front-end development phase of a project (Bosch-Rekveldt, 2011, p. 4). The effort spent in the front-end development phase is called front-end loading. The challenge is to balance front-end loading and the effort spent during the execution of a project, in such a way that there is sufficient front-end development for an optimal result (ibid.). As the project life cycle progresses through its different stages, existing uncertainties and risks are generally reduced, but new uncertainties and risks may come up. Uncertainties and risks invariably play a major role in project management (Hillson and Simon, 2007).

This chapter deals with complexity in decision-making on mega-projects.

Complexity refers to a complicated state of the mega-project itself, to the complicated decision-making process resulting in a mega-project, the complicated dynamic relations between the actors and stakeholders involved in the decision-making process, and finally, the complex state of the relevant markets and the political environment in which the decision-making process develops.

Uncertainties and risks play a crucial role in this complexity. This chapter first presents an overview of theories of project management (Section 5.2). In general terms Section 5.3 explains how to deal with complexity: the central problem statement of this chapter. Risk management is an important component in dealing with complexity (Section 5.4). The changing environment contributes substantially to the complexity of decision-making on mega-projects. Market dynamics and political discontinuity play a crucial role here (Section 5.5).

It is argued in this chapter that the best way to deal with complexity is to adopt redundancy (Section 5.6), resilience (Section 5.7), alternatives and options (Section 5.8), starting in the early project phases. The solution is to adopt different types of adaptation (Section 5.9). Section 5.10 formulates some conclusions. Adaptive capacity is presented here as the key to the management of complex mega-projects.

5.2 THEORIES OF PROJECT MANAGEMENT[1]

We consider complexity as a core characteristic of the decision-making on mega-projects. This was not always the way project management has been approached. Theory development in project management is still in its infancy (Shenhar, 2001). Project management is multi-disciplinary and lacks a unified theoretical basis (Smyth and Morris, 2007). Project management theory can be characterized as pluralist (Söderlund, 2011). Maylor (2005) identifies three stages in the historical development of project management methods:

- pre-1950s: no generally accepted or defined methods;
- 1950s: 'one best way' approach, based on numerical methods established in the USA for managing mega-projects;
- 1990s: a contingent approach based on strategy.

Bosch-Rekveldt (2011, pp. 14–15) argues that in the 1950s, the tools and techniques that were developed to support the management of complex projects, were mainly based on a systems approach, whereby the project was treated as a mechanical activity. The timing of this approach is closely related to the rise of the computer, the emergence of systems engineering and developments in management science. Traditional project management, concerned with topics such as scheduling, cost control and work breakdown structures, started here. Most of the tools and techniques such as the critical path method (CPM) and the program evaluation review technique (PERT) were developed in defence and aerospace engineering and then expanded to embrace other industries including the construction sector (Morris, 1994).

The last stage, from 1990s onwards, is heavily dominated by the changing context in which projects take place (Bosch-Rekveldt, 2011, pp. 15–16). Increasingly complex and large projects are incorporated in programmes, with an important role for communication technology and knowledge management. The project manager acts as a project integrator, paying attention to all the processes taking place around and in projects, rather than concentrating on a single project. There is a growing awareness that a project management approach should be contingent upon its context (Shenhar, 2001). Nevertheless, most of the current project management still seems to underestimate the influence of the dynamic environment (Artto and Wikström, 2005; Koppenjan et al., 2011).

Before the 1990s, project management tried first to define certainties and to look for fixed points and quantitative information. Since the 1990s, awareness is increasing that the social and economic environment changes during the many years of preparation and implementation. A mega-project must perform well during a long lifetime and there must be a positive contingency with the changing context. It is impossible to make reliable predictions about these changes. The core qualities of both a decision-making process and a mega-project are flexibility and resilience (the ability to adapt to changes in the environment and circumstances). Some of the external changes stem from long-term trends (social, economic, demographic, spatial and general technological changes); others are the outcome of emergent events (political decisions and project-specific technological innovations).

In a number of cases long-term fundamental trends and emergent events are interrelated. Take, for example, the gradual development of climate change, depleting resources and energy transition. A new generation of players become aware of those trends and respond innovatively to long-term changes, which are sometimes so revolutionary that one could even speak of a paradigm shift.

In the development of project management approaches we observe different conceptual approaches, which are summarized by Pryke and Smyth (2006) as follows:

- traditional project management approach;
- functional management approach;
- information processing approach;
- relationship approach.

In their view, these four approaches should be seen as complementary rather than adversarial. The traditional project management approach includes many techniques and tools. The functional management approach includes strategic elements such as management of front-end development, supply chain management, partnering and programme and project strategies. The information processing approach is based on an input–output model of project management (Winch, 2002), where the management of information flows is essential. Finally, the relationship approach focuses on the social management of relationships between people, between people and firms and between firms as players in the project. The relationship approach tends towards a process management approach. These complementary approaches illustrate the broadening perspective on project management.

Increasingly it is argued that nowadays a pure project management approach, as compared with Pryke and Smyth's (2006) traditional project management approach, is no longer effective (de Bruijn et al., 2002; de Bruijn and ten Heuvelhof, 2007). This is supposedly caused by the continuous changes that inevitably need to be incorporated in a project that exists in a dynamic environment. Therefore, instead of a pure 'command and control' approach, a broader process management approach of 'prepare and commit' is advocated (Koppenjan et al., 2011).

Handbooks and Body of Knowledge

There are several management handbooks, all aiming to be a reference guide for the fundamental concepts and techniques of project management (Bosch-Rekveldt, 2011, p. 16). The most widely known, but not all embracing, are the *Project Management Handbook* (Cleland and King, 1983), the Project Management Institute (PMI) *Project Management Handbook* (Pinto, 1988), Turner's *Handbook of Project-based Management* (2008), Meredith and Mantel's *Project Management: A Managerial Approach* (2006) and many others such as Kerzner (2003), Pinto (2004) and Turner and Simister (2000). In general, the handbooks are strongly based on a traditional systems perspective. In fact, the idea of a handbook on project management, aiming to prescribe standard procedures, seems contradictory to the unique character of a project. Selective application of these procedures ('scaling not skipping') might resolve this basic tension (Murray, 2009); the project team is responsible for what is applied and when (PMI,

2004; Williams, 2005). Based on certain project characteristics or even company characteristics, the project management approach should be tailored (Turner et al., 2010), hence achieving a fit-for-purpose scaled project management approach, starting from the front-end phase of projects.

Williams (2005, p. 500) argues that the various bodies of knowledge and handbooks are based on three underlying assumptions:

- 'Project management is rational and normative'.
- 'Project management is based on positivism': there is one reality, determined by casual relationships and the observer should be independent of the object under observation. The facts of the situation can be observed.
- 'Project management is particularly concerned with managing scope', by using models of work breakdown structures and project networks. The focus is on analysing by deconstruction, rather than on integration.

These underlying assumptions explain the emphasis of the bodies of knowledge and handbooks on project planning, project control and the decoupling of the project from its environment. Despite the existence of project management handbooks and project management bodies of knowledge, failed projects are still commonplace, suggesting that we might have to broaden our view and adopt a more contextual approach (Bosch-Rekveldt, 2011, p. 17).

Project Management Research

Kloppenborg and Opfer (2002) provide a detailed overview of project management research. They show that it evolved from a focus on planning and scheduling in the 1960s, to the development of automated software for cost and scheduling (in the 1970s) and then to life-cycle costing and risk management in the 1980s. In the 1980s, research on leadership and team-building was published, leading to an even stronger focus on human resources, teams and leadership in the 1990s. Shenhar and Dvir (2007) continue the list in the 2000s, which is characterized by research on project typologies and contingencies, strategic project management and globalization of projects. Their suggestions for further development of the theoretical basis of project management are presented in Table 5.1. They suggest that different parts of the project management problem could be tackled with developments in the different theoretical bases, thereby emphasizing the multi-disciplinary character of project management (Bosch-Rekveldt, 2011, pp. 18–19).

According to Morris (1994), one of the next challenges for the 'bodies of knowledge' would be not to develop a 'one-size-fits-all' approach

Table 5.1 Directions for solving project management problems from different perspectives

Project Management Problem	Theoretical Perspective
Scheduling and resource allocation	Operations research, network theory
Time overruns, escalating resources	Theory of constraints – critical chain
Uncertainty and risk management	Simultaneous management, knowledge and time perspectives
Adapting project management to project differences	Contingency theory – a typological theory of project management, distinction between hard and soft aspects of projects
Project leadership	Transformational leadership
Project strategy	Strategic management

Source: Shenhar and Dvir (2007); Bosch-Rekveldt (2011, p. 18).

irrespective of context and contingency, but an approach where intelligent and reflective practitioners could make their own informed decisions on the principles, concepts, models and techniques to use (Morris et al., 2006b). Suggestions supporting this view were presented in research to update the *APM* [Association for Project Management] *Body of Knowledge* (Morris et al., 2006a). The recommendations include the emphasis on the link to the business purpose, the nature of the context of a project and enhanced positioning of people factors.

Schools of Thought in Project Management Research

Research on project management can be categorized under eight 'schools of thought'. Based on 305 articles in 30 high-ranking journals outside the specific project management journals, seven categories were developed (Söderlund, 2011, p. 158). In this chapter we added the eighth category:

1. *Optimization School* (logic-based, prescriptive research drawing on management science, optimization techniques and systems analysis);
2. *Factor School* (empirical research relying on descriptive statistics on the criteria and factors of project success and failure);
3. *Contingency School* (empirical research, case-study-based and survey-based research on the differences between projects, characteristics of projects and contextual dimensions);
4. *Behaviour School* (interpretative and descriptive research on organizational behaviour, processes and learning in projects);

5. *Governance School* (prescriptive research on governance and contract problems in projects);
6. *Relationship School* (descriptive case-study research on relations between players in projects);
7. *Decision School* (descriptive and interpretative research on politics and decision-making in projects);
8. *Adaptive Management School* (research based on alternatives, uncertainties and no-regret decisions).

These eight 'schools of thought' all have their own analytical focus, research approach and methodology and key questions. In fact they represent eight separate 'theories of project management'. In particular the Contingency School (3), the Behaviour School (4), the Decision School (7) and the Adaptive Management School (8) seem to be most relevant nowadays. Söderlund (ibid., p. 169) stresses the importance of pursuing different perspectives rather than striving for one unified theory of project management: 'by embracing pluralism, project management research might be better equipped to explore and explain the difficulties of generating, forming, managing and even killing projects – such analysis would benefit from a comprehensive view on project processes and the use of multiple theories'.

Focusing on the Contingency School, several researchers suggest a contingency approach in project management (Shenhar and Dvir, 1996; Engwall, 2003; Williams, 2005; Smyth and Morris, 2007; Sauser et al., 2009). They suggest adapting project management to the context of the project in order to improve project performance. Adaptation of project management requires a proactive attitude. Essentially, the research trends in the field of project management are about context. Particularly it is about the context of increasingly complex projects. Given the character of mega-projects, attention should be paid to applying a contingency approach in the project management of mega-projects in order to improve project performance, but not neglecting the other schools of thought. Recent handbooks on the decision-making process on mega-projects of a more eclectic nature are Altshuler and Luberoff (2003) and Priemus et al. (2008).

5.3 DEALING WITH COMPLEXITY[2]

One of the general characteristics of mega-projects, the decision-making processes, the constellation of actors and stakeholders and the markets and political environment, is their complexity. Research of large engineering projects in the process industry shows that complexity of mega-projects

Technical Complexity (17 elements)
High number of project goals
Non-alignment project goals
Unclarity of project goals
Uncertainties in scope
Strict quality requirements
Project duration
Size in CAPEX
Number of locations
Newness of technology (world-wide)
Lack of experience with technology
High number of tasks
High variety of tasks
Dependencies between tasks
Uncertainity in methods
Involvement of different technical disciplines
Conflicting norms and standards
Technical risks

Organizational Complexity (17 elements)
High project schedule drive
Lack of resource & skills availability
Lack of experience with parties involved
Lack of HSSE awareness
Interfaces between diffferent disciplines
Number of financial sources
Number of contracts
Type of contract
Number of different nationalities
Number of different languages
Presence of JV partner
Involment of different time zones
Size of project team
Incompatibility between different project management methods/tools
Lack of trust in project team
Lack of trust in contractor
Organizational risks

External Complexity (13 elements)
External risks
Number of external stakeholders
Variety of external stakeholder's perspectives
Dependencies on external stakeholders
Political influence
Lack of company internal support
Required local content
Interference with existing site
Remoteness of location
Lack of experience in the country
Company internal strategic pressure
Instability of project environment
Level of competition

Note: CAPEX = capital expenditure; HSSE = health, safety, security, environment; JV = joint venture.

Source: Bosch-Rekveldt (2011, p. 213).

Figure 5.1 TOE framework (47 elements in total)

can be split into three categories: technical, organizational and external complexity. Each of these categories (T, O and E) contains a number of elements. The T elements represent the potential causes of complexity in the project related to the project scope or the content of the project. The O elements represent the potential complexity causes in the project related to the project internal organization. The E elements represent all the potential causes of complexity in the project related to external issues or external organizational complexities (Bosch-Rekveldt, 2011, p. 190). The TOE framework contains 47 elements contributing to the complexity of a particular project (Figure 5.1).

Table 5.2 Significant correlations between project performance and project complexity

Variable 1	Variable 2	Correlation Strength (r_s)	Significance (p)	N	Meaning of Correlation
Project performance	Technical complexity	–0.401	0.003	54	Increased technical complexity decreases project performance
	Organizational complexity	–0.308	0.023	54	Increased organizational complexity decreases project performance
	External complexity	–0.221	0.109	54	Increased external complexity decreases project performance

Source: Adapted from Bosch-Rekveldt (2011, p. 111).

Next to providing an identification of (potential) aspects contributing to project complexity by means of the TOE framework, the research by Bosch-Rekveldt (2011, p. 111) also identified relations between project performance (meeting scope, time, cost and quality agreements) and project complexity (Table 5.2).

Table 5.2 shows that on an 'aggregated' level of project complexity, the presence of weak correlations, suggests that increased project complexity (technical, organizational, external) indeed decreases project performance. Assessing project complexity could be important in improving project performance. Each project manager will start his or her assignment by completing the TOE complexity framework for the particular project: in which areas could complexity be expected. This 'complexity footprint' of the project is carved in sand rather than set in stone; it will change throughout the different project phases (Bosch-Rekveldt, 2011, p. 214).

Different players involved may (and will) have different perceptions of project complexity, for example dependent on previous experiences and different roles in the project. Apparently, in Figure 5.1 complexity is an intersubjective characteristic. The research by Bosch-Rekveldt (ibid.) showed that owner and contractor respondents significantly differ in their opinions on how much specific elements would contribute to the complexity of the project. In general, many problems are related to uncertainties and risks.

How could we better deal with different aspects of complexity in order to improve project performance? Bosch-Rekveldt (2011, p. 159) showed that in the front-end project phase, better application of risk management is required, particularly in case of highly (technically or externally) complex projects.

5.4 RISK MANAGEMENT

Risk management can be defined as the way managers deal with risks and uncertainties, related to mega-projects. Risk management should be applied, starting with the earliest stages of the decision-making. Even though the importance of thorough risk management is mostly recognized, it is not yet widely applied (Bosch-Rekveldt, 2011, p. 144). Ideally, risk management entails constant monitoring of uncertainties and new circumstances and their potential effects on the decision-making process, on the mega-project as a whole, or on certain components. More and more we see that a competent official is appointed who reports direct to the management and the supervisory board, or the municipal council and/or parliament, and who provides a periodic overview (e.g., once a quarter) of the current risks. In the early phases it might prove worthwhile to determine the relation between risks and to divide these risks into system risks (relating to the mega-project as a whole) and component risks (relating to specific components, such as foundation techniques, management of the environment and logistics, e.g., the removal of earth). Particular attention is paid more and more to the interface risks between different building components or subsystems. Each risk can be concretely defined in terms of its nature and background, its probability (in percentages), the costs if it does materialize, and the name of the person or department responsible for managing it, that is, the person who must take steps to minimize the probability of the risk and limit the damage if it occurs. The risk manager mostly challenges managers and staff in regular meetings. This broadens the scope for detecting emerging risks and for containing existing risks.

The four-eye principle and periodic external audits are important in the development of an early picture of alternatives, options and risks. Under the four-eye principle all important questions and documents will be promoted by at least two members of staff working independently of each other and whereby one person checks the work of the other. An external audit means that independent external experts are periodically invited to offer critical comments on a particular design, plan or proposal. The persons responsible explain their work and have right of reply to the external critics. 'A fresh pair of eyes' (or, in this case, several pairs) can prove valuable in the preparations for a mega-project. Risk management is partly the organization of checks and balances.

5.5 MARKET DYNAMICS AND POLITICAL DISCONTINUITY: CHANGING ENVIRONMENT[3]

If project management needs to be kept flexible in order to respond effectively to external changes, the next question is: what kind of changes are likely to occur during the decision-making on a mega-project? First, a distinction can be drawn between societal processes, political relationships and markets. Changes in society can re-shape the opinions of stakeholders, including the prospective users. These changes might be demographic in nature, relating to birth and mortality rates, household composition and ageing, immigration and emigration. Changes in migration patterns are particularly difficult to predict. They can be triggered by political changes, wars, natural disasters and famine, but also by wide, often abrupt economic changes in the form of, say, a debt crisis.

Societal changes may be of an economic nature (rise or fall in prosperity, shifts in employment and unemployment, changes in short- and long-term interest) and may express themselves in new preferences and changes in behaviour. Not infrequently, social and economic change goes hand in hand with changing technology, especially over a longer timescale. Consider the introduction of and improvements to automobile and air transport and the growing facilities in and around railway stations and airports. If fundamental societal and economic changes occur between the initial phase and the implementation of the project, they could undermine the prospects of an optimal design and scope. A (non-exhaustive) overview of pitfalls in the management of mega-projects, in relation to market dynamics and political discontinuity is provided below (Priemus, 2010a, 2010b).

Market Dynamics

Mega-projects figure in different phases of decision-making in certain markets and may spill over into many other markets. Facts that can be empirically established usually have only limited validity in specific market constellations. In general, forecasts and estimates – implicit and explicit – are based on assumptions about the trend in supply and demand, and hence the price developments in a number of relevant markets. A whole host of factors come into play, such as the availability of engineers and other experts for the preparation phase, the supply of trades people, building materials, installations and raw materials for the execution phase, developments in energy prices, the overall economic situation, the capital market (including trends in long-term interest rates), inflation and the land market. As most construction markets are regionally oriented, they will be affected by the dynamics in the regional markets. Other developments will be affected by developments in global markets.

All these uncertainties can be 'put into cold storage' until a later date, but this is no guarantee that crucial factors will follow the anticipated pattern. Moreover, certain deviations can make a profound impact on the final analysis of costs and benefits. Mobility patterns can change within the course of a single decade as a result of, amongst others, competition from modes of transport other than those envisioned in the project. Inland shipping, for example, is competing strongly with rail and road for the transport of goods to and from a large port like the port of Rotterdam. And one can safely assume that the growth of budget airlines such as easyJet and Ryanair is reducing the demand for transport by high-speed trains in Europe.

Contested Information

It is easy to spot the impact of market dynamics with the benefit of hindsight. The challenge presented by the decision-making on mega-projects is to identify market dynamics ex ante on the basis of forecasting and scenario analysis. The information on such future developments is always uncertain and it often appears to be contested (Wachs, 1989, 1990; Flyvbjerg et al., 2003; Leijten and de Bruijn, 2008). Contested information is information that is explained in different ways by the different players. Reasons may be the uncertainty of predictions of a future state. The point of the concept is not so much that people lie about it (this may sometimes be the case), but that they make use of the inherent uncertainty and contestability for their strategic goals. Leijten and de Bruijn (2008) recommend that agreements be reached beforehand on how the parties will deal with the information as it becomes available.

The risk of misinformation can be curtailed by deciding together at an early stage on how information is to be treated. Supporters and opponents can agree in advance which sources of information to accept as authoritative. If conflicting information is mobilized by both the supporters and the opponents, those involved can decide which independent expert or institute is to be consulted. Are there any underlying uncertainties? Is it possible to pursue a no-regrets policy that takes these uncertainties into account? Is it clearly understood who bears the risks of underestimations or overestimations? Can these risks still be allocated, if necessary? Does awareness of individual responsibility for risks result in revised estimates for investment costs, management costs and transport performance?

Political Discontinuity

One very well-known pitfall in the decision-making on mega-projects is the frequent changes that occur in the political affiliations of the government responsible for the project (Priemus, 2007a, 2010a). As the entire process, from proposal to handover, takes decades rather than years, every mega-project has to endure government elections and – more often than not – shifts in the balance of political power. Some mega-projects are so emotionally charged and so bound up with differences in political ideologies that they are used as part of the stakes during elections and the formation of coalitions. This happens not only at national level, but also at regional and local level and – most crucially – around the political consensus or dissent between different tiers of governments (central, regional and local). In Europe the projects often cross national borders and thus involve international negotiations and treaties, and sometimes, international tension. In some cases the European Commission also participates in the decision-making if subsidy arrangements and specific EU themes such as the Trans-European Networks are involved. Lack of political continuity and public consensus can have a direct impact on a mega-project; this may stem from diametrically opposed backgrounds and exert an adverse influence on the decision-making as well. When this happens the parties are confronted with tensions that have spilled over from other domains. Fortunately, this can also work in the other direction: if the government units collaborate well in other spheres and if they share similar views, there may be more consensus on the mega-project.

How to Deal with Pitfalls?[4]

An infrastructure project is – at best – a solution. This statement implies that there are one or more problems to which an infrastructure project is the most expedient response – for the moment. A valid problem analysis is essential in order to determine whether a proposed alternative is effective, efficient and legitimate, also for the longer term (Priemus, 2008). The first question that should be asked is: what is or are the problem(s)? And then: what is the problem *now* and what is it likely to become in the short and the long term? And finally, who is affected by the problem? One person's problem might be another person's solution.

Pretty soon the problem will emerge in the form of locations that are insufficiently accessible at present or in the future. This may go hand in hand with an increased risk of economic stagnation (measured in lost vehicle hours) due to growing congestion. Sometimes there are additional health and safety problems that arise as a result of emissions (air quality).

As all of this impinges on mobility, people tend to see the problem in wider terms than just accessibility or stagnation. They point to the decline in residential and economic appeal and the prospect of a deteriorating living climate, reduced quality of life and a decline or stagnation in business leading to job insecurity and uncertain economic growth. This implicit connection between mobility and the living and economic climate is usually difficult to substantiate and often bears witness to a long list of policy ambitions that cannot be supported by valid insights. In practice, it is barely possible to establish a causal relationship between improved accessibility and an upturn in the regional economy (Rietveld, 1989; Vickerman, 1989, 2000; Banister and Berechman, 2000).

As problems are often perceived differently by different parties, it is not only essential to conduct a problem analysis but also to reach the strongest possible consensus. A shared problem analysis in very early project phases enhances the possibility that the selected alternative will still be endorsed by everyone at a later stage.

Any later alternatives must be tested against the problem analysis. Hence, certain aspects need to be concretely and promptly specified:

- the values and criteria involved;
- the objectives of the parties and the political bodies that bear responsibility;
- the boundaries and constraints.

The various parties may have different ideas about these issues, so conflicts can easily arise. The best approach is to identify potential stumbling blocks at an early stage and to establish a workable consensus.

Project Alternatives

Once the problem analysis has been sorted out, it is time to think seriously about potential solutions. It is best to appraise alternatives in the initial stages. An investment project is not always the right answer. The predecessor of the current Dutch Ministry of Infrastructure and the Environment, the Ministry of Transport, Public Works and Water Management (Ministerie van Verkeer en Waterstaat, 2004) differentiated between three types of solution for reducing congestion: utilization, pricing and building. First, attempts can be organized to make better use of the capacity of the existing infrastructure. Congestion might easily arise on certain routes during the rush hour. But can the mobility in the opposite direction be increased? Or the mobility outside rush hours? That is the first question. The second is whether a price tag can be attached to the use of infrastructure in the form of a user charge, such as road pricing. Experience has shown that people curtail their use of infrastructure if it hits their pocket. If the price is differentiated in terms of time and place, pricing can lead to better utilization of infrastructure. If utilization and pricing are not enough, then it is time to consider new infrastructure or expansions to the current infrastructure.

The 'construction' category embraces various alternatives: different routes, different modalities (e.g., road, rail, inland shipping), different cross-sections (e.g., two-lane, four-lane, six-lane) and different types of spatial integration (for instance, to conserve nature or to prevent urban pollution). Situations must be avoided in which alternatives are put forward at the last minute by, for example, only those opposed to the government-favoured plan. Alternatives must be systematically recognized at, if possible, an early stage (Priemus, 2007b, 2008).

Functional Programme and Alternatives

It is advisable to think first in terms of a functional programme of requirements: what criteria does the project have to meet? And which public values need to be secured? Only in later stages is concretization addressed. It is best to spend some time thinking of alternative solutions and even to consciously generate and design extra ones. Then the various options can be tested against the functional programme; the social costs and benefits can be determined in each case. The options can be ranked, starting with the project with, on balance, the best score and finishing with the project with the lowest score. The relevant public authority takes a decision on the basis of this information. If it gives the go-ahead the work can begin. A process that uses a concrete functional programme of requirements as its starting point creates space for a tendering procedure in which candidates compete in terms of quality and innovation as well as price.

Scope of the Project

The scope of the project is decided during the initial phases of the decision-making. Which area will form part of the project – which usually extends beyond the line infrastructure alone? Particular attention will be paid to intersections and junctions, where amenities such as offices, homes, hotels, shops and conference accommodation can be built. In many cases the land near the intersections will rise in value. The question is whether this extra value can be used to co-fund the line infrastructure (value capturing). More generally, the spatial accommodation of various plan alternatives will have to be considered. The best alternative is often selected with a view to the best possible spatial accommodation. The decision-makers will have to decide whether the mega-project is to be realized in one production process or split into phases so that the implementation and details of later phases are decided further down the line.

5.6 REDUNDANCY[5]

A sense of direction and an effective feedback mechanism reduce the chance of an unbalanced result. However, it is also important to still have a choice when tensions arise. The generation of knowledge about alternative development paths is crucial. Not just at the start of the project, but throughout the whole decision-making process, there needs to be a *redundancy* in the form of knowledge about possible alternatives. Such knowledge can be generated by a project organization, but it is just as important to receive knowledge from external sources (Nonaka, 1994; Allen, 2001; Schindler and Eppler, 2003). Thus the concept of redundancy must be introduced with regard to the organization of knowledge and to the constellation of players.

In practice, the tendency when faced with a complex project is to reduce the number of participants in decision-making and to pursue efficiency in the organization of project information (Giezen, 2012b). Still, the feedback of redundant organization and information is needed for deliberation and adaptation at strategic intervals. Otherwise there are high risks of deadlock (Teece et al., 1997) and groupthink (Henningsen et al., 2006).

The concept of redundancy has been used in different scientific disciplines. Although the word refers to everything that is not essential to the immediate operational effectiveness of a system, in many instances it is seen as crucial for long-term survival. In his seminal paper on the principle of redundancy, Landau (1969) underpinned the need for additional information in order to enable the recombination of solutions under unexpected circumstances. An airplane is a widely used example of redundancy. There are about 15000 systems in an airplane even though it would be possible to run a Boeing 777 on a few hundred systems (Low et al., 2003). However, because of the many uncertainties involved in air travel, multiple systems are used for safety purposes. This means that if one system fails an alternative can take over. Several attempts have been made to translate the concept of redundancy into decision-making that focuses especially on the development of alternatives and the selection between these (Keeney, 1996; Kane and del Mistro, 2003; Joumard, 2010).

Redundancy is a way of dealing with uncertainty in policy-making and planning:

> If facts are in question, then we simply do not have knowledge of the appropriate means to use in seeking an outcome. We may have hunches and rules of thumb and we may write elaborate plans that anticipate all conceivable outcomes, but these are only hypotheses. Therefore it seems rational to employ a pragmatic and experimental procedure: that is, a policy of redundancy which permits several, and competing, strategies to be followed both simultaneously and separately. (Landau, 1969, p. 355)

In practice, however, there are tendencies to close the system to external players and information early in the process, especially when a feedback mechanism has not been developed. Thus the process is inadequately equipped for generating a redundancy of alternatives. Decision-making may proceed via the selected trajectories but planners and policy-makers need to strike a balance between moments of re-opening the process time after time to develop a proper feedback mechanism and moments of closing the process in order to move towards the intended goal. This is illustrated by Allen with the Law of Excess Diversity for complex systems: 'For a system to serve as a coherent entity over the medium and long term, it must have a number of internal states greater than those considered requisite to deal with the outside world' (Allen, 2001, p. 175).

Redundancy can be a characteristic of both the decision-making process and the resulting (mega) project. Giezen (2012a, p. 76) presents two operational indicators of redundancy. The first relates to the constellation of actors in the decision-making process. The implementation of mega-projects is generally organized via the closed arrangements of project organizations (the contractual decision-making). However, the process of reflection and decision-making should be wider (open) and provide more feedback mechanisms than is strictly necessary. The second operational indicator is closely related to the open player constellation of decision-making. It focuses on the organization of knowledge to examine different trajectories and realize the project. Knowledge should be fuelled by 'outside-in' strategies instead of being monopolized by stake-holding project management. Closely related to the notion of 'redundancy' is the notion of 'resilience'.

5.7 RESILIENCE[6]

The concept of resilience addresses the ability of the decision-making process to deal with unexpected influences without risking indefinite delays or stalemates in the process. The process should be able to learn and adapt. This involves an ability to accept 'flexibility and adaptability, and preparedness to cope with uncertainties and unanticipated situations and directions' (Handmer et al., 1999, p. 269). Resilience can be reactive or proactive. In other words, decision-making can be aimed at returning to a particular equilibrium or it can be pre-designed to change and adapt.

Reactive resilience is the traditional approach whereby a stable position is assumed that is protected against external shocks. A proactive approach assumes that an unstable environment requires adaptation:

> Moreover, in the face of recognized uncertainty and complexity, policy formulation processes, and the research that supports these – planners – must be open to the possible need for unexpected or unconventional responses to issues. The emphasis becomes the development of an ability to manage a range of possible directions. (Dovers and Handmer, 1992, p. 276)

It is important to manage a redundancy of options, alternatives and directions. Resilience relies on the availability of redundant information in order to recombine different pathways.

In accordance with the notions of strategic ambiguity and redundancy, two conditions are crucial for resilience. First of all, there should be adequate redundancy of information to enable recombination of the policy trajectory. Second, the process should not be closed to external influences more often or sooner than necessary. Resilience implies that key decisions are made in the short term while leaving space for manoeuvre in future decisions. If the mega-project starts as a narrowly defined solution, then everything becomes a threat to it. It becomes path-dependent: options to improve the project more than marginally are unlikely to be generated. From a problem perspective, resilience means that the commitment to the mission and overarching goals remains intact; however, the chosen solution can still change.

Resilience is a characteristic of both the decision-making process and the (mega-)project itself. A resilient mega-project can cope with changing circumstances. Once a mega-project has been realized, it will usually function for a great many years under widely changing circumstances. Mega-projects last for decades, some even for centuries. Nowhere near all the changes that a mega-project will undergo can be determined unequivocally beforehand. It is precisely because of these changes and the associated uncertainties that mega-projects should be flexible and adaptable.

In other words, they need to be resilient enough to be able to adapt to external changes and threats. For instance, mega-projects must continue to perform under changing – sometimes extreme – climatic conditions. Transport infrastructure projects must be able (within certain limits) to cope with increasing traffic flows. It is absolutely essential that the capacity of most mega-projects can be adapted without too many extra costs. Transport infrastructure projects must be protected against the risk of flooding, subsidence and earthquakes (in earthquake-prone regions) if that can be realized at extra costs lower than the additional benefits. Accident risks (collisions, derailments) and consequences should also be limited as long as additional costs are lower than additional benefits. In the wake of a string of disasters the European Commission recently tightened the norms for tunnel safety. In many cases national and international regulations will also have to be observed in the longer term. At the same time, mega-projects should not exert a negative influence on the immediate surroundings in terms of noise hindrance, vibrations and toxic emissions (CO_2, NO_x, particulates), which undermine the air quality. The regulations must be adhered to in these areas as well. In the long run, the regulations may also change (tighter controls versus liberalization), existing transport infrastructure projects will preferably have to comply with these new regulations as well.

The resilience of a mega-project is determined not only by the technical specifications, but also by the professionalism of asset management. Crucial questions, also in the stage of the front-end development of a mega-project, relate to asset management. How is the maintenance organized? How are the necessary functional improvements realized? How is safety guaranteed during the operational phase? This may involve the deployment of detection systems in dynamic traffic management or improving the resistance of technical systems to lightning, arson, computer hacking, copper theft and so on. One increasingly important question is how life cycle analysis can help to improve sustainability in the use of transport infrastructure projects. In short, the resilience of a mega-project, including both process and product, has many dimensions that figure particularly in asset management, and the ability to redefine a project according to the challenges that present itself over time.

5.8 ALTERNATIVES AND OPTIONS

Given the complexity of mega-projects and the physical and social environment, it goes without saying that decisions on the preparations for mega-projects should be taken in an optimal setting. A (business) case should be made for developing a number of alternatives: all realistic options should be kept open (Priemus, 2007b, 2008) and should not be closed earlier than absolutely required to ensure progress. In fact, more attention has to be paid to (or more effort has to be spent on) an extended front-end project phase. As shown in Section 5.6, this calls for redundancy in the collection of information as well as in the participating stakeholders. It is also important to apply risk management in general and to accept uncertainty by ensuring that the mega-project has adequate adaptive capacity to overcome future challenges.

The decision-making on mega-projects has been characterized by a long-standing tradition whereby choices are made in the early stages and an irreversible course of action is set out. Often, the favoured option is selected fairly soon and the others are dropped early after careful consideration. This is the approach advocated by the Elverding Commission (Commissie-Elverding, 2008), who advised the Dutch Minister of Transport, Public Works and Water Management on how to speed up the decision-making on infrastructure projects. It is a classic approach that presupposes that all the feasible and practical options are known in the early stages and that there are very few or no uncertainties in the market conditions or the political landscape. These presuppositions are usually untenable: uncertainties are a fact of life. No one can foresee the duration of the development process. No one knows which stakeholders will be involved before and after the go-ahead or the roles they will play. No one can predict the circumstances on the markets or in the political arena when the go-ahead is given or when the project becomes operational. No one knows how much public money the government is willing and able to commit at the moment of implementation or the kind of opportunities for private (co-)financing that will be presented.

An alternative approach is backcasting: decide what you want to achieve in the longer term and mark it on the timeline in functional terms: in X years there must be a transport connection between A and B with a certain capacity that also meets specific demands in terms of traffic safety, noise nuisance, vibrations and air quality. The short-term decisions should then be taken against the backdrop of a 'no regrets policy': ideal solutions in the longer term must not be compromised by short-term decisions. More than one road lead to Rome. Leaving options open means an extra value that can be quantified in principle. As time passes, as more stakeholders arrive and as relevant markets develop, the uncertainties will gradually dissolve and it will be easier to take well-considered decisions. It may therefore be prudent to defer decisions as more knowledge and greater certainty will become available in later stages.

Keeping the options open and even generating more options is particularly important in the run up to the go-ahead. Contracts that are signed with the construction company before the work starts are formulated in such a way that changes after the go-ahead usually push up the costs. If a design and construct contract is applied, various options can be included in the execution phase, provided they meet sharp functional requirements and the construction firm is responsible for the cost implications (Priemus, 2009). Such an integrated project approach is also shown to be beneficial in large engineering projects outside the area of transportation (Bosch-Rekveldt, 2011).

5.9 ADAPTIVE CAPACITY: KEY TO THE MANAGEMENT OF MEGA-PROJECTS[7]

The crucial way to cope with changes, risks and uncertainties is to mobilize adaptive capacity. Giezen (2012a, p. 50) defines adaptive capacity as the ability to adapt and respond to contextual changes. It is similar to the definition used in ecology (Shrivastava, 1983; Folke et al., 2002, 2005; Hagmann and Chuma, 2002), 'Systems with a high adaptive capacity are able to reconfigure themselves when subject to change without significant declines in crucial functions' (Folke et al., 2005, p. 452). According to this literature, it is crucial for ecological systems to be able to adapt to changes in their environment. Similarly, Giezen (2012a, p. 51) argues that the adaptive capacity of the planning and decision-making process is crucial to the long-term sustainability of a mega-project.

Figure 5.2 presents the conceptual framework adopted by Giezen (2012a). A contextual change triggers adaptive capacity of the planning and decision-making process, leading to different types of adaptation and outcomes depending on the activated mechanisms. There are four types of adaptations, with their learning counterparts in brackets: incremental (single loop learning), radical (double loop learning), socio-historical (triple loop learning), and inertia (zero learning) (Argyris and Schön, 1978; Shrivastava, 1983; Sun and Scott, 2003). The main questions is then: what are the mechanisms that drive a project towards a particular type of adaptation or inertia? And what are the impacts on the process and the project?

Incremental adaptation relates to the idea that change comes in many small steps (Cyert and March, 1963) and that organizations learn incrementally (Argyris and Schön, 1978). Individuals and organizations often adapt because they detect errors that need to be corrected. However, it is usually not desirable to introduce fundamental changes to present policies or objectives as that often requires large investments in time,

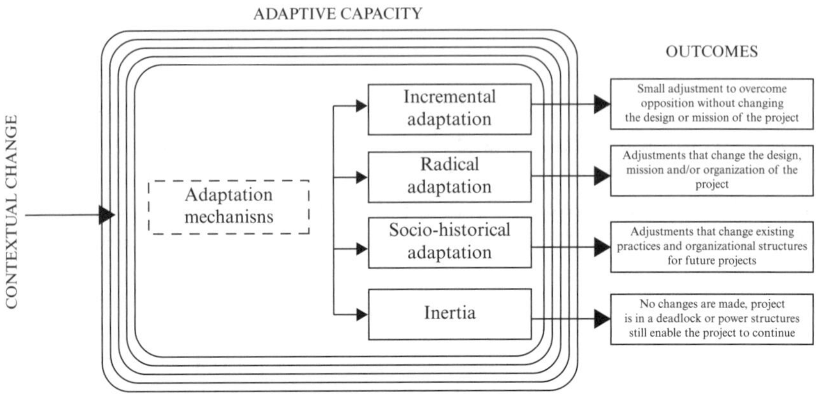

Source: Giezen (2012a, p. 52).

Figure 5.2 Conceptual scheme: adaptive capacity and types of adaptation

money and skills. The benefits may be in the future but the costs are mostly made earlier. However, complex problems can rarely be solved within the safe boundaries of current procedures, objectives and policies. Often more severe, radical adjustments are needed. A radical adaptation involves the fundamental adjustment of objectives, policies and practices. Organizations, for instance, sometimes need to radically renew themselves to survive strong competition and adapt to newly emerging technologies (Crossan et al., 1999). If these adaptations have a lasting impact outside the project, for instance in the institutional setting surrounding mega-projects, we can call them socio-historic adaptations.

Inertia

Protectionist forces are an important mechanism in the creation of an inertia situation. It is the strong protection of vested interests without the willingness to search for a solution that produces inertia. It can be a rewarding strategy for players who are intent on blocking the planning process until their interests or demands are incorporated in the project. Unless an open mindset can be created the planning process will often be plagued by long periods of inertia (Giezen, 2012a, p. 64).

Identifying Adaptation Mechanisms

Incremental adaptations seem primarily a response to emergent technical adversities, the need for impact mitigation strategies, and, more in general, the accommodation of 'protectionist' forces. Solving technical issues and developing mitigation strategies are very common in the planning of mega-projects. And perhaps because of their omnipresence, the potentially disastrous effects are easily neglected. If the decision-makers do not have adequate technical and operational knowledge at their disposal during the construction of a tunnel, small leakages might lead to flooding, houses might subside, or monuments might collapse. Similarly, mitigation strategies are easily promised, but they can have a catastrophic effect on the time and cost budgets if they do not add enough value to the project. Often, protectionist forces are a prime cause of mitigation strategies. They also play a role in emergent technical issues, limiting the possibilities for finding new approaches and solutions. When protectionist forces cannot be accommodated, they can keep the project in a state of limbo. Alternatively, 'taboos' can be created: difficult issues are left out of discussions in order to make progress on other fields. In both cases, total or partial inertia is the result. This seems, however, to offer only a temporary solution: if not dealt with, unsolved issues will surface again later (Giezen, 2012a, p. 64).

In an apparent paradox, *radical adaptations* also seem to require strong oppositional forces in most cases. If there is no strong opposition, it can seem unnecessary to make a more radical change. The difference between the mechanism of the 'protectionist' forces and the 'oppositional' forces seems to be that oppositional forces are open-minded towards change and want to add value to the project. Changes within the institutional setting can aid this process by bringing a breath of fresh air to a deadlocked situation, and thus provide an opportunity for radical adaptation.

Finally, mega-projects can act as major socio-technical experiments that function as frontrunners for larger institutional changes and practices, or socio-historical adaptations. Mega-projects are at the forefront of many developments and are potential agents of change, especially in project management and appraisal methods. They are therefore affected, but also influenced by institutional changes. Table 5.3 provides an overview of the identified mechanisms per adaptation type (Giezen, 2012a, p. 65). As can be seen, the mechanisms supporting radical adaptations all indicate that a redundancy of knowledge and of stakeholders is crucial if strong changes are to be made. Socio-historical adaptations are in this sense similar, yet there is a rearrangement of the stakeholders, institutions and/or practices. In addition, Table 5.3 shows that it is crucial to prevent protectionistic sentiments overtaking the decision-making process. This does not mean that stakeholders should be blocked from the process or ignored, but that it is important to accommodate these sentiments in order to create a productive atmosphere where people feel they are taken seriously.

Table 5.3 Identified adaptation mechanisms

Adaptation Type	Mechanism
Incremental	Solving technical issues Impact mitigation strategies Accommodation of protectionist stakeholders
Radical	Strong oppositional forces (but open to change) Stakeholder acknowledgment of own weaknesses Changes within existing institutions
Socio-historical	Development of new institutions
Inertia	Inflexible protectionist stakeholders Taboos

Source: Giezen (2012a, p. 65).

5.10 CONCLUSIONS

Following Giezen (2012a, p. 66) we conclude that the planning and decision-making of complex mega-projects require adaptations to overcome deadlocks and bottlenecks in the process and unexpected changes in the context, and that these adaptations should be of a type (i.e., incremental, radical or socio-historical) that fits the type of deadlock. Many proponents of mega-projects seem to be fixated on the idea that the first choice is also the best choice and that only technical fixes, mitigation strategies and compromises should be applied to get it through the planning and decision-making process, as in the 'do no harm' approach, proposed by Altshuler and Luberoff (2003). This leads to a built-in preference for inertia or – at the most – incremental adaptations (mostly as a way of acknowledging or accommodating protectionist stakeholders), even where more radical or even socio-historical adaptations (possibly triggered by oppositional forces) could lead to better projects.

Current political strategies and rational planning models applied in government do not seem to be improving on this, but rather they tend to simplify the planning and decision-making processes in mega-projects, for instance by excluding or limiting the involvement of oppositional forces. Such simplification is not the best strategy for dealing with mega-project planning and decision-making. It does not acknowledge the need to adapt the project in all phases of the planning and decision-making process in order to resolve unexpected deadlocks and/or cope with emergent opportunities and threats posed by developments in the broader context. In particular, oppositional forces seem a phenomenon that should be accepted and, if harnessed properly, these forces could lead to more creative solutions and even speed up the process. In more general terms, adaptive capacity should be built into the process in order to keep it responsive to future developments and deadlock. It is crucial to be able to identify the symptoms of particular deadlocks in order to deploy the mechanisms that can prevent them from slowing the project down or masking possible alternatives.

The trends in project management call for a more serious inclusion of the context in project management considerations. Complexity of mega-projects is enlarged by market dynamics and political discontinuity in a changing environment (e.g., particularly the external complexity from the TOE complexity framework). Complexity goes together with uncertainties and risks. Keeping open alternatives and options are essential in dealing with complexity. This makes redundancy and resilience crucial. In more general terms, adaptive capacity is the key to the management of complex mega-projects.

NOTES

1. Section 5.2 draws heavily on Bosch-Rekveldt (2011, pp. 14–17).
2. Section 5.3 is based on Bosch-Rekveldt (2011).
3. Section 5.5 is based on Priemus (2010a).
4. This subsection draws heavily on Priemus (2010b).
5. Section 5.6 is based on Giezen (2012a, pp. 75–6).
6. Section 5.7 is based on Giezen (2012a, pp. 76–7).
7. Section 5.9 is based on Giezen (2012a).

LITERATURE

Achterkamp, M.C. and J.F.J. Vos (2008), 'Investigating the use of the stakeholder notion in project management literature, a meta-analysis', *International Journal of Project Management*, **26**(7), 749–57.

Allen, P.M. (2001), 'A complex systems approach to learning, adaptive networks', *International Journal of Innovation Management*, **5**(2), 149–80.

Altshuler, A. and D. Luberoff (2003), *Mega-projects: The Changing Politics of Urban Public Investment*, Washington, DC: Brookings.

Argyris, C. and D. Schön (1978), *Organizational Learning*, Reading, MA: Addison-Wesley.

Artto, K.A. and K. Wikström (2005), 'What is project business?', *International Journal of Project Management*, **23**(5), 343–53.

Banister, D. and J. Berechman (2000), *Transport Investment and Economic Development*, London: University College London Press.

Bosch-Rekveldt, M.G.C. (2011), 'Managing project complexity: a study into adapting early project phases to improve project performance in large engineering projects', Delft (PhD dissertation TU Delft).

Cleland, D.I. and W.R. King (eds) (1983), *Project Management Handbook*, New York: Van Nostrand Reinhold Company Inc.

Commissie-Elverding (2008), *Sneller en Beter* (*Quicker and Better*), The Hague: Ministerie van Verkeer en Waterstaat.
Crossan, M.M., H.W. Lane and R.E. White (1999), 'An organizational learning framework: from intuition to institution', *The Academy of Management Review*, **24**(3), 522–37.
Cyert, R.M. and J.G. March (1963), *A Behavioral Theory of the Firm*, Englewood Cliffs, NJ: Prentice/Hall.
de Bruijn, J.A. and E.F. ten Heuvelhof (2007), *Management in Netwerken: over Veranderen in een Multi-actorcontext* (*Management in Networks: About Changing in a Multi-actor Context*), 3rd edition, The Hague: Lemma.
de Bruijn, J.A., E.F. ten Heuvelhof and R. In 't Veld (2002), *Procesmanagement: Over procesmanagement en besluitvorming* [*Process Management: About Process Management and Decision-making*], 2nd revised edition, The Hague: Sdu Uitgevers.
Dovers, S.R. and J.W. Handmer (1992), 'Uncertainty, sustainability and change', *Global Environmental Change*, **2**(4), 262–76.
Engwall, M. (2003), 'No project is an island: linking projects to history and context', *Research Policy*, **32**(5), 789–808.
Flyvbjerg, Bent, Nils Bruzelius and Werner Rothengatter (2003), *Megaprojects and Risk: An Anatomy of Ambition*, Cambridge, MA: Cambridge University Press.
Folke, C., T. Hahn, P. Olsson and J. Norberg (2005), 'Adaptive governance of social-ecological systems', *Annual Review of Environment and Resources*, **30**, 441–73.
Folke, C., S. Carpenter, T. Elmqvist, L. Gunderson, C.A. Holling and B. Walker (2002), 'Resilience and sustainable development: building adaptive capacity in a world of transformations', *AMBIO: A Journal of the Human Environment*, **31**(5), 437–40.
Giezen, M. (2012a), 'Navigating mega projects through complexity and uncertainty: strategic and adaptive capacity in planning and decision-making', Amsterdam (PhD dissertation Amsterdam University).
Giezen, M. (2012b), 'Keeping it simple? A case study into the advantages and disadvantages of reducing complexity in mega-projects planning', *International Journal of Project Management*, **30**(7), 781–90.
Giezen, M. (2013), 'Adaptive and strategic capacity: navigating megaprojects through uncertainty and complexity'. *Environment and Planning B: Planning and Design*, **40**(4), 723–741. doi:10.1068/b38184.
Hagmann, J. and E. Chuma (2002), 'Enhancing the adaptive capacity of the resource users in natural resource management', *Agricultural Systems*, **73**(1), 23–9.
Handmer, J.W., S. Dovers and T.E. Downing (1999), 'Societal vulnerability to climate change and variability', *Mitigation and Adaptation Strategies for Global Change*, **4**(3), 267–81.
Henningsen, D.D., M.L.M. Henningsen, J. Eden and M.G. Cruz (2006), 'Examining the symptoms of groupthink and retrospective sensemaking', *Small Group Research*, **37**(1), 36–64.
Hillson, D. and P. Simon (2007), *Practical Project Risk Management – The ATOM Methodology*, Vienna: VA: Management Concepts.
Joumard, R. (2010), 'Transport project assessment methodology within the framework of sustainable development', *Ecological Indicators*, **10**(2), 136–42.
Kane, L. and R. del Mistro (2003), 'Changes in transport planning policy: changes in transport planning methodology', *Transportation*, **30**(2), 113–31.
Keeney, R. (1996), 'Value-focused thinking: identifying decision opportunities and creating alternatives', *European Journal of Operational Research*, **92**(3), 537–49.
Kerzner, P.D. (2003), *Project Management: A Systems Approach to Planning, Scheduling and Controlling*, London: John Wiley.
Kloppenborg, T.J. and W.A. Opfer (2002), 'The current state of project management research: trends, interpretations, and predictions', *Project Management Journal*, **33**(2), 5–18.
Koppenjan, J., W. Veeneman, H. van der Voort, E. ten Heuvelhof and M. Leijten (2011), 'Competing management approaches in large engineering projects: the

Dutch RandstadRail project', *International Journal of Project Management*, **29**(6), 740–50.
Landau, M. (1969), 'Redundancy, rationality, and the problem of duplication and overlap', *Public Administration Review*, **29**(4), 346–58.
Leijten, M. and H. de Bruijn (2008), 'Mega-projects and contested information', in H. Priemus, B. Flyvbjerg and B. van Wee (eds), *Decision-making on Mega-projects: Cost–Benefit Analysis, Planning and Innovation*, Cheltenham, UK and Northampton, MA, USA: Edward Elgar, pp. 84–101.
Low, B., E. Ostrom, C. Simon and J. Wilson (2003), 'Redundancy and diversity: do they influence optimal management', in F. Berkes, J. Colding and C. Folte (eds), *Navigating Social-Ecological Systems*, Cambridge, UK: Cambridge University Press, pp. 53–82.
Maylor, H. (2005), *Project Management*, 3rd edition, Essex: Pearson Education Limited.
Meredith, J.R. and S.J. Mantel (2006), *Project Management: A Managerial Approach*, 6th edition, New York: John Wiley.
Ministerie van Verkeer en Waterstaat (2004), *Nota Mobiliteit* [*Mobility Memorandum*], The Hague: Ministerie van Verkeer en Waterstaat.
Morris, P.W.G. (1994), *The Management of Projects*, London: Thomas Telford.
Morris, P.W.G., A. Jamieson and M.M. Shepherd (2006a), 'Research updating the *APM Body of Knowledge* 4th edition', *International Journal of Project Management*, **24**(6), 416–573.
Morris, P.W.G., L. Crawford, D. Hodgson, M.M. Shepherd and J. Thomas (2006b), 'Exploring the role of formal bodies of knowledge in defining a profession – the case of project management', *International Journal of Project Management*, **24**(8), 710–21.
Murray, A. (2009), *Managing Successful Projects with PRINCE2 (Office of Government Commerce)*, 5th edition, Norwich: The Stationery Office.
Nonaka, I. (1994), 'A dynamic theory of organizational knowledge creation', *Organization Science*, **5**(1), 14–37.
Pinto, J.K. (ed.) (1988), *The Project Management Institute – Project Management Handbook*, 1st edition, San Francisco: Jossey-Bass.
Pinto, J.K. (2004), *The Wiley Guide to Managing Projects*, New York: John Wiley and Sons, Inc.
Priemus, H. (2007a), 'Decision-making on large infrastructure projects: the role of Dutch Parliament', *Transportation Planning and Technology*, **30**(1), 71–93.
Priemus, H. (2007b), 'Development and design of large infrastructure projects: disregarded alternatives and issues of spatial planning', *Environment and Planning B*, **34**(4), 626–44.
Priemus, H. (2008), 'How to improve the early stages of decision-making on mega-projects', in H. Priemus, B. Flyvbjerg and B. van Wee (eds), *Decision-making on Mega-projects: Cost–Benefit Analysis, Planning and Innovation*, Cheltenham, UK and Northampton, MA: Edward Elgar, pp. 105–19.
Priemus, H. (2009), 'Do design and construct contracts for infrastructure projects stimulate innovation? The case of the Dutch high speed railway', *Transportation Planning and Technology*, **32**(4), 335–53.
Priemus, H. (2010a), 'Decision-making on mega-projects: drifting on political discontinuity and market dynamics', *European Journal of Transport and Infrastructure Research*, **10**(1), 19–29.
Priemus, H. (2010b), 'Megaprojects: dealing with pitfalls', *European Planning Studies*, **18**(7), 1023–39.
Priemus, H., B. Flyvbjerg and B. van Wee (eds) (2008), *Decision-making on Mega-projects: Cost–Benefit Analysis, Planning and Innovation*, Cheltenham, UK and Northampton, MA, USA: Edward Elgar.
Project Management Institute (PMI) (2004), *A Guide to the Project Management Body of Knowledge*, 3rd edition, Project Management Institute.
Pryke, S. and H.K. Smyth (2006), *The Management of Complex Projects. A Relationship Approach*, London: Blackwell Publishers.

Rietveld, P. (1989), 'Infrastructure and regional development: a survey of multiregional economic models', *The Annals of Regional Science*, **23**(4), 255–74.
Sauser, B.J., R.R. Reilly and A.J. Shenhar (2009), 'Why projects fail? How contingency theory can provide new insights – a comparative analysis of NASA's Mars Climate Orbiter loss', *International Journal of Project Management*, **27**(7), 665–79.
Schindler, M. and M. Eppler (2003), 'Harvesting project knowledge: a review of project learning methods and success factors', *International Journal of Project Management*, **21**(3), 219–28.
Shenhar, A.J. (2001), 'One size does not fit all projects: exploring classical contingency domains', *Management Science*, **47**(3), 394–414.
Shenhar, A.J. and D. Dvir (1996), 'Toward a typological theory of project management', *Research Policy*, **25**(4), 607–32.
Shenhar, A.J. and D. Dvir (2007), 'Project management research: the challenge and opportunity', *Project Management Journal*, **38**(2), 93–9.
Shrivastava, P. (1983), 'A typology of organizational learning systems', *Journal of Management Studies*, **20**(1), 7–28.
Smyth, H.J. and P.W.G. Morris (2007), 'An epistemological evaluation of research into projects and their management: methodological issues', *International Journal of Project Management*, **25**(4), 423–36.
Sun, P.Y.T. and J.L. Scott (2003), 'Exploring the divide – organizational learning organization', *The Learning Organization*, **10**(4), 202–15.
Söderlund, J. (2011), 'Pluralism in project management: navigating the crossroads of specialization and fragmentation', *International Journal of Management Reviews*, **13**(2), 153–76.
Teece, D.J., G. Pisano and A. Shuen (1997), 'Dynamic capabilities and strategic management', *Strategic Management Journal*, **18**(7), 509–33.
Turner, J.R. (2008), *The Handbook of Project-based Management*, 3rd edition, London: McGraw-Hill.
Turner, J.R., A. Ledwith and J. Kelly (2010), 'Project management in small to medium-sized enterprises: matching processes to the nature of the firm', *International Journal of Project Management*, **28**(8), 744–55.
Turner, J.R. and S.J. Simister (eds) (2000), *Gower Handbook of Project Management*, 3rd edition, Aldershot: Gower Publishing Limited.
Vickerman, R. (1989), 'Measuring changes in regional competitiveness: the effect of international infrastructure investments', *The Annals of Regional Science*, **23**(4), 275–86.
Vickerman, R. (2000), 'Evaluation methodologies for transport projects in the United Kingdom', *Transport Policy*, **7**(1), 7–16.
Wachs, M. (1989), 'When planners lie with numbers', *Journal of the American Planning Association*, **55**(4), 476–9.
Wachs, M. (1990), 'Ethics and advocacy in forecasting for public policy', *Business and Professional Ethics Journal*, **9**(1–2), 141–57.
Williams, T.M. (2005), 'Assessing and moving on from the dominant project management discourse in the light of project overruns', *IEEE Transactions on Engineering Management*, **52**(4), 497–508.
Winch, G.M. (2002), *Managing Construction Projects*, Oxford: Blackwell Science.

6. New Public Management and the new features of strategic behaviour

Ernst ten Heuvelhof and Martijn Leijten

6.1 BACKGROUND AND PROBLEM DEFINITION

During the 1980s and 1990s New Public Management (NPM) (Hood, 1991; Osborne and Gaebler, 1992; Pollitt and Bouckaert, 2004) appeared as a reaction to the government management policies of the previous decades that were viewed as having become too 'self-centred'. Governments were accused of focusing too much on political objectives rather than meeting the needs of citizens. According to proponents of NPM, government bodies and state-owned companies were not sufficiently customer-oriented, and were not innovative and were inefficient. In their view, government bodies should provide better service to citizens in efficient and innovative ways. In doing so, they should use private enterprise as an example. NPM supporters claimed that private companies are aware that their survival depends on their ability to meet the needs of their customers. Competition and self-interest stimulate companies to do this efficiently. NPM aims at introducing arrangements that enable and stimulate competition and/or give more room for pursuing self-interest. These criticisms also applied, with the necessary modifications, to public transportation companies, including railway, tram and underground rail companies. These companies were also accused of being insufficiently customer-oriented, inefficient and lacking innovation.

For this reason, it was hoped that public transport companies would become more like private companies (Pollitt and Smith, 2002; Parker, 2009). Just like private companies, these organizations should be stimulated to operate effectively and efficiently. They should have specific clients and operate like an enterprise. Where possible, this should also be in competition with other parties. Companies involved should feel more incentives to operate more effectively and efficiently. In other words, the public transport companies were required to become more market-oriented. Having said this, NPM is not a concrete 'how to' manual. On the contrary, it is more a way of thinking. During the last few decades, changes have been made to organizational structures and contracts that have made it appear feasible to approach this 'ideal' of a market-driven enterprise.

These changes were intended to introduce market-based stimuli and a generally more commercial approach. These changes are archetypal of the NPM approach and, in fact, amount to institutional reform.

NPM-like Reforms with Regard to Railway Projects

Institutional changes were introduced to the world of railway companies and projects at two levels within this context of NPM (Koppenjan, 2012). The first level concerned the structure of public transport companies. It was thought that the splitting up of previously integrated companies to form smaller entities would enable a situation to be achieved that would be closer to the ideal market situation (Evans, 2003; Gomez-Ibanez, 2003; Gomez-Ibanez and De Rus, 2006). By splitting the production chain into different fields, carried out by separate organizations, quality and price could be approached in a more commercial manner. A common partition of fields is to make separate organizations responsible for maintaining the infrastructure and the provision of transport services. This enables a rise in possibilities for competition and is ultimately intended to improve quality and efficiency. This relationship between competition on the one hand and quality on the other hand is a typical example of the NPM way of thinking. In this chapter we distinguish three fields that may be split up (van de Velde and ten Heuvelhof, 2008), for example, transport services, trains and infrastructure. Companies that operate in fields where competition is possible could become more independent from government or even privatized. These privatized companies were supposed to feel more incentives to operate efficiently.

The second level concerns the activities that are defined in standard contracts, like design, build, financing, maintenance and operation. For these activities, there is a clear tendency towards more integral contracts (van Herk et al., 2006). Activities and responsibilities that were previously the subject of separate contracts are now included in integral contracts. According to the NPM approach, these activities and responsibilities are (re)connected to each other (in other words, integrated) by means of contracts. By making these 'connections', the best results for all parties can – in theory – be approached more effectively. The former separate contracts were sub-optimal at least partly due to the fact that governments are obliged to work with budgets based on the annual cash budget system. This used to result in sub-optimal arranged projects (low project costs, high maintenance costs). The privatization of companies promoted the acceptance of multi-year budgeting systems that would enable the introduction of life cycle cost systems. Integrated projects and contracts fit in better with these life cycle cost systems. The combination of fields and activities results in the conceptual scheme shown in Table 6.1.

Table 6.1 Fields and activities in realizing and running rail projects

Fields	Transport Services	Trains	Infrastructure
Activities			
Design			
Build			
Financing			
Maintenance			
Operation			

In NPM-like approaches there is a tendency to split up the fields and to reconnect the activities. Moreover, two additional changes are worth mentioning. First, to promote competition there was a tendency to make, whenever possible, smaller contracts. This would give more opportunities for smaller companies to enter the market. This was supposed to promote competition. Second, the growing independence of the organizations involved from government and the privatization of these organizations made the introduction of more lump-sum-like contracts attractive. A lump sum arrangement appeals to the self-interest of the organization that receives the lump sum. This is considered to be an incentive to operate efficiently.

In this section a number of NPM-like arrangements have been introduced: separation of fields, connecting activities, privatization, whenever possible smaller contracts and lump sum financing arrangements. These arrangements are all meant to promote more competition and to introduce incentives to operate more effectively and efficiently. These arrangements are examples of NPM-like arrangements and are by no means a complete enumeration of all possible NPM-like arrangements. In the case studies in this chapter we will come back to these arrangements and analyse the impact of these arrangements.

Problem Definition

The splitting up and reconnection operations led to old interfaces disappearing and new ones appearing. New fragmentation problems arose related to these interfaces, which are described in detail elsewhere (Gomez-Ibanez and De Rus, 2006). In this chapter, we wish to take a step beyond providing another discussion of the various advantages and disadvantages. Instead, we wish to make a contribution towards explaining how the disadvantages come about. To do this, we will take a detailed look at one of the possible explanations of why these disadvantages arise: the strategic behaviour of parties that operate in and around these new interfaces. In addition to this, we analyse forms of strategic behaviour that are caused by other NPM-like arrangements.

Three caveats are worth mentioning. First, by this we do not claim that strategic behaviour has exclusively emerged in NPM-like conditions. The previous way of organizing had its particular variants of strategic behaviour as well. Second, the introduction of NPM is flanked by macro-developments, such as the decline of public expenditure in public transport. It is difficult to distinguish the effects of these developments from the effects of particular variants of strategic behaviour. Third, we have selected failing cases, because we would like to explore new forms of strategic behaviour that might arise in new conditions. From this one cannot conclude that NPM-like conditions may or may not give more room for strategic behaviour than previously.

We will investigate three large railway projects that have used the NPM approach to see whether the parties have acted strategically. We will do this by first defining the vague concept of strategic behaviour more clearly. We will then describe three large rail projects. We will sketch how they are organized in an NPM-like way, the resulting benefits and disadvantages and the forms of strategic behaviours that have been developed. We will then draw some conclusions.

6.2 STRATEGIC BEHAVIOUR

A famous description of strategic behaviour is as follows: a 'propensity to shirk, to be opportunistic, to maximize his or her self-interest, to act with guile and to behave in ways that constitute a moral hazard' (Donaldson, 1990, p. 372; see also Williamson, 1985). Strategic behaviour is also 'based on the assumption of rational behaviour – not just of intelligent behaviour, but of behaviour motivated by a conscious calculation of advantages' (Schelling, 1960, p. 4) Both descriptions have strongly negative connotations, but there is also a different aspect to strategic behaviour. Strategic behaviour also assumes insight on the part of the strategic actor – an entrepreneurial attitude and the ability to be calculating (ten Heuvelhof et al., 2009). Rather more positive qualities, in other words. Strategic behaviour seems to lie somewhere between being clever and being cunning.

Strategic behaviour is always based on the self-interest of the actor, even if this harms any private interests or even the public interest. Strategic actors behave in a calculating way and this is partly why they are able to camouflage their intentions, sometimes even by claiming virtuous motives, which often makes it difficult for the outside world to unmask the actor's true intentions.

There are sufficient reasons to provoke the assumption that strategic behaviour can arise during the realization of railway infrastructure. One reason is that the theory of strategic behaviour assumes that this type of behaviour will thrive within so-called 'coopetitive' relationships (Dixit and Nalebuff, 1991) – in other words, in situations where both common and conflicting interests exist between actors (Schelling, 1960). Actors involved in the realization of infrastructure projects are indeed related to each other in this way. They are either the other actor's supplier or customer, or they are competitors. These positions encourage ruthless, business-like behaviour in which the actor's own position is of the highest priority. At the same time, they are mutually responsible for the quality and competitiveness of the same end product, which encourages cooperative behaviour.

A second reason is that there are very substantial interests involved in the realization of infrastructure. The projects themselves are enormously expensive, which means that there is much to be won and lost. During the construction phase, it is also possible to gain advantage with respect to the operational phase, which again involves very large potential benefits.

In view of the above, it is not surprising that strategic behaviour has been linked to the realization of infrastructure projects, in particular with respect to the often high costs of realizing infrastructure (Cantarelli, 2011). In many infrastructure projects, the original estimates of costs and revenues differ from the figures actually achieved by a very large margin (Cantarelli, 2011; van Wee, 2011) If this were only due to incompetence, one would expect the positive and negative differences to balance each other out. However, this is not the case in practice. The costs appear to be underestimated in many more cases than they are overestimated, while the revenues are very often lower than estimated (Flyvbjerg et al., 2003b; van Wee, 2004). This means that – rather than being randomly distributed – the inaccuracy of estimates is strongly biased, in the sense that estimates are tailored to ensure the realization of the infrastructure. It should not be surprising that strategic behaviour is often suggested as an explanation for these problems, although a justification for this claim is not always given (Wachs, 1990; Trujillo et al., 2002; Flyvbjerg et al., 2003a).

As previously mentioned, we will focus on strategic behaviour in NPM-like arrangements as a possible explanation. By doing this, we do not mean that strategic behaviour emerges in NPM-like conditions only. On the contrary, strategic behaviour tends to emerge in any conditions. We argue, however, that there is a strong and particular relation between NPM-like conditions and strategic behaviour.

It goes without saying that strategic behaviour in relation to the realization of infrastructure is not limited to the estimation of costs and revenues. Tendering processes also provide opportunities for strategic behaviour. Many other benefits are equally conceivable.

Strategic behaviour is difficult to prove, partly because the actors involved are seldom prepared to admit that they have acted in a strategic manner. This caveat also applies to the forms of strategic behaviour described in this chapter. The methodological status of the forms of strategic behaviours described in this chapter should, therefore, be regarded as hypothetical.

6.3 CASE STUDIES

The realization of three large railway projects in the Netherlands is described below. These are: RandstadRail in The Hague and surrounding area, the High Speed Rail Line South, and the North/South Metro Line in Amsterdam. The reason for selecting these projects is that these have NPM-like characteristics and that these have been studied by the authors of this chapter. The description of the cases is structured as follows. An introduction describes the rail project and some significant issues related to the realization of the project. This is followed by a description of the NPM-like arrangements in the case, the related strategic behaviour and the results of these arrangements. The results are summarized in Table 6.2.

RandstadRail

RandstadRail is a public rail transport service in the Rotterdam and The Hague agglomerations in the western Netherlands (TU Delft, 2008). It was created by linking up two converted conventional commuter rail lines between Rotterdam and The Hague and between The Hague and its satellite town Zoetermeer, together with the Rotterdam underground and two tram lines in The Hague. Light rail rolling stock is being used for the new system.

The project was split up into many small contracts, which enabled contracts to be awarded at lower prices. This meant that the costs were lower than initially budgeted, which provided financial headroom to expand the scope; in other words, to realize more than had been initially planned and for the same budget. However, at the end of the realization it turned out that some of the money that was redistributed to other projects was necessary after all. This led to so much political commotion that a councillor was forced to resign.

Table 6.2 NPM-like arrangements, strategic behaviour and effects for complex rail projects

Project	NPM Arrangement	Hypothetical Strategic Behaviour	Result of NPM Arrangements and Strategic Behaviour
RandstadRail	Lump sum Different parties responsible for operation and maintenance on the one hand and construction on the other Tendering for small contracts	Shirking Dragging feet Potential abuse of information asymmetry	Cheap contracts that enabled the scope to be expanded Chaos during the conversion test and trail period resulting in derailments and suspension of operations Moral hazard or fending off of input from engineers due to fear of strategic behaviour
High Speed Rail Line South	Privatization of the construction and operation/ maintenance For the superstructure, design, construction and operation were 'reconnected'	Collusion Risk shifting Unwillingness to optimize the project as a whole	Cost overruns Serious delays
North/South Metro Line in Amsterdam	Lump sum Design and con- struct contracts	Risk avoidance and risk shifting	Cost overruns Serious delays

Within the first few weeks of operation, there were four derailments; one of them resulting in injuries to passengers. As a result of this event, the Transport Inspectorate decided to shut the system down. It was eventually reopened almost a year later, after the structural cause of the system's malfunction had finally been uncovered and repaired.

NPM-like arrangements

The RandstadRail project was set up in line with the New Public Management approach. The largest part of the funding came from central government (Ministry of Transport). This subsidy was transferred lump sum, including all risks, responsibilities and possible benefits, to the regional authorities. Since the regional authorities did not have the skills or staff to manage the project, they transferred the implementation of the project (excluding decision-making authority, but including risks and financial management) to the municipality of The Hague, its largest constituent. We consider these kinds of arrangement as NPM-like arrangements because the actor who receives this lump sum will feel a strong incentive to operate effectively and efficiently.

Regional authorities had, on the instigation of central government, started the separation of the activities of local public transport operator HTM from governmental tasks. Previously, HTM had been part of the municipality of The Hague. This was meant to finally lead to full privatization of HTM as well as competitive tenders of concessions for operation and management of transport systems. A hole-and-corner contract, or in fact any responsibilities for the development of the RandstadRail system delegated to HTM, would disrupt the level playing field.

The drive to outsource had several implications, both positive and negative. The managers of RandstadRail decided that all parts of the system were to be developed independently, with separate contracts to make maximum use of the expertise in the market. As a consequence, the project managers could benefit from favourable conditions, in a market that was eager for work. Moreover, the management of the project could adjust to emerging developments, such as new insights and emerging information on light rail, of which there were many in this project. Because it was begun with very rough terms of reference, the scope and design changed considerably during the preparation. The management changed plans on the basis of emerging issues and optimized the system in such a way that the functionality of the completed system was of greater scope than originally defined, and for, by and large, the same amount of money, due to some windfall in several contracts (Koppenjan et al., 2011). Changes were made when information emerged, indicating that optimizations could be made or parts of the plan were not implementable with the new rolling stock or in cooperation with hesitant third party actors.

The downside emerged during the conversion period, when there were so many different contracts and contractors that proper coordination was hardly possible. The various contractors did not know what the others were doing. The project management did set up a configuration control board to improve coordination capabilities, but this was done rather late in the preparation phase and the actors involved were not accustomed to using it. In practice, the configuration control board always lagged behind the real events.

This situation was exacerbated by the large fragmentation of contracts. For example, the municipality of The Hague was responsible for infrastructure, HTM for rolling stock and the regional authorities for design decisions. The specifications of the rolling stock (such as the shape of the wheels) depended heavily on the geometry of the railway infrastructure (such as the required corner radiuses and the shape of the points) and vice versa. The consequences occurred in many cases in issues emerging in the preparation and operation phases. So, the interface problems of RandstadRail occurred in almost all fields of Table 6.1.

The derailment that led to the shutting down of the system occurred at points that had been damaged in an earlier unknown event; probably during the chaotic conversion works. Coordination had been a problem throughout the entire preparation and implementation, even to the extent that different contractors worked with different versions of the reference design. One contractor allegedly broke up what others had just built.

Strategic behaviour

Shirking One issue emerged at the interface of the rolling stock and infrastructure columns and the interface of design and operation. Despite the unbundling of HTM activities from the client's public responsibilities, the involvement of HTM was indispensable, or at least desirable. It had all the knowledge of the existing street tram tracks in The Hague and it was expected to order the rolling stock, even though too much involvement had to be prevented to keep the level playing field intact and HTM was not sure whether it would actually get the concessions. When HTM had to order the rolling stock to make sure the trains were delivered on time, many of the required specifications were still unknown. It was, for example, unclear how the power supply would be organized when the conventional railway tracks were disconnected from the heavy rail grid (see below) and how the geometry of the wheels would combine with certain types of points in the former heavy rail sections (many of which were different from what HTM was accustomed to). In fact, HTM was waiting for specifications from the infrastructure project managers and the regional authority decision-makers, whereas the latter were waiting for the specifications of the rolling stock, to be provided by HTM. Since HTM had been denied a hole-and-corner concession for operation and maintenance throughout a major part of the preparation, it was not inclined to put a lot of effort into solving this deadlock. Very late in the process, HTM did get such a concession without tender, after special permission from the Ministry of Transport.

Dragging feet Further complications during the project occurred due to a troubled relationship between the owners of RandstadRail and ProRail, the national railway infrastructure manager. The owner had expected that he could, at least for the first period of operation, make use of the power supply that was already available from the conventional rail operation. It was also expected that a part of a shunting yard would be made available. Negotiations with ProRail were, however, far from smooth. ProRail was not happy with the loss of a part of its network and was also in conflict with RandstadRail about the availability of platforms in the central railway station in The Hague for RandstadRail trains. It appeared to be impossible for RandstadRail to make a durable deal on power supply. The shunting yard was cut into two sections, but RandstadRail unexpectedly had to pay a sum of money that it had assumed was to come from ProRail, on the basis of an investment in future replacement of depreciated parts.

Potential abuse of information asymmetry As a result of the strong fragmentation in the implementation of the project, there was an important interface between managers of the client (regional authorities) in the position of decision-maker and the engineers of the municipality of The Hague, responsible for implementation. Engineers of the municipality feared that the time schedules for the conversion works were too optimistic for the complex work to be achieved. The managers were, however, reluctant to extend the construction period. Engineers could not indicate objectively where problems as a result of fragmented works under pressure would occur. They had developed these trepidations from experience and from an extensive understanding of the project at system level. Particularly, they had a very good understanding of the consequences of strong fragmentation and subsequent interface risks. The managers, acting from a completely different frame of reference, did not comprehend and were afraid that the input from engineers might be a strategically driven attempt to gain more time, which would make life a lot easier for them. However, in such a scenario, budget and time schedules would be overrun.

In an attempt to avoid becoming victim to such perverse incentives, the client fended off this potential strategic behaviour and maintained the schedules. With hindsight, one could maintain that the engineers' concern was justified. But even that might be too quick a conclusion. The engineers might still have had a strategic motivation, but were also coincidentally proved to be right. The point is that adverse effects can occur in an organizational arrangement like this, regardless of the motive. Fending off inconvenient input implies that valuable information can be neglected (Leijten et al., 2010). Not only strategic behaviour itself, but even the fear of strategic behaviour can have adverse effects, as it can precipitate decision-makers to throw out the baby with the bath water. Either the client is misled, or they may neglect valuable input that is necessary for a sound project. The double bind character of this dilemma is a common adverse effect of principal–agent relationships (Jensen and Meckling, 1976; Leijten, 2012). NPM-like arrangements are susceptible to this.

The conclusion at the end of this section is that NPM arrangements made a complex project even more complex due to coordination, responsibility and planning difficulties. In addition, the NPM-fuelled half-and-half involvement of the future privatized operator hampered a smooth implementation.

High Speed Rail Line South

The HSL-South is the first high speed rail line in the Netherlands (Tweede Kamer der Staten Generaal, 2004). It runs from the Belgian border to Amsterdam. Its construction was one of the largest infrastructure projects ever carried out in the Netherlands. The Dutch government acted as client through its Ministry of Transport. The project was built between 2000 and 2006, but it was not opened until 2009 and it was only in 2012 when the new high speed trains of the national service started operation, with many technical problems. There were also major cost overruns. Design and build issues on infrastructure are the fields in the matrix that are most particularly discussed in this section, but this project has experienced complexity and difficulties in many fields of the matrix.

NPM-like arrangements

The project was split into four parts: the substructure (foundation, tunnels, viaducts etc.), the superstructure (tracks, overhead wiring, electronic systems), the stations and operation. Market research had indicated that potential contractors considered the project as a whole to be too complex. It would confront them with too many risks and uncertainties. Unlike a public actor, they would not be able to offset these risks with other (sub) projects or with tax revenues. This could have either of the following consequences. One possibility was that the project would be too large for any potential bidder, or that there would be a very limited number of bidders capable of doing the job, leading to a lack of competition in the tender.

The other possibility was that a contractor might be found, but they would be likely to include a large risk reservation in their bid, which was considered unfavourable to the client, because it would make the contract very expensive. Another reason for the splitting up of the project was that the preparation of the project and its privatization – particularly due to political discussions about the route and the explorations of the preferable type of contracts – had taken so long that a single contract could no longer be completed within the set time framework. If contracts were split up, some works could be done in parallel.

The contract for the substructure was split up into seven smaller contracts (five when excluding the separate contracts for the large Groene Hart Tunnel and the connections to the existing rail infrastructure), because the client once again considered the contract too large for a single contractor and feared that, also due to the size and complexity of the work, the competition in the tender might be limited. Again, a job of this size could only be done by a limited number of companies if it had been contracted out as a whole. The substructure contracts were all design and construct contracts. The superstructure contract was a design/build/finance/maintain contract.

The contracting strategy enabled the client to optimize contracts to obtain the best and most efficient results, through maximum competition in the tenders. Originally, the client had 21 separate, relatively small contracts in mind for the substructure, but considered the coordination effort and interface risks too large. However, as mentioned above, a single large contract was not expected to provide the desired level of competition in the tender, so an intermediate option was chosen. Intermediate contracts were also expected to attract more foreign bidders than many small contracts would do, thus increasing the competition.

It did not work out that way. Whereas the Groene Hart Tunnel was built by a combination led by a French company, no foreign contractor led a bid for any of the five sections. Moreover, the outcome of the tenders was disappointing for the client. The total sum of the bids was approximately half a billion euros higher than the budget cap. To keep total costs acceptable, the client cut back the scope of the contracts in such a way that financial managers feared that the contracts would, after all, have to be expanded, but now in the form of additional works. A quick scan indicated that only some 200 million of the half billion euros in cutbacks were actually guaranteed. The rest remained as financial risks for the client. These risks were often related to interfaces between contracts and the possible strategic behaviour that resulted from it. We will discuss this in the following sections (Tweede Kamer der Staten Generaal, 2004; Koppenjan and Leijten, 2007).

There were a number of specific problems related to interfaces that resulted from the contracting strategy. Who, for instance, designed the interfaces? Both the substructure and superstructure contracts included design components, but the two could not be designed in isolation. Designing efforts included subsystems that had a physical interface with other subsystems, across the contract boundaries. In the substructure, for instance, fixation points were to be pre-installed for overhead wiring portals. These fixation points, however, partly determined what the infraprovider could design and build on top of them. The design/build/finance/maintain contract for the superstructure implied that the infraprovider had freedom of design of these portals, but the possibilities were strongly limited by the substructure installations. The contracts did not provide an incentive to take the system as a whole into consideration. Originally, the responsibility for interface issues was included in the contract, but it was transferred back to the client in negotiations with the bidders when the total sum of the contracts turned out to be too high for the client's budget. The awareness of the consequences of this decision may have fallen short.

Strategic behaviour

Collusion (Fudenberg and Tirole, 1989; Shapiro, 1989). The contracting strategy was aimed at attracting many bidders, including foreign bidders. It did not work out that way. Except for the Groene Hart Tunnel, no foreign contractor led a bid for the substructure contracts. Now that the contract was split into five larger contracts, the major Dutch construction firms divided the work among themselves. It is presumed that the competition between the companies was limited as a result of the availability of multiple large contracts (ibid.) This seems to have led to collusion.

Risk shifting The situation worsened when substructure contractors started to lag behind in the provision of specifications and locations of the fixation points. It put the infraprovider at a disadvantage. Since the client had taken back this interface risk responsibility in the contract negotiations, they were in default and had to pay a fine to the infraprovider. Effectuating risks like these caused the client to lose control over budgets and time schedules. It gave the project a bad reputation.

The final conclusion must be that, due to the strategic behaviour, the ministry's ambitions regarding NPM-like arrangement have not been fulfilled. The tendering process proved difficult to steer and the fragmentation of contracts did not incentivize contractors to take optimization of the whole project into account.

North/South Metro Line in Amsterdam

The North/South Line is a metro rail line under construction in Amsterdam (ten Heuvelhof and van der Heijden, 2010). The line will have a length of 9.7 km. Part of the line will be underground in a bored tunnel. The total length of the bored tunnel will be 3.8 km.

Many problems have attended the North/South Line construction project in Amsterdam. Estimates of the costs of the project have been adjusted upwards time and again and the expected delivery date has been pushed back repeatedly. On 27 November 1996, the Amsterdam City Council approved the initial resolution to construct the North/South Line. At that time, the overall project costs were estimated to be 817 million euros. Currently, the estimate of the overall costs is more than 3.1 billion euros. This represents a cost overrun of more than 380 per cent when compared to the 1996 estimate. The originally planned construction time of eight years has since been extended to 14 years.

NPM-like arrangements

On 29 June 1998, the City of Amsterdam applied to the Ministry of Transport and Public Works for subsidy of the North/South Line. At that time, the overall project costs were estimated to be just under 911 million euros. The Ministry of Transport and Public Works did grant the subsidy, in late December 1999. The ministry also offered to buy off the risks involved. Additionally, the ministry also made a lump sum available for related projects and an amount towards VAT costs. In total, the lump sum provided by the Dutch central government amounted to 1113.6 million euros.

During the first tendering round (June 2000), the construction of three stations was put up for tender. The contracts would take the form of engineering and construct contracts. However, the consortiums of construction companies appeared to have difficulty in estimating the technical and management risks. The project organizers then allowed them to give a basic price (without incorporation of risks) and supply a separate catalogue of risks. The catalogue of risks would specify the additional remuneration for which the construction company would be willing to bear responsibility for a particular risk. The result of the bidding during the first round of tenders was unsatisfactory. The prices of the bids (excluding the separate risk catalogues) were 50–100 per cent higher than the estimate, with the exception of the bids for constructing the bored tunnels. The City of Amsterdam had only made allowance for a reserve of 10 per cent above the estimates including all risks for tendering the contracts. It was thus impossible to grant the contracts within the available budget.

For this reason, a different method was employed during the second tendering round (October 2011). The management estimates were adjusted and the contracts were split up into smaller packages and changed to traditional specifications. After this second round, the mayor and the council decided on 13 February 2002 that the project budget needed to be increased by 132 million euros.

A third tendering round turned out to be necessary for further negotiations. During this third round, the City of Amsterdam again took on more risks. For example, in the contract for subterranean stations, provisional sums were included amounting to 76 million euros over a total contractual sum of 223 million euros. This is 34 per cent of the total. No separate reserves were set aside. The contract for the Central Station placed a number of high-risk activities in the public domain. The City of Amsterdam was liable for these risks. The public domain amounted to 25 per cent of the total contractual sum for this project. The City of Amsterdam reserved just 2.5 million euros to cover these risks. This amount would be supplemented with the yield from potential savings, but these were very uncertain. A final example: the contractor had priced the risks in the risk catalogue for the bored tunnel contract at 40 million euros. The City of Amsterdam covered these risks and reserved 12 million euros.

On 9 October 2002, the Amsterdam City Council gave the go ahead. The estimate at that time was a total of 1.47 billion euros, including reserves to cover risks. The project budget at the time that the go ahead was given was 61 per cent higher than the amount estimated in the application for subsidy in June 1998. Over the same period, the share of City of Amsterdam in the project budget had risen from 5 per cent to 23 per cent. In April 2003, construction of the North/South Line began.

It may be concluded that there were a number of NPM-like arrangements associated with the project from the start. Particular examples of this are the lump sum character of the subsidy and the engineering and construct contracts. Over the course of time, the engineering and construct contracts were replaced by traditional specification-based contracts. The fact that the risks associated with the project were returned to the City of Amsterdam was significant because the lump sum nature of the subsidy from the Dutch central government meant that the City of Amsterdam was not able to share these risks with the central government.

Strategic behaviour

*Risk avoiding and risk shifting (*Hood, *2002)* The golden rule in risk management is that a risk must be borne by the party best able to manage the risk. This does not mean that this party is necessarily the cause of the risk and it does not mean that this party has an interest in minimizing the risk. Therefore, it is not self-evident that the party best able to manage a risk will feel an incentive to actually do so. This fact, in combination with the eagerness of the public party to realize the infrastructure project, can easily lead to other parties trying to arrange matters so that the risks are shifted to the initiator. Seen from the viewpoint of public interest, this is obviously not the optimal way to allocate risks because there is no guarantee whatsoever that this actor is in a position to manage the risks in an optimal way.

This shifting of risks to the initiator applies to the decision-making process regarding the North/South Line. The other parties succeeded in limiting their risks and shifting them to the City of Amsterdam. First, the City of Amsterdam accepted the offer from the Dutch central government for funding in the form a lump sum. In this way, the Dutch central government shifted a large risk to Amsterdam. Second, the City of Amsterdam gradually took on an increasing number of risks during the tendering process. Four examples:

1. After an unsuccessful first tendering round, the engineering and construct contracts were replaced by classic specification-based contracts. This meant that the City of Amsterdam took on responsibility for the design and for any additional work due to lack of clarity in the contract.
2. The City of Amsterdam split the project up into smaller contracts and tendered these separately. The effect of this can be that more parties submit bids than would have otherwise been the case. Specialized or smaller businesses will bid for limited contracts, when large and extensive contracts would not have been of interest to them. Obviously, this will exert downwards pressure on prices. The reduction in prices can be broadly presented as a success in the political and administrative discourse. However, the splitting up of contracts has a downside. Coordination problems grow as the number of contracts increase. The City of Amsterdam bears the responsibility for integrating the separate contracts and managing the interfaces. These responsibilities carry risks and it is tempting to present these risks as being low.
3. Many contracts involved relatively high provisional costs. Provisional costs can be ambiguous and presented either as risks or as potential benefits. Many of the provisional costs turned out negatively and this resulted in the overall costs of the contract being higher than anticipated.
4. The City of Amsterdam took on risks for a substantially lower amount than the prices specified by the contractors in the catalogue of risks.

One can conclude that the private actors managed to shift the risks to the City of Amsterdam, which, in the end, had to bear the effects of the risks. The lump sum arrangement meant that the City of Amsterdam had to cover these costs.

6.4 CONCLUSION

Table 6.2 provides an overview of which NPM arrangements were introduced into each project, the hypothetical resulting strategic behaviour and the effects of the NPM arrangements and strategic behaviour for each project.

In all three cases, NPM-like arrangements were introduced. These led to new forms of strategic behaviour. These forms of strategic behaviour should be regarded more as hypotheses than as empirical facts. There is an almost insoluble methodological problem attached to strategic behaviour: parties that behave strategically are seldom willing to admit that their behaviour is actually strategic. This makes empirical verification almost impossible. This chapter is mainly based on the investigators' own analysis and assessment, supplemented by the assessments of other actors.

It seems likely that new forms of strategic behaviours have contributed to higher costs for society. The increased costs for society can be attributed to two factors in the above cases. (1) In the context of NPM, the parties seem to withdraw into the small corner for which they are responsible. They optimize their own subsystem. Nobody seems to be primarily concerned with the system as a whole. Naturally, the public body commissioning the project ultimately bears these costs. (2) Parties try to shift risks onto others. This results in the many risks being carried by the government body commissioning the project, which is not the party best able to manage these risks. From the perspective of society as whole, this is not an optimal way to allocate risks.

6.5 DISCUSSION

The valuation of the different forms of strategic behaviours is difficult. On the one hand, they seem to have led to extensive problems, which are ultimately borne by society. On the other hand, the strategic actors have not done anything wrong from a legal perspective. They have kept to the letter of the law. This being said, if these actors had exhibited more flexibility, mindfulness and concern for the community, they could have prevented serious problems from arising. However, it can be said in defence of the actors that their behaviour was encouraged by the NPM-like arrangements that call on all parties to exhibit a more business-like approach than in the past, but which are all too easily countered by a more commercial approach by the strategic actors. The eagerness of principals to realize infrastructure projects plays into the hands of strategic actors. Other parties must have felt that initiator aspired to realize the project regardless of the cost. This is one of the reasons why they believed they could push matters very far with their strategic behaviour.

Although NPM had led to many benefits (Koppenjan, 2012), it has not led to all the benefits the proponents of NPM had expected. Based on the analysis presented in this chapter, it can be concluded that it is probable that the relatively disappointing results are partly caused by the forms of strategic behaviour that can arise due to NPM-like arrangements. On the other hand, traditional public management, the predecessor of NPM, had had its own variants of strategic behaviour. So, the conclusion is that any form of management will cause its forms of strategic behaviour. It is rather naive to introduce any new form of management without analysing and anticipating its related forms of strategic behaviour.

LITERATURE

Cantarelli, C.C. (2011), 'Cost overruns in large-scale transport infrastructure projects: a theoretical and empirical exploration for the Netherlands and worldwide' (dissertation), Delft: Delft University of Technology.

Dixit, A.K. and B.J. Nalebuff (1991), *Thinking Strategically: The Competitive Edge in Business, Politics and Everyday Life*, New York: Norton.

Donaldson, L. (1990), 'The ethereal hand: organizational economics and management theory', *Academy of Management Review*, **15**(3), 369–81.

Evans, J. (2003), 'The case for separation of infrastructure', European Transport Forum ETF.

Flyvbjerg, B., N. Bruzelius and W. Rothengatter (2003a), *Megaprojects and Risks: An Anatomy of Ambition*, Cambridge, UK: Cambridge University Press.

Flyvbjerg, B., M.K. Skamris Holm and S.L. Buhl (2003b), 'How common and how large are cost overruns in transport infrastructure projects?', *Transport Reviews*, **23**(1), 71–88.

Fudenberg, D. and J. Tirole (1989), 'Noncooperative game theory for industrial organization: an introduction and overview', in R. Schmalensee and R.D. Willig (eds), *Handbook of Industrial Organization*, Vol. 1, Amsterdam: Elsevier Science Publishers, pp. 261–305.

Gomez-Ibanez, J.A. (2003), *Regulating Infrastructure: Monopoly, Contracts, and Discretion*, Cambridge, MA: Harvard University Press.

Gomez-Ibanez, J.A. and G. de Rus (eds) (2006), *Competition in the Railway Industry: An International Comparative Analysis*, Cheltenham, UK and Northampton, MA, USA: Edward Elgar.

Hood, C. (1991), 'A public management for all seasons', *Public Administration*, **69**(1), 3–9.

Hood, C. (2002), 'The risk game and the blame game', *Government and Opposition*, **37**(1), 15–37.

Jensen, M.C. and W.H. Meckling (1976), 'Theory of the firm, managerial behavior, agency costs and ownership structure', *Journal of Financial Economics*, **3**(4), 305–60.

Koppenjan, J. (2012), *The New Public Governance in Public Service Delivery*, The Hague: Eleven International Publishing.
Koppenjan, J.F.M. and M. Leijten (2007), 'How to sell a railroad?', *European Journal of Transport and Infrastructure Research*, **7**(3), 201–22.
Koppenjan, J., W. Veeneman, H. van der Voort, E. ten Heuvelhof and M. Leijten (2011), 'Competing management approaches in large engineering projects: the Dutch RandstadRail project', *International Journal of Project Management*, **29**(6), 740–50.
Leijten, M. (2012), 'Risk versus risk: double bind dilemmas in multi-actor decision-making on complex projects', paper presented at the XVI International Research Seminar on Public Management. Rome, 11–13 April.
Leijten, M., J. Koppenjan, E. ten Heuvelhof, W. Veeneman and H. van der Voort (2010), 'Dealing with competing project management values under uncertainty: the case of RandstadRail', *European Journal of Transport and Infrastructure Research*, **10**(1), 63–76.
Osborne, D. and T. Gaebler (1992), *Reinventing Government: How the Entrepreneurial Spirit is Transforming the Public Sector*, Reading, MA: Addison-Wesley.
Parker, D. (2009), *The Official History of Privatization*, London: Routledge.
Pollitt, C. and G. Bouckaert (2004), *Public Management Reform: A Comparative Analysis*, Oxford: Oxford University Press.
Pollitt, M.G. and A.S.J. Smith (2002), 'The restructuring and privatization of British Rail: was it really that bad?', *Fiscal Studies*, **23**(4), 463–502.
Schelling, Th.C. (1960), *The Strategy of Conflict*, Cambridge, MA: Harvard University Press.
Shapiro, C. (1989), 'Theories of oligopoly behaviour', in R. Schmalensee and R.D. Willig (eds), *Handbook of Industrial Organization*, Vol. 1, Amsterdam: Elsevier Science Publishers, pp. 330–414.
ten Heuvelhof, E.F. and J. van der Heijden (2010), 'Noord/Zuidlijn Amsterdam' (North-South Line Amsterdam), *Bouwrecht*, **9**, 882–9.
ten Heuvelhof, E.F., M. de Jong, M. Kars and H. Stout (2009), *Strategic Behaviour in Network Industries: A Multidisciplinary Approach*, Cheltenham, UK and Northampton, MA, USA: Edward Elgar.
Trujillo, L., E. Quinet and A. Estache (2002), 'Dealing with demand forecasting games in transport privatization', *Transport Policy*, **9**(4), 325–34.
TU Delft (2008), 'Het RandstadRail-project: Lightrail, zware opgave: Onafhankelijk onderzoek RandstadRail Haagse deel' [The Randstad Rail project: light rail, heavy challenge], Stadsgewest Haaglanden, Delft: Delft University of Technology.
Tweede Kamer der Staten Generaal (2004), 'Reconstructie HSL-Zuid: De besluitvorming uitvergroot' [Reconstruction HSL South: the decision-making enlarged], Tijdelijke Commissie Infrastructuurprojecten [Temporary Parliamentary Inquiry Committee on Infrastructure Projects], Tweede Kamer der Staten-Generaal, The Hague: Sdu Uitgevers.
van de Velde, D. and E.F. ten Heuvelhof (2008), 'Provision and management of dedicated railway systems: how to arrange competition', in Hugo Priemus, Bent Flyvbjerg and Bert van Wee, *Decision-making on Mega-projects. Cost–Benefit Analysis, Planning and Innovation*, Cheltenham, UK and Northampton, MA, USA: Edward Elgar, pp. 263–81.
Van Herk, S., P.M. Herder, W.M. de Jong and D.S.M. Alma (2006), 'Innovative contracting in infrastructure design and maintenance', *International Journal of Critical Infrastructures*, **2**(2/3), 187–200.
van Wee, B. (2004), 'Grote Infrastructuurprojecten: de kwaliteit van kostenschattingen en vervoersprognoses: Een literatuuroverzicht' [Large infrastructure projects: the quality of cost estimates and traffic forecasts: an overview of the literature], Contribution to the Colloquium Vervoersplanologisch Speurwerk, Zeist, 25–26 November.
van Wee, B. (2011), *Transport and Ethics: Ethics and the Evaluation of Transport Policies and Project*s, Cheltenham, UK and Northampton, MA, USA: Edward Elgar.
Wachs, M. (1990), 'Ethics and advocacy in forecasting for public policy', *Business and Professional Ethics Journal*, **9**(1&2), 141–57.
Williamson, O.E. (1985), *The Economic Institutions of Capitalism*, New York: Free Press.

PART II

PUBLIC–PRIVATE PARTNERSHIP AND MULTI-ACTOR ANALYSIS

7. Public–private partnerships in mega-projects: successes and tensions

Matti Siemiatycki

7.1 INTRODUCTION

Around the world, public–private partnerships (PPPs) have increasingly become the preferred procurement model for delivering mega-projects. Between 1986 and 2010, 1000 highways, bridges, tunnels, railways, urban transit lines, seaports and airports have been built or rehabilitated through this project delivery model, with concessions valued at over $648 billion (Public Works Financing, 2012). PPPs represent an important form of multi-level governance, involving complex relationships between different government agencies and departments, and various private sector firms that serve as project advisors, construction contractors, operators and insurers.

PPPs are widely promoted based on a narrative of improved collaboration between different stakeholders. By aligning the interests of the multiple parties to encourage closer and more productive working relationships, it is argued that public–private partnerships support innovative project designs and deliver value for money by better controlling project risks. Despite the promises, however, relationships between the various partners in PPPs have often turned from collaborative to confrontational, threatening the success of the project.

This chapter unpacks the complicated partnership relationships that underpin PPPs in transportation infrastructure projects in general, and mega-projects in particular. It begins by defining the structure of the relationships between the various partners involved in the PPP, and categorizes the incentives in place for each partner. Then examples of mega-projects delivered globally are presented to identify key tension points that can arise between the various partners. A key argument put forward is that the structure of the partnerships, and in particular the incentives and interests for each of the partners in the partnership, can meaningfully impact the level of success of the project outcomes. The chapter concludes by reflecting on the factors that support successful partnerships in the context of multi-level governance arrangements.

7.2 WHY PARTNER IN THE FIRST PLACE?

Public–private partnerships are guided by a simple belief: that governments and firms working in meaningful collaboration will deliver mega-projects that have better outcomes than any one party could deliver on their own. 'Not only have they [PPPs] become seen as a cost-efficient and effective mechanism for the implementation of public policy across a range of policy agendas' writes Stephen Osborne (2000, p. 1), an early scholar of PPPs, 'they have also been articulated as bringing significant benefits in their own right – particularly in terms of developing socially inclusive communities'.

For McQuaid (2000, p. 9), the benefits of a partnership approach come specifically from 'a recognition that any one local actor often does not have all the competencies or resources to deal with the interconnected issues raised in many policy areas'. Rather, because of the interdependence between different actors involved in the successful delivery of an infrastructure mega-project, the strength of the partnership approach is derived from the aligning of interests between the partners. 'Our central proposition is that the PPP is a strongly incentive-compatible contracting arrangement' argue Grimsey and Lewis (2004, p. 6):

> The cost effectiveness of a PPP relative to traditional procurement is a result of up-front engineering of the design solution and the financing structure combined with downstream management of project delivery and the revenue streams. All of this is a consequence of the incentives built in to the services payment mechanism and the risk transfer in the PPP model.

Thus, for PPP proponents, maximizing the benefits of multi-level governance is formally interwoven directly into the fabric of the PPP.

While PPPs may be based on a belief in the benefits of partnership, the structure of the relationships between multiple government and private sector partners is anything but simple. The planning and delivery of infrastructure mega-projects has always involved partnerships between governments and private sector firms. These partnerships have taken a variety of different forms. Dating back to the nineteenth century, for instance, the French government used concession contracts with private firms to build and operate roads over a specified period, with the firms recouping their initial investment through toll charges; likewise the first turnpikes in the United States were built and operated by private firms under exclusive concession agreements with the governments of the day. In Canada in 1881, the fledgling national government contracted a private firm to build, own and operate the strategically important TransCanada Railroad. In exchange the firm was provided with a small up-front public invest-

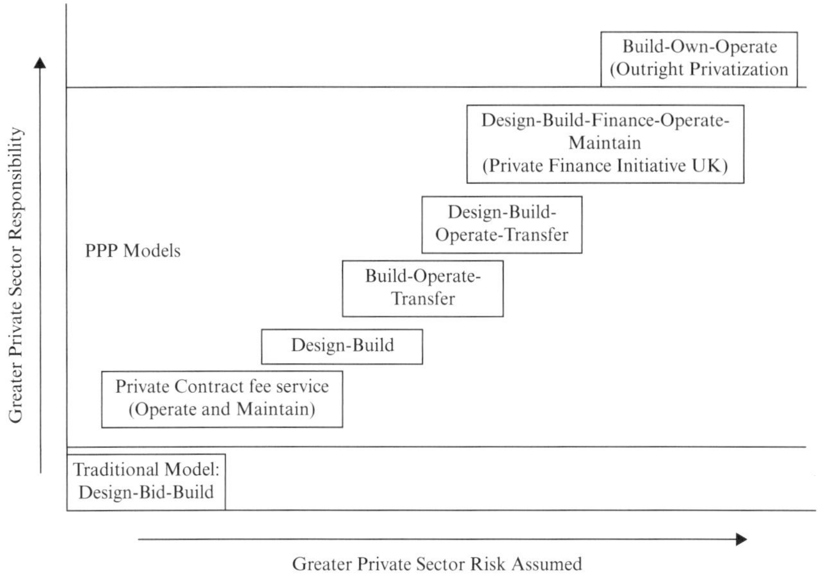

Source: CCPPP (2012).

Figure 7.1 Contemporary PPP models

ment, a massive land grant and a 20-year deferral on their property taxes. Developing countries have also extensively partnered with private sector firms to deliver transportation infrastructure. In Mumbai, India, the construction of the Prince's Dock in the 1870s was initiated by the quasi-government Bombay Port Trust, financed by the state and national governments, and built by a private sector contractor. These varied examples of partnerships highlight the long history of public–private collaborations in the delivery of public infrastructure (Garvin, 2010; Wettenhall, 2010).

In contemporary infrastructure project delivery, as shown in Figure 7.1, partnership structures of all kinds are still used, and range on a continuum from more public sector responsibility to more private sector responsibility. Definitions of PPPs typically have three key components. First, the partnership is structured around a long-term contractual relationship intended to provide mutual benefit to each partner. Second, the partnership involves a private concessionaire providing a mix of facility design, construction, operation and maintenance. Third, the identified risks of the project are allocated to the partner that is best able to manage them (Garvin, 2010; Regan et al., 2010).

PPPs are thus centrally based around a long-term, contractual approach to partnerships, which involve a diversity of public and private sector entities. In fact, both the public and private sector partners in a PPP typically involve complex internal partnerships between a variety of organizations. As will be shown below, the structure, terms and incentives built into these relationships are of central importance in understanding both the patterns of investment at a global scale, the types of projects that are most typically delivered, and the success of an individual PPP project within its local environment. In order to contextualize the inter-organizational dynamics that accompany the PPP, it is helpful to first review the partnership approach used in the traditional model of project delivery, and the types of challenges that have commonly arisen.

7.3 THE TRADITIONAL PROJECT DELIVERY APPROACH

Worldwide, there is a diversity of 'traditional' approaches that have been used to deliver transportation mega-projects. In some countries, projects have been planned, built and operated directly by government departments or arm's length government corporations; in other cases it is the norm for governments to enter into concessions with private sector partners to build and operate infrastructure. In many contexts, including North America and Northern Europe, the traditional model of project delivery has coalesced around what is commonly known as the design-bid-build (DBB) approach (Flyvbjerg et al., 2003). In this procurement model, a government department or agency works with a team of private consultants and advisors to develop the planning rationale and design for the project. The government partner then carries out a competitive procurement process to select a contractor to build the facility as designed. Lowest cost is often the primary criterion used to select the winning bidder, and in fact in many cases this is mandated by law. Project construction is financed through government-issued debt or bonds, and the facility is operated and maintained by public sector employees (Siemiatycki, 2006, 2011a). On transit projects, repayment of some public borrowing for capital costs may come from transit fares, but the bulk is typically funded through general tax revenues. On road projects, tolls may cover some or all of the initial capital costs as well as operating expenses.

In the traditional model of contracting, as shown in Figure 7.2, there are four main parties involved in a DBB project: the lead project sponsor, typically a government department, ministry or agency; the construction contractor, which may be comprised of a consortium of firms and subcontractors; the engineering advisors to the government; and the financial

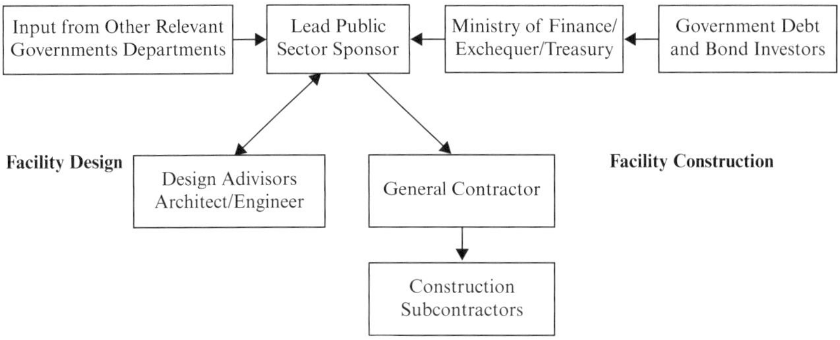

Figure 7.2 Typical organizational structure of a design-bid-build procurement

lenders. Each of the main parties involved in a DBB project have their own unique set of objectives and interests, some of which overlap and others of which are in conflict.

For the lead public sector project sponsor, their primary objective is to deliver a project that has the lowest up-front construction costs, and meets the needs of their stakeholders. Providing input to the lead project sponsor are typically agencies and departments representing other levels of government, who may have some jurisdictional responsibility, or may be brought on board to participate as funding partners. For the lead project sponsor and their government partners, the DBB approach is seen to be advantageous because they maintain a high level of input and control over the evaluation of project alternatives, facility location, alignment, design and finishes. In some jurisdictions, it is legally required that infrastructure projects are procured using the DBB method. In practice, a challenge with the DBB approach has been that governments have often selected the lowest-cost construction option, rather than the design that maximizes long-term value. 'We tend to cheap it out' under the DBB approach, a senior public sector project manager from Canada explained in our personal interview, 'because we go through an exercise, of almost inevitably, value engineering the project towards the end to meet a budget and we take out a lot of the good to have things' (personal communication).

The objective of the contractor varies from that of the government agency; it is to turn a profit on the construction of the project. This can be achieved by delivering the project on time and on budget, which can sometimes be rewarded by a bonus payment. Additionally, once a fixed price contract for the construction work has been signed, the contractor has an incentive to use every technique available to manage risk and lower delivery costs in order to maximize their profit. Because the contractor does not have a long-term stake in the project following construction completion, building the facility quickly and at a low cost may supersede quality considerations. Moreover, because the engineering design was developed and signed off by the government agency and not developed with input from the contractor, there may be trouble with the handover, and the contractor has an incentive to submit change orders for any miscalculations or required deviations that add to the cost of construction. The cost of accepted change orders are paid by the government sponsor.

The engineering advisors to the project sponsor have a similar motivation to earn a profit on the job. Yet their profit is rooted in providing what is seen to be a comprehensive project design and a high-quality service to the government agency. A project that is well designed and functions well upon completion can serve as important exposure and help the engineering advisor to win future work. To this end, the engineering advisors have an incentive to collaborate with the winning contractor to see the successful realization of their plans, especially if they are retained by the public sector agency to oversee the project's construction phase. Yet collaboration may turn to confrontation if there are disputes about whether costly change orders originated with the contractor or errors rooted in the original engineering designs.

Government lenders are the final party involved in a DBB procurement. Debt financing that is used to fund infrastructure capital costs typically comes through the government's normal borrowing facility and is not tied to a given project. When this is the case, the lenders have little incentive to vet the priorities, merits or outcomes of any given project. Lenders will lend money to government regardless of their specific investment choices, provided that they are confident of being repaid. Thus the lenders are not particularly concerned about the viability of any given transport project or its outcomes, as long as they are convinced that the government has the capacity to repay their overall loan.

Within this constellation of involved parties and their interests, a common set of challenges have beset infrastructure delivered through traditional procurement models. These include significant cost overruns, construction delays, poor workmanship and inaccurate demand forecasts (Flyvbjerg et al., 2003; van Wee, 2007). The causes of these poor project outcomes have been variously identified as the lack of alignment of partner interests and missing accountability mechanisms from DBB structure. Siemiatycki (2009) found that a common challenge is the lack of coordination between the project designers and facility builders during the initial planning stages of a project, leading to incomplete designs and costly change orders. For Flyvbjerg (2007) and van Wee (2007), poor outcomes are more commonly the result of the unsuitable allocation of risk between the partners, and a lack of enforceable penalties to discourage opportunistic behaviour on the part of project promoters and developers where mechanisms are not in place to align short and long-term interests.

Finally, the level of government involved in funding the project can create perverse incentives in project selection, location and design decisions. As Pickrell (1992) shows, there is a strong incentive for local promoters to underestimate project costs and overestimate project benefits in order to be competitive and attract funding from senior levels of government. Projects funded directly by government can be sited to maximize political benefit with limited regard for demand, efficiency or operating cost recovery. Facilities can also be overdesigned or overbuilt at significant additional costs, often to limit the harm to surrounding communities that may oppose the scheme. With funding coming from senior levels of government, there are strong incentives for local project planners to select expensive technologies that have capacities in excess of what can be justified based on expected ridership, or choose costly underground transit alignments to limit unpopular impacts at street level (Altshuler and Luberoff, 2003).

7.4 THE PPP MODEL

Public–private partnerships have been specifically designed as a procurement model to rectify the challenges that have plagued traditional approaches to government contracting in countries around the world. In particular, PPPs aim to align the short- and long-term incentives and rewards for each partner so that project risks are effectively managed by the partner best able to control them. This includes risks associated with major construction cost overruns and delays, and facility operations that do not meet their projected standards in terms of performance, maintenance or revenue (Siemiatycki, 2010).

This chapter focuses specifically on concession-based approaches to partnerships that can last between 25 and 99 years depending on the asset type. While there may be some regional variation in their design, concession-based approaches to partnership have become the state-of-the-art in both developed and developing countries, and thus it is possible to draw some general observations that are relevant across national boundaries. In these concessions, a single concessionaire is awarded a contract to provide some combination of facility design, construction, up-front project financing, operations and maintenance. In return for their ongoing participation in the project, the private sector concessionaire

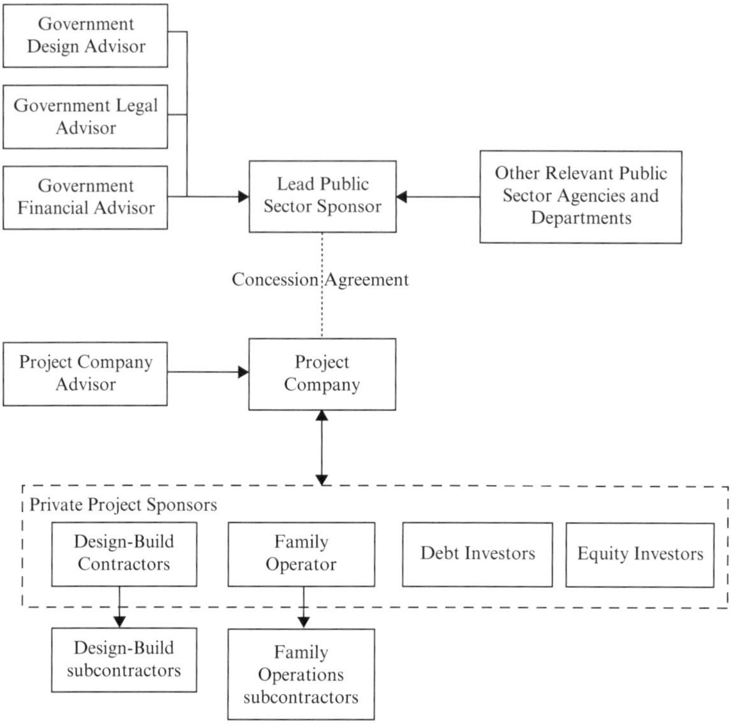

Source: Siemiatycki (2011a).

Figure 7.3 Typical PPP concession structure

either receives user fee revenues or is paid a fixed annual fee over the lifespan of the concession agreement. The PPP concession is designed with a sufficient revenue stream so that provided the facility is built on time and budget and operates as expected, the private sector concessionaire will be able to cover the initial capital outlay, operating expenses and a profit margin (Smyth and Edkins, 2007). In this model of partnership, the primary driver of improved project performance is identified as the investment of private sector risk capital, which provides the concessionaire with an incentive to effectively identify and manage project risks and meet their stated objectives (Grimsey and Lewis, 2004).

While there are now a diversity of PPP models, as shown in Figure 7.3, PPPs globally are typically delivered through a common set of underlying relationships between a variety of government departments and agencies and their private advisors, and multiple private sector firms that comprise and advise the concessionaire. Like with the traditional DBB contracting approach, each government agency and each firm involved in the PPP has its own goals, risks and desired rewards, some of which are congruent and others that may diverge. By briefly examining the interests of each party to the PPP arrangement, it is possible to underscore how PPPs differ from more traditional approaches to project procurement.

The Public Sector Sponsor

The public sector partner in a PPP concession is usually headed by one government agency or department known as the lead public sector sponsor or commissioning agency, with other relevant levels of government, departments and agencies serving as collaborators or advisors. Additionally, while a common objective of the PPP model is to raise private sector financing for infrastructure, it is not uncommon for the public sector sponsor and its partner departments to directly fund up to two-thirds of the cost of the project through public debt. As such, even as PPPs emphasize the partnership between the public and private sectors, they continue to be shaped by important dynamics of multi-level government collaboration.

In the PPP procurement model the role of the public sponsor is shifted from a producer and provider of infrastructure to a purchaser of public services that meet a pre-specified set of output-based performance standards. To this end, the PPP approach is for the public sponsor to identify required performance output specifications and then invite private sector bidders to submit proposals that best meet the specifications at the lowest cost. The winning bid is selected based on its potential to deliver the best value over the project's life cycle rather than strictly the lowest construction cost. One feature of the PPP process is therefore that the public sponsor and its government partners have less control over the specific project design, construction methods, and finishes, provided that the best-value proposal meets the performance specifications. Throughout the long-term operating period, an important objective for the government partner is to maintain some control over key project planning responsibilities such as the setting of service levels, quality and safety standards, user fee rates, and facility expansion plans. These are critical government responsibilities that contribute to protecting the public interest. At the same time, the political party in power can become vulnerable to public outcry in cases where control has been contractually transferred to the private sector partner, enabling unpopular decisions by the private sector partner (Siemiatycki, 2010).

The Public Sector Advisors

Private sector advisors to government have become important participants in PPP delivery. Many project sponsors, especially smaller agencies or governments that do not procure large projects regularly, feel that they do not have the specialized expertise necessary to structure and execute a successful project. Thus as part of the PPP procurement process, it is common that the lead public sector sponsor and any other government partners will hire multiple firms to act as independent project advisors. This includes the hiring of firms to provide legal, financial, insurance and technical engineering advice, and these firms may further subcontract components of their workflow to more specialized firms. The hiring of specialized expertise is seen by project sponsors as a way to level the playing field in terms of information and expertise when dealing with experienced private sector partners, and ensure that the public sector partner is making decisions and drafting concession agreements that best protect the public interest.

Like in the DBB model, advisory firms are compensated based on a fee-for-service basis. Their objective is to generate a profit through their advisory services, and their services do not come cheaply; advisory services and transaction costs commonly account for between 2 per cent and 3 per cent of the total capital cost of a mega-project. Given the lucrative nature of the PPP advisory business, these firms have an interest in seeing projects proceed successfully as PPPs and the PPP model further adopted locally and abroad, since this could position them for future commissions with either the public or private sector partners (Shaoul et al., 2007; Hodge et al., 2010).

The Private Sector Partner

Similarly to the public sector partner, the private sector partner is made up of numerous different firms who are brought together through a complicated set of relationships. At the core of the private sector's participation in a PPP is the formation of a special purpose vehicle (SPV) or project company. For each PPP, the consortium of sponsor firms that are chosen as the winning bidder forms a new project company. It is this project company that enters into contractual agreements with the public sector sponsor, subcontractors, advisors and investors. This legal structure provides two key benefits for its corporate sponsors: it means that the parent companies do not have to account for borrowing by the project company on their own balance sheets; and it protects the sponsor firms from taking on financial responsibility for losses or bankruptcy by the project company (Shaoul et al., 2008).

The lead project sponsor in most private sector consortiums for PPPs is a major construction contractor or design-build engineering firm, which has a reputation for successfully delivering projects in the selected asset class. The project company is filled out with large sponsor firms that will provide services that are critical to the successful realization of the concession, including facility operation and maintenance, and project financing. In a typical PPP structure, the sponsors of the project company will each be the primary firm contracted by the project company to provide services within their area of expertise, and the sponsor firms may then subcontract pieces of work to more specialized firms as required. The project company also commonly complements their own in-house staff by hiring more specialized financial, technical and insurance advisors on a fee-for-service basis, to aid with the bid production and project delivery process.

A critical aspect of the PPP model is that each sponsor of the project company is expected to make an equity investment in the project that typically amounts to a total of 10 per cent of the private sector's expected share of project financing (anywhere from one-third to 100 per cent of the project's capital cost). With their own risk capital at stake, in theory the firms that comprise the project company are strongly incentivized to develop innovative project designs, construction strategies and operational plans that minimize costs over the entire life cycle of the project, since their initial investment is repaid in instalments over the long-term operating period. Additionally, the integration of facility design and construction alongside facility operations and maintenance into the private sector's project company and bundle of services is meant to incentivize the production of more complete initial designs, limit errors in the hand-off of the project from the designer to the builder to the operator, and create strong financial incentives to manage construction risks, and deliver the project on time, on budget and to a high quality.

For the concessionaire, then, their objective in the contract with the public sector sponsor is to try and lock in as many project contingencies as early on in the planning process as possible. This enables the concessionaire to identify and price project risks appropriately, and then manage them over the course of the construction and operating contract. To this end, concessionaires have demanded strict contractual terms that limit direct competition for the service, pre-specify toll rates and escalation schedules, and levy severe penalties for government initiated breach of contract, even though such measure conflict with the public sponsor's objective of maintaining their long-term control and flexibility over the project and associated policy decisions.

In practice, the theoretical incentives built into the concession agreement have not always delivered their desired outcomes. Equity financing carries a high cost premium, so project sponsors have often accepted small equity contributions in order to make the PPP financially competitive with traditional procurement. An observed pattern has been that some members of the initial project delivery consortium have sold their equity stake in the project early, limiting the long-term incentives built into the PPP model. Moreover, the project company may have an incentive to prioritize design and architectural mediocrity over excellence to save on costs. And tested technologies may be prioritized over innovations or building flexibility into project designs, since these can add costs and increase the risk of penalties if they do not meet the initial performance specifications.

The Private Investors

While sponsors of the project company commonly invest up to 10 per cent of the private sector's contribution in equity, privately issued debt or bonds are used to raise the remaining 90 per cent of the private sector's up-front funding contribution. Numerous bank arrangers are used as intermediaries to identify and organize the private financiers (Siemiatycki, 2011a). Tapping into global capital markets can be an expensive way to finance public infrastructure projects. In the transit sector, for instance, privately raised capital typically comes with a premium of between 100 to 200 basis points above the rates available to governments, adding some $20–40 million in borrowing costs per $100 million borrowed privately over a 35-year term.

While private sector borrowing carries a cost premium, the presence of private sector financiers is identified as an important contributor to value for money in the PPP model. It is expected that the presence of private financiers with their own risk capital on the line will bring a greater level of scrutiny and discipline to the planning, delivery and operation of a project. Unlike in the DBB approach, private sector investors are investing specifically in a project, and their return is based to varying degrees on the success of the project. When the contract stipulates that investors are repaid entirely through collected user fees, the investors have a strong incentive to scrutinize the ridership forecasts and project plans at the outset, countering some of the overly optimistic rationales and projections that may be put forward by project promoters that do not have the same personal 'skin in the game'.

Even if the private investors are repaid directly through government payments based on the facility being available and performing to the expected standards, the contracts can be structured to align the interests of the public sector partner and the investors. This is especially around achieving an on time and on budget project. When the contracts specify that the private sector partner does not begin receiving government payments until the project is completed, the investors are incentivized to closely scrutinize the project delivery team to ensure that the project is built on time and on budget, and they can intervene to demand changes in process or management if results are not meeting expectations.

7.5 TENSION POINTS IN PPPs

For each partner in a PPP, their risks and rewards are established through the contractual structure of the concession agreement as well as the way that private financing is infused into the PPP arrangement. In the ideally structured partnership, the interests of the partners are effectively aligned, creating incentives for both partners to control the project risks within their purview and meet their contractual obligations (Siemiatycki, 2011a). In practice, however, the relationship between the partners is specified in a concession agreement that often stretches over thousands of pages, and is invariably incomplete in envisioning all eventualities for an uncertain future that stretches over a quarter-century or more. PPPs are thus living, breathing agreements, sensitive to all of the risks and uncertainties of planning in contexts characterized by competing interests and change over time.

Against this backdrop, in the vast body of literature on PPPs, scholars and practitioners have identified an array of tension points where the theory of partnership meets the messiness of planning practice. At their core, these tensions are predicated on questions about how the incentives and interdependencies in PPP arrangements alter the policy-making context, impact on the processes through which investment decisions are made, drive varied project outcomes and introduce new political dimensions. The following section focuses on a selection of four key tension points associated with delivering transportation mega-projects through PPPs that I have identified as particularly important through my research, and explains them by focusing on the multi-level governance models and public–private interrelationships that underpin the partnership.

Do PPPs Support Sustainable Transportation?

A first issue relates to the very types of transportation infrastructure that are conducive to being built through PPPs. Around the world, governments of all levels are grappling with the challenge of how to finance and successfully deliver the next generation of sustainable transportation infrastructure, to address issues of climate change, air pollution, automobile dependence and diminishing supplies of easily accessible oil. Broadly put, governments have defined sustainable transportation to mean ways of moving around that limit pollution emissions and draw on renewable resources, are affordable and equitable in their access, and support economic growth and prosperity. Common examples include public transit, carpools and car sharing, as well as active modes of transport like cycling and walking. For cities and countries that have been designed to encourage long-distance travel and automobile usage, at the core of this transition towards more sustainable transportation are investments in public transit mega-projects, including both large-scale urban rapid transit lines and inter-urban railroads.

Increasingly, both national and local governments in countries as diverse as Canada, the United States, Britain, South Africa, Brazil and India are holding up PPPs as a key strategy to expedite and expand investment in sustainable transportation projects. PPPs, the governments argue, make it possible to tap into private sector capital and expertise to realize sustainable transportation projects sooner and more efficiently than if left to more traditional government funding and delivery models. Given the interest in using PPPs to deliver sustainable transportation, an important question is therefore, are PPPs actually conducive to such projects? Or do the partnership structures and the allocations of project risks embedded within contemporary PPP models make sustainable transportation projects less feasible?

At the simplest level, the global experience to date suggests that there are challenges in using PPPs to deliver sustainable surface transportation projects. Globally between 1984 and 2010, more than five times as many road projects were delivered as PPPs than rail schemes. In cities, moreover, less than one-third of all transportation PPPs are urban transit projects such as subways and commuter railway lines that provide viable alternatives to the automobile. Only in Western Europe has there been a substantial number of urban transit mega-projects built through PPPs (see Siemiatycki, 2011b). In the cities in developing countries, by comparison, PPPs have been particularly skewed towards auto-oriented projects, especially ring roads and upgraded connections to urban-satellite towns around the periphery of the major cities. These investments encourage further urban decentralization and auto dependence, which can increase air pollution and traffic congestion (Newman and Kenworthy, 1999).

To be certain, the disproportionate investment in road as compared to sustainable transit projects is an extension of transportation investment trends over the past half-century, highlighting how PPPs remain a product of the political and governance contexts in which they are built. Transit projects often require approvals and funding from overlapping levels of government, making them dependent upon collaboration between agencies that can have significantly different interests. Conversely, road projects are more likely to be the sole responsibility of a single government agency or department such as a highway agency or department of transport, making it simpler to proceed.

At the same time, the relatively limited use of PPPs to deliver large-scale sustainable transportation projects are also rooted in the incentives built into the PPP delivery model. First, sustainable transportation projects often require ongoing capital and operating subsidies from governments to make them financially viable. As such, while PPPs may provide a strategy for governments to privately finance the up-front capital costs of transit, they do not alleviate the need for long-term public funding, making approvals politically difficult. This challenge can be alleviated for some road schemes that are able to recover costs through tolls and other motor vehicle charges.

Second, in contrast to freestanding greenfield projects that are typical of road schemes, the high level of system-wide integration and coordination requirements for transit systems means that PPPs may provide only minimal opportunity to realize innovations or risk transfer from deeper private sector participation, key drivers of value for money. Planning for a $22 billion investment in rail projects across Los Angeles in the early 2010s provides a case in point. County officials were keen to exploit the benefits of the PPP to successfully realize their once-in-a-generation investment in sustainable transportation infrastructure. However, a feasibility study exploring the prospects of using PPPs to deliver this investment found that such an approach would provide little additional value. There would be challenges integrating public and private operations and maintenance in a regionally coordinated transit system. Meaningfully transferring construction risk to the private sector would be difficult in a busy urban environment. And a highly unionized workforce could restrict the transferring of facility operations to the private sector (Schneider, 2011). Due to the limitations of the PPP model in this context, the investment is being examined for delivery through more traditional government procurement models.

While PPPs may have limited application for large-scale urban rail projects, the introduction of tolls on road PPPs can serve to manage growing usage demand, and provide an additional perspective on the sustainability of road PPPs. Although road tolls can be implemented on both government-owned and privately operated highways, an identified benefit of PPPs with long-term operating contracts is that they can lock in toll rates at levels that are sufficiently high to actually impact on facility demand, and generate sufficient revenues to cover capital and operating expenses. By comparison, in the many jurisdictions where motorists disdain road tolls, reducing or eliminating road tolls on facilities controlled by government has been a popular political strategy, even when this contradicts policies of environmental or fiscal sustainability.

Meaningful Public Engagement in Project Planning

A second key tension point relates to the processes of planning large-scale infrastructure through PPPs, and whether the differing interests of the public and private sector partners enable meaningful public consultation and community engagement in project planning. It is now well understood that transparency and meaningful public engagement in PPP procurements add legitimacy to the planning process, provide a level of democratic oversight, and can improve the design quality and likelihood of successful implementation for the selected projects (Siemiatycki, 2007; Shaoul et al., 2010).

Although information transparency is identified as a key condition for accountable decision-making on PPPs, the need to withhold the release of certain information has also been commonly articulated by public and private sector participants in PPPs. The core of this tension is succinctly captured by Hedlund and Chase (2005, p. 10): 'On the one hand, disclosure of proposed projects is necessary for them [PPPs] to gain public legitimacy. On the other hand, the private sector will be unwilling to participate if certain information about them and their business secrets must be disclosed'.

The rationales for keeping information confidential vary at different stages of the procurement process, as does the partner that encourages the withholding of key information. Early in the planning and competitive procurement process, public sector agencies have often withheld extensive information around their preferred construction methods, specific technologies and designs, detailed budgetary information and assessments of the project's value for money as a PPP. The limited release of this information is meant to preserve the greatest incentive for private sector innovations, limit allegations of biasing the tender outcome, and maintain the public sector sponsor's negotiating position with the winning bidder.

During the competitive tendering process, confidentiality is primarily invoked to ensure integrity of the bidding process, and protect the commercial position of the participating bidders so that robust competition between firms is achieved. In particular, commercially sensitive bidder information is restricted from public release by the government project sponsor running the tendering process, including material that could divulge technological innovations, corporate strategies, financing models or expected rates of return. This restriction on the release of information during the procurement process can serve to limit the public's capacity to meaningfully assess and provide feedback on the pros and cons of specific mega-projects in their community (Siemiatycki, 2007).

Finally, at the last stage of the PPP procurement process where negotiations are being carried out with the winning bidder, confidentiality is typically invoked to maintain the public sector sponsor's bargaining position. In this context, a bargaining advantage could be provided to the private sector concessionaire if they had access to the premature release of information such as the specific amount of government money available or which system features could be value engineered to save on costs.

While there is clearly a need to maintain confidentiality of some information at certain key moments in the PPP procurement process, the Australasian Council of Auditors General (1997) has questioned the government's motives for invoking secrecy in some instances: 'Recent experiences in Australia would indicate that Government agencies are tending to use the pretext of commercial confidentiality as a shield against the disclosure of information which is commercially embarrassing to the Government or which raises issues of probity'.

The issues of secrecy and confidentiality during project planning processes have become one of the key public critiques of PPPs, as politicians and citizens seek to assess whether the PPP model provides value for money in their community. As an opposition party politician in Ontario articulated in an interview, his top concern with PPPs is 'accountability, first and foremost, and transparency through the process for the investments on the public side. I think that it does hide the true costs on projects to the public at large' (personal communication). Indeed, some recent experiences with transport PPPs highlight the negative implications of limited transparency and limited public accountability. In California, for instance, residents in Orange County strenuously protested when it was discovered that a previously undisclosed non-competition clause in a PPP contract restricted the government from undertaking a necessary expansion of a highway adjacent to the SR-91 express toll lanes that had been delivered by a private concessionaire. And in Vancouver, a protracted law suit was initiated by a business owner after it was announced that the winning concessionaire for an underground rail line had chosen to build the system using an invasive cut-and-cover construction method, rather than a less disruptive deep bore tunnelling approach as expected. Thus limited transparency can affect not only the planning process and project outcomes, but also create political risks for government decision-makers.

On Time and on Budget? At What Cost?

A third key tension point in PPP project delivery is the extent to which such models of project delivery successfully control unexpected cost escalations, and at what cost. On large-scale infrastructure projects, risk tends to be concentrated in two stages of the project: construction, and demand and operations. In recent years, governments procuring mega-projects have identified on time and on budget project delivery as the key motivation that drives the use of PPPs. Indeed, the extent to which PPPs provide value for money to the public largely hinges on transferring construction period risks to the private sector partner.

Historically, transportation mega-projects delivered through traditional procurement models have been plagued by large construction cost overruns and late project delivery, which have often been covered by contractor claims for additional government investment (Flyvbjerg et al., 2003; van Wee, 2007; Siemiatycki, 2009). By involving the private sector earlier in the project planning process, bundling facility design and construction into a single contract, creating tight legal agreements, and bringing on board investors who only recoup their investment when the project is completed, PPPs have been proposed as a way to create incentives that clamp down on the underlying causes of cost overruns. As Bain (2007, p. 6) argues, while conflicts between partners over costly change order claims have been common in traditional procurement, in PPPs '[t] he incentive for contractors to complete has replaced the incentive to claim'. Thus for the public sector partner, budget certainty is the central benefit of proceeding with a PPP procurement, rather than the elimination of cost overruns so long as they are borne by the private sector concessionaire.

To date, the limited empirical research on whether PPPs are better at providing on time and on budget project delivery is decidedly mixed. Many governments, such as those in the Canadian provinces of Ontario and British Columbia, boast that the PPP model is revolutionizing project delivery, with every major PPP (both transportation and other large buildings) approved since 2003 being achieved on time and on budget. As the head of the British Columbia agency responsible for delivering PPPs proclaimed:

> All British Columbia public private partnerships (PPPs) to date have been delivered on time and on budget. Performance-based, fixed-price contracts ensure that cost and schedule overruns don't happen and that project risks are transferred to the private partner. Taxpayers don't pay for a design that doesn't work or for a service that isn't provided to the contractually bound standards set by government. (Blain, 2009, p. 1)

Such contentions are supported by a large comparative study from researchers in Australia, which found that PPPs have had fewer incidences of cost overruns and construction delays than traditionally built projects (Allen Consulting Group, 2007). While proponents of PPPs have trumpeted their success in delivering cost certainty for governments, Hodge's (2010) review of dozens of studies reveals that most are based on unreliable data or methodologies, and are prone to changing goal posts about what is considered on time and on budget. In one of the few detailed studies comparing the unit costs of delivering roads through traditional and PPP models, the European Investment Bank concluded that the ex ante predicted costs for road PPPs were 24 per cent more than the predicted cost of delivering comparable traditionally procured roads, primarily due to the higher costs of private finance and premiums for risk transfer built into the contracts. At the same time, while traditionally built projects may have had lower estimated costs ex ante, they commonly experienced 24 per cent ex post cost escalations, cancelling out any potential savings (Blanc-Brude et al., 2006). Yet one feature of PPPs is that they have been identified as generating very high profits for the private sector participants in the project. As Acerete et al. (2009, p. 20) conclude based on their examination of the first eight DBFO (design-build-finance-operate) road PPPs in the UK: 'Its private sector partners reported a post-tax return on capital of 29 per cent and an effective cost of capital of 11 per cent in 2002, more than twice the UK cost of public finance (approximately 4.5 per cent), a high price for risk transfer'.

Beyond high returns, Boardman et al. (2005) note that while the private sector has become skilled at ensuring that they are well compensated for taking on risk, they have gone to considerable lengths to transfer costs back to the public in cases when conflicts arise and things go wrong. The structure of the private concessionaire as a special purpose vehicle means that the parent companies face limited recourse if the concession collapses and bankruptcy is declared. Members of the concession team have also limited their equity participation in PPPs by extensively relying on financial leverage and third party financing. Thus risk transferred in theory may not always be risk transferred in practice.

Conflict Between the Partners

A final point of tension in PPPs is the prevalence of conflict between the public and private sector partners. Despite the widely held belief that PPPs are predicated on the formation of trusting long-term relationships between the public and private sector, conflict between the partners has been a common aspect of PPPs. Conflicts in PPPs are rooted in the differing interests and incentives that various partners have in a project. This is not altogether surprising as the stakes can be very high. Even minor changes to the contract terms can be the difference between profit or loss for the private sector concessionaire, or the need for greater government subsidies. Additionally, PPPs tend to cover high-profile public infrastructure projects. As such public sector dealings with the concessionaire are replete with political risks for the government in power. On the one hand, governments may be the ultimate holder of all financial risks if a strategically important project goes bankrupt (Shaoul et al., 2010). On the other, they may face intense public criticism if they are seen to be protecting corporate interests over those of facility users and the general public.

To be certain, disputes in PPPs have arisen over which partner should bear the costs for unexpected construction cost escalations. However, the dominant source of conflict in transportation PPPs has related to facility demand and service quality over the long-term operating period of the concession. On early transportation PPPs, public sector sponsors sought to transfer risks associated with lower than expected traffic volumes and poor service quality to the private sector partner. This was achieved through the application of free-standing PPPs in which all private sector capital investment and operating costs were recouped directly through user fees. Examples of free-standing transportation PPPs include the Croydon Tramlink in London, the Orlyval rail shuttle to Orly Airport near Paris, the State Route 91 express toll lanes in Orange County California, Highway 407 in Toronto, the Cross City Tunnel in Sydney Australia, the Bangkok Skytrain, the Kuala Lumpur rapid transit projects, and the Las Vegas Monorail (Siemiatycki and Friedman, 2012).

Yet these projects have faced common challenges, and as reported in a World Bank study, 'allocating all demand risk to private operators has a poor track record' (Menzies and Mandri-Perrott, 2010, p. 2). First, traffic volumes and revenues on transportation PPPs have often failed to meet expectations, challenging the financial viability of the concessionaire, and contributing to demands by the private sector partner to renegotiate the terms of the PPP relationship. As Guasch (2004, p. 13) shows, within the first four years of a concession, over half of all Latin American transportation concession agreements were renegotiated, often leading to additional costs or risks assumed by the public sector partner.

Second, contractual clauses designed to protect the long-term revenues of the private sector investors have resulted in governments losing control over fee setting and system-wide planning, functions that are key to protecting the public benefit of infrastructure projects. Non-competition agreements are a feature of some road PPPs, restricting where governments can build future infrastructure facilities. PPP concessions have also sometimes included contractual terms that lock in long-term decisions that may not be acceptable to future governments, and result in conflict and in some cases legal actions. In the case of the Cross City Tunnel in Sydney, an incoming government faced public pressure to drop the toll rates and reverse some road closures that accompanied the project, a move that was criticized by the concessionaire as threatening the financial success of the project (Joint Select Committee on the Cross City Tunnel, 2006).

Third, competing interpretations of service level and facility maintenance agreements have contributed to conflicts between the partners. In London, Mayor Ken Livingstone publicly admonished the Croydon Tramlink concessionaire for their poor maintenance record and insufficient service frequency (Livingstone, 2007). The mayor also publicly criticized the national government for imposing expensive transportation PPPs on the British capital, and mused about tasking his staff with exploring options to bring PPP concessions back in house. The war of words between the partners was carried out publicly in the media, and resulted in a deterioration of any trust in the relationships.

Not surprisingly, the contract management costs associated with remediating conflicts have been high for all partners involved. However, one surprising aspect of early transportation PPPs has been the number of projects that have been cancelled or gone bankrupt before the scheduled conclusion of the concession period. As examples, the Croydon Tramlink, SR-91 express toll lanes and the Orlyval rail shuttle were each bought out by the public sector partner at significant cost, in order to facilitate improved service quality and system-wide integration. At the same time, the original concessionaires involved in the Las Vegas Monorail and Cross City Tunnel have each gone bankrupt, resulting in efforts to restructure the services under private sector control.

As a result of the poor track record of transportation PPPs that transfer traffic volume and operations risk to the private sector, governments and investors have become increasingly reticent to participate in PPPs that involve the transferring of all traffic volume risk to the private sector. In response, one adjustment that has been made in recent years is the move towards PPP models that pay the concessionaire a guaranteed annual payment provided the facility is available and meeting performance criteria. Under such models, the public sector partner can maintain control over the setting of user fee rates and regional planning objectives. Terms are also included in some concessions so that if profit or traffic volume exceeds or falls below a certain level, the contract is rebalanced to compensate the losing partner. The inclusion of rebalancing provisions in contemporary transportation PPPs provide an incentive for both the public and private sector partners to continue to collaborate throughout the partnership, while removing some of the key sources of conflict that have challenged the viability of PPPs (Siemiatycki and Friedman, 2012).

7.6 CONCLUSIONS

As illustrated in this chapter, public–private partnerships are an important form of multi-level governance, bringing together partners from both the public and the private sector to deliver infrastructure mega-projects. In theory, incentives built into the PPP contracts that structure the multi-party collaboration are designed to align the interests of the partners and encourage project results that are better than any one party could achieve on their own. In particular, private finance is considered the glue that holds the partnership together, incentivizing the private sector partner to meet their construction and operation obligations in order to recoup their investment.

In practice, PPPs have had mixed results: the prospect of construction cost and delivery time certainty for the government partner is balanced off against high financing and transaction costs; there has been limited applicability to date in the sustainable transportation sector; meaningful public consultation has sometimes been undermined by the incomplete release of key project information; and frequent tensions have arisen between the partners.

These experiences point to the settings and conditions under which PPPs can be an appropriate tool for delivering mega-projects. PPPs are most effective in settings such as major inter-urban highways or urban ring roads, airports and seaports, where it is in essence possible to identify each facility as a stand-alone unbundled asset, and define and delineate the roles and responsibilities of each partner. Moreover, a single level of government typically has financial and planning jurisdiction over these types of transportation assets, thereby reducing the prevalence of intergovernmental conflicts. Partnerships become increasingly complex and prone to tensions in infrastructure that is deeply interwoven into a dense interconnected network of facilities, such as an urban transit system, which requires funding, service integration and coordination involving multiple levels of government to maximize user benefits.

Thus a key feature in creating successful partnerships is implementing models that enable each partner to maintain control over the areas in which they have the capacity and incentive to best identify and manage risks. To this end, partnership models are required that enable the public sector partner to maintain control over key public policy issues such as ensuring meaningful community engagement in decision-making, service coordination, rate setting and facility upgrades over time. This means that governments should carefully consider the trade-offs associated with entering into PPPs that involve long-term facility operations and maintenance concessions and those that transfer demand risk to the private sector, as these PPP elements serve to lock-in future public decision-making. Conversely, bundling facility design, construction and financing into a single concession can leverage competitive forces and risk capital at stake to improve the management of project implementation.

To be certain, PPPs are not a static model of project delivery. Just as partnerships between the public and private sector have always existed in the provision of public infrastructure and have evolved over time, growing awareness of the shortcoming of PPPs provide an opportunity for innovation to address these contemporary challenges. Already, innovations in PPPs have begun to take place, highlighting instances where PPPs may be tailored to the local setting.

For instance, PPP models that repay up-front private sector investment through availability payments rather than user fees have made urban transit projects more viable, particularly in North America. Such approaches have also reduced the need for controversial contractual clauses that limit the long-term flexibility of governments to set user fee rates and make planning decisions that provide public benefit. PPP planners have also taken steps to make the planning process more transparent, releasing the complete concession agreements and summary documents on project value for money once an agreement is finalized. Indeed, it is now not entirely uncommon for more information to be publicly available about PPPs than traditionally procured projects. And more robust dispute resolution protocols are being built into PPP concession agreements that mandate non-legal remedies for conflicts between the partners, with legal proceedings identified as a last resort. One particular approach has been the introduction of contract clauses that rebalance the terms of the agreement if conditions exceed or fall below certain thresholds, which act to share rather than fully transfer risks between the partners.

Despite the advancements in PPP models and project delivery approaches, pressing challenges still remain. While PPPs have grown in popularity, they still face stiff opposition from labour unions and communities concerned about creeping privatization, loss of long-term public control of key public assets, and the loss of democratic input and accountability over critical infrastructure investment decisions. Given the long history of partnerships between the public and private sectors to deliver major public infrastructure, it is clear that multi-stakeholder, government–private-sector collaboration will continue to be central in the delivery of transportation mega-projects. A key challenge for the future is to develop PPP models that leverage the collaborative advantage of partnership through the alignment of risks and rewards, in order to deliver mega-projects that are procedurally accountable, efficient, equitable and environmentally sustainable.

LITERATURE

Acerete, B., J. Shaoul and A. Stafford (2009), 'Taking its toll: the private financing of roads in Spain', *Public Money & Management*, **29**(1), 19–26.

Allen Consulting Group (2007), *Performance of PPPs and Traditional Procurement in Australia*, accessed 11 June 2013 at http://www.irfnet.ch/files-upload/knowledges/IPA_Performance%20of%20PPPs_2007.pdf.

Altshuler, A. and D. Luberoff (2003), *Mega-projects: The Changing Politics of Urban Public Investments*, Washington, DC: Brookings Institution.

Australasian Council of Auditors-General (1997), 'Statement of principles: commercial confidentiality and the public interest', accessed 30 July 2007 at http://www.acag.org.au/ccpi.htm.

Bain, R. (2007), 'Anatomy of construction risk: lessons from a millennium of PPP experience', *Standard and Poor's*, accessed 27 January 2012, at http://www.robbain.com/The%20Anatomy%20Of%20Construction%20Risk.pdf.

Blain, L. (2009), 'PPPs provide benefits to BC', *Partnerships British Columbia*, accessed 27 January 2012 at http://www.partnershipsbc.ca/files/documents/20090407BCWideOP.pdf.

Blanc-Brude, F., H. Goldsmith and T. Välila (2006), *Ex Ante Construction Costs in the European Road Sector: A Comparison of Public–Private Partnerships and Traditional Public Procurement*, Economic and Financial Report 2006/01, accessed 21 November 2012 at http://www.eib.org/attachments/efs/efr_2006_v01_en.pdf.

Boardman, A.E., F. Poschmann and A. Vining (2005), 'North American infrastructure P3s: examples and lessons learned', in G. Hodge and C. Greve (eds), *The Challenge of Public–Private Partnerships: Learning from International Experience*, Cheltenham, UK and Northampton, MA, USA: Edward Elgar.

CCPPP (2012), 'Models of public–private partnership', accessed 21 November 2012 at http://www.pppcouncil.ca/resources/about-ppp/models.html.

Flyvbjerg, B. (2007), 'Policy and planning for large-infrastructure projects: problems, causes, cures', *Environment and Planning B*, **34**(4), 578–97.

Flyvbjerg, B., N. Bruzelius and W. Rothengatter (2003), *Megaprojects and Risk: An Anatomy of Ambition*, New York: Cambridge University Press.

Garvin, M. (2010), 'Enabling development of the transportation public–private partnership market in the United States', *Journal of Construction Engineering and Management*, **136**(4), 402–11.

Grimsey, D. and M. Lewis (2004), *Public–Private Partnerships: The Worldwide Revolution in Infrastructure Provision and Project Finance*, Cheltenham, UK and Northampton, MA, USA: Edward Elgar.

Guasch, J.L. (2004), *Granting and Renegotiating Infrastructure Concessions: Avoiding the Pitfalls*, Washington, DC: The World Bank Institute of Development Studies.

Hedlund, K.J. and B.F. Chase (2005), *Overview of Key Elements and Sample Provisions: State PPP Enabling Legislation for Highway Projects*, accessed 11 June 2013 at http://www.fhwa.dot.gov/ipd/pdfs/legis_key_elements.pdf.

Hodge, G.A. (2010), 'Reviewing public–private partnerships: some thoughts on evaluation', in G.A. Hodge, C. Greve and A.E. Boardman (eds), *International Handbook on Public–Private Partnerships*, Cheltenham, UK and Northampton, MA, USA: Edward Elgar, pp. 81–112.

Hodge, G.A., C. Greve and A.E. Boardman (2010), *International Handbook on Public–Private Partnerships*, Cheltenham, UK and Northampton, MA, USA: Edward Elgar.
Joint Select Committee on the Cross City Tunnel (2006), *First Report: Cross City Tunnel*, Sydney: Parliament of New South Wales.
Livingstone, K. (2007), 'Press release: mayor calls on Croydon Tramlink operator to improve service for passengers', accessed 11 June 2013 at http://www.london.gov.uk/media/mayor-press-releases/2007/01/mayor-calls-on-croydon-tramlink-operator-to-improve-service-for-passengers.
McQuaid, R.W. (2000), 'The theory of partnership', in S.P. Osborne (ed.), *Public–Private Partnerships: Theory and Practice in International Perspective*, New York: Routledge, pp. 9–36.
Menzies, I. and C. Mandri-Perrott (2010), 'Private sector participation in urban rail: getting the structure right', *Grid Lines*, **54**, 1–4.
Newman, P. and J. Kenworthy (1999), *Sustainability and Cities: Overcoming Automobile Dependence*, Washington, DC: Island Press.
Osborne, Stephen (2000), *Public–Private Partnerships: Theory and Practice in International Perspective*, New York: Routledge.
Pickrell, D.H. (1992), 'A desire named streetcar: fantasy and fact in rail transit planning', *Journal of the American Planning Association*, **58**(2), 158–76.
Public Works Financing (2012), International Major Projects Database, accessed 14 November 2012 at http://pwfinance.net/projects-database/.
Regan, M., J. Smith and P. Love (2010), 'Infrastructure procurement: learning from private–public partnership experiences "down under"', *Environment and Planning C*, **29**(2), 363–78.
Schneider, M. (2011), 'LA Metro's bold vision for P3s', *Public Works Financing*, **266**, 14–18.
Shaoul, J., A. Stafford and P. Stapleton (2007), 'Partnerships and the role of financial advisors: private control over public policy?', *Policy & Politics*, **35**(3), 479–95.
Shaoul, J., A. Stafford and P. Stapleton (2008), 'The cost of using private finance to build, finance and operate hospitals', *Public Money and Management*, **28**(2), 101–8.
Shaoul, J., A. Stafford and P. Stapleton (2010), 'Financial black holes: the disclosure and transparency of privately financed roads in the UK', *Accounting, Auditing & Accountability Journal*, **23**(2), 229–55.
Siemiatycki, M. (2006), 'Implications of public–private partnerships on the development of urban transit infrastructure', *Journal of Planning Education and Research*, **26**(4), 137–51.
Siemiatycki, M. (2007), 'What's the secret: confidentiality in planning infrastructure using public/private partnerships', *Journal of the American Planning Association*, **73**(4), 388–403.
Siemiatycki, M. (2009), 'Academics and auditors: comparing perspectives on transportation project cost overruns', *Journal of Planning Education and Research*, **29**(2), 142–56.
Siemiatycki, M. (2010), 'Delivering transportation infrastructure through public–private partnerships: planning concerns', *Journal of the American Planning Association*, **76**(1), 43–58.
Siemiatycki, M. (2011a), 'Public–private partnership networks: business–government networks in United Kingdom transportation projects', *Economic Geography*, **87**(3), 309–34.
Siemiatycki, M. (2011b), 'Urban transportation public–private partnerships: drivers of uneven development?', *Environment and Planning A*, **43**(7), 1707–22.
Siemiatycki, M. and J. Friedman (2012), 'The trade-offs of transferring traffic demand risk on transit public–private partnerships', *Public Works Management and Policy*, **17**(2), 283–302.
Smyth, H. and A. Edkins (2007), 'Relationship management in the management of PFI/PPP projects in the UK', *International Journal of Project Management*, **25**(3), 232–40.
van Wee, B. (2007), 'Large infrastructure projects: a review of the quality of demand forecasts and cost estimation', *Environment and Planning B*, **34**(4), 611–25.
Wettenhall, R. (2010), 'Mixes and partnerships through time', in G.A. Hodge, C. Greve and A.E. Boardman (eds), *International Handbook on Public–Private Partnerships*, Cheltenham, UK and Northampton, MA, USA: Edward Elgar, pp. 17–42.

8. The political economy of urban infrastructure

Kevin Dwarka and Eran Feitelson

8.1 INTRODUCTION

The Infrastructure Revolution

Beginning in the early 1980s, the resurgence of private sector involvement in the development of infrastructure revolutionized the provision of public services (Grimsey and Lewis, 2004). Anchored by the neoliberal ideology of Reagan and Thatcher, new policy regimes crystallized around the contraction of public expenditures and the liberalization of private capital flows (Prasad, 2006). Deregulation programs transformed the way local, state, and federal governments operated and built highways, railways, power plants, and water treatment facilities (Gómez-Ibáñez, 2003; Winston, 2010; Finger and Künneke, 2011). In both the industrialized and developing worlds, the private sector expanded the scope of its services beyond engineering and construction and assumed primary responsibility for the design, operation, and maintenance of new infrastructure (Roland, 2008; Grigg, 2010). The most sweeping change, however, was the financialization of new infrastructure. Countries began to sell off their infrastructure assets to private investors. Engineering firms and venture capital funds formed new infrastructure products. Infrastructure, no longer simply a public good, became bought and sold as a globally traded asset class (Torrance, 2009a; Weber and Alfen, 2010). Meanwhile, new legal frameworks like private finance initiative (PFI), design-build-operate-maintain (DBOM), and build-operate-transfer (BOT) subjected service delivery to private contractual agreements rather than agency protocols and public regulation.

Scale Infrastructure Market

Today, the global infrastructure market is a massive business. Data collected by the World Bank shows that between 1990 and 2011, the scale of annual private sector investment in the global infrastructure market grew from US$12.7 billion in 1990 to US$162.7 billion in 2011 (The World

Bank Group, 2012). The economic recession that began in 2007 has not reversed the trend of rising private investment in infrastructure. Even with the collapse of global capital markets and the emergence of state-led stimulation programs, the growth of the global infrastructure market has continued almost unabated. In fact, the World Bank data indicate that private investment in infrastructure has never been as high as it was in 2010 and 2011.

The Global LRT Market

One of the largest sectors within the urban infrastructure market is urban light rail transit ('LRT'), a market expected to reach US$7.5 billion by 2015 (Global Industry Analytics, 2010). Often tied to larger urban regeneration initiatives, LRT projects generally aim either to stimulate economic development or improve access along congested corridors (Cohen-Blankshtain and Feitelson, 2011). In LRT projects that are structured as design-build-operate-finance-maintain ('DBOFM'), a multi-disciplinary consortium of private companies not only builds the project but also secures its own financing. Under a long-term contract generally lasting between 25 and 30 years, the consortium might also assume revenue risk for the system's operation. Proponents of DBOFM agreements contend that this approach is superior to more traditional forms of project delivery because it reduces public sector costs, transfers risks to the private sector, spreads costs out over a long period of time, and contractually assigns a fixed price to a project, thereby insulating the public sector from cost inflations.

The actual percentage of an LRT's total costs that is financed with private capital is highly variable from project to project. Also highly variable is the private borrower's means of repaying its debts. The private sector may recover a portion of its investments from farebox revenue but it may also be reimbursed from the government in the form of capital grants attached to construction milestones as well as availability payments provided in exchange for service provision. Nonetheless, projects are generally characterized as 'privately financed' as long as the private sector assumes responsibility for at least some amount of up-front financing for the capital infrastructure regardless of the downstream financial obligations of the public sector.

While private financing may define an initial plan for an LRT project, it is not uncommon for government sponsors to significantly modify contracts in ways that reverse the risk transfers or extinguish the private financing element altogether. In North America, for example, private financing was initially considered but not ultimately adopted for the Hudson-Bergen Light Rail (Dwarka, 2012) as well as the BART Oakland

Airport Connector (BART, 2008). Meanwhile, the Las Vegas Monorail was financed by private investors but the project subsequently went bankrupt (United States Bankruptcy Court, 2011). In Canada, the best example of a currently operating privately financed LRT project is Vancouver's Canada Line.

More extensive use of DBOFM arrangements, however, can be found in the United Kingdom where private capital was used for key parts of the Docklands Light Railway ('DLR') including the Lewisham, London City Airport, and Woolwich Arsenal extensions (London Docklands Development Corporation, 1997). At the end of 2011, Transport for London reclaimed public responsibility for the financing of the latter two DLR extensions. Just a few years earlier, the same agency had taken over the privately financed Croydon Tramlink (Transport for London, Rail and Underground Panel, 2011). Other LRT projects in the UK that have enlisted private capital include the Phase 2 Extension of the Manchester Metrolink and the Nottingham Express Transit.

Outside the United Kingdom, few other European countries have privately financed the construction of LRT projects. Although the private sector is extensively involved in the operations of systems under concession contracts, public financing for the capital costs is still the norm and facilitated by the taxing powers of local authorities (Gannon and Smith, 2009).

In Australia, the Sydney LRT was originally financed with private capital. However, in 2012, the investor transferred its shares back to the government, thereby transferring ownership to the public sector (Tan, 2012). In Israel, private capital was used to finance the first phase of the Jerusalem Light Rail Transit but subsequent extensions will be publicly financed after extensive controversy surrounding the project's cost and delays (Dwarka, 2012). A consortium was selected for the planned Tel Aviv Light Rail but the contract along with its private financing approach was shelved in favor of starting anew with a publicly financed system.

Private finance has also been used in Asia. In Malaysia, two different LRT projects in Kuala Lumpur were initially financed and owned by private companies and subsequently taken over by the national government in 2002 (Abdul-Aziz, 2006). In Thailand, private capital was used to finance Bangkok Skytrain, an elevated light rail system that has remained under private control in spite of threats of nationalization (Phang, 2007). In the Philippines, the 17-km Blue Line in Manila was originally conceived as a purely privately financed project with only fundamental guarantees from the national government. However, the government ultimately offered a more expansive commitment of sovereign guarantees in order to help the private sector secure lower financing costs from senior lenders (Llanto, 2007).

The widespread volatility with private finance arrangements for LRT projects, however, does not mean the end of DBOFM as a worldwide method of project delivery. On the contrary, the lure of private capital remains especially compelling in the North American markets. In Denver, for example, a new commuter rail line structured as a DBOFM is currently under construction (Nichols, 2011). In Detroit, a non-profit organization has developed a proposal for an LRT line that would be financed entirely by private investors and philanthropic organizations (Heims, 2012). A similar proposal is underway in Pittsburgh where private investors have been invited to finance a new transit connection in exchange for development rights (Schmitz, 2012). In Canada, private finance arrangements are currently planned for four new light rail lines in Toronto (Grant, 2012): Ottawa's Confederation Line (CBC News, 2012), another transit line in Vancouver (Strandberg, 2012), the southeast LRT line in Edmonton (Kent, 2012), and a new LRT line connecting the Ontario cities of Cambridge, Kitchener, and Waterloo (Smith, 2012). And in Queensland, Australia, private capital is currently helping to finance the construction of the Gold Coast Rapid Transit Project (GoldLinQ, 2011). Given the breadth of privately financed LRT projects that are either already built or in the pipeline, now is an opportune time to study the implications of this form of project delivery on the infrastructure development process.

8.2 RESEARCH QUESTIONS AND CHAPTER SCOPE

The use of private capital for urban infrastructure is not a new phenomenon. After all, infrastructure projects throughout the industrializing world in the late nineteenth century were routinely built with private capital (Gunderson, 1989; Larson, 2001; Roth, 2006). In the United States, for example, real estate developers financed streetcar systems in order to maximize returns on property development beyond the city center (Warner, 1978). Still, the more recent insertion of private capital into LRT projects is revolutionary because it comes on the heels of the post-World War II approach to infrastructure finance that emphasized public investment as the prerequisite to economic recovery.

The re-privatization and re-marketization of infrastructure therefore provokes questions about the ways in which the private sector is reshaping the governance of urban transport systems, especially with regard to the siting, scale, and intended beneficiaries of new projects. This chapter tries to illuminate the urban infrastructure development process in the era of neoliberalism. Of particular concern is the degree to which global agents are now influencing the various stages of the infrastructure development process from a project's first gestation to its actual implementation.

So far, only a few analysts have examined how the globalization and marketization of infrastructure has affected the governance of infrastructure projects (Graham and Marvin, 2001; Siemiatycki, 2005, 2006, 2009, 2011a, 2011b; Torrance, 2008, 2009a, 2009b). In the absence of a large theoretical literature on the governance of privately financed infrastructure, the next section of this chapter identifies theoretical streams that may at least suggest some of the key players and core dynamics in the infrastructure development process. The subsequent Section 8.3, the heart of this chapter, then enlists these various theories to build a political economy framework of urban infrastructure development.

The infrastructure development process (Section 8.4) can be seen as comprising seven distinct stages. Based on the literature and the insights gained from various empirical studies of LRT we propose that the role of the different actors varies from stage to stage. These changes in roles are spelled out in the framework.

While potentially applicable to a broad range of infrastructures, the political economy framework proposed here is intertwined with empirical references to the global LRT market. The purpose of these references is not to provide unequivocal proof that a given hypothesis is valid but to help illustrate the hypothesis itself. By no means is this framework intended as a complete theory of urban infrastructure production nor does it represent an exhaustive empirical review of LRT projects. Rather, this framework is offered as a starting point for identifying the agents and processes governing a restructured infrastructure market and utilizes the global LRT market as a setting to identify and present the role of various agents in the different stages of the infrastructure development process. Section 8.5 presents some conclusions.

8.3 REVIEW OF THEORETICAL LITERATURE

A relatively small number of scholars have directly addressed the political economy of infrastructure. Through planning histories of London's ill fated 'third airport', London's motorways, and the San Francisco Bay Area's commuter rail network, Hall (1982) identifies the role of pressure groups, bureaucracies, and politicians in driving failed infrastructure planning processes. Altshuler and Luberoff's (2003) more recent analysis deals with the United States's post-war public investments in transportation infrastructure and connects its empirical findings with a variety of theoretical currents in urban theory.

While Hall and Altshuler & Luberoff offer useful insights into infrastructure as a public investment, they do not engage with private finance or globalization. More germane to the political economy of privately financed infrastructure is Siemiatycki's (2005, 2011a, 2011b) scholarship, which offers an in-depth case study of Vancouver's privately financed LRT line, analyzes the composition of partnerships building privately financed transportation projects in the United Kingdom, and studies the pattern of uneven development accompanying the use of public–private partnerships for transportation infrastructure. Also relevant is Torrance's (2007, 2009a) scholarship that examines the role of institutional investors in the global infrastructure market.

What is missing from most existing infrastructure theory is a broader understanding of infrastructure production as a complete development process with political outcomes directed by the forces of globalization and marketization. Filling this void is Graham and Marvin's (2001) *Splintering Urbanism*, which contends that the deregulation and globalization of network infrastructure has resulted in the substitution of universal services with highly bifurcated and socially stratified systems. The authors are not concerned with the decision-making process for a particular project. Theorizing instead at a higher scale of analysis, Graham and Marvin charge that globalization has re-territorialized the physical and financial space of infrastructure by linking geographically discontiguous projects through shared financial instruments and managerial entities. Their argument begins with the observation that 'public and private monopolies are being replaced by contested, profit-driven markets' (Graham and Marvin, 2001, p. 13). With the rising role of global capital as a major source of funding large-scale infrastructure projects, Graham and Marvin identify the emergence of a new global infrastructure network, one that is linked transnationally through financial flows but results in fragmented local landscapes. Consequently, service delivery is no longer provided according to a comprehensive planning ideal or the public interest standard of 'universal access'. Instead, infrastructure projects are built in a fragmented fashion in which 'the most highly valued spaces in global city cores are being provided with their own dedicated, high quality infrastructural connections' (ibid., p. 313). Graham and Marvin note that the emergence of these global enclaves, connected more to other global enclaves than their physical adjacent areas, 'undermines the economic prospects' of those larger urban areas in which they reside (ibid., p. 377). That process of undermining occurs as new projects bypass poorer or more industrial areas, leaving them behind as power and access are concentrated in a new transnational space inhabited by global elites.

Absent from Graham and Marvin's meta-analysis is a fine-grain analysis that specifies the agents and interactions associated with the production of infrastructure. Logan and Molotch's (2007) urban growth machine theory offers an actor-based interpretation of governance in which identifiable agents manipulate the transactions and use of urban space. Though principally concerned with real estate development rather than infrastructure development, urban growth machine theory nonetheless offers a useful pathway into the human interactions guiding a development process. In contrast to the structuralist concept of splintering urbanism, growth machine theory suggests that power over infrastructure decisions is local and concentrated rather than global and diffuse. Specifically, real estate developers, driven by the desire for higher returns on property investments, drive the infrastructure development process. An informal alliance emerges between these developers and pro-growth advocates, including elected officials, unions, and the media. Elected officials are either captured by real estate developers or the elected officials are real estate developers themselves. This 'machine' strategically embarks upon the maximization of urban growth even if the consequent development does not necessarily result in well-distributed economic benefits. Kirkpatrick and Smith (2011, p. 478) observe that 'the growth machine's viability is predicated upon the ability of coalition partners to secure an infrastructural framework that can physically support economic growth and land-use intensification. Under the growth machine, all politics are local'. As Logan and Molotch (2007, p. xviii) note, 'The global entrepreneurs, including huge financial institutions, are backers – offering finance and forms of expertise (marketing, architecture); the locals run the interference'.

Neither the splintering urbanism concept nor urban growth machine theory offers a clear understanding of the infrastructure development as an interactive process comprising sequential stages. One way of conceptually ordering the infrastructure development process is the rational planning model, a five-stage model developed by Banfield (1955, 1959). Under this model, planning decisions are systematically performed as a series of five steps (1) definition of goals, (2) development of alternatives, (3) evaluation of alternatives, (4) selection of preferred alternative, and (5) implementation of selected alternative. Banfield's model came to be established as the desired norm for planning processes and continues to shape the administrative procedures for complex planning initiatives. More recently, Innes and Booher (2010) have offered a variation of the rational planning model in the concept of collaborative rationality. Under this framework, diverse stakeholders (who represent a wide cross-section of interests, institutions, and jurisdictions) define goals, strategies, and plans through a process of ongoing collaboration, reciprocal learning, and consensus building. Under collaborative rationality, 'problems are treated as puzzles as participants work jointly to put pieces together to create a shared picture of the future and a strategy for getting there' (ibid., p. 9)

8.4 URBAN INFRASTRUCTURE DEVELOPMENT PROCESS

None of the theories reviewed above offer a unified theory of urban infrastructure development process. Moreover, the theories are not necessarily inapposite to each other but address different aspects of a planning process. Splintering urbanism, for example, addresses the political outcome of the global infrastructure markets whereas urban growth machine theory reveals finer-grain concepts of urban governance in relation to the use and distribution of land. Provided below is a political economy framework that attempts to repackage these various theoretical streams into a stream of hypotheses related to the production of privately financed infrastructure. The framework, organized around seven proposed stages of the infrastructure development process, is not purely theoretical or speculative. Interwoven throughout this framework are empirical references to privately financed LRT projects. As mentioned earlier, however, these references are offered as empirical illustrations rather than proof.

Stage I: Entrepreneurship

Infrastructure decisions, especially ones related to large transformative projects, are not routinely made as part of a city's day to day governance. By their nature, infrastructure projects are ambitious, risky, expensive, and time-consuming. Their formulation requires vision as well as intimate knowledge of a city's political, geographic, and legal landscape. Moreover, the financial and environmental obstacles to implementing an infrastructure project are formidable. For all these reasons, urban infrastructure projects are inherently acts of entrepreneurship.

Contrary to the assumptions of collaborative rationality, infrastructure projects do not always emerge as the product of deliberations by diverse stakeholders in which 'many actors – experts, stakeholders, elected officials, and the public – are engaging jointly to address planning and policy problems' (Innes and Booher, 2010, p. 5). Instead, urban infrastructure schemes are also launched from the creative vision of an entrepreneurial-minded individual committed to enacting dramatic change in a city, such as Robert Moses in New York (Caro, 1974). In the case of real estate development, Logan and Molotch (2007, p. 29) conceived of 'place entrepreneurs' as modern urban rentiers who 'have the job of trapping human activity at the sites of their pecuniary interests'.

Infrastructure entrepreneurs, however, are not necessarily the owners and purveyors of infrastructure as a discrete physical product but a broader social program. Consistent with Kingdon's (2011, p. 179) concept of a policy entrepreneur, infrastructure entrepreneurs 'are willing to invest their resources – time, energy, reputation, money – to promote a position in return for anticipated future gain in the form of material, purposive, or solidarity benefits'. Through the erection of grand public projects, preferably large in physical scale and branded as exemplars of global ingenuity, infrastructure entrepreneurs are committed to the physical and economic reshaping of a city.

The most likely candidate for an infrastructure entrepreneur is an elected official who recognizes that 'infrastructure is a necessary precondition for urban growth to be achieved' (Kirkpatrick and Smith, 2011, p. 477). The official's interest in development may stem from an interest in strengthening a city's tax base, generating new jobs, or capturing public financing from the central government. But infrastructure projects also enable elected officials to satisfy the development interests of the real estate community and also leave a lasting legacy of their political achievements in the form of a physical marker.

The infrastructure entrepreneur does not necessarily invent the infrastructure concept such as a light rail but creates the structure that allows a physical idea to blossom as a political vision. The entrepreneur might be a local official such as Mayor Ehud Olmert in the case of the Jerusalem Light Rail Project (Dwarka, 2012). In the concept of a light rail system for Israel's capital city, Olmert saw an opportunity to upgrade the real estate values in Jerusalem's city center. However, the infrastructure entrepreneur does not necessarily have to be a representative of a particular municipality but could instead serve at a higher level of governance. In the case of Hudson Bergen Light Rail, for example, it was the Governor of New Jersey, Thomas Kean, who acted as the infrastructure entrepreneur, the person who first identified the need to analyze the transportation barriers to development along the Hudson River waterfront (ibid.). Similarly, the regeneration of the London Docklands and the construction of the Dockland Light Railway were fueled by the leadership of Michael Heseltine in his capacity as a Member of Parliament and Secretary of State for the Environment (Mohammadi, 2001).

The elected official is not the only party with infrastructural longings. The infrastructure entrepreneur could also be an agency head, especially one with political ambitions in the style of Robert Moses (Caro, 1974).

But agency heads are often invisible politically, lacking the combination of charisma and contacts that enable entrepreneurialism.

Real estate developers might also conceive of infrastructure projects but the complexity and scale of a project like a LRT project is likely to dissuade them from taking as active of a role as an elected official. Global business elites are also candidates for infrastructure entrepreneurs. Multinational engineering companies and investors search for low-risk investments with the maximum rate of return. But multinational engineers are constrained by their lack of familiarity with a city's physical composition and local institutions. Meanwhile, financial institutions are usually in the business of financing schemes that are already developed rather than developing new projects themselves.

Non-government organizations, advocacy organizations, the media and the public at large are interested in infrastructure as an opportunity for enhancing service delivery. They may try to build political capital for their ideas by forming advocacy organizations, writing newspaper articles and blogs, joining committees, or arranging meetings with elected officials. But these actions rarely result in the initiation of infrastructure as a political concept, a phenomena requiring a concurrence of technological ingenuity, authority, and institutional leadership. Ultimately, infrastructure projects are so risky, costly, complicated, and time-consuming that their production requires the entrepreneurship of a local political elite, someone whose entire identity is defined by creating long-term physical change in the urban landscape. The availability of global financial markets for financing infrastructure does not upend this requirement.

Stage II: Agenda Setting

Once an infrastructure entrepreneur embraces the rehabilitation of an urban area through infrastructure investment, the time comes for the entrepreneur to place a specific infrastructure concept on the policy agenda, 'the list of subjects or problems to which government officials, and people outside government closely associated with those officials, are paying some attention at any given time' (Kingdon, 2011, p. 3). The infrastructure entrepreneur thereby commences an initiation process, what Polsby (1984, p. 3) characterizes as 'the politics of inventing, winnowing, and finding and gaining adherents for policy alternatives before they are made part of the "program"'.

Generally, a single individual cannot maneuver an infrastructure concept through the various political hurdles standing in the way of implementation. The entrepreneur's success in placing a proposal on the policy agenda requires a transformation of the entrepreneurship driving the infrastructure development process from one of individual entrepreneurship to systemic entrepreneurship. Individual entrepreneurship entails a single individual marshaling contacts and authority in order to create change. Systemic entrepreneurship occurs when 'several actors and several organizations participate. The innovative output of each is combined to create a completely new situation' (Bernier, 2007, p.488). In the case of infrastructure, the entrepreneur forms an infrastructure alliance in order to ensure cooperation between the multiple agencies representing various scales of jurisdiction from the local to the state to the national. The alliance is composed of the entrepreneur and other infrastructure advocates who may include elected officials, agency heads, and real estate developers.

The infrastructure entrepreneur's first task in the agenda-setting process will most likely be to identify the local and state agency heads most likely to serve as allies in support of an infrastructure concept. Agency heads often assume leadership after having worked for years as a public servant and amassing extensive knowledge of a particular city's laws, policies, and institutions (Caro, 1974). As such, they sometimes have the greatest depth of institutional knowledge of a city's planning process and the broadest understanding of its needs. Though public stewards, agency heads are not removed from self-interests (Chowdhury, 2006; Dal Bo, 2006). Especially in the context where an agency head may have control not only over planning but also implementing infrastructure, committing to a complex long-term undertaking offers a form of job security that will persist across multiple administrations. Also, embracing the infrastructure agenda of an influential politician often empowers the agency head to remain at the helm of an agency or transfer to a more prestigious or remunerative title. Agency heads usually have nothing to gain by opposing an elected official's agenda.

In many cases, the entrepreneur does not ally with an existing agency head but creates a new administrative agency and then appoints the head of that agenda based upon their fit with the infrastructure's development agenda. Secretary of State Heseltine, for example, established the London Docklands Development Corporation ('LDDC') and appointed Reg Ward to lead the new unelected body that would have complete authority for planning approvals (*The Telegraph*, 2011). Acting in the capacity of chief executive of the LDDC, Ward was able to define not only the land use agenda for the Docklands area but also position the light railway as essential to the area's regeneration.

Besides agency heads, infrastructure entrepreneurs may also ally with real estate developers who support urban infrastructure as an opportunity to make their present and future land investments more accessible and better connect their properties to commercial centers. It was precisely for these reasons that the real estate division of the Hartz Corporation was so committed to the concept of a transit project along the Hudson River waterfront in New Jersey (Dwarka, 2012).

Developers also view infrastructure as an opportunity to improve the overall marketability of their development sites through broader public investment. The development of an infrastructure project routinely enlists local government in a broad range of activities including the upgrading of utilities, re-parcelization of land, deployment of eminent domain, and environmental mitigations. As Logan and Molotch (2007, p. 36) note, 'By working through a local government, moreover, the efforts of an elite gain the appearance of a civic campaign waged on behalf of a legal entity, and its citizens, rather than of a conspiracy of vested interests'.

Regardless of their divergent motivations, what unites members of the infrastructure alliance is their shared desire to create large-scale physical and economic change in the city as well as their power to create that change through collaboration. Power in the agenda-setting process therefore rests not in a singular individual or agency but in the networked interactions of members of the alliance. As McGuirk (2000, p. 652) notes:

> The organisational forms through which power is socially produced in urban governance involve co-operation, interdependencies between organisations, a multiplicity of actors and the mobilisation of networks to access the various resources essential to creating the capacity to govern and to achieve policy goals.

Stage III: Project Development

Elected officials may possess the political authority to initiate an infrastructure project but they lack the technical knowledge and institutional leadership to concretize an infrastructure agenda or develop a project. However, the heads of major agencies within city governments do have the technical knowledge and institutional leadership that is required to translate the development goals of elected officials into a formal infrastructure proposal. For example, in the case of the Jerusalem Light Rail, city's mayor, Ehud Olmert, may have been the infrastructure entrepreneur for a new light rail system for Jerusalem. However, the materialization of that concept into an actual project required the expertise of Moshe Hirsh, the head of the city's master transportation planning agency (Dwarka, 2012).

Similarly, the core of a real estate developer's business is buildings rather than infrastructure. In most cases, the technical requirements of an infrastructure project are too specialized for a real estate developer to develop a serious infrastructure project. The technical and institutional knowledge required for developing an infrastructure scheme is far more likely to be found in a city agency rather than a real estate company. The elected official and developers eagerly anticipate the project's ribbon-cutting ceremony but only an agency head can do the work of translating an infrastructure idea into a built reality.

Agency heads acquire technical knowledge from high levels of formal education as well as years of practical experience managing specific projects in a particular discipline. More importantly, agency heads have access to a wide global network of professional contacts who have successfully implemented new technologies in similar locales. The agency head of a large municipal agency also controls the work assignments of tens if not hundreds of senior, middle-level, and junior bureaucrats. Whereas an elected official may seek technical counsel from a few politically appointed policy advisers, the agency head can assemble multiple teams of in-house experts while also contracting out further planning responsibilities to independent consultants.

The maturation of an infrastructure concept into a detailed proposal includes definition of extensive technical specifications, operational standards, approaches to financing, and implementation strategies. During this stage, the local planning agency will review alternative proposals but these alternatives are not necessarily viable options. Rather, they constitute 'synthetic alternatives', proposals that are designed as part of a learning process in which an infrastructure plan's goals are synthesized and evaluated (Feitelson, 2011).

The production of the alternatives analysis does not always accord with the professionalism and objectivity presumed by rational planning theory. Planning documents and feasibility studies are sometimes prepared to evoke the execution of objective professional assessment. The calculation of cost estimates, implementation times, and revenue projections is especially ripe for distortion (Flyvbjerg, 2007). The effect of these distortions is to privilege the creation of ambitious projects whose stated objectives might have been better served with a lower-cost alternative. The Jerusalem Light Rail Project, for example, opened in 2011 severely over budget and six years later than anticipated (Dwarka, 2012). A more accurate estimation of its actual costs and implementation time might have compelled project planners to pursue a bus rapid transit option instead of light rail.

Meanwhile, even accurate capital cost estimates do not address the full costs of a project. The planning costs and administrative costs of an infrastructure project are rarely if ever included in the capital cost estimations of a project that are published in the media. These costs begin accruing during the project initiation phase and continue for the full lifespan of a project's operation. Even if a project's capital construction and operations are tendered to a private operator, the public sector continues to bear the ongoing costs of monitoring, contract administration, and planning of extensions.

Professional planners within and without the agency are unlikely to question the legitimacy of the preferred alternative or the planning process (Wachs, 1988). The reasons for the planner's reticence are numerous. First, infrastructure is inherently a specialized complex undertaking requiring highly specialized expertise in order to critically engage with its development. As such, the overwhelming majority of professional planners in any given city will not have knowledge of the engineering requirements, financial risks, or implementation challenges of a particular infrastructure initiative. Land use planners, for example, may anticipate the development impacts of a proposed project but they lack professional training in construction, engineering, infrastructure finance, and operations. As such, a city's professional planning staff may remain agnostic while the alliance develops their project.

Second, infrastructure entrepreneurs seek the installation of an advanced technology, a form of physical intervention that may be unprecedented in their city. The revolutionary nature of this proposed scheme inherently means that even specialized planners will have limited experience with the proposed technology. For example, in Jerusalem, the JLRT was the first light rail project ever built in Israel. As such, most Israeli planners had no prior experience of the complexity of installing or operating such a technology.

Finally, the infrastructure alliance carefully defines the infrastructure agenda not only as a specific infrastructure scheme but also as a long-term restructuring of local governance. The infrastructure development process generates new employment opportunities in the public sector, the termination of certain positions, and the awarding of consulting contracts. Professional planners weigh their ethical obligations against the competing desire to maintain their livelihoods (ibid.). Driven by the desire to be on the right side of history, professional planners are disincentivized to interrogate the alliance's preferred alternative.

Stage IV: Project Approval

An infrastructure concept is approved, rejected, deferred, or changed during the project approval phase. Just as the scale of an infrastructure project varies considerably by the nature of its technology and the extent of its service area, the approval bodies for an infrastructure scheme also vary depending on the project. Whereas some projects may require only the approval of a city legislature, other projects may require approval at the regional, state, or national level.

With few exceptions (mainly transboundary cases), the approval of infrastructure projects does not require supra-national approvals, at least in developed countries. Foreign companies and banks are not involved in deciding whether or not a project is approved by a legislative body. While decision-makers may be in dialogue with engineering companies and visit built projects in other countries, the approval process remains a local game. Formal corruption is unlikely to occur during the approval of an infrastructure project. Unlike real estate deals, infrastructure projects are generally voted upon before any contractor has been selected to construct a project. As such, infrastructure developers are generally not in a position to bribe an elected official to authorize a particular project. However, the absence of global interference and formal corruption does not mean that the decision-making process is necessarily rational. To win over political support for the proposed project, the infrastructure alliance makes four key claims to authenticate the legitimacy of the proposed infrastructure concept:

- The first claim is that crisis conditions compel a major change in the status quo. As Kingdon notes, 'Conditions must deteriorate to crisis proportions before the subject achieves enough visibility to become an active agenda item' (Kingdon, 2011, p. 95).
- The second claim is that the scenario envisioned by the infrastructure alliance is the only scenario that will resolve the crisis. Unless the project is built, crisis conditions will continue. The proposed project thereby emerges as a symbol of success and power (Richmond, 2005), while continuing crisis conditions all but ensure that the project becomes an inevitable policy choice (Garb, 2004).
- The third claim is that the project is feasible with regard to cost, implementation, and revenue. But as noted above, planning studies may exaggerate project benefits, underestimate project costs, underestimate implementation times, and promote a flawed sense of risk allocation (Kain, 1990; Flyvbjerg et al., 2003).
- The fourth claim, especially in the context of privately financed infrastructure, is that the project will entail a transfer of risk from the public sector to the private sector. The disjuncture between the term 'private finance' and the actual level of risk assumed by the private sector opens the door for projects to be approved according to false assumptions. Projects that are 'privately financed' actually require extensive public investment even if the nature of those investments is not formally inscribed in a state's annual budget. Decision-makers may be approving projects without fully understanding the actual sharing of risks between the public and private sectors. In

Jerusalem, for example, the Israeli government approved the JLRT as a privately financed infrastructure project even though the Israeli government was ultimately responsible for the overwhelming majority of the project's costs (Dwarka, 2012).

Stage V: Selection of Contractor

The global infrastructure community enters into the infrastructure development process once the project is approved and a request for a proposal ('RFP'), qualifications, or expressions of interest is released by the sponsoring public agency. The tenders for major infrastructure projects are open to applicants from around the world but most bidders will be sure to include local firms on their team.

Prospective teams are not passive respondents to the tender but actively involved in shaping its terms through an extended negotiation process. The teams are in dialogue with the sponsors of the tender with regard to the contract terms, financing requirements, performance requirements, and technical standards. As in the case of the RFP for Denver's Eagle P3 project, prospective teams may be able to review a draft copy of the RFP and submit their comments 'to assure that the latest thoughts and innovations that the industry has developed are allowed for in the project'(RTD, n.d.).

Banks and institutional lenders are also involved in the process for privately financed infrastructure since prospective teams must also include a financial proposal in their submitted bid. In this regard, the banks can play a significant role in defining the risk allocation structure by making certain loans to a private consortium contingent upon the guarantees and reimbursements from the public sector.

Proposals are usually reviewed by a committee of leading public agency representatives. In the case of developing countries, dependent as they frequently are on foreign capital for infrastructure development, international lending institutions may flex their muscle during the procurement process. For example, the procurement process for a light rail project in the Philippines was allegedly interrupted by the intercession of state officials from Japan who threatened to pull already committed financing from the Japanese Bank for International Cooperation unless the Philippines government reconsidered the eligibility of Japanese firms for the development contract (Aquino, 2000).

Whether or not contracts are awarded on the basis of professional assessment of the proposals is difficult if not impossible to evaluate because of the secretive nature of the tendering process. In regard to Vancouver's Canada Line, Siemiatycki (2005) points out the decision-making process was deficient in terms of transparency and availability of information due to the confidentiality of the tendering process.

So far, there has not been a case where the winner of a privately financed LRT contract has been charged with winning the contract through bribery. Still, speculation about the fairness of contract selection processes persists given the closed nature of infrastructure deals. In December 2012, for example, the contract for Ottawa's LRT was awarded to the engineering company SNC-Lavalin during the arrest of the company's CEO on fraud-related charges as well as other claims of corruption leveled at senior company staff (Marowitz, 2012).

Stage VI: Financing

The financial architecture of a project is defined by the approach to financing its planning, design, capital construction, operation, and maintenance. Financing may come from public sources, private sources, or a combination of both. Moreover, a project's financial architecture does not remain static but is subject to constant renegotiation for the duration of a project's lifetime. Privately financed projects require infrastructure developers to secure financing from global capital markets. However, the pursuit of that financing does not remove the public sector from the financing process. On the contrary, the public sector serves as a guarantor for private bank loans, provides loan reimbursements and grants to contractors upon the completion of their work, promises ongoing operating subsidies, and assumes the financial burden for many aspects of supposedly private projects. These sorts of financial burdens assumed by the public sector are difficult to track because they are not conventionally budgeted.

Local planning agencies are not always in full command of deciding how to finance a local infrastructure project. State or national finance departments and treasuries may have greater influence on determining the financing approach than local planning agencies. For example, the commitment to using a private finance approach for the Jerusalem Light Rail mainly came from the Israel's national finance ministry rather than Jerusalem's local planning offices (Dwarka, 2012). Siemiatycki's (2005, p. 72) analysis of the Vancouver Canada Line reveals that federal and provincial governments actively promoted the use of public–private partnership 'in spite of repeated requests by local officials to examine a more traditional public service delivery mechanism' Siemiatycki notes that empirical evidence does not reveal formal corruption behind the government's involvement with Vancouver's Canada Line. Nonetheless, he notes that a variety of self-interested parties undergirded the project's framing as a public–private partnership. Specifically, Siemiatycki (ibid.) observes that 'many parties involved in the analysis process and those with a direct interest in the project proceeding have been financial contributors to both the provincial and federal Liberal parties, who were in power at the time of the RAV planning'. Referring to the consulting firms hired to help plan the Canada Line, Siemiatycki (ibid., p. 75) further states that 'Many of the firms hired to provide financial and feasibility analysis were overt supporters of private–public partnerships and stood to gain financially from the proliferation of this funding model'.

Once the contractor is selected, the ability of the contractor to reach finance closure is subject to the volatility of the capital markets. In the case of the Jerusalem Light Rail, for example, the contractor's ability to secure financing took 28 months longer than was anticipated by the project planners (Dwarka, 2012). Moreover, the achievement of financial closure is only the starting point for continued negotiations between the sponsoring public agency and the selected contractor. The private sector renegotiates the financial terms of the contract agreed upon at the conclusion of the procurement process. These renegotiations may occur regardless of whether a project is financed through private capital or public revenues. In both cases, the private sector attempts to minimize risk by revising the project scope, pressing the government for more subsidies, and limiting equity investments. These negotiations occur with little oversight and are frequently removed from a government's accounting of current expenditures (Engel et al., 2009). The renegotiation of a project contract may thus dramatically increase the public costs of a project but those costs are rarely transparent whether or not the project is financed publicly or privately.

During the negotiations, the contractor has a clear bargaining advantage due to the government's negotiating levers constrained by what Lonsdale (2005) calls the 'post-contractual lock-in'. Once the government is locked into a contractual relationship with the consortium, reversing course becomes near impossible. The government's failure to comply with the demands of the contractor may result in even larger public sector costs as a result of litigation, delay, or project implosion. Unlike the pre-contract phase, the government may not rely upon competition in order to secure a more favorable set of outcomes from the consortium. The government is contractually locked into negotiating public service provision with a monopoly power. In the case of the Jerusalem Light Rail, the Mayor of Jerusalem suggested in 2008 that the light rail project be suspended on account of its excessive costs, construction impacts, and delays. However, the mayor was unable to reverse the course of the project as the city was contractually tied to the consortium charged with completing construction and commencing operation (Dwarka, 2012).

Stage VII: Implementation

An infrastructure concept enters the implementation stage once it is formally approved, the project achieves financial closure, and construction begins. The insertion of private actors into the financing of a major infrastructure project does not guarantee a smooth implementation process. In the case of the Jerusalem Light Rail project, the construction of the project was significantly delayed as a result of ongoing disputes between the government and the private sector consortium (Dwarka, 2012). The project delays further exacerbated the impact of construction on the city's residents and local businesses.

Contracts do not guarantee that the contracting team will remain stable during the length of the contract. As occurred with both the Hudson Bergen Light Rail and the Jerusalem Light Rail, the composition of teams is subject to change as companies are bought and sold, merged and acquired, or liquidated. Privately financed infrastructure projects also suffer from inefficiencies that manifest in time delays and cost-overruns as occurred with the Jerusalem Light Rail. As Ng and Loosemore (2007, p. 66) note, 'Too often, risks are underestimated and allocated to parties without the knowledge, resources and capabilities to manage them effectively. The result is increased costs, project delays and services which fail to deliver value-for-money to the community'.

Whereas the early stages of the infrastructure development process are shrouded in secrecy, the infrastructure alliance is unable to hide these types of injuries. Project opponents might form an anti-growth coalition and conduct their own set of impact analyses, charging that the project is costly or damaging and therefore must be stopped, delayed, or re-analyzed (Dyble, 2007). However, the mobilization of the anti-growth coalition often emerges too late in the infrastructure development process. By the time project opponents have formalized a grounded critique of the project's feasibility, construction of the project is already underway. The public at large and non-governmental associations will usually not be able to cancel a project. However, as occurred with the Jerusalem Light Rail, opposition groups may influence a project's construction process and alter the approach to future extensions.

In accordance with Graham and Marvin's (2001) splintering urbanism concept, the insertion of privately financed infrastructure may undermine a city's provision of universal service by providing fragmented or even competing services. A study of light rail outcomes conducted by a British parliament committee, for example, noted that the newly built light rail systems in the UK were competing rather than connecting with deregulated bus systems (House of Commons Committee of Public Accounts, 2005).

On the other hand, the privatization of infrastructure finance is subject to change. As noted at the beginning of this chapter, the government often decides to buy out the private sector and assume public control over the project's financing. In the case of LRT systems, governments may also decide to change their approach to the planning of new extensions based upon lessons learned from prior segments. In this regard, the infrastructure development process becomes iterative and introduces an unexpected rationality. While the choices of investment and technology may be originally clouded by narrow interests and analytical distortions, the failure of projects to meet their objectives indeed does compel changes in the planning process and approaches to designing a project's financial architecture. For example, the second phase of the Manchester LRT system required the private sector to significantly finance capital costs and assume all of the downside revenue risk. The third phase of the Manchester LRT, however, involves no private capital and the public sector will assume responsibility for the revenue risk (Mandri-Perrott, 2010). The election of this approach followed evolving awareness in the UK that the DBOFM model can increase costs as a result of the private sector adding a premium to offset the risks it assumes (Knowles, 2007). Similarly, in Israel, planners in Haifa observed the risks of building a privately financed light rail system in Jerusalem and so instead opted for a publicly financed bus rapid transit line as the first step to upgrading their city's transit network (Dwarka, 2012).

8.5 CONCLUSIONS

The infrastructure development process comprises seven stages. The actors and power relations between them vary from stage to stage. In the early stages, local knowledge and entrepreneurship are central. Hence, elected officials and agency heads with professional expertise are major power brokers in these stages. Once the project has been developed and moves to the approval and contracting stages the planners and agency heads may take a back seat to local or national-level politicians (depending on the scope of the project). In private–public partnership projects (many of which are in the neoliberal era), the power gradually shifts toward the private interests, including contractors and banks, as government is increasingly constrained by the post-contractual lock-in (Lonsdale, 2005).

Overall, the preceding framework suggests that the locus of power in the infrastructure development process still resides with local and/or national government despite the globalization and marketization of infrastructure. The inclusion of global agents in the infrastructure development process, the entrance of infrastructure developers into foreign markets, and the rising use of global finance has only a limited impact on a country's or city's adoption of a particular infrastructure project. Locals initiate projects, set local agendas, shepherd projects through project authorization, and decide upon a project's financial architecture.

A different scenario may play out in less developed countries, where multinational companies and lending authorities may exert greater control over the infrastructure decision-making process. But in the case of countries with established systems of governance and law, multinational engineering companies and global financial institutions only become influential during the procurement, financing, and implementation phases of an infrastructure project. Though these stages of the process are significant sites of local and global negotiation, the production of infrastructure development remains tethered to local laws, regulations, and policy frameworks. While privately financed projects may indeed result in a splintering of urban space, it may be that local real estate interest in tandem with pro-growth elected officials and agency heads continue to define the local infrastructure program. And in the case of planning failure, where the promise of private finance proves unworkable, governments have demonstrated a willingness to revert back to public finance not simply as a means of bailing out a beleaguered project but also for redefining the project delivery approach for future extensions.

LITERATURE

Abdul-Aziz, A.R. (2006), 'Privatization of fixed-rail transit systems: a case study of Malaysia's STAR and Putra', *Canadian Journal of Civil Engineering*, **33**(7), 846–53.

Altshuler, A. and D. Luberoff (2003), *Mega-projects: The Changing Politics of Urban Public Investments*, Washington, DC: Brookings Institution.

Aquino, N. (2000), 'Senate body cites alleged meddling in LRT-II auction', *Business World*, 6 July.

Banfield, E. (1955), 'Note on a conceptual scheme', in *Politics, Planning, and the Public Interest: The Case of Public Housing in Chicago*, Glencoe, IL: Free Press.

Banfield, E. (1959), 'Ends and means in planning', *International Science Journal*, **11**(3), 361–8.

BART (2008), 'Public–private partnerships', presented at the California Public & Community Transportation Conference, Monterey, 7 December.

Bernier, L. (2007), 'The changing nature of public entrepreneurship', *Public Administration Review*, **67**(3), 488–503.

Caro, R. (1974), *The Power Broker: Robert Moses and the Fall of New York*, 1st edition, New York: Knopf.

CBC News (2012), 'Confederation Line LRT project approved by council', accessed 30 December 2012, at http://www.cbc.ca/news/canada/ottawa/story/2012/12/19/ottawa-lrt-approved-confederation-line-light-rail-council.html.

Chowdhury, F. (2006), *Corrupt Bureaucracy and Privatization of Tax Enforcement in Bangladesh*, Dhaka: Pathak Shamabesh.

Cohen-Blankshtain, G. and E. Feitelson (2011), 'Light rail routing: do goals matter', *Transportation*, **38**(2), 343–61.

Dal Bo, E. (2006), 'Regulatory capture: a review', *Oxford Review of Economic Policy*, **22**(2), 203–25.

Dwarka, K.R. (2012), 'The political economy of infrastructure: the case of urban light rail' (unpublished doctoral dissertation).

Dyble, L. (2007), 'Revolt against sprawl', *Journal of Urban History*, **34**(1), 38–66.

Engel, E., R. Fischer and A. Galetovic (2009), 'Soft budgets and renegotiations in public–private partnerships', Working Paper No. 15300, Cambridge, MA: National Bureau of Economic Research.

Feitelson, E. (2011), 'Issue generating assessment: bridging the gap between evaluation theory and practice', *Planning Theory and Practice*, **12**(1), 549–68.

Finger, M. and R.W. Künneke (2011), *International Handbook of Network Industries: The Liberalization of Infrastructure*, Cheltenham, UK and Northampton, MA, USA: Edward Elgar Publishing.

Flyvbjerg, B. (2007), 'Cost overruns and demand shortfalls in urban rail and other infrastructure', *Transportation Planning and Technology*, **30**(1), 9–30.

Flyvbjerg, B., N. Bruzelius and W. Rothengatter (2003), *Megaprojects and Risk: An Anatomy of Ambition*, Cambridge, UK and New York: Cambridge University Press.

Gannon, M. and N. Smith (2009), 'The rise and fall of public–private-partnerships: how should LRT/Metro transport infrastructure be funded in the United Kingdom?', paper presented at the European Transport Conference 2009, Association for European Transport.

Garb, Y. (2004), 'Constructing the Trans-Israel Highway's inevitability', *Israel Studies*, **9**(2), 180–217.

Global Industry Analytics (2010), *Light Rail: A Global Strategic Business Report*, San José, CA: Global Industry Analytics (self-published).

GoldLinQ (2011), 'Financial close achieved for Gold Coast rapid transit project', Press Release, 29 October, accessed 14 June 2013 at http://www.plenarygroup.com/news-and-media/news-articles-and-press-releases/2011/financial-close-achieved-for-gold-coast-rapid-transit-project.html.

Gómez-Ibáñez, J. (2003), *Regulating Infrastructure: Monopoly, Contracts, and Discretion*, Cambridge, MA: Harvard University Press.

Graham, S. and S. Marvin (2001), *Splintering Urbanism: Networked Infrastructures, Technological Mobilities and the Urban Condition*, London: Routledge.

Grant, K. (2012), 'TTC to operate new LRTs in deal struck with Metrolinx', *The Globe and Mail*, 3 October accessed 30 December 2012, at http://www.theglobeandmail.com/news/toronto/ttc-to-operate-new-lrts-in-deal-struck-with-metrolinx/article4585560/.

Grigg, N.S. (2010), *Infrastructure Finance: The Business of Infrastructure for a Sustainable Future*, Hoboken, NJ: John Wiley & Sons.

Grimsey, D. and M. Lewis (2004), *Public–Private Partnerships: The Worldwide Revolution in Infrastructure Provision and Project Finance*, Cheltenham, UK and Northampton, MA, USA: Edward Elgar.

Gunderson, G. (1989), 'Privatization and the 19th-century turnpike', *Cato Journal*, **9**(1), 191–200, accessed 14 June 2013 at http://www.cato.org/sites/cato.org/files/serials/files/cato-journal/1989/5/cj9n1-9.pdf.

Hall, P. (1982), *Great Planning Disasters*, Berkeley, CA: University of California Press.

Heims, M. (2012), 'Woodward light rail line group says it will pay for first 10 years of operations', Detroit Free Press, accessed 30 December 2012 at http://www.freep.com/article/20120423/NEWS01/120423048.

House of Commons Committee of Public Accounts (2005), 'Improving public transport in England through light rail', Eleventh Report of Session 2004–05, accessed 13 June 2013 at http://www.publications.parliament.uk/pa/cm200405/cmselect/cmpubacc/440/440.pdf.

Innes, J.E. and D.E. Booher (2010), *Planning With Complexity: An Introduction to Collaborative Rationality for Public Policy*, Abingdon, Oxon/New York: Routledge.

Kain, J. (1990), 'Deception in Dallas: strategic misrepresentation in rail transit promotion and evaluation', *Journal of the American Planning Association*, **56**(2), 184–96.
Kent, G. (2012), 'Council approves P3 funding plan for southeast LRT line', *Edmonton Journal*, 18 October, accessed 14 June 2013 at http://www2.canada.com/edmontonjournal/news/story.html?id=d17f8a82-fd73-4b6d-a18f-73db6f5dbb11.
Kingdon, J. (2011), *Agendas, Alternatives, and Public Policies*, 1st edition, Boston: Little Brown and Co.
Kirkpatrick, L.O. and M. Smith (2011), 'The infrastructural limits to growth: rethinking the urban growth machine in times of fiscal crisis', *International Journal of Urban and Regional Research*, **35**(3), 477–503.
Knowles, R.D. (2007), 'What future for light rail in the UK after Ten Year Transport Plan targets are scrapped?', *Transport Policy*, **14**(1), 81–93.
Larson, J. (2001), *Internal Improvement: National Public Works and the Promise of Popular Government in the Early United States*, Chapel Hill, NC and London: University of North Carolina Press.
Llanto, G.M. (2007), 'Dealing with contingent liabilities: the Philippines', in *Fiscal Policy and Management in East Asia*, Vol. 16, Chicago: University of Chicago Press.
Logan, J.R. and H.L. Molotch (2007), *Urban Fortune*, Berkeley and Los Angeles, CA: University of California Press.
London Docklands Development Corporation (1997), *Starting from Scratch: The Development of Transport in London Docklands*, accessed 14 June 2013 at http://www.lddc-history.org.uk/transport/tranmon2.html.
Lonsdale, C. (2005), 'Post-contractual lock-in and the UK private finance initiative (PFI): the cases of national savings and investments and the Lord Chancellor's Department', *Public Administration*, **83**(1), 67–88.
Mandri-Perrott, C. (2010), *Private Sector Participation in Light Rail–Light Metro Transit Initiatives*, Washington, DC: World Bank.
Marowitz, R. (2012), 'SNC-Lavalin Wins Ottawa Light Rail Project Despite Scandals, Arrests', 12 May, accessed 25 June 2013, at http://www.huffingtonpost.ca/2012/12/05/snc-lavalin-ottawa-light-rail_n_2245964.html.
McGuirk, P. (2000), 'Power and policy networks in urban governance: local government and property-led regeneration in Dublin', *Urban Studies*, **37**(4), 651–72.
Mohammadi, K. (2001), 'Michael Heseltine interview, Canary 2001', accessed 14 June 2013 at http://www.kamin.co.uk/Hesel.html.
Ng, A. and M. Loosemore (2007), 'Risk allocation in the private provision of public infrastructure', *International Journal of Project Management*, **25**(1), 66–76.
Nichols, C. (2011), 'PPP profiles: EagleP3, a section of Denver's comprehensive transit expansion, FasTracks', Metropolitan Planning Council, accessed 30 December 2012 at http://www.metroplanning.org/news-events/article/6139.
Phang, S. (2007), 'Urban rail transit PPPs: survey and risk assessment of recent strategies', *Transport Policy*, **14**(3), 214–31.
Polsby, N. (1984), 'Political innovation in America: the politics of policy initiation', New Haven, CT: Yale University Press.
Prasad, M. (2006), *The Politics of Free Markets: The Rise of Neoliberal Economic Policies in Britain, France, Germany, and the United States*, Chicago: University of Chicago Press.
Richmond, J. (2005), *Transport of Delight – The Mythical Conception of Rail Transit in Los Angeles*, Akron, OH: University of Akron Press.
Roland, G. (2008), *Privatization : Successes and Failures*, New York: Columbia University Press.
Roth, G. (2006), *Street Smart : Competition, Entrepreneurship, and the Future of Roads*, New Brunswick, NJ: Transaction.
RTD (n.d.), 'RTD breaks ground on Third Eagle Project Rail Line', RTD website, accessed 13 June 2013 at http://www.rtd-fastracks.com/ep3_2.
Schmitz, J. (2012), 'Oakland transit line explored', *Pittsburgh Post Gazette*, 28 March, accessed

30 December 2012 at http://www.post-gazette.com/stories/local/neighborhoods-city/oakland-transit-line-explored-234904/.
Siemiatycki, M. (2005), 'The making of a mega project in the neoliberal city', *City*, **9**(1), 67–83.
Siemiatycki, M. (2006), 'Implications of private–public partnerships on the development of urban public transit infrastructure', *Journal of Planning Education and Research*, **26**(2), 137–51.
Siemiatycki, M. (2009), 'Delivering transportation infrastructure through public–private partnerships: planning concerns', *Journal of the American Planning Association*, **76**(1), 43–58.
Siemiatycki, M. (2011a), 'Public–private partnership networks: exploring business–government relationships in United Kingdom transportation projects', *Economic Geography*, **87**(3), 309–34.
Siemiatycki, M. (2011b), 'Urban transportation public–private partnerships: drivers of uneven development?', *Environment and Planning A*, **43**(7), 1707–22.
Smith, K. (2012), 'Canada's light rail renaissance', *International Railway Journal*, 29 October, accessed 14 June 2013 at http://www.railjournal.com/index.php/light-rail/canadas-light-rail-renaissance.html.
Strandberg, D. (2012), 'SNC-Lavalin on track to build Evergreen', The Tri-City News, 4 October, accessed 1 January 2013 at http://www.tricitynews.com/news/172702541.html.
Tan, G. (2012), 'AIX sells metro transport stake to NSW government', 23 March, accessed 14 June 2013 at http://blogs.wsj.com/dealjournalaustralia/2012/03/23/aix-sells-metro-transport-stake-to-nsw-government/.
The Telegraph (2011), 'Reg Ward obituary', Telegraph.co.uk, 11 January, accessed 14 June 2013 at http://www.telegraph.co.uk/news/obituaries/8253519/Reg-Ward.html.
The World Bank Group (2012), Private Participation in Infrastructure Database, 'Featured rankings, 1990 to 2011' accessed 14 June 2012 at http://ppi.worldbank.org/explore/ppi_exploreRankings.aspx.
Torrance, M. (2007), 'The power of governance in financial relationships: governing tensions in exotic infrastructure territory', *Growth and Change*, **38**(4), 671–95.
Torrance, M. (2008), 'Forging glocal governance? Urban infrastructures as networked financial products', *International Journal of Urban and Regional Research*, **32**(1), 1–21.
Torrance, M. (2009a), 'The rise of a global infrastructure market through relational investing', *Economic Geography*, **85**(1), 75–97.
Torrance, M. (2009b), 'Reconceptualizing urban governance through a new paradigm for urban infrastructure networks', *Journal of Economic Geography*, **9**(6), 805–22.
Transport for London, Rail and Underground Panel (2011), 'Rail and Underground Panel meeting paper: Tramlink operations', Agenda Item 6. Transport for London, accessed 14 June 2013 at http://www.tfl.gov.uk/assets/downloads/Item06-RUP-12-July-2011-Tramlink_Operations-v2SC.pdf.
United States Bankruptcy Court (2011), *In re Las Vegas Monorail Co.* (462 BR 795 – Bankr. Court, D. Nevada, 2011), No.462 B.R. 795 (United States Bankruptcy Court, D. Nevada Nov. 18, 2011), accessed 14 June 2013 at http://chapter11cases.com/in-re-las-vegas-monorail-co-462-br-795-bankr-court-d-nevada-2011/.
Wachs, M. (1988), *When Planners Lie with Numbers: An Exploration of Data, Analysis, and Planning Ethics*, Los Angeles, CA: School of Architecture and Urban Planning University of California Los Angeles.
Warner, S. (1978), *Streetcar Suburbs*, 2nd edition, Cambridge, MA and London: Harvard University Press.
Weber, B. and H.W. Alfen (2010), *Infrastructure as an Asset Class: Investment Strategies, Project Finance and PPP*, Chichester: John Wiley & Sons.
Winston, C. (2010), *Last Exit: Privatization and Deregulation of the U.S. Transportation System*, Washington, DC: Brookings Institution Press.

9. Public–private partnership in developing and governing mega-projects

Graeme Hodge and Carsten Greve

9.1 INTRODUCTION

Public–private partnership somehow captures the imagination, and for political leaders, is capable of delivering high-profile infrastructure projects that demonstrate political leadership. But despite the popularity of the concept, the arena is still highly contested and much of the literature is filled with either ideological advocacy or criticism. There is little doubt that the PPP experiment has been filled with well-rehearsed arguments over public versus private sector efficiency and it has been a strong policy preference for governments such as the United Kingdom, Australia and Canada. There is equally, though, a need now to think more carefully about the PPP phenomenon and to bring this concept to our present discussion on mega-projects. This chapter aims to do just that.

So, what defines a mega-project? Priemus et al. (2008, p. 2) described mega-projects in terms of project characteristics: colossal in size; captivating and aesthetic; costly; controversial; complex; and with control issues. Mega-projects were to them often a 'tour de force', with an innovative character and at the cutting edge of technological complexity along with significant social complexity. But above all, mega-projects seem to capture the Zeitgeist, fill us with a sense of awe and wonder (Nye, 1994; Frick, 2008) and enrol everyone in an exciting possible future. The parallel question here is what defines a PPP? Several years ago we commented that scholars were divided in their answers to this issue: some viewed PPPs as a tool of governance while others saw it as a 'language game' (Teisman and Klijn, 2002; Hodge and Greve, 2007). We now know that PPP is both; it is public policy rhetoric, as well as a long-term infrastructure contract (LTIC) arrangement.

PPP is in reality a broad phenomenon, and has much in common with the concept of mega-projects. Perhaps mega-projects are 'PPP in action' at one level or another. There is much written on the important technical aspects of delivering PPPs and mega-projects including legal, engineering, management and financial matters. This chapter instead emphasizes non-technical matters that in reality are also crucial to developing both

PPPs and mega-projects (Flyvbjerg et al., 2003). It cautions that whilst infrastructure delivery methods such as private finance initiative (PFI) type partnerships have been popular for infrastructure, they have also remained inherently risky as well as controversial, with judgements as to performance highly contested. Today's post-global-financial-crisis turbulence is only likely to magnify these characteristics.

By way of structure, this chapter seeks first to articulate the notion of PPP more formally (Section 9.2). We outline the PPP pedigree, and present a conceptual framework for understanding PPPs as LTIC arrangements for delivering infrastructure. Section 9.3 weighs into the continuing debate around the performance of PPP including its goals and its relative performance against these. Section 9.4 then proposes some meta-lessons gained from experience to date and examines the implications of this knowledge for developing and managing mega-projects. Conclusions are offered in Section 9.5. The chapter therefore provides a 'reality check' on what we now know about infrastructure PPP amidst contested policy positions and interests, and brings this knowledge to discussions on mega-projects.

9.2 UNDERSTANDING THE PPP NOTION

Understanding the PPP Notion: Across Time

The idea of getting the best from both the public and private sectors has a long, but insufficiently acknowledged, pedigree. Relegating history to a few opening paragraphs before describing more exciting 'new' applications denies both history as well as the possibility to learn from it (Wettenhall, 2010, p. 23). With PPP playing a hugely important symbolic role in modern governance thinking, we need to achieve a balanced appreciation of the PPP phenomenon as well as discerning just what is new and what is not.

Many authors have written on the rich past of marrying public and private endeavours, and we will draw on the work of only a few. The overarching thrust of authors such as Wettenhall (2005, 2010) and Bovaird (2004, 2010) is fourfold:

1. The time lineage of the public–private movement is long.
2. The scope of alternative structural and institutional arrangements has been huge.
3. The disciplinary contributions and intellectual provenance is varied.
4. This rich PPP history matters, because it has real implications for today.

Indeed, Wettenhall (ibid.) and Bovaird (ibid.) between them draw on the work of over 300 authors and well illustrate the many cultural threads, the non-linearity of ideas and the various parallel paths followed through time as we have sought the ideal of marrying the public and private sectors. Wettenhall (2005, p. 22), for example, reminds today's PPP commentators that 'whatever the new enthusiasts may think, there is nothing new about the mixing of public–private endeavours'. He identifies several separate theatres of economic and social activity in which such public–private 'mixing'[1] could be observed over two millennia:

- privateer shipping;
- mercenary armies;
- trade, commerce and colonial expansion;
- treasury and public finance;
- collaboration in agriculture, health and education;
- infrastructure provision;
- organizing hallmark events; and
- public and mixed enterprises.

Cases such as privateer shipping and the early government treasury function are colourful and illustrate lessons from experience. They deserve careful reflection.

Bovaird (2004, p. 223) notes that the use of the phrase 'PPP' dates back to the 1940s and was popularized through the US urban regeneration experience of the 1960s and 1970s. To this we could add the clear current post-modern attraction of the PPP semantic and the way in which the PPP language game fits the modern public sector like a glove. Tony Blair's re-branding of the UK's PFI scheme as a public–private partnership policy was indeed a masterful political move, and guaranteed a high political legitimacy for PPP. In countries that have since copy-catted the UK's PPP policy platform, PPP today symbolizes positive business relationships, a new way of governing, sophistication, innovation and performance. Yet PPP has also remained 'deliciously ambiguous' (Hodge, 2009).

The point here is that there is a rich history of public–private mixing across multiple lineages. It did not begin with the PFI policy in the UK! Today, clear distinctions between the public and private realms are blurred, and the state must work with markets, with market actors and with a variety of non-state parties amidst an intricate network of connections and a variety of interests (Wettenhall, 2010, p. 20). The old 'public versus private' assumption has been replaced by a 'public + private' reality as Salamon (2002, p. 14) put it. And PPP continues to exhibit multiple grammars (Linder, 1999). A richer discourse is needed if we are to understand the phenomenon and its application to mega-projects.

Understanding the PPP Notion: Today

Given the breadth of differing ideas, positions and interests in mixing public and private activities, it is perhaps little surprise that notions of PPP remain heavily contested. For example, whilst all Australian state governments advertise PPP mainly in terms of their current private finance infrastructure policy platforms, Hodge and Greve (2007) argued half a decade ago that the PPP semantic is used across at least five different families:

1. Institutional cooperation for joint production and risk sharing (such as the Netherlands Port Authority).
2. Long-term infrastructure contracts (LTICs), which emphasize tight specification of outputs in long-term legal contracts (as exemplified in UK private finance initiative projects).
3. Public policy networks (in which loose stakeholder relationships are emphasized).
4. Civil society and community development.
5. Urban renewal and downtown economic development (and where, in the USA, a portfolio of local economic development and urban re-growth measures are pursued).

These five PPP families[2] cover a wide array of governance types.[3] The UK's National Audit Office (2009, p. 6) likewise noted that the narrow view of PPP as a specific type of long-term infrastructure contract was not accurate. It stated that whilst its review had concentrated mainly 'on the widely used PPP model called the Private Finance Initiative (PFI) . . . there are also hundreds of other types of PPPs, ranging from small joint ventures to the London Underground PPPs which have a capital value of £18 billion'.

Concentrating on LTIC-type PPPs as one of the above-mentioned families, we should also recognize that the single family of LTIC-type PPPs is itself a large group. De Bettignies and Ross (2010), for instance, suggest that an LTIC-type PPP project generally involves planning, designing, financing, building, maintaining, operating and paying for a facility, and there is clearly a wide range of possible combinations as to how the two sectors can work together.[4] Traditionally, we view LTICs covering a continuum of possibilities[5] ranging from a public emphasis at one extreme to a private emphasis at the other.[6] These arrangements include, for example, the O&M (operations and maintenance) contract, BOOT

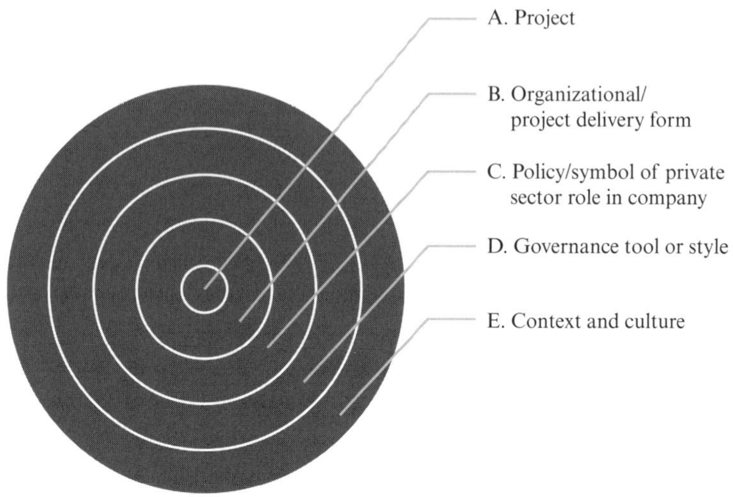

Source: Adapted from Hodge and Greve (2013).

Figure 9.1 Dimensions to the public–private partnership phenomenon

(build-own-operate-transfer), BTO (build-transfer-operate), WAA (wrap-around addition), and DBFO (design-build-finance-operate), along with a host of other acronyms.

So, how then, might we marry together in a conceptual model the various meanings inherent in the single LTIC family of PPP in order to contribute to PPP and mega-project debates around the globe? Our view of PPP is as a broad phenomenon at five levels (Hodge and Greve, 2013), as shown in Figure 9.1. The phrase PPP may exist in five ways:

A A specific infrastructure project or activity.
B An organizational form, project delivery form or a management tool.
C A policy, statement or symbol as to the role of the private sector in a mixed economy.
D A tool in the modern governance task.
E A phenomenon within the context of a broader national history and set of cultural assumptions.

At the narrowest level (A), therefore, PPP is viewed as a single project. At level B, PPP is viewed as a specific type of infrastructure project delivery mechanism involving the use of contracted private finance to initially fund all works. The rationale is that private financing incentives encourage excellent project performance and early delivery. This view is typical of the engineering and project finance disciplines, and emphasizes the preference for private finance, the bundling of contracts through a consortium and new governance and accountability assumptions. The next conceptual level (C) takes this project tool one step further and sets the private finance delivery of PPP infrastructure as a policy preference for a jurisdiction. It may also operate at a wider policy level not as one single PPP type, but acknowledging a wide variety of alternative project delivery options available to governments such as the OECD's list of acronyms. It is therefore essentially a policy statement that the private sector has a crucial role to play in today's mixed economy, whatever technical delivery option is chosen. Broadening out again, level D represents the degree to which PPP is a regulatory tool integral to governing. Large economic incentives can be employed to ensure that the promise of the early delivery of government objectives is met – even for complex projects and in controversial circumstances. PPP at this level also marks a particular style of governance. The Labour government of the UK throughout the 1990s, for instance, struggled to develop its relationship with the City of London. But as Hellowell (2010, p. 310) points out, PPP provided the incoming Tony Blair and his 'New Labour' government with advantages. It not only had the crucial political advantage that new private finance borrowing did not score against the main calculations of national debt but also assisted UK New Labour in establishing and cementing a stronger relationship with the City of London (Hellowell, 2010). PPP thus continues to have an inherently political, and thus governance, context as well as any functional engineering or economic meaning. In our conceptual model, each of these four levels of PPP meaning are bound together, and they also exist within a broader historical and cultural context (E).

An alternative and complementary meta-view to understand PPP is the provocative suggestion of Klijn (2010): PPP is simply a brand. He argues that PPP evades the clear definition, symmetrical conceptual constructions and accurate analytics sought by those assuming PPP to be a science. It is a 'hybrid idea' that by definition is ambiguous and aims to evoke images and emotions rather than precision. This brand has power, too, because it enables governments to adopt partnership and PPP in different ways for different purposes, all imbued with the suggestion of doing things differently and tackling problems together. It promises political success by symbolizing innovation and forward thinking from both sectors. And from observation, it is also a brand in which there has been much political capital invested around the globe.

Understanding Today's LTIC PPPs

Using the narrow lens of level B from our conceptual model, we may now view PPP as a project delivery mechanism for LTICs. Many options are possible, however. On this score, Duffield (2010) neatly defines the major roles of both the public and private actors participating in an LTIC PPP. Also, he articulates some eight additional (counterfactual) project delivery options (including 'in house') delivery. These provide a set of counterfactuals against which a comparison can be made for assessment of PPP efficacy. The private finance initiative-based conception of PPP provides the largest scope of work transferred to the private parties, and in terms of a decreasing works scope, these alternative options include:

- public–private partnership (PPP)/private finance initiative (PFI);
- relationship contracting; alliances are currently popular and are a specific form of relationship contract;
- managing contractor;
- project management;
- design and construct (also termed engineer, procure, construct or design-build);
- document and construct;
- construction management;
- construct only (traditional);
- in house by government (public works).

He also describes what each sector's role is for each alternative throughout the project lifecycle: from the project inception, project definition and concept development, through to the phases of construction, commissioning and operation. His summary is included in Figure 9.2.

What is key here is that PFI type infrastructure is seen as one of nine possible methods of delivering infrastructure, two of which are seen as 'traditional'.

One of the key arguments for PPP has always been the issue of best managing risks. Duffield's work is again useful in that he summarizes for us both who bears which cost risks (i.e., either the private or public party) as well as who makes the main decisions at different points during project delivery. This is summarized in Figure 9.3.

Of course the reality of who bears which risks with mega-projects is always more complex than this figure shows, and is an empirical question.[7] This work demonstrates not only the complexity of possible LTIC options involving both sectors as well as Australia's PPP arrangement, but the

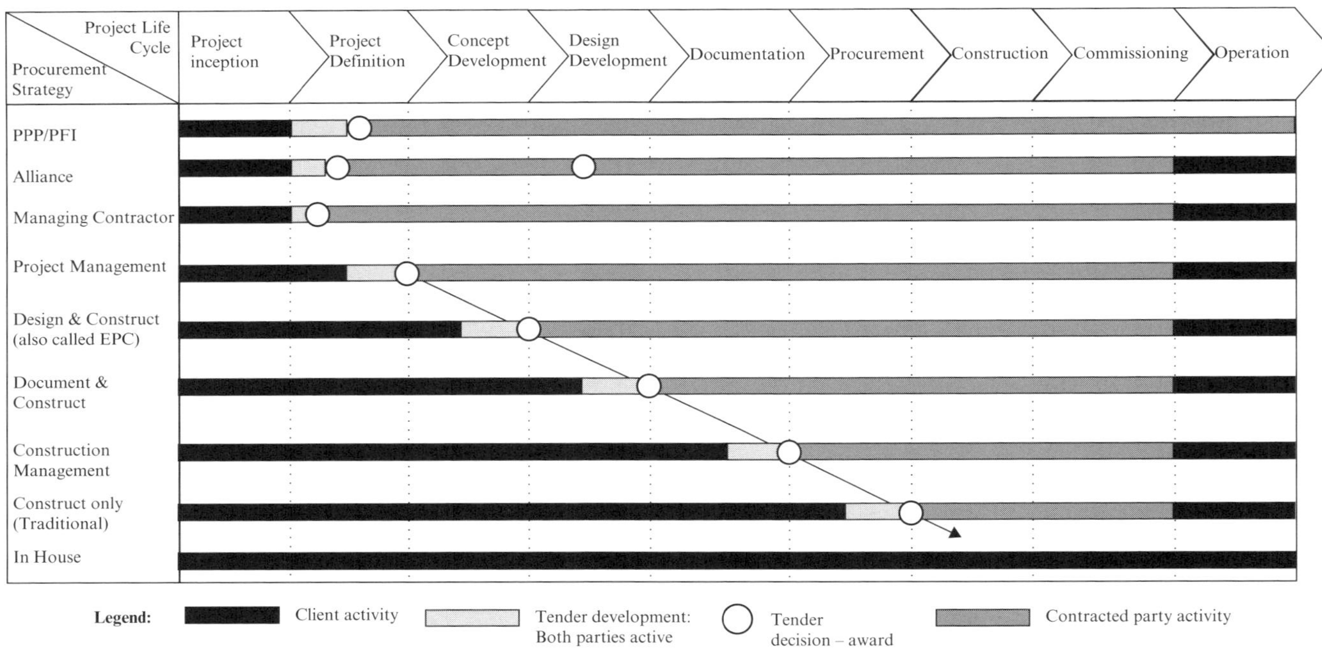

Source: Duffield (2010, p. 193).

Figure 9.2 Procurement strategy versus project lifecycle

High Private sector risk

	Predominant Payment Method				Main Decision Maker			
Procurement strategy	Concept	Design	Construct	Maintain & Operate	Concept	Design	Construct	Maintain & Operate
PPP	Fixed	Fixed	Fixed	Fixed	SPV	SPV-Contractor	SPV-Contractor	SPV-Operator
Design & construct	Actual	Fixed	Fixed	Actual	Owner	Contractor	Contractor	Owner
Early Contractor Involvement	Actual	Fixed	Fixed	Actual	Shared	Contractor	Contractor	Owner
Managing Contractor	Actual	Fixed	Actual	Actual	Shared	Contractor	Contractor	Owner
Project Management	Actual	Fixed	Fixed	Actual	Owner	Owner	Contractor	Owner
Construct only	Actual	Actual	Fixed	Actual	Owner	Owner	Contractor	Owner
Construction Management	Actual	Actual	Actual	Actual	Owner	Contractor	Contractor	Owner
Relationship contract – alliance	Actual	Actual	Actual	Actual	Owner	Shared	Shared	Owner
Public Works	Actual	Actual	Actual	Actual	Owner	Owner	Owner	Owner

Risk continuum

High Owner Risk

Notes:
Fixed – Cost risk with Contractor
Actual – Cost risk with Owner
SPV– Special Purpose Vehicle management
SPV: Contractor – SPV generally sub-contracts this work as Design and Construct
SPV: Operator – SPV generally sub-contracts this work to an Operator or Facilities Management firm

Source: Duffield (2010, p. 196).

Figure 9.3 Risk transfer continuum

complexity of the various alternatives (including traditional practices) as well. In this environment, we begin to appreciate the difficulty of making generalized conclusions about the efficacy or otherwise of different infrastructure delivery methods.

9.3 ASSESSING PPP PERFORMANCE

Our deep interest in PPP today is matched by the equally strong interest in assessing their worth, importance and value. In other words: in evaluating PPP. In this section, we address the continuing debate around the performance of PPP, and argue that since they are as political a phenomenon as they are technical, many lenses may be relevant in an assessment.

PPP Goals and Performance Dimensions

In concept, partnership performance could be judged at each of the five levels indicated in Figure 9.1. So, what do we mean by partnership success from the narrowest of these perspectives (at the project level), to a broader organizational level; and through to the perspective of government, and the widest levels of societal change and benefit?

At the narrowest level, the literature is full of claims of project success. We certainly all enjoy brand new infrastructure, and when it is delivered to expected standards, this is itself a measure of success. It is certain, visible and has common-sense appeal. But the reasons for governments adopting PPP ideas have been more sophisticated than simply delivering a project. Historically, the reasons for adoption have been manifold:[8]

1. John Major's initial rationale was to get around the UK's restrictions on formal public-sector debt levels. Private financing promised infrastructure without increasing the public-sector borrowing requirement.
2. This was followed by the promise that PPPs would 'reduce pressure on public-sector budgets'.[9]
3. The third promise of PPPs was that this delivery mechanism provides better value-for-money for taxpayers – a policy promise most worthy of examination.
4. Added to these three initial promises have been ten more – some explicit such as: reduced risk to government from projects, better accountability, better on-time and on-budget delivery, and greater innovation; and some implicit such as encouraging a more innovative public sector, improved business confidence, improved palatability for user funding for infrastructure, provision for long-term infrastructure lifecycle costs, and boosted sales of professional PPP services abroad. To these 13 PPP objectives, we might nowadays also add two more objectives following the recent credit market failures and stock market downturns. It may well be that two new implicit objectives for PPPs will be the desire for governments to broadly support businesses and preferentially adopt the PPP mechanism in difficult market circumstances (the objective of business assistance) or the broader societal objective of economic development.

Whilst additional objectives are also possible, the point here is clear. Many separate objectives have been set for PPPs, and these objectives have also altered over time. Together, they also form a series of promises at the level of project delivery mechanism (or organizational form); at the policy level and at the level of governance. Whilst there is no neat one to one correspondence and categories overlap, governments clearly expect PPP to deliver benefits across a far wider base than often discussed. So, returning to our thoughts about assessing PPP performance, how might we determine if PPP has been successful? And what dimensions might be crucial in such an evaluation framework?

Jeffares et al. (2013) build on the work of Skelcher and Sullivan (2008) and focus on measuring the performance of partnership through a theory-based evaluation. Jeffares et al. (2013) articulate six 'performance domains' linked explicitly to acknowledged bodies of theory: democracy (democratic theory); policy goal achievement (network theory); transformation to produce new public sector behaviours (institutional theory); connectivity to stimulate innovation (innovation theory, network theory); coordination to achieve synergies (resource dependency); and coalition/sustainability to achieve sustainable partnerships (discourse theory). Each is valuable and brings different PPP values into the spotlight.

Crucially, Jeffares et al. (2013) are clear about the 'politically loaded' nature of PPPs as public policy instruments. As they rightly state, 'PPPs are as much political as they are managerial entities' (p. 171). Importantly too, Jeffares et al. (2013) see both a 'narrow' and a 'broad' definition of partnership performance, which neatly confirms our thoughts thus far. In the narrow definition, 'partnership performance is narrowly conceived as concerned with the achievement of particular service or outcome targets as set out in the partnership agreement' (p. 170) and assessed in relation to factors such as the operational cost. An assessment under a wider definition, however, would contemplate the degree to which 'partnership performance may be more broadly conceived and include consideration of the longer term relationship that might exist beyond the delivery of a particular project or programme, the wider benefits to particular individuals or partner organisations or indeed to citizens and service users' (ibid.).

Huxman and Hubbert (2009) likewise see high performance in terms of multiple dimensions: (1) achieving outcomes, (2) getting the process to work, (3) reaching emergent milestones, (4) gaining recognition from others and (5) acknowledging personal pride in championing a partnership. Their point is that whilst the first dimension is well known and often considered to be the primary arbiter in judging success, goals such as 'getting the process to work' are also fundamental to modern governments seeking to be more networked and adaptable. Skelcher (2010) writes about PPP performance from another angle – that of governance. He defines four different types of governance: legal governance, regulatory governance, democratic governance and corporate governance. And crucially, his view is that the corporate governance aspect of PPP has been the least examined dimension of PPP. At an even broader level again, too, there are different kinds of criteria for 'performance' that are associated more with disciplinary perspectives. Economists tend to look at economic factors concerning PPP while political scientists and public policy scholars are likely to see if the political mandate is being fulfilled, and sociologists want to know the difference PPP makes at a broader societal level including being clear about who the winners were as well as the losers.

The straight technical challenge presented to the evaluator when assessing the relative success of a PPP is another alternative lens on evaluation. Hodge (2010), for example, defines six serious infrastructure PPP evaluation challenges. The challenge: of defining the evaluand (i.e., the subject which is put under scrutiny); of multiple PPP objectives; of multiple discourses and disciplines; of the evaluator's role; of evaluative rigour for an individual PPP; and of accurately summarizing multiple evaluation studies.

It is thus not at all clear what governments mean when they proclaim PPP a 'success'. As McConnell (2010) reminds us, 'success' is like talk of 'good' governance and 'better' regulation; an attractive linguistic. It is not 'all or nothing', though, and governments may achieve policy success to a degree across many fronts. McConnell's realistic view is that three dimensions are crucial. To his mind, governments do process (defining issues as problems, examining options, consulting, and so on), they do programmes (using a wide variety and combinations of policy instruments), and they do politics (engaging in activities that can influence electoral prospects, maintaining capacity to govern and steering policy direction) (McConnell, 2010, p. 54).[10] Clearly, success can reside in each of these three spheres as well as having a temporal dimension in terms of durability. These insights are central to discussions on PPP performance.

But with all these different conceptual models for PPP, wide-ranging performance dimensions and multiple criteria within each as well as the usual technical challenges inherent in evaluation exercises, there is an obvious question – is PPP evaluation tractable? Perhaps, as with any inherently political assessment the answer lies in acknowledging up front the breadth of the PPP phenomenon, and the chosen evaluand, and then providing as rigorously as possible another clue to be added to the contested terrain of PPP evaluation. In other words, the reality is that a comprehensive assessment across all five levels of the PPP phenomenon model encompassing all goals and using all identified performance dimensions would be impossible. Most real life evaluations do not for an instant contemplate such a complex task; they focus on a few performance dimensions and criteria that they personally regard as important from their own perspective.

What is also clear here is that whilst some goals of PPP are explicit, many are not. A potentially useful framework to view goal-focused

Table 9.1 Taxonomy of goals and criteria for assessing the PPP phenomenon

Formality/ Technicality	Technical	Non-technical
Explicit	Value-for-money for taxpayers On-time delivery On-budget delivery Improved accountability Enable visibility of full lifecycle costs	'Reduced pressure' on public sector budgets PPP as a friendly policy label Increased project innovation culture LTICs enable government infrastructure priorities to be agreed then delivered Visible symbolic use of market discipline and private sector capacity
Implicit	Project risks managed away from government Improve government financial credentials Strengthen economic development	PPP is a political brand differentiating government and symbolizing progress Enable 'crash through' delivery of mega-projects under private contract law Enable user pays provision for road infrastructure Business assistance in turbulent times Business and financial markets are confident and happy A more innovative public sector Help to put infrastructure funding needs/projects on public agenda Boost sales of professional services abroad Strengthened links in networked/ collaborative government Enhance electoral prospects Ease the business of governing

evaluations of PPP might therefore be that shown in Table 9.1, in which we articulate 24 goals of PPP and suggest the degree to which each is technical and explicit.

This table shows the large number of goals evident for PPPs, as well as the small number that are explicit (rather than implied), and technical (rather than non-technical). Perhaps the PPP phenomenon is an iceberg that lies mostly underwater, with its visible surface characteristics not as important as less visible weightier matters?

PPP Performance Evaluation

There is now considerable experience with the LTIC PPP family around the world, and much commentary. Performance assessments have been couched around two broad domains; questions of project performance (including matters such as value-for-money (VfM), and issues of 'on-time' or 'on-budget' delivery), and questions of governance performance (encompassing matters such as governance arrangements and accountability concerns). We shall skate over both domains:

1. The first observation to be made on the project performance domain is that substantive empirical performance measurements made to date have been limited, despite numerous professional glossy reports such as PricewaterhouseCoopers (2005), Deloitte (2006), Ernst & Young (2007) and OECD (2008). Real VfM performance of PPPs therefore remains surprisingly open from an empirical perspective.
2. There are no high-level rigorous statistical reviews summarizing multiple quantitative PPP performance results to date, although several narrative assessments have attempted to go past polarized advocacy or criticism, and covered either more general ground[11] or focused on particular PPP concerns.[12]
3. Because individual evaluation studies using primary data have not been particularly rigorous from a statistical perspective, and failed to employ control groups for example, review stories of PPP success and failure should be treated with considerable caution from a strict statistical perspective.[13]
4. The reality is that the counterfactual of 'traditional procurement' is usually both horribly vague and largely unquantified in most assessments. This has left study conclusions correspondingly unreliable.
5. It is apparent that many studies of 'cost' measurement have been business case projections rather than measurements of actual costs. Some exceptions exist, however, including multiple studies by Shaoul (2005) as well as Fitzgerald (2004), Blanc-Brude et al. (2006), Allen Consulting group (2007), and Leviakangas (2007).
6. A sixth observation is that two separate academic areas of PPP literature exist, in political science/public policy/public administration, and in economics/engineering/project finance, but few evaluation reviews cover both well. Economists have been examining PPPs carefully. Some of the most detailed work comes from Canadian economists Boardman, de Bettignies, Ross and Vining. Economic theory here contributes knowledge to what the potential costs and benefits are in infrastructure projects and focus on efficiency – will PPP projects

provide the most desired output for the least input? (de Bettignies and Ross, 2010). Some economists propose that PPPs be compared with the public sector alternative using 'social costs', that is, production costs plus transaction costs plus externalities and argue that proper cost–benefit analysis needs to be performed for PPPs. But very few independent cost–benefit analyses of PPPs exist (Boardman and Vining, 2010). Other economic analyses of PPPs include Yescombe (2007) and Delmon (2011).

7. The seventh point concerns the VfM results themselves. As Hodge and Greve (2009) showed, a large group of evaluations over the past decade support high PPP performance compared to traditional infrastructure delivery. Mainly through the calculus of risk transfers, lower cost estimates (of up to 20 per cent) are reported compared to traditional procurement. These have been bolstered by reports that PPPs were delivered on time more often (76 per cent compared to 30 per cent for traditional projects) and on budget (78 per cent compared to 27 per cent for traditional arrangements) (Mott MacDonald, 2002 and National Audit Office, 2003). An equal-sized group of studies, though, opposed this conclusion, and did not support a judgement of PPP superiority. Serious concerns from this opposing group included excessive returns to investors (Vecchi et al., 2010), a VfM appraisal methodology biased in favour of policy expansion, and pitiful availability of information needed for project evaluation and scrutiny (Shaoul, 2005). Even the UK Public Accounts Committee of Parliament labelled the PSC (Public Sector Comparator) process as clearly 'manipulation' (Corner, 2005, p. 50). Ball et al. (2007) noted 'almost entirely subjective' risk analyses, and the UK Audit Commission (2003, p. 21) 'found no evidence that PFI projects delivered schools more quickly than projects funded in more conventional ways'. Also, Pollock et al. (2007, p. 133) criticized the abovementioned on-time and on-budget findings as having no solid evidence base, stating that 'all claims based on [this] are misleading'.[14] In addition, Hodge and Greve (2009) observed a third group of studies, where a slightly greater number of studies doubted claims of PPP success and concluded that far greater analytical care was required before PPPs could be judged as superior to traditional methods. Blanc-Brude et al. (2006), for example, conducted careful regression analyses across EU countries and found PPPs were 24 per cent more expensive than our expectations from traditional procurement – ironically, at about the same magnitude of traditional project cost overruns.[15] Fitzgerald (2004) argued that the size of cost savings claimed in his Australian PPP assessment was largely dependent on the discount rate used (with

> a lower discount rate suggesting a cost increase of 6 per cent rather than the 9 per cent cost saving estimated using the higher discount rate). Both Fitzgerald (2004) and Hodge (2005) concluded government treasuries needed to employ the philosophy of 'buyer beware' and be more of a steward for public funds rather than a PPP advocate. Vining and Boardman (2008) judged only one half of the Canadian PPPs reviewed as successes, and Jupe (2009) viewed PPPs as 'imperfect solutions' for transport in the UK.

On the second broad performance domain, governance, there have also been a range of illuminating commentaries. Indeed, questions of PPP governance and the legitimacy of PPPs as a governance tool have been just as controversial as matters of project efficiency and effectiveness. Multiple accusations have been levelled: ongoing analytical manipulation with public sector comparisons lacking legitimacy and favouring private finance delivery; decision-making arrangements lacking transparency; large complex commercial deals clearly being done with business partners rather than with citizens also as equal 'partners'; traditional methods of gaining access to information and review through Freedom of Information or Administrative Law not now available to citizens under private law contracts; and governments lacking accountability. Little wonder that PPPs have been labelled 'the illegitimate child' of the PPP LTIC family (Hodge, 2006, p. 324).

In one sense, such concerns are hardly surprising. Governance matters are particularly important in that the public interest needs to be protected despite the delegation of authority to private concerns. But at the centre of this governance challenge there is an inherent and continuing tension. As Skelcher (2010) said, tight governance is needed to protect the public interest, but weaker governance is also required to enable risk-taking and innovation, along with incentivized private actor participation. These mechanisms can together provide a fair basis for potential investors as well as a framework that should reduce risks of corruption and opportunism. But PPPs equally 'raise important issues of democratic governance', and whilst 'organizations in the public domain are required to account for their activities in the public arena of discourse', 'forms of third party government like PPPs muddy the waters of accountability', and may lead to a 'democratic deficit' (Skelcher, 2010, p. 299). Interestingly, PPPs are much like a form of quasi-governmental body, emerging in a multiplicity of forms through ad hoc processes, and frequently a function of executive rather than legislative decision. So to Skelcher, creating effective constitutional oversight remains a priority challenge for PPP. Having said this, observers such as Willems and van Dooren (2011, 2012) argue that such accountability concerns are overstated and fail to understand the breadth of today's multiple and complex avenues through which communities hold governments to account. Perhaps the counterfactual of traditional accountability and transparency mechanisms has also tended to be overly optimistic and romantic as well.

9.4 META-LESSONS FROM PPPS AND IMPLICATIONS FOR MEGA-PROJECTS

Looking back, there are multiple lessons from our PPP experience to date, with implications for mega-projects. The first clear lesson from PPP experience has been the attractiveness of PPPs as a 'buy-now, pay-later' political arrangement. Crystal clear in jurisdictions such as the UK, Canada and the Australian States has been the support of major political parties and the political pay-offs in terms of project delivery as well as considerably strengthening the governments' relationships with city financiers. Despite some visible failures and policy U-turns, there have been clear political attractions in these jurisdictions for PPP.

Next have been the mixed findings as to performance to date and the ongoing contests in judging performance. Even the auditors appear to have been evaluating PPP experiences more harshly in recent times. NAO (2009, p. 6) in the UK, for instance, warned that PFI was 'one of many routes of delivery', and that while it 'can work well', it was 'not suitable at any price or in every circumstance'. The NAO found financial modelling that was 'error-ridden and given undue influence as the basis for decisions', and in which 'too much weight [was] placed upon subjective judgments of risk, which can easily be adjusted to show private finance is cheaper' (p. 8). It also explicitly noted the difficulty in properly evaluating the UK's use of PPP, and stated '[so] government cannot satisfy itself that private finance represents the best VfM option'. Perhaps the UK NAO developed more independence in its judgements after the global financial turmoil of 2008? Likewise, the Government Accountability Office (GAO) in the USA examined PPPs in several sectors, with its judgements reflected in titles such as: *Highway Public–Private Partnerships: Securing Potential Benefits and Protecting the Public Interest Could Result from More Rigorous Up-front Analysis* (GAO, 2008).[16]

Other disciplinary contributions have also been informative. De Bettignies and Ross (2010) in economics, for instance, found that whilst conditions exist under which we might expect privately financed infrastructure projects to deliver superior VfM to traditional projects, we still have a considerable distance to go to properly calibrate these theoretical ideas with empirical data so that decision-making is evidence-based. Boardman and Vining (2010, p. 180) add provocatively that 'no government has performed normatively appropriate analyses of P3' (as PPPs are called in Canada). Moreover, they judge criteria such as 'on time', 'on budget', or 'VfM' as all 'weak', and recommend that economic evaluation be undertaken on the basis of lowest 'total social cost'. Likewise, Davies (2008, p. 200) also rises above the popular rhetoric and observes that for alliance contracts, Australian governments 'all provide directions for managers to achieve value for money, but are silent on how value for money should be measured'. To him, VfM is 'a nebulous concept' that 'frightens auditors' (pp. 216, 242).

Governments themselves have also contributed to the spread of PPPs and their policy success through initiatives including supportive legislation and regulatory governance arrangements, central PPP units and taskforces, and supporting loan arrangements (Boardman and Vining, 2010; Hammerschmid and Ysa, 2010). But an even more crucial requirement has been the obvious need for strong and professional capacity inside of government to take on these deals. This has been no small issue, as we have previously observed throughout the history of contracting-out government services (Hodge, 2000; Greve, 2008).

What is beyond doubt across the globe has therefore been the powerful role of political dynamics as well as the crucial role PPP has played in linking governments to the business sector. Equally clear, too, has been the sense that many of the empirical results on PPP performance seem to have differed greatly from past proclamations of success by advocating governments. The UK government, for example, has now signed up to over 700 projects through the PFI (PPP) technique, and despite many criticisms on technical matters such as poor VfM and loss of face over manipulated business cases, this government has clearly seen its PPP policy as successful. Even the most recent UK review (HM Treasury, 2012) addressing 'fundamental concerns' expressed by Parliament, the public sector and taxpayers simply revised its former PFI policy to become 'PF2', rather than reversing it. Likewise, three successive state governments of Victoria, Australia, have also pushed ahead with a PPP policy over the past decade, and it continues to be a popular choice in other jurisdictions such as British Columbia and many states of Canada.

For advocating governments, PPP success seems to have been inevitable. It is clear that there continues to be real benefits to governments to proceed down this road in the face of policy critics. Put another way, despite controversial legitimacy and VfM findings, PPPs have usually been politically effective for reformist governments (Hodge et al., 2010). We therefore need to think far more seriously about how PPPs contribute politically, and develop stronger analytical frameworks to analyse PPP as a governing mechanism with political pay-offs. Having said this, we ought to remember that not all governments have taken the PPP policy road. Many have not, and Scandinavian countries such as Denmark and Norway on one side of the globe and New Zealand on the other exemplify those who have strongly resisted such attempts. As Greve and Mörth (2010, p. 454) stated, 'governments in Scandinavia mostly steered clear of promoting PPP policies' because in their view, these countries were under little financial or political pressure to spend beyond their means.

The global financial crisis has led to turbulence in both markets and national politics, and the future of PPPs in this new environment is uncertain. The PPP debate has been recast (Flinders, 2010). A strengthened questioning of market fundamentalism may now occur. But equally it may be that PPP will have a bright future, because one overwhelming lesson from experience to date is that the PPP ideal is a powerful one, and this will continue. To our minds, therefore, there will of course be increased attention on the many technical issues central to our continuing assessments of success. But the power of the PPP ideal as well as the political drivers of PPP success is likely to continue to capture the hearts of elected leaders. These drivers, as well as the breadth and inherent flexibility of the PPP phenomenon itself, will enable PPP to adapt to the needs of a turbulent future.

Where does all this leave us? We have mapped the complex terrain covered by both the PPP phenomenon itself and the matter of PPP performance. And whilst we did not discover any single neat meta-framework for evaluating PPP success, we at least now have some broad dimensions that would seem central to any serious analysis of PPP. So for all types of PPP, issues of legitimacy, sustainability and innovation matter; utilitarian notions of meeting policy objectives, achieving outcomes and delivering benefits to target groups matter; and issues of enhancing one's own electoral prospects and sustaining the broad values of government also matter. In other words, PPP performance and success would seem from this chapter to be as much about politics and the business of governing strongly and legitimately as it is about policy objectives and technical concerns. Importantly, too, there is as much that matters to PPP success that is implicit and non-technical in nature (as well as explicit and technical).

As we develop and manage mega-projects, we need to take on board these meta-lessons. But how? The word 'develop' itself has a fascinatingly wide richness of meanings and covers nuances such as natural growth or evolution, the sense of something becoming gradually visible or the sense that we can bring out the possibilities in something and make it more useable. Mega-projects are by definition therefore an inherently 'developmental' process themselves. They are a story, a phenomenon that grows from a seed to a reality, where a faint idea gradually unfolds and then becomes a visible image. They also bring out the possibilities in us as a community as technological achievers and symbolize an exciting future where our technologies enable us all to immediately become more useful and effective. Past these semantic observations, as well, there is a deeper issue: perhaps we need to get outside the PPP phenomenon rather than further dissecting it, in order to better understand it and learn about how notions of PPP interact with mega-projects. The fascinating work of Sturup (2013) is central here.

Examining three transport mega-projects in Australia through the governmentality lens of Michel Foucault, Sturup's investigation centred around how the amalgam of rationality, technology and knowledge generated a specific art of governing mega-projects. Through this, she was able to explain how actors involved in mega-projects behaved. Her approach to investigating the art of government was founded on the idea that particular technologies reinforced certain rationalities that leveraged specific sets of knowledge and thus encouraged 'right behaviour' (Sturup, 2013, p. 133). In other words, governing was not about overt domination, but about 'creat[ing] the conditions from which right behavior is generated by the individuals themselves'. Interestingly, her project cases included two iconic PPP mega-projects (Melbourne's City Link and Sydney's Cross City Tunnel) as well as a traditional mega-project delivered through a publicly funded construction contract (the Perth to Mandurah Railway).

She argued that 'PPPs have been touted as the solution to the problems of mega-projects, especially the ability to deliver them on time and budget, without risk to government. However, the technology consistently fails to deliver as expected' (p. 144). Crucially, she saw this to be a result not because we misunderstand the technology of PPPs, but because we misunderstand the art of governing mega-projects. To her, 'the art of government of mega-projects follows a logic of power which is strongly sovereign or pharonic' (Boyce, 1990). The logic is that 'my will be done, I am the King'. Project management technology, where object X is to be produced by time Y, worked to support this. Decision-making follows the logic of the project, the legitimacy of decisions is presumed and 'the question of power is largely avoided' (Sturup, 2013, p. 138). The project management body of knowledge further focuses attention on the 'build' element of the project. Moreover, mega-projects are also seen as part of the rationalities around the relationship between problem design and solution. She goes as far as to say that:

> Problems are generated to fit the solutions which are at hand (Li, 2007). In each of the projects studied the problem and the solution to it were articulated

> and re-articulated until the solution was to build a piece of infrastructure. The generation of the problem and solution produce the rationality for the project. The rationality given for the problem is therefore bounded by, but also bounds the rationality of the solution and subsequently the design of the project. Once this process is complete the solution proposed (the mega-project) occurs as the only rational solution. By the time the project reaches what Miller and Lessard (2008) call the 'ramp up phase', the logic of the problem and solution are embedded in the project. (Ibid.)

In other words, what might have been intense political struggles are rearticulated 'as a technical problem solvable by construction'. This art of government of mega-projects is reinforced by PPP. Many examples exist: the logic of sovereignty is reinforced through the PPP contract; PPP also supports and reinforces the technology of project; and the contract places boundaries around the project and keeps it free of political interference. Authority for contracted parties to act is granted by the sovereign. But PPP also interferes with governing too because the idea of partnership in PPPs is rendered meaningless with little basis in equality. Also, negotiating and writing the contract 'acts to support proper identification, allocation and costing of risks as well as creating clarity about the exact parameters of the project'. But it equally 'exacerbate[s] the tendency of projects to focus on the deliverable, the construction phase, rather than the business phase (operations) which in urban transport mega-projects is often considerably longer and arguably more important' (Sturup, 2013, p. 145).

Importantly as well, because the art of government of urban mega-transport projects is strengthened, PPPs fundamentally reinforce the 'sublime' of mega-projects. Three elements are reinforced here: the technical sublime (where we are in awe of the beauty and graceful lines of the project); the political sublime (where politicians achieve rock star appeal when they solve the problem and open the bridge); and the 'managerial sublime' (where chaotic activities are brought under control). Sturup (ibid.) even warned that the sublime may actually 'reduce our capacity to resist the siren song' of mega-projects, so that political questions that should be contested 'are rendered technical, to the detriment of the project and the society in which they are built'.

The lesson is clear, overall. The psychological dimensions of governance and the art of the 'project' are major determinants of what makes a mega-project tick as well as engineering and technical determinants. Indeed, Sturup's work suggests controversially that from the perspective of psychology our model of the PPP phenomenon (with the project as the narrowest conception, broadening out to organization, policy and governance dimensions) should be reversed. The project and its logic becomes the all powerful paradigm, with policy and governance occurring within this – not the other way around. As Sturup (ibid., p. 143) says, 'once people have committed themselves to the project, they become the project'. Daring to question the project rationale leaves one with 'an unjustified existence'. Perhaps 'this is why mega-projects don't really fail, their failures rather get reinterpreted into justified outcomes'.

The symbolic nature of mega-projects will not change. And our search will continue for the PPP ideal. Photographs of ministers opening new infrastructure will continue to be evidence of success as much as any complex utilitarian or academic analysis. We will continue to debate project delivery success and whether structural issues matter most or whether 'it's the management stupid' (Klijn, 2008, p. 1). And we will continue to be interested in overseeing fair financial returns for risk taking, and investigating the potential of pension schemes to fund large infrastructure initiatives.

9.5 CONCLUSIONS

The overriding sense through this chapter has been that the PPP phenomenon has much in common with the mega-project. The public–private mixing applying to both throughout history, the rich dimensions relevant to assessing performance in both cases, and the complexity and multi-dimensionality of mega-project goals are all clear. Indeed there are probably more non-technical and implicit goals in PPPs and mega-projects than there are technical and explicit goals. Given the degree to which PPPs and mega-projects are inherently political, this is perhaps of little surprise. But we are only now just growing aware of why such mixed performance results appear to have occurred to date, why such results remain so strongly contested, and why large infrastructure projects remain so politically popular. There is still much to learn.

We now need to move past the PPP and mega-project performance assessment technical controversies and think more seriously about how, despite long-running project efficiency and governance concerns, PPPs and mega-projects contribute politically. It is through this lens that we will develop a better evidence base and stronger analytical frameworks to analyse how infrastructure projects provide political as well as social pay-offs. In our post-global-financial-crisis era of market turbulence, and amidst powerful financial interests, the need to understand PPP and mega-projects in governance terms is crucial.

NOTES

1. To Wettenhall (2005, p. 22; 2010, p. 22), the terminology of public–private 'mix' is more intellectually defensible than the popular rhetorical label of 'partnership'. Partnership in reality requires a relationship between two agents involving 'a degree of trust, equality or reciprocity' rather than a straightforward market-style contract.
2. See also Weihe (2005) for her meta-view outlining five alternative PPP 'approaches' including: local regeneration, policy, infrastructure, governance and development.
3. Neither of these two views of PPP matches the most popular use of the phrase around the world: that of the shared delivery of health services in developing countries.
4. From first principles there are perhaps 128 different ways (i.e., 2^7) of organizing these seven tasks between the two sectors.
5. See, for example, Allan (1989), Savas (2000), Berg et al. (2002), Grimsey and Lewis (2004) or OECD (2008) here.
6. OECD (2008, p. 20), for instance, also places PPPs somewhere in the middle of the continuum between purely public and purely private. The five points along this continuum in order of increasing privateness were complete government production and delivery, traditional public procurement, PPPs, concessions and, lastly, privatization. Alternatively, Grimsey and Lewis (2004, p. 54) nominate some 21 alternative public–private business models in between either fully public provision or outright privatization, Savas (2000, p. 241) nominates ten models, and OECD (2008, p. 22) nominates 14 options.
7. See Monteiro (2010), for example.
8. Note that this chapter focuses simply on the PPP objectives of government.
9. We might reflect that the private financing of a long-term infrastructure does not strictly reduce the call on the budget. All public infrastructure debts must be repaid in the end, at hopefully minimum interest rates to ensure efficiency, except where a government enters an infrastructure deal and requires users or citizens to pay directly, such as tolls on a new road.
10. McConnell gives an example of each: flood control in the Netherlands (for utilitarian 'programme' success); Prime Minister Kevin Rudd's historic 'sorry' speech at Parliament House in 2007 following Australia's forced removal of perhaps up to one-third of aboriginal children from their families over the period 1910 to 1970 (for success in terms of 'politics'); and electoral system reform in British Columbia, Canada (for the case of 'process' success).
11. See for example, Perrot and Chatelus (2000), Vaillancourt Rosenau (2000), Savas (2000), Osborne (2001), Berg et al. (2002), Bovaird (2004), Edwards et al. (2004), Ghobadian et al. (2004), Grimsey and Lewis (2004), Pollitt (2005), Shaoul (2005), and Hodge and Greve (2007).
12. See National Audit Office (2000, 2009), Mott MacDonald (2002), Pollock et al. (2002) and Flinders (2005) for examples of PPP reviews taking a more specific focus.
13. Hodge et al. (2010) argue indeed that early contracting-out evaluations, for example, were also found to be statistically unreliable compared to the more careful later assessment of teams such as Domberger et al. (1986). This later assessment was careful to control for eight variables and their results showed the overwhelming importance of controlling for the amount of work done as well as its characteristics before we proselytized over matters such as the sector undertaking the work. Such careful statistical work is only now starting to appear in the PPP field.
14. Difficulties in extracting this research data from behind government claims of 'commercial-in-confidence' also amplified the concern that peer review scrutiny was not welcomed because this well-publicized study lacked rigour.
15. This review rightly cautioned against making any further VfM conclusions, however, arguing that lifecycle costs over the longer term were still unknown.
16. A further activity in Europe has also been the Supreme Audit Institutions of the European Union and their examination of PPP audits (Bundesrechnungshof, 2011).

LITERATURE

Allan, J.R. (1989), 'Public–private partnerships', Institute for Public Policy, Public Private Partnerships, Working Paper Series, Yale University.

Allen Consulting Group (2007), *Performance of PPPs and Traditional Procurement in Australia*, Final Report to Infrastructure Partnerships Australia, 30 November.

Audit Commission (2003), *PFI in Schools*, London: Audit Commission.

Ball, R., M. Heafey and D. King (2007), 'The private finance initiative in the UK', *Public Management Review*, **9**(2), 289–310.

Berg, S., M. Pollitt and M. Tsuji (eds) (2002), *Private Initiatives in Infrastructure: Priorities, Incentives and Performance*, Cheltenham, UK and Northampton, MA, USA: Edward Elgar.

Blanc-Brude, F., H. Goldsmith and T. Valila (2006), *Ex Ante Construction Costs in the European Road Sector: A Comparison of Public–Private Partnerships and Traditional Public Procurement*, Economic and Financial Report 2006/01, European Investment Bank.

Boardman, A.E. and A.R. Vining (2010), 'Assessing the economic worth of public–private partnerships', in G.A. Hodge, C. Greve and A.E. Boardman (eds), *International Handbook on Public–Private Partnerships*, Cheltenham, UK and Northampton, MA, USA: Edward Elgar, pp. 159–86.

Bovaird, T. (2004), 'Public–private partnerships in Western Europe and the US: new growths from old roots', in A. Ghobadian, D. Gallear, N. O'Regan and H. Viney (eds), *Public–Private Partnerships: Policy and Experience*, Basingstoke: Palgrave Macmillan, pp. 221–50.

Bovaird, T. (2010), 'A brief intellectual history of the public–private partnership movement', in G.A. Hodge, C. Greve and A.E. Boardman (eds), *International Handbook on Public–Private Partnerships*, Cheltenham, UK and Northampton, MA, USA: Edward Elgar, pp. 43–67.

Boyce, J.K. (1990), 'Birth of a mega-project – political economy of flood control in Bangladesh', *Environmental Management*, **14**(4), 419–28.

Bundesrechnungshof (2011), 'The audit of public–private partnerships', seminar in Bonn, 9–11 February, Germany.

Corner, D. (2005), 'The United Kingdom private finance initiative: the challenge of allocating risk', in Graeme A. Hodge and Carsten Greve (eds), *The Challenge of Public–Private Partnerships: Learning from International Experience*, Cheltenham, UK and Northampton, MA, USA: Edward Elgar, pp. 44–61.

Davies, J. (2008), 'Alliance contracts and public sector governance', PhD thesis, Griffith University, August, unpublished.

de Bettignies, J.E. and T.W. Ross (2010), 'The economics of public–private partnerships: some theoretical contributions', in G.A. Hodge, C. Greve and A.E. Boardman (eds), *International Handbook on Public–Private Partnerships*, Cheltenham, UK and Northampton, MA, USA: Edward Elgar, pp. 132–58.

Delmon, J. (2011), *Public–Private Partnerships in Infrastructure. An Essential Guide for Policy Makers*, Cambridge, UK: Cambridge University Press.

Deloitte (2006), *Closing the Infrastructure Gap: The Role of Public–Private Partnerships*, A Deloitte Research Study, New York.

Domberger, A., S.A. Meadowcroft and D.J. Thomson (1986), 'Competitive tendering and efficiency: the case of refuse collection', *Fiscal Studies*, **7**(4), 69–87.

Duffield, C.F. (2010), 'Different delivery models', in G.A. Hodge, C. Greve and A.E. Boardman (eds), *International Handbook on Public–Private Partnerships*, Cheltenham, UK and Northampton, MA, USA: Edward Elgar, pp. 187–215.

Edwards, P., J. Shaoul, A. Stafford and L. Arblaster (2004), *Evaluating the Operation of PFI in Roads and Hospitals*, London: Certified Accountants Education Trust.

Ernst & Young (2007), *The Road Ahead: Future of PPP in Australian Road Infrastructure*, Australia: Ernst & Young.

Fitzgerald, P. (2004), *Review of 'Partnerships Victoria' Provided Infrastructure*, Melbourne: Growth Solutions Group.

Flinders, M. (2005), 'The politics of public–private partnerships', *British Journal of Political and International Relations*, **7**(2), 215–39.
Flinders, M. (2010), 'Splintered logic and political debate', in G.A. Hodge, C. Greve and A.E. Boardman (eds), *International Handbook on Public–Private Partnerships*, Cheltenham, UK and Northampton, MA, USA: Edward Elgar, pp. 115–31.
Flyvbjerg, B., N. Bruzelius and W. Rothengatter (2003), *Megaprojects and Risk: An Anatomy of Ambition*, Cambridge, UK: Cambridge University Press.
Frick, K.T.Y. (2008), 'The cost of the technological sublime: daring ingenuity and the new San Francisco-Oakland Bay Bridge', in H. Priemus, B. Flyvbjerg and B. van Wee (eds), *Decision-making on Mega-projects: Cost–Benefit Analysis, Planning and Innovation*, Cheltenham, UK and Northampton, MA, USA: Edward Elgar, pp. 239–62.
Ghobadian, A., D. Gallear, N. O'Regan and H. Viney (eds) (2004), *Public–Private Partnerships: Policy and Experience*, London: Palgrave Macmillan.
Government Accountability Office (GAO) (2008), *Highway Public–Private Partnerships: Securing Potential Benefits and Protecting the Public Interest Could Result from More Rigorous Up-front Analysis*, Washington, DC: GAO.
Greve, C. (2008), *Contracting for Public Services*, Abingdon, Oxon/New York: Routledge.
Greve, C. and U. Mörth (2010), 'Public–private partnerships: the Scandinavian experience', in G.A. Hodge, C. Greve and A.E. Boardman (eds), *International Handbook on Public–Private Partnerships*, Cheltenham, UK and Northampton, MA, USA: Edward Elgar, pp. 439–55.
Grimsey, D. and M. Lewis (2004), *Public–Private Partnerships: The Worldwide Revolution in Infrastructure Provision and Project Finance*, Cheltenham, UK and Northampton, MA, USA: Edward Elgar.
Hammerschmid, G. and T. Ysa (2010), 'Empirical PPP experiences in Europe: national variations of a global concept', in G.A. Hodge, C. Greve and A.E. Boardman (eds), *International Handbook on Public–Private Partnerships*, Cheltenham, UK and Northampton, MA, USA: Edward Elgar, pp. 333–53.
Hellowell, M. (2010), 'The UK's private finance initiative: history, evaluation, prospects', in G.A. Hodge, C. Greve and A.E. Boardman (eds), *International Handbook on Public–Private Partnerships*, Cheltenham, UK and Northampton, MA, USA: Edward Elgar, pp. 307–32.
HM Treasury (2012), 'A new approach to public private partnerships', 5 December, p. 99.
Hodge, G.A. (2000), *Privatization: An International Review of Performance*, Boulder, CO: Perseus Books/Westview Press.
Hodge, G.A. (2005), 'Public–private partnerships: the Australian experience with physical infrastructure', in G.A. Hodge and C. Greve (eds), *The Challenge of Public–Private Partnerships: Learning from International Experience*, Cheltenham, UK and Northampton, MA, USA: Edward Elgar, pp. 305–31.
Hodge, G.A. (2006), 'Public–private partnerships and legitimacy', *University of New South Wales Law Journal*, Forum, **29**(3), 318–27.
Hodge, G.A. (2009), 'Public–private partnerships: the phenomenon, the brand and the future', presentation to Civil Contractors Federation National Conference, 21–25 October, Perth.
Hodge, G.A. (2010), 'Reviewing public–private partnerships: some thoughts on evaluation', in G.A. Hodge, C. Greve and A.E. Boardman (eds), *International Handbook on Public–Private Partnerships*, Cheltenham, UK and Northampton, MA, USA: Edward Elgar, pp. 81–112.
Hodge, G.A. and C. Greve (2007), 'Public–private partnerships: an international performance review', *Public Administration Review*, **67**(3), 545–58.
Hodge, G.A. and C. Greve (2009), 'PPPs: the passage of time permits a sober reflection', *Economic Affairs*, **29**(1), 33–9.
Hodge, G.A. and C. Greve, (2013), 'Introduction: public–private partnership in turbulent times', in C. Greve and G.A. Hodge (eds), *Rethinking Public–Private Partnerships: Strategies for Turbulent Times*, Abingdon, Oxon/New York: Routledge, pp. 1–32.

Hodge, G.A., C. Greve and A. Boardman (2010), 'Conclusions: public–private partnerships – international experiences and future challenges', in G.A. Hodge, C. Greve and A.E. Boardman (eds), *International Handbook on Public–Private Partnerships*, Cheltenham, UK and Northampton, MA, USA: Edward Elgar, pp. 594–610.
Huxman, C. and P. Hubbert (2009), 'Hit or myth? Stories of collaborative success', in J. O'Flynn and J. Wanna (eds), *Collaborative Governance*, Canberra: ANU Press, pp. 45–50.
Jeffares, S., H. Sullivan and T. Bovaird (2013), 'Beyond the contract: the challenge of evaluating the performance(s) of public–private partnerships', in C. Greve and G.A. Hodge (eds), *Rethinking Public–Private Partnerships: Strategies for Turbulent Times*, Abingdon, Oxon/New York: Routledge, pp. 166–87.
Jupe, R. (2009), 'New Labour, public private partnerships and rail transport', *Economic Affairs*, **29**(1), 20–25.
Klijn, E.H. (2008), 'It's the management, stupid!: on the importance of management in complex policy issues', The Hague: Uitgeverij LEMMA.
Klijn, E.H. (2010), 'Public–private partnerships: deciphering meaning, message and phenomenon', in G.A. Hodge, C. Greve and A.E. Boardman (eds), *International Handbook on Public–Private Partnerships*, Cheltenham, UK and Northampton, MA, USA: Edward Elgar, pp. 68–80.
Leviakangas, P. (2007), *Private Finance of Transport Infrastructure Projects: Value and Risk Analysis of a Finnish Shadow Toll Road Project*, ESPOO 2007, VTT Publications.
Li, T.M. (2007), *The Will to Improve: Governmentality, Development and the Practice of Politics*, Durham, NC and London: Duke University Press.
Linder, S. (1999), 'Coming to terms with the public–private partnership: a grammar of multiple meanings', *The American Behavioral Scientist*, **43**(1), 35–51.
McConnell, A. (2010), *Understanding Policy Success: Rethinking Public Policy*, Basingstoke: Palgrave Macmillan.
Miller, R. and D.R. Lessard (2008), 'Evolving strategy: risk management and the shaping of mega-projects', in Hugo Priemus, Bent Flyvbjerg and Bert van Wee (eds), *Decision-making on Mega-projects: Cost–Benefit Analysis, Planning and Innovation*, Cheltenham, UK and Northampton, MA, USA: Edward Elgar, pp. 145–72.
Monteiro, R.S. (2010), 'Risk management', in G.A. Hodge, C. Greve and A.E. Boardman (eds), *International Handbook on Public–Private Partnerships*, Cheltenham, UK and Northampton, MA, USA: Edward Elgar, pp. 262–91.
Mott MacDonald (2002), *Review of Large Public Procurement in the UK*, London: Mott Macdonald.
National Audit Office (NAO) (2000), *Examining the Value for Money of Deals under the Private Finance Initiative*, London: The Stationery Office.
National Audit Office (NAO) (2003), *PFI: Construction Performance*, London: The Stationery Office.
National Audit Office (NAO) (2009), 'Private finance projects', a paper for the Lords Economic Affairs Committee, accessed 14 June 2013 at http://www.nao.org.uk/wp-content/uploads/2009/11/HL_Private_Finance_Projects.pdf.
Nye, D.E. (1994), *American Technological Sublime*, Cambridge, MA: MIT Press.
OECD (2008), *Public–Private Partnerships: In Pursuit of Risk Sharing and Value for Money*, Paris: OECD.
Osborne, S. (ed.) (2001), *Public–Private Partnerships: Theory and Practice in International Perspective*, New York: Routledge.
Perrot, J.Y. and G. Chatelus (eds) (2000), *Financing of Major Infrastructure and Public Service Projects: Public Private Partnerships, Lessons from French Experience Throughout the World*, Paris: Presses de l'Ecole Nationale des Ponts et Chaussées.
Pollitt, M. (2005), 'Learning from the UK private finance initiative experience', in G. Hodge and C. Greve (eds), *The Challenge of Public–Private Partnerships: Learning from International Experience*, Cheltenham, UK and Northampton, MA, USA: Edward Elgar, pp. 207–30.

Pollock, A., D. Price and S. Playe (2007), 'An examination of the UK Treasury's evidence base for cost and time overrun data in UK value-for-money policy and appraisal', *Public Money and Management*, **27**(2), 127–33.
Pollock, A., J. Shaoul and N. Vickers (2002), 'Private finance and value for money in NHS hospitals: a policy in search of a rationale?', *British Medical Journal*, **324**(7347), 1205–8.
PriceWaterhouseCoopers (2005), *Delivering the PPP Promise. A Review of PPP Issues and Activities*, accessed 26 November 2008 at http://www.pwc.com/en_GX/gx/government-infrastructure/pdf/promisereport.pdf.
Priemus, H., B. Flyvbjerg and B. van Wee (eds) (2008), 'Introduction: scope of book', in H. Priemus, B. Flyvbjerg and B. van Wee (eds), *Decision-making on Mega-projects: Cost–Benefit Analysis, Planning and Innovation*, Cheltenham UK and Northampton, MA: Edward Elgar, pp. 1–20.
Salamon, L.M. (2002), 'The new governance and the tools of public action: an introduction', in *The Tools of Government: A Guide to the New Governance*, New York: Oxford University Press, pp. 1–47.
Savas, E.S. (2000), *Privatization and Public–Private Partnerships*, New York: Chatham House Publishers and Seven Bridges Press.
Shaoul, J. (2005), 'The private finance initiative or the public funding of private profit', in G. Hodge and C. Greve (eds), *The Challenge of Public–Private Partnerships: Learning from International Experienc*e, Cheltenham, UK and Northampton, MA, USA: Edward Elgar, pp. 190–206.
Skelcher, C. (2010), 'Governing partnerships', in G.A. Hodge, C. Greve and A.E. Boardman (eds), *International Handbook on Public–Private Partnership*s, Cheltenham, UK and Northampton, MA, USA: Edward Elgar, pp. 292–304.
Skelcher, C. and H. Sullivan (2008), 'Theory driven approaches to analysing collaborative performance', *Public Management Review*, **10**(6), 751–77.
Sturup, S. (2013), 'A Foucault-perspective on public–private partnership mega-projects', in C. Greve and G. Hodge (eds), *Rethinking Public–Private Partnerships: Strategies for Turbulent Time*s, Abingdon, Oxon/New York: Routledge, pp. 132–47.
Teisman, G. and E.-H. Klijn (2002), 'Partnership arrangements: governmental rhetoric or governance scheme?', *Public Administration Review*, **62**(2), 197–205.
Vaillancourt Rosenau, P. (ed.) (2000), *Public–Private Policy Partnership*s, Cambridge, MA: MIT Press.
Vecchi, V., M. Hellowell and F. Longo (2010), 'Are Italian healthcare organizations paying too much for their public–private partnerships?', *Public Money and Management*, **30**(2), 125–32.
Vining, A. and A. Boardman (2008), 'Public–private partnerships in Canada. Theory and evidence', *Canadian Public Administration*, **51**(1), 9–44.
Weihe, G. (2005), 'Public–private partnerships: addressing a nebulous concept', Working Paper No. 16, International Centre for Business and Politics, Copenhagen Business School, Denmark.
Wettenhall, R. (2005), 'The public–private interface: surveying the history', in G. Hodge and C. Greve (eds), *The Challenge of Public–Private Partnerships: Learning from International Experience*, Cheltenham, UK and Northampton, MA, USA: Edward Elgar, pp. 22–43.
Wettenhall, R. (2010), 'Mixes and partnerships through time', in G.A. Hodge, C. Greve and A.E. Boardman (eds), *International Handbook on Public–Private Partnerships*, Cheltenham, UK and Northampton, MA, USA: Edward Elgar, pp. 17–42.
Willems, T. and W. van Dooren (2011), 'Lost in diffusion? How collaborative arrangements lead to an accountability paradox', *International Review of Administrative Sciences*, **77**(3), 506–30.
Willems, T. and W. van Dooren (2012), 'Coming to terms with accountability: combining multiple forums and functions', *Public Management Review*, **14**(7), 1011–36.
Yescombe, E.R. (2007), *Public–Private Partnerships. Principles of Policy and Finance*, London: Butterworth-Heinemann.

10. Mega-projects in intermodal freight transport: innovation adoption

Arjan van Binsbergen, Rob Konings, Lóri Tavasszy and Ron van Duin

10.1 INTRODUCTION

Intermodal transport technology has been a, if not the, main driving force behind the spectacular and ongoing growth of international transport in the post-war world. Many books have been written on the concept of standardized freight unitization (see, e.g., Levinson, 2006), which has allowed massive scale economies to develop in global transport. Investments in ports followed as the throughput of major seaside transhipment hubs and transport flows into their hinterland approached millions of containers per year. Clearly, intermodal transport facilities had become mega-projects. These were, however, not only visible by their sheer scale (the planned Rotterdam coastal land reclamation, for example, spans 2000 hectares and costs 2.7 billion euros, not counting private investments in terminals) (Port Authority Rotterdam, 2012), but mostly by their enormous complexity. Intermodal transport not only by definition links different actors (service providers of different modes of transport, infrastructure providers, terminal operators), it also comprises a complicated chain of activities. Because of the limited number of users of transhipment terminals (several orders of magnitude lower than in passenger transport, often not more than a handful) it involves investments in service connections and in synchronized operations. In addition, it involves a more far-reaching intrusion into the natural or built environment than uni-modal transport projects. Transhipment generates additional activities that cluster around and provide employment, it is space extensive, produces local emissions and noise annoyance and involves public–private investments. The planning of intermodal transport facilities often has an even longer lead time than other transport infrastructures because of the needed coordination between different network operators, and requires close involvement of public and private stakeholders. Besides the traditional investments in seaport and inland transport infrastructure, new logistics service networks are also developing, connecting these terminals and infrastructures into new networks. These networks involve a substantial industrial innovation effort, reorganizing logistics networks of the users, and closely interacting with the effort of infrastructure development. This complex of infrastructures and services is the main subject of this chapter on mega-projects for freight transport. Our definition of mega-projects therefore is somewhat broader than the traditional one, which focuses on single infrastructural objects. We take the complexity and magnitude of the system innovation as the decisive principle of labelling an initiative a 'mega-project'; in such mega-projects developments in transport technology, ICT and logistics reorganization go hand in hand with infrastructure development.

Many mega-projects for intermodal transport have been proposed in the recent past, incorporating new technologies, new logistics organization and/or innovative infrastructure development. Interestingly, only a few of them resulted in operational systems. In this chapter we explore why these mega-projects in intermodal transport are difficult to realize successfully and how barriers for their successful implementation could be overcome. The theoretical perspective that we take for our analysis, given our definition of mega-projects as complex and multi-dimensional systems, is that of innovation adoption. Our focus is on European initiatives.

The chapter is organized as follows. By means of an introduction to the subject, Section 10.2 provides a brief outline of intermodal transport in Europe, explaining the main challenges the intermodal transport sector is facing. In Section 10.3 we review some recent, complex, public–private intermodal initiatives in Europe. This review includes ideas that have materialized and those that did not succeed in becoming implemented. Besides infrastructural projects we include major logistical innovations that have a natural linkage to intermodal systems and require large investments in infrastructure. In Section 10.4, we explore briefly some theoretical notions about innovation and implementation processes, to understand success and failure factors. From these general notions key factors are derived that we use to evaluate the success or failure in realizing intermodal mega-projects. Section 10.5 reviews the mega-projects and identifies critical issues in the implementation of these mega-projects. Section 10.6 concludes the chapter with an outlook on desirable conditions for the successful implementation of future mega-projects in intermodal transport, based on the lessons learned from previous projects.

10.2 INTERMODAL TRANSPORT IN EUROPE: STATE OF THE ART AND CHALLENGES

Barge and rail transport represented a major market in European inland freight transport in the 1960s, but since then these modes have lost much business to the roads. In 2008 road transport counted for 76 per cent of the total transport performance (in tonnes/km), while rail and barge had a share of 18 per cent and 6 per cent respectively (Eurostat, 2011).

A major explanation for the loss of market share of rail and barge are structural changes in freight transport demand that have resulted in a shift in the composition of cargo towards types of goods and related distribution patterns that have historically less affinity with rail and barge transport and/or a less optimal fit with the characteristics of these modes (i.e., a shift from base materials like ores to semi-finished and consumer goods). In addition, new logistic concepts and changing customer demands have resulted in smaller and more frequent consignments of goods that have strongly favoured and increased the role of road transport at the cost of rail and barge transport (Konings, 2009).

The introduction of cargo unitization (palletization, containerization), as a solution to labour-intensive, time-consuming and therefore expensive handling of general cargo, however, has opened up new perspectives for a revival of rail and barge transport within an intermodal operation, either in transport markets they were not involved in before or in the markets they lost to road transport (e.g., general cargo, which was previously a major market for rail). Transporting cargo in load units made it possible to combine benefits of barge and rail transport with the advantages of road transport, that is, low transport costs for covering larger distances and high flexibility and accessibility to collect and distribute cargo.

The development of this type of transport – known as intermodal freight transport[1] – has not only offered opportunities to recapture market share by rail and barge, but has also gained much political interest, because of its supposed important contribution to sustainable mobility as the exhaust of pollutant emissions and energy use per tonne-kilometre are generally lower in barge and rail transport than in road transport. In looking over the development of intermodal transport its success is diverse, both in intermodal barge transport and intermodal rail transport.

Intermodal Barge Transport

The development of intermodal barge transport in Northwest Europe has been very successful in its role as a system for container transport in the hinterland of seaports. The presence and quality of a waterway network is a major factor in its development. The ports of Rotterdam and Antwerp, both well connected to Europe's largest river, the Rhine, and to a fine-structured national inland waterway network, put their mark on container barge transport in Europe.

In 2010 the barge volume handled in Rotterdam was 2.4 million TEU[2] and 2.3 million TEU in Antwerp. These volumes corresponded with a market share in hinterland transport of 33 per cent for Rotterdam and 34 per cent for Antwerp. In other major container seaports the volumes and the share of barge transport are still modest (Le Havre: 170000 TEU [7 per cent], Marseille: 59000 TEU [6 per cent]; Hamburg: 95000 TEU [1 per cent]).

The success of barge transport in hinterland transport is also the result of the ability of the sector to adapt itself to the demand of shippers and the specific requirements of container transport. New logistical concepts but also technological improvements (both in vessels and handling equipment) have greatly supported the spectacular growth of container barge transport.

It is generally believed that there is still a great potential as well as a need for container barge transport to expand its role in hinterland transport. For instance, the target for the Port of Rotterdam in the Maasvlakte area where the majority of container handling takes place is to increase its share from 39 per cent in 2011 to 45 per cent in 2035. This ambition implies that the barge volume for the Maasvlakte area will more than quadruple from 1.8 million TEU in 2011 to 7.5 million in 2035 (Port Authority Rotterdam, 2011). In view of the current problems perceived in container barge transport it is also believed that such large volumes can only be accommodated if major innovations both in logistics and technology are implemented.

Barge container transport in Europe, however, still functions almost exclusively as a hinterland transport system, and although the current total container volume transported by barge (over 5 million TEU) is impressive, it is only a fraction (about 1 per cent) of total inland freight transport (in tonne-kilometres) in Europe. Hence there is also a great challenge to really open up the market of intermodal barge transport for continental flows, that is, cargo flows that are not related to seaports. A few isolated successful examples exist, such as the Danube floating motorway service (roll-on-roll-off service) of Donau-Lloyd-MAT, which started operation in 1982 between Germany and Bulgaria over a distance of 1435 km (Platz, 2009). Among several initiatives, pallet transport by barge is considered a high potential growth market, but a wide breakthrough has not yet been achieved.

Intermodal Rail Transport

Intermodal rail transport shows a different development path. Intermodal rail transport can take place in many forms. Following common definitions it may consist of unaccompanied transport, that is, containers, swap bodies and trailers, and accompanied transport, that is, rail carriage of entire road vehicles (including the driver). In addition, intermodal transport is applied both in hinterland transport and continental transport in the whole of Europe. Moreover, many operators are involved in the intermodal rail transport market.

In the market of unaccompanied transport the total volume in the European Union (excluding Sweden and Finland, and including Switzerland, Turkey, Croatia, Serbia and Macedonia) was estimated at 15.5 million TEU in 2009 (International Union of Railways, 2010). Although the history of intermodal rail transport started with continental transport shipments it seems that its development has been boosted by the emergence of hinterland transport by rail. About 57 per cent of the total unaccompanied volume in 2009 was hinterland transport, while 43 per cent consisted of continental transport. Within these market segments there is also a clear difference regarding the shares of domestic and international transport: domestic services counted for 73 per cent of hinterland shipments and only for 38 per cent in continental transport. A major explanation is that in general the transport distance in continental services must be larger than in hinterland services in order to be competitive to road transport, because in the continental services pre- and end-haulage and transhipments are needed – and the costs of these additional activities offset the initial benefits of the cheaper-per-kilometre transport modes. Particularly in countries with a rather small territory such as the Netherlands, Belgium or Denmark domestic transport distances are usually too short for intermodal transport to compete with road transport.

The large size of countries like Germany, France and Italy is one of the reasons why intermodal rail transport in these countries has developed quite well. This holds for the continental transport flows as well as for the maritime-based hinterland transport flows. Major seaports in these countries have a much larger share of rail in container hinterland transport than the ports of Rotterdam and Antwerp, which have much better opportunities to accommodate barges (e.g., the rail share in Bremen and Hamburg is 57 per cent and 29 per cent respectively, while in Rotterdam and Antwerp it is 10 per cent and 11 per cent).

The volumes of accompanied intermodal rail transport are much smaller: about 1 million TEU in the European Union in 2009, which represents about 5 per cent of the intermodal rail transport market (International Union of Railways, 2010). Moreover, these flows are even more geographically concentrated: mainly in the corridors crossing the Alpine states of Austria and Switzerland and the Channel Tunnel. These accompanied intermodal flows are largely a result of specific geographical and infrastructure conditions (ranges of mountains or seaway crossings only possible by train) or national transport policies of these countries pursuing a modal shift aiming at reducing the negative impacts of road transport especially cross-border and transit road traffic.

As opposed to barge transport, launching a new intermodal rail service is much more complex because of the necessary negotiations with various national railway operators and the technical and operational differences in national railway systems, and involves higher costs and financial risks. Finding the necessary critical mass in transport volume is a challenge. This is especially the case in continental transport relations where cargo flows tend to be more fragmented and dispersed. A major strategy to attract small flows and expand the market for intermodal rail transport is pursuing network innovations that accommodate bundling of cargo flows, which are most effectively supported by terminal innovations (Kreutzberger, 2008), but so far it has been difficult to accomplish these innovations in practice.

From this brief overview we can conclude that, although intermodal transport is a more complex way of freight transport compared to road-only transport, it can be a competitive and attractive alternative to road transport. However, its development has in general been modest, in terms of current market share.

The costs and quality performance of intermodal transport compared to road-only transport are in the end decisive for the potential success of intermodal transport. It is clear that major innovations can significantly improve the cost and/or quality of intermodal transport and hence are crucial for a breakthrough in its development. From this perspective it is useful to learn about the conditions to realize innovations successfully as well as to learn about the success and failure factors regarding their implementation. Therefore, we will review different intermodal transport innovations that have been implemented and some that did not materialize.

10.3 OVERVIEW OF MEGA-PROJECTS IN INTERMODAL TRANSPORT

In intermodal freight transport in Europe a great number of innovation efforts have focused on improving the exchange process of cargo between modes, because of the relatively large share of this link in the intermodal chain costs. This holds in particular for intermodal barge transport. However, the driver for innovation in this link is also related to the increasing importance of the terminal performance in the overall quality performance (e.g., reliability and transit time) of the intermodal chain (see also Rodrigue, 1999). Many innovations in intermodal transport have a technical dimension, while other innovations include new logistics organization or innovative infrastructure development. However, innovations often cover a combination of these dimensions.

For extensive overviews of innovations in intermodal freight transport we refer to Woxenius (1998), Bontekoning and Kreutzberger (1999), Vleugel et al. (2001), Peterlini (2001), van Gorp and van der Zandt (2003) and University of Antwerp et al. (2012). In our selection of projects to review we have aimed to cover the diversity of intermodal transport innovations, that is, they range from strongly infrastructure-oriented projects, transport system development projects (that include new transport infrastructure, vehicle and transhipment technology) to projects in which the role of infrastructure development is related only to new terminal and transhipment technology. The selection aimed to cover initiatives in different countries across Europe. However, Western European countries are leading in intermodal transport innovation. The project reviews start with infrastructure projects followed by projects in which infrastructure development has a less profound role.

Future Seaport Terminal Areas: Maasvlakte 2 and London Gateway

In order to prepare for the expected growth of container transport in the coming decades, all ports in Western Europe have stepped up their efforts to extend the capacity of the container terminals. At least two of these initiatives can be classified as mega-projects, not so much because of their innovative nature (although the most modern container transhipment equipment is expected to be deployed here), but mostly because of their sheer size and complexity (Figure 10.1). The Maasvlakte 2 area at Rotterdam port and the new London Gateway terminal are expected to cover over 2000 and 700 hectares respectively of land to be used for various port-related industrial activities. The planned capacity for container transhipment lies at around 16 million TEU vs 3.5 million TEU respectively. Investment figures quoted go up to 3.5 billion euros for the Maasvlakte 2 port extension (Port Authority Rotterdam, 2012) and 1.8 billion euros for London Gateway (London Gateway, 2012). Besides transhipment, warehousing, distribution and transport activities will be hosted, requiring further investments. The complexity of the projects is enhanced because intermodal hinterland infrastructures must also be realized. For Maasvlakte 2 a 5 billion euro investment has already been made in a rail line connecting the port area to the German hinterland (the so-called Betuwe Line), but the expansion of the capacity of the main hinterland road axis in the port (estimated at 2 billion euros) is still a project under construction. Depending on the growth of container trade, the

Figure 10.1 Seaport extension projects: Maasvlakte 2 Rotterdam (L) and London Gateway (R)

reclaimed land will take one to two decades to be claimed and furbished completely. The first terminals at both sites are expected to open in 2013.

The challenges associated with implementing these extensions are manifold. Technological challenges include the problem of introducing a completely new built area, with massive traffic generation effects, on the border of world cities. Hinterland transport requires special organizational measures, limiting the share of road transport movements around terminals by contract, creating advanced multi-modal transport concepts. During the preparation of political decision-making about Maasvlakte 2, and the negotiations about the plans, the champion of the development, the Port of Rotterdam Authority, adopted and proactively developed ideas of issue and stakeholder management, conflict resolution and mediation (rooted in the ideas of Fisher and Ury, 1991). This resulted in an extensive environmental mitigation plan, including a multitude of additional 'nature compensation' projects scattered over a large region. New governance skills were required from both the Port Authority and the private investors to tackle all the technological, environmental, social and economic challenges, to such an extent that one talks of a renaissance in the Port Authority, providing it with a new function as community manager (Verhoeven, 2010).

Seine-Nord Canal

Seine-Nord is a major inland waterway transport infrastructure project in France that is currently in preparation. The construction of this 106-km-long canal will replace an existing canal between Compiègne and Cambrai that can accommodate only small vessels. It will provide a missing link of European importance, by connecting the River Seine basin (France) via Belgium to the Rhine river basin (Netherlands, Germany, Switzerland) and the main European inland waterway network (Figure 10.2). The project also includes some upgrading of other waterways in this corridor, both in France and Belgium. Some inland investment plans in the Netherlands have a close relation with this Seine-Nord project. The aim of the project is to enable economies of scale in barge transport (to support a modal shift) both in transport of bulk goods as well as in intermodal transport. The canal leads to an extension of the hinterland of both the French and Benelux container seaports.

The preparation involves a close cooperation between France, the Flanders and Wallonia regions in Belgium and the Netherlands regarding the financial coordination of the project, coordination of research and procedures, harmonization of pricing conditions on the cross-border section and the harmonization of the traffic management conditions

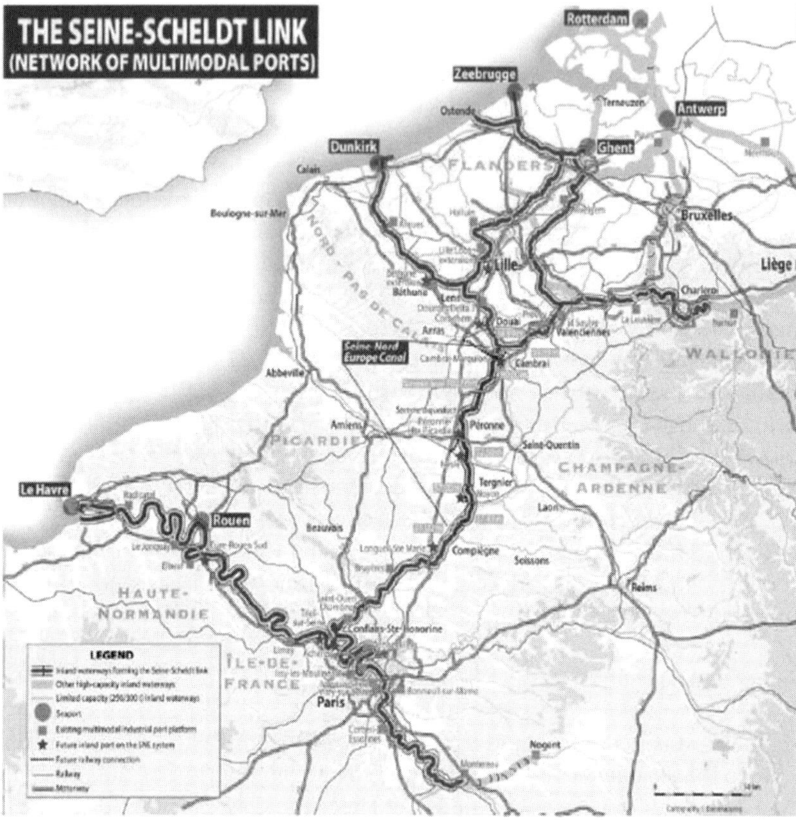

Source: VNF.

Figure 10.2 Seine-Nord Canal: missing link in the European inland waterway network

(Mialocq, 2011). Studies indicate that the benefits of the project are largest in France (75 per cent), followed by Belgium (15 per cent), the Netherlands (7 per cent) and Germany (3 per cent) (VNF, 2011). However, the position of French actors seems critical for the timing or even the realization of project implementation.

Envisaged construction costs have significantly increased from initially 4.7 billion euros to about 6 billion euros now (end of 2012). Although the project receives EU grants and is planned to be financed in public–private partnerships the required large contribution of the French state (2.2 billion euros) is becoming an impediment. Moreover, the Port of Le Havre and the French barge skippers are conducting a lobby against the project, because of fear of competition from the Belgian and Dutch seaports and the Belgian and Dutch shipping sector. The relative advantage of the project is apparently perceived differently by the actors, and this seems related to the different characteristics of the port and barge transport industry in the different countries.

Combi-Road

The Combi-Road project was established in the Netherlands to facilitate the movement of maritime containers from the Port of Rotterdam to inland freight terminals where they could be transferred to long-distance trucks or trains for connections throughout Europe. It was developed as a public–private partnership between the government and the freight transport industry, both of whom had an interest in improving freight movement and in developing alternatives to conventional road and rail transport means. One of the key features of the concept was the use of special purpose automated freight transport vehicles that would operate on their own guideway, completely segregated from other traffic in order to avoid congestion and safety problems (Figure 10.3).

Combi-Road was defined at several levels, ranging from a broad

Source: Projectbureau Combi-Road.

Figure 10.3 Combi-Road prototype vehicle on test track

logistics concept for freight handling, to the development of its special purpose freight guideway along a specific alignment for the lateral guidance of vehicles, to the design of an automated, driverless, electrically propelled vehicle (van der Heijden and Heere, 1997). A prototype of the Combi-Road vehicle was built, tested and demonstrated on a short track facility in Ridderkerk in the Netherlands in 1998.

Combi-Road did not advance beyond the concept definition and prototype vehicle testing stage. The large investment costs needed for Combi-Road were a barrier to further developing the system, including the construction of a pilot track. Moreover, commitment of potential users of the system was lacking. At public level the project was faced with political challenges associated with the development of a competing rail freight line (the Betuwe Line) parallel to the intended route of Combi-Road. A strong lobby for the Betuwe Line led the government to decide to construct this dedicated rail freight line.

OLS (Underground Logistic System) Schiphol

In this project the aim was to develop an underground freight transport network (covering approximately 20 km) for air cargo and flowers, which would connect Schiphol Airport to the flower auction in Aalsmeer and a new rail terminal in Hoofddorp (Figure 10.4). The project was set up in that area in order to address the fact that deteriorating accessibility, increasing traffic congestion, and growing costs were threatening the economic position of the national airport and the flower auction market.

After positive feasibility studies that were completed in 1996, the (conceptual) design of the system was started in 1997 and continued through 1998 and 1999. A test site was realized in Delft (the Netherlands) to test prototypes of the various automated vehicles and handling systems and to develop and test the control system (Pielage, 2005).

The huge investments (about 250 to 500 million euros) that would be needed to develop the system gave cause to revise the original concept, including, for instance, the decision not to build completely underground but largely on the surface using dedicated lanes. Despite these concessions the project financing remained a barrier. Related to this, in the project a real problem owner was missing, and hence a strong driving force for project implementation. As a matter of fact, many actors were involved and they had different interests, goals and ideas, and this made the project even more complex, on top of the fact that new transport technologies were also envisaged (Wiegmans et al., 2010).

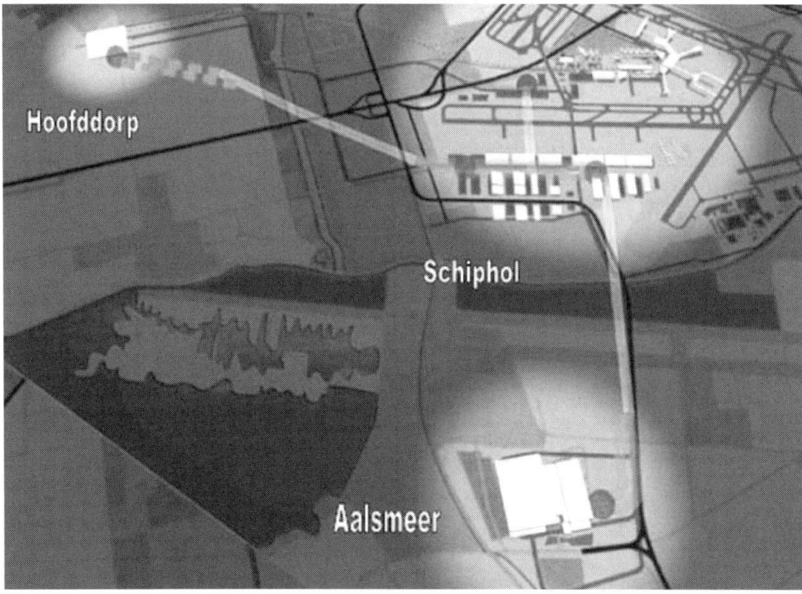

Source: Pielage (2000).

Figure 10.4 Overview of the OLS Schiphol network

Rolling Highways: Modalohr

With respect to terminal infrastructure projects a notable cluster of projects comprises roll-on-roll-off transhipment concepts in rail transport. These terminal concepts are aimed at a fast and inexpensive transhipment avoiding the use of cranes. As these solutions are in principle focused on rail carriage of accompanied units (complete truck and driver), although also unaccompanied units can be carried, they are often denoted as rolling highways.

The main challenges of these innovative handling technologies are to enable handling of all kinds of semi-trailer/load units and to limit required investments in the wagon fleet and/or terminals. Among proposed solutions, for instance, the Swedish MegaSwing concept only requires special freight wagons (Widell and Linde, 2010), while the German CargoBeamer and French Modalohr system require both special wagons and terminals (CargoBeamer, 2012; Modalohr, 2012). Further, the transhipment in CargoBeamer is an automated process. MegaSwing and CargoBeamer are still in a prototype or test phase, but since Modalohr has been introduced into the market it makes this concept more relevant for discussion.

The development of the Modalohr system was driven by the idea that

Source: www.modalohr.com.

Figure 10.5 Modalohr terminal at Bourgneuf-Aiton (near Chambéry, France)

'the rail must adapt to the road' to make rail transport attractive to road hauliers. Key elements of the system consist of special wagons and terminals (Figure 10.5). The low-floor wagons can swing out in the terminal and hence enable a truck driver to drive their complete unit on the wagon or to drop the semi-trailer onto the wagon. The wagons are passive, that is, the necessary technology (to swing out) is built into the tracks of the terminal.

The system allows fast and simultaneous loading/unloading operations of trains and saves on terminal staff costs. However, large investments in wagons and special Modalohr terminals are required. Due to its system characteristics it is designed for regular block train services within a special Modalohr network. The system was implemented in 2003 in the cross-border Alpine route (AFA) between Aiton (France) and Orbassano (Italy) over a distance of 175 km. The possibility to implement Modalohr can be attributed to the energy of its designer and manufacturer (Lohr) and the strong interests of public authorities (because of environmental considerations and safety concerns regarding truck transport through the Alps). In addition, road hauliers, being the primary customers of the service, could be committed to the project. Furthermore, a large French industrial shipper of dangerous goods played a very supportive role in the development of the system by instructing its transport companies to use the system (University of Antwerp et al., 2011).

The system functions well, since major technical problems have not been reported, but the system is not profitable. Since the beginning of operations up till now the system has faced operational deficits, which have been settled by subsidies from the two involved states. The traffic volume is much smaller than a priori forecasted. In 2011 26 000 trucks were carried, while 100 000 trucks were expected when the service was launched. Despite this the line was kept and will remain in service, a second line came into operation in 2007 and the launch of a third line was decided upon at the end of 2012. The driving force for these decisions is the political interest to encourage sustainable transport solutions as well as to support the French rail industry, Modalohr in particular.

Commutor

The Commutor concept is based upon technologies to automatically transfer containers between multiple trains at hubs, thus avoiding time- and space-consuming shunting operations (i.e., replacing the marshalling yard by a terminal) (Figure 10.6). An important driver for this concept was the desire to improve the productivity of rail transport and that of the

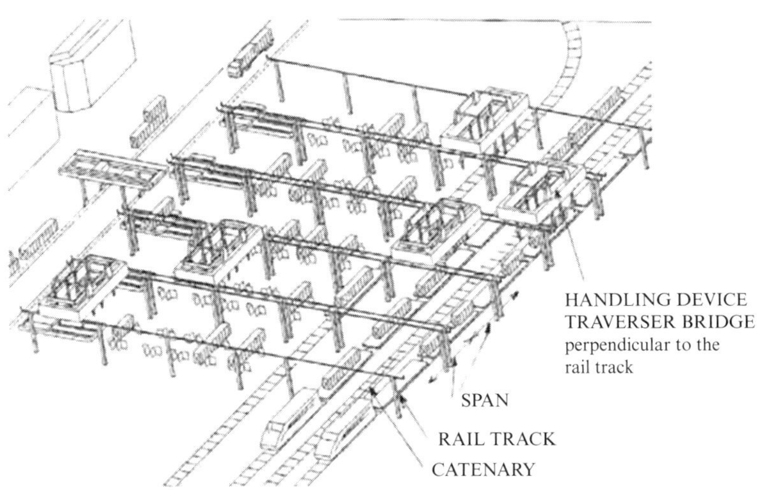

Source: Technicatome (1996) (adapted from Woxenius, 1998).

Figure 10.6 Commutor terminal system

wagonload traffic in particular. Later in the development, interfaces with road transport were foreseen.

From 1987, the French Railways (SNCF) and some 20 companies specialized in mechanical engineering and industrial robotics worked to find solutions to automate the handling processes. From 1990 to 1994, SNCF and its partners used an experimental site in Trappes in the Paris suburbs. At the test site positioning technologies for railway carriages, automated handling equipment and container storage, sorting and internal transport systems were tested (Desessard, 1994). Originally, the use of one standard size railway wagon was part of the concept, but due to technological developments later on some nine different sizes of – still adapted – wagons could be handled. Eventually, hubs servicing up to nine parallel tracks were foreseen, able to handle up to seven trains of 33 wagons a day (14 hours operation a day). Since these automated hubs enable high transfer capacities and very short transfer times, it would make them well suited to serving a hub-and-spoke design suitable for France, or eventually a multinode system serving an even larger area. The costs of the commuter system were estimated at 150 million euros (O'Mahony, 1994).

Critical issues in this system that resulted in the abortion of its development were the complicated technology (including a high degree of automation) causing high investment costs and the requirement to use dedicated rail wagons. Hence, the technology would have restricted its application to an isolated hub-and-spoke network (Woxenius, 1998).

MegaHub

MegaHub is, just like Commutor, a terminal system to improve the exchange of containers between trains, but the motive for its development as well as its technical design were very different from Commutor. MegaHub is a terminal system for container trains that was developed for the transportation of container volumes that are considered too small to enable cost-effective direct train transport and otherwise would be left to be served by truck transport (Avery, 2000; Franke, 2008).

In the MegaHub, containers that arrive on a train that have different destinations are sorted and regrouped to other trains according to their destination. A key feature of this concept is that the container exchange process takes place through transhipment instead of shunting (Figure 10.7). As a result the MegaHub leads to much shorter handling times of trains, lower costs per transfer and more efficient land use.

Container transfers are carried out using electrically powered and semiautomated cantilevered yard gantry cranes that span the transfer area in which six trains can be handled simultaneously. Transfers over very short

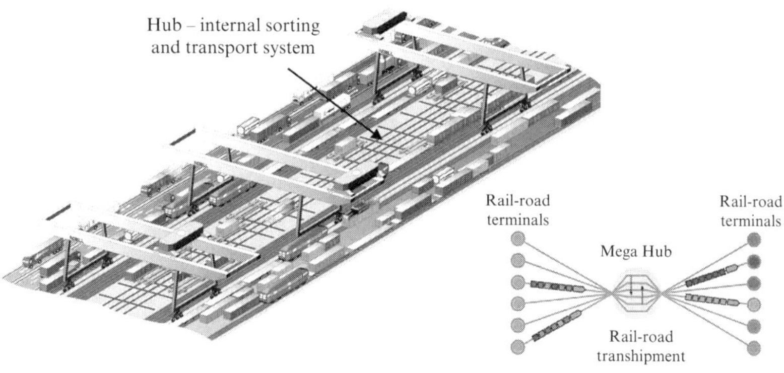

Source: Franke (2000).

Figure 10.7 MegaHub terminal

distances are performed by crane movements, while the transfer between trains over long distances at the terminal are supported by linear motor-driven shuttle cars, which can move along and across the sorting area.

A test site was built on the premises of crane manufacturer Noell in Germany, which designed and developed the MegaHub concept. Ever since its first design, which was a response to a design contest organized by Deutsche Bahn (DB) in 1995, the plan has been to implement the first MegaHub near Hannover (Lehrte) in Germany. Despite the very promising high performances of the MegaHub a final decision was not taken. The reason for postponement was initially the lack of confidence that the freight flows would be large enough to exploit the hub profitable. Later, the significant investments committed by DB in Maschen Marshalling Yard at Hamburg caused that the interest in MegaHub faded.

Moreover, reorganizations in DB cut investment budgets. After a planning phase that lasted almost 15 years the construction may still get underway as German government authorities and Deutsche Bahn have agreed to finance this 100 million euro project.

BargeExpress

A barge transport system named BargeExpress was proposed in the mid-1990s as a way to boost the development of container barge transport in the hinterland of Rotterdam (Figure 10.8). The concept aimed at time and cost reductions in handling barges in the seaport as well as cost savings through increasing scale of operations in barging. To accomplish these

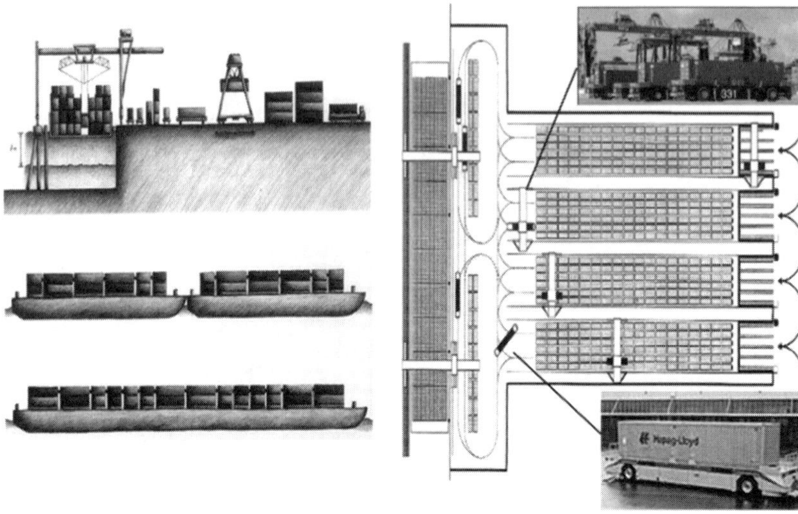

Source: TRAIL Research School (1996).

Figure 10.8 BargeExpress concept: terminal and vessels (L) and terminal layout (R) (top view)

benefits the concept includes push-boat–push-barge formations in which giant push barges are operated with automation/robotization of the loading and unloading process. The barges are equipped with cell guides to facilitate the robotized container handling process. Automated guided vehicles (AGVs) and automated stacking cranes (ASCs) that were already applied by Europe Container Terminals in Rotterdam were envisaged to support the logistical process of barge handling.

The initiators, the government together with a group of scientists, were envisaging a rapid development process, because almost all elements of the concept were based on proven technology, except for the automated quay crane. Moreover, applying proven technology could keep the investment costs as well as the associated costs within limits. Detailed studies showed the technical and economic feasibility of the concept, that is, cost savings in the barge chain (handling and sailing) was in the range of 10 to 15 per cent (TRAIL Research School, 1996). However, the fact that the barge transport system assumed point-to-point operations between the seaport and a few inland terminals revealed that the container flows were too small at that time. Moreover, there was no perspective to accomplish sufficiently large flows by bundling at the planned BargeExpress terminals for economic reasons and the unwillingness of barge operators to cooperate.

10.4 INTERMODAL MEGA-PROJECTS: AN INNOVATION ADOPTION FRAMEWORK

An innovation can be defined as an idea, practice or object that is perceived as new by a unit of adoption (Freeman, 1989). These adopters can be individuals (e.g., customers) or organizations (e.g., companies). Every innovation goes through an innovation development process (Rogers, 1983). This process consists of a series of actions and choices over time through which an individual or organization evaluates the innovation and decides whether or not to incorporate it into practice. According to Rogers the process covers five phases:

1. *Knowledge:* the awareness and exploration of a new solution to a problem.
2. *Persuasion:* the unit of adoption from a favourable or unfavourable attitude towards the innovation. The characteristics of the innovation are especially important in this stage.
3. *Decision:* the phase in which it is decided to adopt or reject the innovation.
4. *Implementation:* the phase in which the innovation is being developed and tested.
5. *Confirmation:* the adopter evaluates the decision that was taken to adopt the innovation.

Although abundant literature exists on the adoption and diffusion of innovations in general, literature that applies these issues to freight transport innovations is still rather scarce. NEA, the transport training and research company (1998), specifically focused on diffusion of innovations in the freight transport sector and based its conceptual model on the more general model of Rogers (1983). Bontekoning (2002) developed an analytical model, building upon the work of Rogers (1983), Frambach (1991), Moon and Bretschneider (1997) and NEA (1998), to identify potential obstacles for the implementation of advanced (e.g., robotized) intermodal terminals. The main groups of explaining variables in Bontekoning's model relate to:

- perceived characteristics of the innovation;
- characteristics of the potential adopting organization;
- characteristics of the communication process, and of the information that is communicated;
- characteristics of the social system to which the adopting organization belongs;

- characteristics of the competitors of the potential adopting organization;
- the role of the government;
- characteristics of the innovator/supplier.

The role of the government in fostering intermodal transport innovations has been highlighted by Holguin-Veras et al. (2008). Focusing on the American freight transport system the authors identify different sets of factors that explain the difficult challenge government has in fostering innovations: lack of cooperative tradition between the government and the freight transport industry, mismatched planning horizons of the private and public sector, lack of identification between private industry success and national policy objectives and last but not least the typical industry structure (size and complexity of the transport system) and transport modality-based priorities.

Wiegmans et al. (2010) have also been inspired by the general conceptual model of Rogers and adapted the model to three key factors to explain whether an innovation will materialize or not:

1. *User requirements:* the operationalization of the relative advantage of the innovation over the existing transport system performance in terms of reliability, costs, efficiency, flexibility, safety/security, speed and catchment area.
2. *Product characteristics (attributes of the innovation):* compatibility, simplicity, try-out possibilities, social context and relative advantage.
3. *The innovation system:* focusing on the role that all kind of actors and their relationships play in the innovation process.

Wiegmans et al. (2010) used this model to review the barriers and enablers for the development of underground logistic systems in the Netherlands.

Although all phases of the innovation process are important to achieve a successful adoption of an innovation there is much empirical evidence that the implementation phase is one of the most difficult and critical stages in the whole process (see e.g., van Binsbergen, 2007). In this phase more and other actors usually become involved and other skills and competences are needed than in the study phase, and this increases the complexity of the process.

Based on the above notions about the innovation process and the critical stages in this process we can conclude that the bottom line for a successful implementation of an innovation is the quality and complexity (perceived characteristics) of an innovation on the one hand and the process and social context in which an innovation should materialize (the innovation system) on the other. We consider these aspects as key decisive factors to evaluate potential success or failure in our review of large-scale innovations (mega-projects). We define these aspects as follows:

Perceived characteristics

- *Relative advantage:* the degree to which the intermodal transport innovation is perceived to perform better than the existing intermodal transport option or competing modes (e.g., road-only transport). The better performance may, for instance, relate to transport costs, transit time, reliability and/or flexibility.
- *Compatibility:* the degree to which an intermodal transport innovation fits into existing transport and logistics chains. Compatibility can be an issue from technological and/or organizational perspective.
- *Complexity:* the degree to which the intermodal transport innovation is perceived as relatively easy to develop (e.g., using proven-technology), understand and use.
- *Testability:* the degree to which an innovation can be experienced and tested.

Innovation system and process

- *Composition and diversity of actors involved (stakeholders):* number and type of actors and their interests, balance of power of actors, distribution of costs and revenues between actors, the role of investment actors (capital/subsidies), the role of lobby groups and/or public opinion.
- *Characteristics of competitors:* degree of market competition, possibility for niche-market development.
- *The role of the government:* the government can be involved in different ways and levels (facilitating, initiating, developing/financial, legal, coordination).

10.5 CRITICAL SUCCESS FACTORS

In the previous section we discussed the characteristics of innovations that are critical for the implementation of innovations. In Table 10.1 we summarize which of these characteristics have played a decisive role for the intermodal mega-projects we presented in Section 10.3.

Following the findings in our review of mega-projects in intermodal transport and their key success and failure factors as summarized in this

Table 10.1 Key success and failure factors of freight transport mega-projects

Project/ Initiative	Initiator – Participants/ Stakeholders	Result/Status	Key Success/Failure Factor Regarding Implementation
Seaport terminal areas: MV2/ London Gateway	Seaport authorities/national governments	Under construction	Innovation system: – common shared interest of stakeholder – strong role of national government
Seine-Nord	Inland waterway manager/national governments	In preparation	Innovation system: – funding problem – role of lobby groups
Combi-Road	Engineering company/ consultants	Pre-design, physical test site and demo; stopped	Perceived characteristics: – too complex Innovation system: – funding problem – role of government
OLS Schiphol	Flower auction/ freight cargo handlers/Schiphol Airport	Pre-design and physical test site; stopped	Perceived characteristics: – too complex Innovation system: – insufficient commitment of potential users – funding problem
Modalohr	Truck/trailer manufacturer railway companies, road hauliers	In operation	Perceived characteristics: – simple technology – relative advantage: time savings Innovation system: – commitment of customers – involvement of public authorities
Commutor	French railways/ engineers	System components tested; stopped	Perceived characteristics: – too complex – not compatible
Noell MegaHub	German Railways/crane manufacturer	Pre-design and physical test site; still under discussion	Innovation system: – role of stakeholders – funding problem
BargeExpress	Government/ knowledge institutes/barge operators, Port Authority	Feasibility studies, so far not been followed up	Innovation system: – misinterpretation of market/wrong timing (too small cargo flows)

table we can define a number of issues that are in general critical for the implementation of modal mega-projects:

Level of Investment Costs (Funding Problems)

The intermodal transport industry is a highly capital-intensive industry. In general, large budgets are required for investments in intermodal equipment (vehicles and handling facilities) and in particular when intermodal investments include infrastructure development (e.g., construction of rail lines, canals or locks, or dedicated infrastructures e.g., in the case of the Seine-Nord project, Combi-Road and OLS). Such intermodal investment costs are even higher when innovations are concerned, because the transfer facilities are innovative, that is, they are produced for the first time, so it is not possible to benefit from economies of scale in production. This is clearly illustrated by the MegaHub, Commutor, BargeExpress and OLS cases as described earlier. Also, when specialized transport vehicles are needed, high initial investment costs can hamper a successful implementation, as is illustrated by Combi-Road and OLS (automated vehicles).

For individual commercial actors the large investment budgets that are needed may be a problem in itself. As far as the innovation is developed and to be implemented by a consortium other financial issues may arise, for example, distribution of costs and revenues between the partners in the project. It seems, however, inevitable that commercial actors that invest will be confronted with higher costs in the start-up phase than their non-participating competitors. This puts the investing actors in an unfavourable competitive position, and it may therefore raise the investment threshold, although the innovation may offer promising perspectives. Van Binsbergen (2007) defines this situation as a prisoners' dilemma. As far as the innovation is concerned with infrastructural developments the involvement of the public sector is a prerequisite to enabling such developments.

Distribution of Costs and Benefits

When innovation projects require cooperation or joint investments in equipment and/or infrastructure to accomplish the comparative advantages of the innovation it is often difficult to establish a fair mechanism to distribute the costs and revenues between the participants. If participants believe that their partners will have greater benefits or lower investments than themselves they will be less willing to cooperate. This attitude will be reinforced if efficiency gains cannot easily be reaped by the initiators of the innovation, for instance if the transport market in which they operate is so competitive that they actually have to pass on their gains to the shippers. In the case of OLS, the new system would reduce truck traffic on public roads. However, public authorities were not willing to 'pay' for this reduction in truck traffic. This problem of failing to achieve an accepted distribution of costs and revenues has been one of the most manifest and persistent barriers for many innovations that have been proposed to improve the handling of barges in the Port of Rotterdam (see van Binsbergen et al., 2009). In principle this distribution issue plays a part in every project that requires cooperation, but it increasingly endangers the viability of a project when the required investments and/or the potential profits are large.

Innovations are increasingly focused on contributing to sustainable mobility, for example, reduction of emissions and noise and efficient land use. As a result such innovation projects usually score positive in social cost–benefit analyses. However, these social benefits generate very limited monetary benefits to the actors that implement the innovation in practice. So although the innovation may be socially desirable, in the end the business case must be promising.

Effects on the Power and Identity of Actors in the Transport Chain

Intended participants in an innovation project may believe that the implementation of the innovation may lead to (unintentional) changes in power relations between the participants. These expected changes may, for instance, relate to losing customer contacts, and related to that loss in commercial identity, and/or losing grip on operational processes. These effects particularly emerge when new logistics concepts and/or new transport concepts are introduced, such as in the examples of MegaHub and Commutor ('new' railway concepts) and Combi-Road (new modality), or when infrastructure investments change the competition playing field (Seine-Nord Canal). It is also possible that on a strategic level this may even affect the dependency of a company, for instance regarding the issue of whether business units can still be sold if they are embedded in the materialization of the innovation. Potential changes in power relations are an issue that plays a part in almost any concept that is based on cooperation, both in situations of chain cooperation (vertical) and in situations of horizontal cooperation, for example, intermodal transport operators that have to bundle flows to make a new concept profitable.

Continuity of Consortia and Concepts: Sufficiently Long Period of Testing

Transport and logistics innovations have a long-lasting impact: investments are made in equipment, software, staff, buildings and so on. Along with these investments a transformation to new logistic processes needs to take place and this is usually a rather slow process. Pilot and test projects are often scheduled for a too short period of time, in which this transformation has not been accomplished, and related to that, the pilot or test results may be disappointing. When pilots or tests have a longer time schedule it is important that sufficient commitment of the involved actors can be retained, even if some actors withdraw. In this context, the role and attitude (commitment) of sufficient employees of the involved companies seem to be of utmost importance: project support should not be based on the support of just one key person in the company. In fact, all mega-projects have to deal with this aspect, as either huge investments or (costs made for) significant adaptations in logistics processes and/or vehicle fleet have long pay-back periods and all mega-projects need multiple actors to stay involved over a longer period of time. For example, in the Seine-Nord Canal project the role of one crucial partner (the French state) is uncertain, endangering the whole project.

Minimum Required Scale of Operation

In several concepts the real comparative advantages of the innovation do not materialize to their full extent when the concept is tried out in a pilot or test phase, because the scale of operation is too limited. The limited scale of operation may relate to a minimum number of participants (users of the innovation), a minimum transport volume, a minimum amount of equipment (vehicles, cranes), a minimum service level, and so on. In general, budget restrictions are a major explanation for setting up small-scale pilot projects. Due to the biased performance of the innovation it becomes much more difficult to roll out the concept to wider application. In particular, mega-projects that require fundamental changes in logistics operations (such as MegaHub, Commutor and BargeExpress) and/or require the use of dedicated vehicles and infrastructures (OLS, Combi-Road) are not scalable and need a significant transport flow from the start to be able to grow into a competitive position.

Institutional Context: Role of Governments

Intermodal freight transport systems are typically created (planned, designed, financed, operated, maintained) in a public–private context. The strong interaction required by these parties is fuelled by, amongst others, the existence of regulations that affect the choice of technologies, the need to join or align financing for infrastructure and equipment, and the responsibility to prepare spatial plans and involve the local citizenship and industry stakeholders. Plans are seldom well aligned, however, because of the mismatch of private and public actors' objectives, perceptions or beliefs. It is at this stage, of early planning, that the root cause of failure lies. While governments can play an important role as innovation agent, sometimes covering first year losses of new systems (the cornerstone of the European Marco Polo funds for intermodal systems), they sometimes resort to negative measures such as restrictive actions for competing modes (Platz, 2009) or ongoing subsidization of operations. For example, Modalohr is still in operation by the grace of state subsidies. Still, fundamental aspects – some would say flaws – in traditional waterway, rail and road transport markets, hamper successful introduction of new, alternative concepts. Examples of such flaws are the misbalance between modes of infrastructure costs/tariffs, low vehicle costs due to outdated equipment (rail, barge), low labour costs due to loopholes in legislation (road), low transport tariffs due to pricing strategies (especially road), and legislation/regulation not adapted to new developments. Also, there can be a conflict of interest at different (policy) scales. For example, the new hinterland rail link (Betuwe Line) and Maasvlakte 2 land reclamation projects would support intermodal transport with the supposed environmental advantages. However, the projects themselves were a heavy burden on the local environment, and governments enforced the development of environmental mitigation (nature compensation) measures. An early alignment between private and public interests may not only increase the chances of success, but also ensure acceptance of discontinued projects (van Duin et al., 2010).

Changing External Conditions

Several innovations require a long-term commitment of governments and/or private companies. Due to internal or external causes some of these actors are no longer able (or willing) to maintain their commitment. Examples can be changes in the political scene, leading to changing long-term visions, changes in the government, mergers/takeovers, reorganizations and strategic reorientations of governments or companies. In addition, social and economic developments at national or even global level can have impact on the commitment for an innovation. For example, the financial crisis that started in 2008 has dramatically curbed the interest in large investment projects (such as MegaHub), and changing freight market conditions combined with the inflow of a relatively cheap labour force as a result of the extension of the European Community reduced the advantages for automated and high-capacity transport (such as Combi-Road, OLS and new rail systems). To some extent such developments cannot be foreseen, but innovations are more likely to successfully materialize if they can somehow be robust to such changing external conditions. Nowadays an innovation that is not just focused on profitability but can also score well on sustainability criteria will have better prospects of success.

Overestimation of Potential of 'Hardware' Solutions, Underestimation of Importance and Impact of 'Orgware' Solutions

In general there is the perception that technological innovations can have a ground-breaking impact on the performances of systems. This view is also noticeable in the intermodal transport industry, since many innovations have a technical dimension. This perception is strengthened by the fact that these innovations are often well tested under laboratory conditions (including simulations, etc.) and therefore show very promising results. However, performance claims often cannot be fulfilled in practice. The reliability of innovative technologies usually has shortcomings when they are introduced in applications. In a very competitive environment, such as the intermodal transport industry, unreliable performances can therefore endanger market competitiveness. For this reason potential users may be reluctant to be the first user of these new technologies. These kind of barriers may arise in 'hardware' innovations (engineering developments), but also arise in 'software' innovations (IT/software developments). In fact, most mega-project examples have a strong technology orientation – MegaHub, Commutor, OLS and Combi-Road related to infrastructure and equipment, and OLS, Combi-Road and Commutor also even to vehicles. All these new technologies are largely new, hardly tested in practice, and argued to be vulnerable in the harsh environment of freight transport. In addition, most mega-projects require important changes in logistics operations and/or a change in habits, and such changes are hard to implement. Moreover, where strong, technologically oriented innovations are concerned the financial issues and organizational impacts are often neglected in the R&D process and turn out to be serious barriers when it comes to implementation. The intermodal transport industry is a typical multi-actor environment where innovations in inter-organizational coordination and cooperation can be even more effective in improving the performance of the intermodal transport system.

Innovation Project Management

A critical issue for the successful materialization of an innovation is proper management of the whole development process of the innovation.

In the first place, several innovations have suffered from the fact that the initiators have been insufficiently aware of the (international) state of the art and/or experiences with similar initiatives. Innovation projects often start from scratch and often face the same kind of barriers as previous projects. The concept of Modalohr, for example, is almost identical to the Walda system developed about a decade earlier in the Netherlands, and the MegaHub concept is very similar to Commutor. Previous initiatives can provide useful insights into avoiding pitfalls in developing new initiatives. It is questionable whether the initiators of the 'newer' systems knew the ins and outs of the earlier initiatives.

Major causes of the lack of quality in the process management are related to financial structures and conditions (e.g., budgets are provided in small amounts, one by one and other strict conditions regarding spending budgets) and a lack of a strong project manager. In addition, problems and challenges in the innovation project that are identified or defined in the early phase of a project are not always adequately dealt with in later phases of the innovation development. This may relate to very fundamental issues, such as 'Does the innovation really contribute to solving a problem?' or 'Can the innovation really be implemented in practice?' For instance, in the Combi-Road project the development process was strongly technology driven, while as the project progressed it became clear that the technology that was chosen did not fit very well to the envisaged application of this automated transport system. The causes of such fallacies can be attributed to a group process in which participants are not really able to review and revise their project visions or are not willing to do so, because one dominant participant or some of them have a vast interest in developing a project according to the initially defined plan.

Finally, innovation projects that have a large scope, both in terms of the number of new system elements (regarding technologies, logistics organization and infrastructure development) and in number of actors (companies and individuals) that are involved, will face typical management problems, because in view of their large scope, participants will be less committed and feel less responsible.

10.6 CONCLUSIONS

Innovations in intermodal freight transport face many different barriers and challenges during the process of implementation. This especially holds for intermodal mega-projects – projects that ask for heavy investments and/or demand fundamental organizational changes throughout the transport process. As with most mega-projects, acquiring funding is nowadays an important challenge as infrastructural development requires large budgets, pay-back periods are long and future profits uncertain. Also, as investment relies heavily (though not uniquely) on public funding, long-term project impacts are important.

Not only there should be a long-term net societal benefit, the private business case must also be(come) viable. For initiatives with a net societal profit but a negative business case, some way of compensation – for example by subsidies for the introduction and operational phase – could be considered. Authorities, however, can be reluctant to subsidize because of apprehension about causing distortion of competition in the transport market. Moreover, alignment of public and private strategies is needed well beyond the stage of political decision-making. During the (private) operation of facilities, public regulations determine the effectiveness and efficiency of the new infrastructure. So, size does complicate the realization of projects.

The sheer scale of intermodal freight transport projects is not the main reason for projects to be challenging, however. The key critical factors that we have identified here are typical in the whole freight transport industry. While this industry is very competitive and profit margins on operations are generally low, intermodal transport systems require operators of competing modes to collaborate. This raises complex questions concerning alignment of strategic objectives, synchronization of services, sharing of investments (in physical or ICT infrastructure) and sharing of gains. In short, in a world of heavy competition, intermodal transport is a multi-actor service that all of a sudden requires good cooperation between the actors – often competitors – in the logistic chain. To complicate things further, changes in transport services can impact on the broader supply chain, influencing inventory management (through, e.g., changes in transport schedules) and possibly the quality of delivery of goods. This influence affects the business of the shipper, who has to consider changes in the supply chain surrounding the transport service. If these changes are too complex and do not result in an overall, supply chain level improvement, shippers will not accept this change. A reluctance by companies to pioneer such innovations can be explained by the difficulty in creating a balanced outcome. These barriers will be highest in the start-up phase, in particular when the performance of the innovation does not yet meet expectation.

Solutions to overcoming these barriers will have to focus on some main substantive critical factors. First, the relative advantage of the new technology needs to be clear. Second, the compatibility with the existing system has to be understood by all parties, irrespective of the question of whether the innovation is transformational or incremental. Third, the lower the complexity of the change, the higher the probability of implementation. Fourth, the innovation has to be such that it can be experienced and tested, if necessary on a large scale. Finally, the new concept must eventually be based on a positive, private business case that can compete with alternatives; this could imply the introduction of subsidies in the introduction phase and in some cases even in the operational phase.

Where the innovation process itself is concerned, there is a need for a strong process management during the whole development process, starting from the elaboration of the idea until implementation of the innovation. The freight projects discussed in this chapter show that this is only possible if stakeholders are willing to invest in the process, first in the role of championing institutes, later in the role of mediation and aligning of preferences, and finally in joint decision-making in implementation.

The potential success of an intermodal transport innovation, however, will depend on the reaction of competing intermodal actors, but also on the reaction of competing modes, the road transport sector in particular. It is striking that road hauliers, while confronted with continuous increasing operating costs, have still managed to improve their productivity to keep up their strong competitive position towards intermodal transport. These improvements could not have been accomplished without road transport innovations also taking place, such as more intelligent (dynamic) route planning systems and cooperative agreements between hauliers to improve vehicle utilization rates and to avoid trips with empty containers. From this perspective, positive experiments with so-called longer and heavier vehicles (LHVs) up to 25.25 metres length and 60 tons gross weight that are taking place in some European countries are considered a threat to rail and barge transport (both in traditional and intermodal operations of rail and barge). However, it remains to be seen to what extent and under which conditions access to these trucks will be permitted.

In view of the major social ambition to make our transport system more sustainable it would be more useful to focus on the complementarities of the different modes rather than propagating intermodal transport as the only recipe for sustainable transport. Governments, including the European Commission, increasingly acknowledge that striving for optimal combinations of various modes, including road transport (so called co-modality) is a more preferred option in achieving sustainable transport. However, it is evident that to make co-modality really work there remains a need for innovations. It is most likely that these innovations would be most needed in information and telecommunication technology and organizational issues.

NOTES

1. Intermodal freight transport is generally defined as the movement of goods in one and the same loading unit or vehicle by successive modes of transport without handling of the goods themselves when changing modes (European Conference of Ministers of Transport et al., 1997). Loading units can be containers, swap bodies and trailers.
2. Twenty Foot Equivalent Units, a standardized computing unit to compare different sizes of containers.

LITERATURE

Avery, P. (2000), 'MegaHub gains momentum', *Cargo Systems*, London: IRR Publications.

Bontekoning, Y.M. (2002), *Towards New-generation Terminal Operations: Identifying Implementation Obstacles*, TRAIL Reports in Transportation Planning, R2002/02, Delft: DUP Science.

Bontekoning, Y. and E. Kreutzberger (1999), *Concepts of New-generation Terminals and Terminal Nodes*, R99/01, TRAIL Reports in Transportation Planning, Delft: Delft University Press.

CargoBeamer (2012), 'CargoBeamer Prospekt', www.cargobeamer.com.

Desessard, J.F. (1994), 'Commutor, la gare futuriste du fret' [Commutor, futuristic freight station], BE France, No. 8, 1 November – ADIT/ADIT, accessed 19 June 2013 at www.bulletins-electroniques.com/actualites/34867.htm.

European Conference of Ministers of Transport, United Nations Economic Commission for Europe Statistical Division and European Union Eurostat (1997), 'Glossary for transport statistics'.

Eurostat (2011), *Europe in Figures – Eurostat Yearbook 2011*, Luxembourg: Publications Office of the European Union.

Fisher, R. and W. Ury (1991), *Getting to Yes: Negotiation Agreement Without Giving In*, 2nd edition, Boston: Houghton Mifflin.

Frambach, R.T. (1991), 'The diffusion of innovations: the influence of supply-side factors', Tilburg: Tilburg University Department of Economics Research Memorandum.

Franke, K.P. (2000), 'Boosting efficiency of split container terminals by innovative technology', Memorandum, Noell Crane Systems GmbH, Würzburg.

Franke, K.P. (2008), 'A technical approach to the Agile Port System', in R. Konings, H. Priemus and P. Nijkamp (eds), *The Future of Intermodal Freight Transport, Operations, Design and Policy*, Cheltenham, UK and Northampton, MA, USA: Edward Elgar Publishing.

Freeman, J.L. (1989), 'An empirical test of a model of the innovation-decision process in organizations', doctoral dissertation, Atlanta: Georgia State University.

Holguin-Veras, J., R. Paaswell and A. Perl (2008), 'The role of government in fostering intermodal transport innovations: perceived lessons and obstacles in the United States', in R. Konings, H. Priemus and P. Nijkamp, *The Future of Intermodal Freight Transport: Operations, Design and Policy*, Cheltenham, UK and Northampton, MA, USA: Edward Elgar Publishing.

Institut für Seeverkehrswirtschaft und Logistik (ISL) (2004), Intermodal transhipment interfaces, working paper, Work Package/Working Group WG3 Intermodality & Interoperability, European Strategies to Promote Inland Navigation (SPIN-TN) EU FP5-project, Bremen.

International Union of Railways (2010), *2010 Report on Combined Transport in Europe*, Paris: IUR.

Konings, R. (2009), 'Intermodal barge transport: network design, nodes and competitiveness', TRAIL Thesis Series No. T2009/11, Delft.

Kreutzberger, E.K. (2008), 'The innovation of intermodal rail freight bundling networks in Europe: concepts, developments and performances', TRAIL Thesis Series No. T2008/16, Delft.
Levinson, M. (2006), *How the Shipping Container Made the World Smaller and the World Economy Bigger*, Princeton, NJ: Princeton University Press.
London Gateway (2012), 'Overview of London Gateway', www.londongateway.com.
Mialocq, G. (2011), 'Future challenges for the inland navigation sector: the Seine–Scheldt link and its perspectives for 2030', in C. Sys and T. Vanelslander (eds), *Future Challenges for Inland Navigation: A Scientific Appraisal of the Consequences of Possible Strategic and Economic Developments up to 2030*, Brussels: UPA.
Modalohr (2012), 'Road on rail and info sheet', February 2006, www.modalohr.com.
Moon, M.J. and S. Bretschneider (1997), 'Can state government actions affect innovation and its diffusion? An extended communication model and empirical test', *Technological Forecasting and Social Change*, **54**(1), 57–77.
NEA (1998), *Diffusie van innovaties in het goederenvervoer* [*Diffusion of Innovations in Freight Transport*], The Hague: Pb IVVS.
O'Mahony (1994), 'Waiting on the Commutor line', *Cargo Systems*, No. 7 (July), 55–7.
Peterlini, E. (2001), 'State of the art of conventional and innovative techniques in intermodal transport: survey on intermodal transfer technologies', Deliverable D1, Annex 1 of EU-Project Innovative Technologies for Intermodal Transfer Points (ITIP), EU FP4-project, Milan.
Pielage, B.A. (2000), 'Design approach and prototyping of automated underground freight transport systems in the Netherlands', International Symposium on Underground Freight Transportation (ISUFT 2000) conference proceedings, Delft.
Pielage, B.A. (2005), 'Conceptual design of automated freight transport systems: methodology and practice', PhD thesis, Delft: TRAIL Research School.
Platz, T.E. (2009), 'The efficient integration of inland shipping into continental intermodal transport chains: measures and decisive factors', TRAIL Thesis Series No. T2009/7, Delft.
Port Authority Rotterdam (2011), 'Havenvisie 2030 – Port Compass', Rotterdam.
Port Authority Rotterdam (2012), 'Maasvlakte 2: Space for the future', www.maasvlakte2.com.
Rodrigue, J.P. (1999), 'Globalization and the synchronization of transport terminals', *Journal of Transport Geography*, **7**(4), 255–61.
Rogers, E.M. (1983), *Diffusion of Innovations*, 3rd edition, New York: The Free Press.
TRAIL Research School (1996), *Barge Express: perspectief voor grootschalige binnenvaart* [*Barge Express: Perspective for Large-scale Barge Transport*], Delft: TRAIL.
University of Antwerp, University of Aegean, University of Genova, University of Delft, CNRS, LCA Europe (2011), 'Deliverable D4 and D5 – Topical assessment of innovative successes and not-yet-successes', 2, EU FP7-Project INNOSUTRA, Brussels.
University of Antwerp, University of Aegean, University of Genova, University of Delft, CNRS, LCA Europe (2012), 'Innovation process in surface transport (INNOSUTRA)', EU FP7-project, http://www.innosutra.eu/.
van Binsbergen, A.J. (2007), 'Succes- en faalfactoren bij implementatie complexe logistieke concepten' [Success and failure factors regarding the implementation of complex logistic concepts], in F. Witlox and C. Ruijgrok, *Bijdragen 14de Vervoerslogistieke Werkdagen* [*Contributions to 14th Transport Logistical Workshops*], Grobbendonk.
van Binsbergen, A.J., M. van der Horst, R. Konings and A. Veenstra (2009), 'Containerlogistiek in de binnenvaart: een vergelijking tussen Nederlandse en buitenlandse zeehavens' [Container logistics in inland shipping: a comparison between Dutch and foreign seaports], Delft: TRAIL Research School.
van der Heijden, B. and E. Heere (1997), 'Combi-Road is on the move', Proceedings of Fourth World Congress on Intelligent Transport Systems, Berlin, Paper No. 2284.
van Duin, J.H.R., H. Quak and J. Muñuzuri (2010), 'New challenges for urban consolidation centres: a case study in The Hague', *Procedia – Social and Behavioral Sciences*, **2**(3), 6177–88.

van Gorp, H.A. and M.M. van der Zandt (2003), 'Trailers-on-train, de praktische invulling, eindrapportage', [the practical realisation, final report] commissioned by the Ministerie van Verkeer en Waterstaat, The Hague.
Verhoeven, P. (2010), 'A review of port authority functions: towards a renaissance?', *Maritime Policy & Management*, **37**(3), 247–70.
Vleugel, J., E. Kreutzberger and Y. Bontekoning (2001), 'Concepts of innovative bundling networks', R2001/03, TRAIL Reports in Transportation Planning, Delft: Delft University Press.
VNF (Voies Navigables de France) (2011), *Seine-Nord Europe Canal*, Paris.
Widell, B. and P. Linde (2010), 'Piggyback potential', *Railway Gazette International*, September, 149–50.
Wiegmans, B., J. Visser, R. Konings and B.J. Pielage (2010), 'Review of underground logistic systems in the Netherlands: an ex-post evaluation of barriers, enablers and spin-offs', *European Transport*, **45**, 1–16.
Woxenius, J. (1998), 'Development of small-scaled intermodal transportation in a systems context', dissertation, Report No. 34, Gothenburg: Chalmers University of Technology.

11. Multi-actor and multi-criteria analysis in evaluating mega-projects

Cathy Macharis and Peter Nijkamp

11.1 INTRODUCTION

Mega-projects, such as the Channel Tunnel (Norman and Vickerman, 1999), the Vasco da Gama Bridge in Portugal (Branco et al., 2000), the Millau Viaduct in France (Campagnac, 2010) and the Rion-Antirrion Bridge in Greece (Kaparos, 2010), imply a great political, economic and environmental impact (Flyvbjerg et al., 2003). These impacts have recently been given considerably more attention due to the growing number of regulatory restrictions concerning the environment, the economy and other important aspects. Also the fact that many projects have shown poor results with regard to their planning and implementation (Priemus et al., 2008) is an important reason for an increasing interest in the search for a framework that is able to deal with a multiplicity of planning aspects.

Mega-projects involve great risks on account of the extended planning and construction time. First, mega-projects involve complex interactions between the project itself and reality, which can incorporate many risks when these interactions are not properly dealt with. Second, there are many actors involved in the decision-making process who often have conflicting interests. These actors who have a vested interest in a problem, because they can influence it and/or are influenced by it, can be called stakeholders (Banville et al., 1998). Third, the ambition and range of the project can change over time, making it more or less ambitious than initially planned. This can directly influence the overall impact of the project. The fourth characteristic is the fact that unplanned events are not explicitly taken into account when determining the budget, making this budget planning incorrect. This may prompt misunderstandings and an underestimation of the costs, benefits and risks of the project.

As more and more transport infrastructure projects are increasing in size, they face a great number of problems due to their complex nature. Mega-projects affect the economy, the environment and society as a whole. On top of that, predictions about costs and benefits are often incomplete or incorrect, which may lead to financial problems during the building and exploitation stage of the project. Moreover, these difficulties are exacerbated when we look at the project's performance from an economic, environmental and social perspective. Most mega-projects have a poor performance in terms of planning and costs. These poor results often put an enormous pressure on the viability of these projects. The Channel Tunnel, for instance, faced construction costs of €6.8 billion. These construction costs were equal to a cost overrun of 80 per cent, causing several near bankruptcies. The forecasted financial costs and revenues were also too optimistic, causing a financial cost overrun of 140 per cent and overestimated revenues by 50 per cent (Flyvbjerg et al., 2003). Such mistakes in project assessment may be caused by inability of planners and designers to come up with reliable cost estimates (especially in case of non-routine projects), but also by deliberate neglect of relevant costs in order to come up with a more favourable outcome.

As mentioned before, mega-projects involve multiple stakeholders with different objectives and opinions. As such projects become more complex it becomes more difficult to align these different points of view. Often during the planning phase, various stakeholder groups take action to prevent implementation of the project on account of bias or incompleteness in the planning and design. In this chapter, a general and integrative evaluation framework, called multi-actor multi-criteria analysis (MAMCA), is presented. This extension of traditional multi-criteria analysis (MCA) allows the explicit involvement of relevant stakeholders during the project analysis. It was developed by Macharis (2000, 2004). Mega-projects face many difficulties during the decision-making process. Explicit stakeholder involvement is a way to address these difficulties by providing a structured view of the decision-making problem in a visual and understandable way.

MAMCA has already been used for several decision-making problems in the field of evaluating transport projects; for an overview, see Macharis et al. (2009). In this chapter, an illustrative application for the evaluation of mega-projects will be given. The case of the Oosterweel Connection in Antwerp, Flanders is a perfect example of a mega-project for which the stakeholders were not sufficiently involved in the process from the beginning, leading to the emergence of several action groups and heated public debate. The project preparation has already lasted for 15 years, and has hardly got off the ground.

11.2 ASSUMING THERE ARE WINNERS AND LOSERS

Most of the research concerning the planning and implementation of mega-projects focuses on cost estimations and traffic forecasts (Skamris and Flyvbjerg, 1997; Flyvbjerg et al., 2005, 2006). But most of these projects not only have an economic impact, there are also social, demographic and environmental aspects that need to be taken into account when evaluating projects of this magnitude. Gellert and Lynch (2003) interpret the development of mega-projects as an extension of Schumpeter's creative destruction. Such projects involve a transformation of landscapes and communities, and thus have a substantial influence on multiple levels and groups in our society. It is obvious that these levels should be heard and represented during the decision-making process. There are, for example, environmental pressure groups that are opposing the environmental implications of a certain project, or citizens who are against the idea that a bridge is being built in their backyard. But in reality this involvement is often forgotten by policy-makers. As said by Bryson (2004, p. 23), a 'failure to attend to the information and concerns of stakeholders clearly is a kind of flaw in thinking or action that too often and too predictably leads to poor performance, outright failure or even disaster'. The case study of the Oosterweel Connection will show that mega-projects that lack stakeholder involvement are much more difficult to implement owing to pressure from actors whose opinions have not been explicitly and sufficiently recognized.

Implementing such mega-projects implies that there will be winners and losers. The real difficulty is how one can integrate these varying opinions and get to a solution where everyone is reasonably satisfied (or where at least standard 'democratic rules' are met). Within Bryson (2004), a set of possible stakeholder identification and analysis approaches is described that can be used in a general context. Rothengatter (2008) provides two possible approaches to stakeholder involvement when planning mega-projects.

The first approach is to use spider diagrams where all the performance indicators are scored with regard to the project. However, this method is based on rough calculations, which might be misleading when not using the correct information. That is why this method might be useful in the preliminary phase of the project to investigate its feasibility, when the final design has not yet been decided. By comparing the minimum positions of a stakeholder group's preferences with the expected performance of each indicator, these spider diagrams can serve as a tool for further discussion and research.

A second method is constraint logic programming (CLP), which is a method originating from artificial intelligence, and with roots in operational research (ibid.). This method tries to satisfy a multiple number of constraints at the same time by using heuristics. The constraint-solver generates variable domains that satisfy the set of criteria. In order to do so, a minimum boundary is set for each criterion. Then, on the basis of the Kaldor-Hicks criterion (Hicks, 1939; Kaldor, 1939), which states that a project is acceptable for society when the advantaged parties compensate the disadvantaged parties, and have a net surplus, a project is accepted or rejected. The goal of this criterion is to determine whether the advantages of a given project outweigh the disadvantages. CLP may serve as a valuable tool to initiate the negotiation process, where stakeholders determine the conditions under which they are willing to accept a project. However, the main problem with this method is that it only looks at the economic advantages, which is basically like performing a traditional cost–benefit analysis where the economic benefits are compared with the economic costs (Mishan and Quah, 2007).

It is, however, not desirable to evaluate mega-projects by using only financial variables, even if the evaluation integrates stakeholders in the decision-making process. For the evaluation of external costs, already a great deal of effort is often made to obtain monetary values for external effects such as noise and congestion in order to include them in a social cost–benefit analysis. However, other criteria such as image, comfort, and so on, are often also crucial factors for the stakeholders. So, there is a need for a framework that can look at all implications of a project, especially the non-monetary ones, while taking into account the preferences and objectives of all relevant stakeholders. MAMCA provides a framework in which these different opinions can be integrated in a structured and objective way (see Macharis, 2000, 2005).

In the next section, different possible evaluation methods are discussed and the importance of stakeholder involvement is explained. Section 11.4 provides a general explanation of the multi-actor multi-criteria methodology. In Section 11.5 the way MAMCA can be used is illustrated by the Oosterweel Connection application.

11.3 EVALUATION METHODS FOR MEGA-PROJECTS

Socioeconomic Evaluation Methods

Transport projects are often complex decision problems with different alternatives and stakeholders who each have their own goals. To deal with these complex problems, policy-makers have the possibility to use several evaluation techniques with different backgrounds. The goal of these tools is not to replace the decision-makers, but to support them by solving the problem in a structured and objective way (Brans, 2004). According to van Mierlo and Macharis (2005, p.487), an evaluation is 'systematically analyzing the concept, design, implementation and utility of social intervention programs by using social research procedures'.

Over the years, several socioeconomic evaluation methods have been introduced to evaluate transport projects. The most important ones are: cost-effectiveness analysis (CEA); economic-effects analysis (EEA); cost–benefit analysis (CBA); private investment analysis (PIA); and social cost–benefit analysis (SCBA).

CEA is a neoclassical method that is based on one single actor (often the government) and one single criterion (money). It looks at the effectiveness of a certain policy measure in terms of the investments made by the government. The analysis is therefore performed with regard to one single objective (Macharis, 2005). A second method is economic-effects analysis (EEA), which looks at the economic implications of a transport project (ibid.). For instance, new transport infrastructure can have an impact on a country's GDP, employment rate and government revenue. However, it is more a descriptive method, which means that it is not useful when evaluating new policy measures concerning transport infrastructure (de Brucker et al., 1998). CBA is similar to CEA, a neoclassical evaluation method. It simply tries to sum up all the relevant costs and benefits, in order to evaluate if the planned investments will be efficient. A PIA is a CBA, but performed from the point of view of the private investor (Macharis, 2007). Using a benefit ratio to calculate the return on investment, the best alternative is chosen. An SCBA is an extension of the basic CBA, because the latter does not take into account the point of view of the whole society. External effects like environmental and social effects are becoming as important as the monetary ones. Mega-projects affect multiple layers of our society, who have different interests and needs. In that case, looking at the direct economic effects will not suffice, because there is a need to evaluate the project from the point of view of society as a whole. The main disadvantage of this method is that everything has to be transformed into monetary values, causing several problems, especially in terms of external effects, which are difficult to determine (de Brucker et al., 1998; Erke et al., 2008).

Multi-criteria Analysis

CEA, EEA and CBA have limitations, in particular when there is stakeholder involvement (Macharis, 2005). Projects that are becoming more complex involve more actors and non-economic factors that need to be included in the decision-making process. In this section, multi-criteria analysis (MCA) is discussed. Originating from operational research, this evaluation method is able to evaluate a project using multiple criteria (see Nijkamp et al., 1991; Triantaphyllou et al., 1998).

MCA is an evaluation method that has become more important in the last quarter of the twentieth century. Research on this method evolved rapidly during this period, leading to a number of 'schools of thought', for example, the French with outranking methods, and the American School with utility functions. MCA is used when a set of possible alternatives has to be evaluated with regard to multiple criteria that can be conflicting with each other (Belton and Stewart, 2002). This evaluation can be based on both qualitative and quantitative information and is not bounded to one single measuring unit as it is in the SCBA.

There are two main phases in an MCA that each involve a number of steps. The first phase is the analytical phase, where the problem definition is organized in a clear format. The second phase is more synthetic, and contains the actual evaluation. Following de Brucker et al. (1998) we define six steps to perform an MCA, four in the analytical phase and two in the synthetic phase: Step 1 is the problem definition. This involves collecting all the relevant information, making sure that the problem is well documented and formulated. Step 2 involves defining the different solutions for the problem definition of Step 1. Each solution will have its specific implications and consequences, so it is important that these alternatives are defined very clearly. The evaluation of the alternatives will be based upon a number of objectives or criteria. These criteria laid down in Step 3 represent the relevant characteristics of the decision problem. In Step 4 every alternative will be evaluated with regard to one single criterion in an evaluation matrix. These performances are then aggregated in Step 5 to a general evaluation. This aggregation is in fact the synthesis of the previous steps (de Brucker et al., 1998). Step 6 is the actual implementation. The results of the analysis can be transformed into real policy measures.

The Need for Stakeholder Involvement

Mega-projects are characterized by the (direct or indirect) involvement of different stakeholders. Over the years, this stakeholder approach has attracted a great deal of interest in the field of MCA (Macharis, 2005, 2007). The concept of stakeholders was introduced in the research field of strategic management (Williamson, 1991) in the context of corporate social responsibility (Donaldson and Preston, 1995; Buysse and Verbeke, 2003). Freeman (1984) defines a stakeholder as an individual or a group of individuals who can influence the objectives of an organization, or who can be influenced themselves by these objectives. Their explicit involvement can happen for two reasons. First, it is possible that the researcher is not able to guarantee a valid solution due to the lack of relevant information (Macharis, 2005). Second, their involvement can also be useful when the decision-making problem is highly controversial and has a low acceptance rate (Macharis, 2007).

Stakeholder involvement is often inadequately integrated in the decision-making process because MCA lacks the properties necessary to cope with group decision-making (GDM) (Banville et al., 1998). However, this involvement might be crucial for the successful implementation of transport projects. The rate of acceptance will be higher when all the interests of the different stakeholders are taken into account (Walker, 2000). Banville et al. (1998) suggest that the ideas of these stakeholders can indeed be implemented into the multi-criteria decision-making process. Their proposal is an improvement that integrates socio-political aspects into the decision-making process, based on the stakeholder integration into MCA. Macharis (2005) states clearly that this integration can be successful in group decision-making and can be implemented in a more complex methodology, that is, multi-actor multi-criteria analysis.

Integrating several actors in the decision-making process by using MCA has evolved over the years. Group decision-making tries to achieve a consensus between the different actors in the decision-making process (Leyva-Lopez, 2010). This can be very difficult because each stakeholder has a unique perception about the outcome of a certain decision-making problem. There have been several attempts to classify group decision-making problems that use MCA techniques to support a group decision (for an overview, see Alvarez-Carrillo et al., 2010). These methods focus mainly on how the information is brought together in the decision-making process.

There are many different ways in which stakeholder participation can be organized. Sometimes stakeholder involvement is included in the entire analysis through well-defined and structured steps. However, in most of the current MCA transport projects, stakeholder participation is not arranged that profoundly. Their input is often only used in the preliminary investigation, or in the very first stages of the MCA in order to gather enough information to build an initial framework. Another type of stakeholder participation that is used frequently happens at the end of the analysis, when stakeholders are asked to provide feedback on the results of the analysis. A combination of the last two techniques mentioned above has also been applied several times. The way in which the stakeholders are integrated into the analysis may also vary according to the specific MCA technique that is applied. Mostly, a few extra steps are simply carried out before or after the classical MCA method. Only in a few exceptional cases is the stakeholder input seen as the most crucial element for the analysis, as, for example, in the multi-actor multi-criteria analysis developed by Macharis (2000, 2005).

11.4 MULTI-ACTOR MULTI-CRITERIA ANALYSIS

Multi-actor multi-criteria analysis (MAMCA) allows different alternatives (policy measures, scenarios, technologies) to be evaluated from the perspective of the objectives of the different stakeholders who are involved. Unlike a conventional MCA where alternatives are evaluated using several criteria, the MAMCA methodology explicitly includes the points of view of the different stakeholders. It has been developed by Macharis (2000, 2005). It has been applied to several transport-related decision problems (for an overview see Macharis et al., 2009). The methodology consists of seven steps (see Figure 11.1).

Step 1 is the definition of the problem and the identification of the alternatives. These alternatives can take different forms according to the problem situation. They can be different technological solutions, different policy measures, long-term strategic options, and so on. In Step 2, the relevant stakeholders are identified. Stakeholders are people who have an interest, financial or otherwise, in the consequences of any decisions

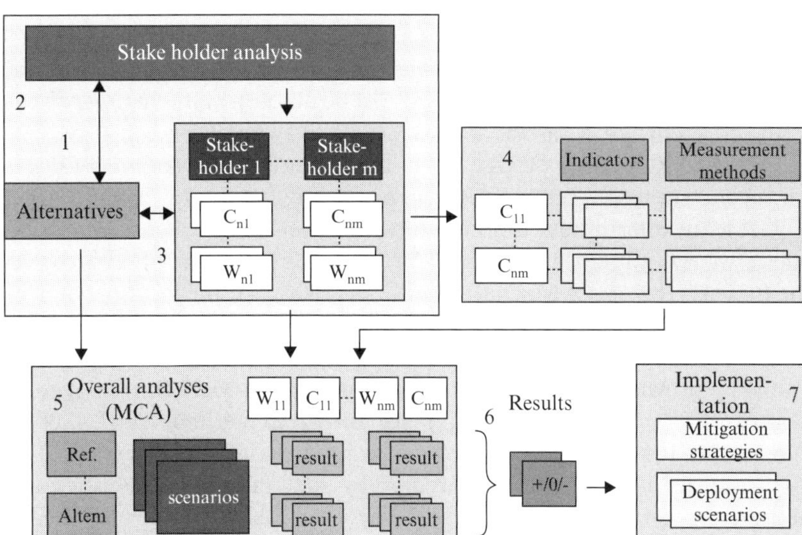

Source: Macharis (2007).

Figure 11.1 The MAMCA methodology

taken. In Step 3, the key objectives of the stakeholders are identified, and the stakeholders express the relative importance or priority (weights) they attach to them. In Step 4, for each criterion, one or more indicators are constructed (e.g., direct quantitative indicators, such as money spent, number of lives saved, reductions in CO_2 emissions achieved, etc. or scores on an ordinal indicator such as high/medium/low for criteria with values that are difficult to express in quantitative terms). The measurement method for each indicator is also made explicit (for instance, willingness-to-pay and quantitative scores based on macroscopic computer simulation). This allows each alternative performance to be measured in terms of its contribution to the objectives of specific stakeholder groups. Steps 1 to 4 can be considered as mainly analytical, and they precede the 'overall analysis', which takes into account the objectives of all stakeholder groups simultaneously and is more 'synthetic' in nature. Step 5 is the construction of the evaluation matrix. The alternatives are further described and translated into scenarios that also describe the contexts in which the policy options will be implemented. The different scenarios are then scored on the objectives of each stakeholder group. A multi-criteria analysis (MCA) is performed for each stakeholder. The different points of view are brought together in a multi-actor view. In Step 6 this multi-actor multi-criteria analysis yields a ranking of the various alternatives, and reveals their strengths and weaknesses. The stability of the ranking can be assessed through a sensitivity analysis. Step 7, the last stage of the methodology includes the actual implementation. Based on the insights obtained from the analysis, an implementation can be developed, taking the wishes of the different actors into account.

The MAMCA methodology has in the meantime proven its usefulness for several transport-related decision problems. It was, for instance, used to tackle an inter-modal terminal location decision problem (Macharis, 2000); for a study on the choice between waste transport alternatives in the Brussels region see Macharis and Boel (2004); for the location choices of a new high-speed train terminal see Meeus et al. (2004); for the evaluation of DHL's hub strategy at Brussels airport see Dooms et al., 2006 and Dooms and Macharis (2005); in the project 'Night Deli' for the evaluation of different night distribution scenarios see Verlinde et al. (2009); and in the 'Flanders in Action' process to structure the discussions on how to turn Flanders into a top region by 2020 in terms of logistics and mobility see Macharis et al. (2010). For a complete overview of theory and applications of the MAMCA methodology we refer to Macharis et al. (2009).

11.5 CASE STUDY: THE OOSTERWEEL CONNECTION

A good example of the use of MAMCA is an evaluation of the different possibilities to solve the serious mobility problems in and around Antwerp, a main transportation hub in Belgium. The Antwerp ring road is faced with heavy congestion due to international transit and port-related traffic. This congestion is an economic cost for the Flemish economy, making it less competitive. In 1995, the Flemish government initiated a project to present the ring road in an entire circle, and therefore to create extra capacity. Fifteen years later, the project is still in a preparatory phase, mainly due to many internal discussions and public protests against the proposals of the Flemish government.

This case study will show how difficult it is to plan and implement mega-projects. The involvement of multiple stakeholders is very clear in this case because of the project's large economic, social, political and environmental effects. This section goes through the different steps of the MAMCA in the analysis of the Oosterweel Connection. The decision-support software used for this analysis is Expert Choice, which uses the analytical hierarchy process method (Saaty, 1982) as the MCA technique, which provides the advantage that the outcomes can be visualized and allows an extra layer to include the stakeholders (Macharis, 2005).

Alternatives

The first step of the methodology consists of identifying and classifying the possible alternatives submitted for evaluation. For this case, five alternatives were selected, based on their relevance at that particular point in time. Since then, there have been other proposals that could not be included in the analysis because our model was already in its final phase when these proposals were presented.

The first alternative is the BAM route with the highly contested bridge (the 'Lange Wapper'). It is part of the Antwerp Mobility Master Plan, which is a large-scale mobility plan with initiatives in public and road transport to provide optimal mobility for the City of Antwerp. The BAM route closes the R1-Ring, which will make the BAM a complete ring road around Antwerp. The connection is made between the R1 (Kennedy Tunnel) – E17 – E34 (Left Bank) and the R1 (Merksem Viaduct) – E19 – A12 (Right Bank). The first part of this route will be a 1.5-km sunk tunnel under the River Scheldt with 2 × 3 lanes and two separate tunnels for pedestrians and safety purposes, in order to conform with the European Union's Tunnel Guideline 2004/54/EG. The second part of the BAM route is a double-deck viaduct that will be 2.4 km long and consist of 2 × 3 lanes. This route will be implemented together with a truck ban in the Kennedy Tunnel, in the hope of relieving this tunnel from congestion.

The second project is the ArupSum alternative or AS route. This was an unsolicited proposal made by bureau ArupUK/SUMResearch during its independent analysis of the Oosterweel Connection. It consists of a drilled tunnel that will be 4.3 km long, with two cylinders, each having three lanes. The AS route will run from Left Bank to the A12 in Ekeren where a new traffic complex will be built to manage the new traffic flows.

The third alternative is a proposal by a Flemish Member of Parliament Ivan Sabbe to optimize the current infrastructure (the Liefkenshoek Tunnel) so that the existing capacity can be used more efficiently in a short- to mid-term perspective. The Liefkenshoek Tunnel was built in 1991 and is part of Antwerp's great ring road, R2. The main argument for this alternative is that the existing tunnel is currently used below its capacity level with approximately 19 000 vehicles per day compared with its maximum capacity level of 59 000 vehicles. In order to implement this alternative, minor adjustments have to be made to the existing infrastructure.

The fourth alternative is the optimization of the road tax in the Kennedy Tunnel. It was proposed in a research paper by de Borger and Proost (2009). Like the previous alternative, this proposal focuses on the optimization of the use of the current infrastructure by implementing a road tax that will vary according to the traffic volume. However, this alternative should be seen as a short-term solution in order to gain time to further investigate the Oosterweel Connection.

Finally, the 'Going Concern' scenario is the continuation of the current situation. The 'Going Concern' will serve as a benchmark scenario to be compared with the four proposals. The different alternatives will be described more in detail below.

Stakeholders

For this analysis, three stakeholder groups were identified. The first relevant stakeholder group is clearly the Flemish government. This stakeholder is in fact the decision-maker in this project. It did not want the project to interfere with its other obligations and policy measures, so it set up a public company, the BAM, to realize the objectives concerning the Master Plan so that its projects could also be financed with private investments (BAM, 2009). In the public–private partnership (PPP), BAM would act as the public partner. The second stakeholder group in the analysis is the City of Antwerp, comprising its citizens and, in that sense, also the action groups. The importance of the project for Antwerp and its citizens became very clear in the referendum of 18 October 2009. This referendum had only one single question: 'Should the City of Antwerp give a positive opinion concerning the building permit of the Oosterweel Connection on the anticipated route between Left Bank and Merksem/Deurne? Yes or no?' Almost 60 per cent voted against the BAM route (ibid.). The last stakeholder group is the Port of Antwerp, which is important for the economic development of Flanders and Belgium. Being the second largest port in Europe, it is one of the gateways into the continent. Currently, 31 per cent of the total transhipment (157.8 million tonnes in 2009) is being transported via trucks. This puts a lot of pressure on the road infrastructure of Antwerp. Then again, only one-fifth of the total truck transport on the ring road is port related. It also acts as a node in international truck transport. The port community not only covers the Port Authority, but also all companies that are located in and close to the port and the different trade associations. The stake of the port community is clear in this transport project: adequate transport infrastructure is crucial for the port in order to stay competitive and develop economically in the future.

Criteria and Weights

In this step, a predetermined list of criteria was discussed with the members of each stakeholder group. This preliminary list was set up on the basis of an extensive literature review, together with a detailed study of the decision-making problem and the context in which this project is situated. The task of the stakeholders was twofold: first of all, the preliminary criteria list had to be validated by the stakeholders; and, second, the stakeholders were asked to assign weights to the definitive list of criteria. To assign the weights, all the members of the stakeholder groups had 100 points to divide among their list of criteria. In order to reach the weights for each stakeholder, the mean was taken of the score for each criterion given by every individual member of the stakeholder group. The weight of each criterion is given in Table 11.1.

In order to get a clear view of this complex decision-making problem, a criteria tree or 'hierarchical tree' has been set up to structure the problem of the Oosterweel Connection (Figure 11.2).

Indicators

If the alternatives need to be evaluated with regard to the different criteria, there is a need for operational indicators that allow the researcher to measure the performance of a certain alternative on a single criterion. In most cases, these indicators or metrics are quantitative by nature, but it is

Table 11.1 Criteria and weights

Criterion	Weights (in %)
Flemish government	Flemish government
Financial feasibility	25
Environmental impact	10
Efficiency traffic flows	25
Duration	10
Traffic safety	10
Prestige	20
City of Antwerp	City of Antwerp
Air quality	12.5
Mobility	10
Noise effects	12.5
Barrier formation and visual hindrance	30
Nature	30
Prestige	5
Port community	Port community
Economic development	32.5
Direct access	27.5
Competitive position	40

possible to work with an ordinal scale as well. It is also possible that there are several indicators to measure the performance on one criterion or that one indicator is used to evaluate with respect to multiple criteria. The indicators used for this analysis are shown in Table 11.2.

Analysis

The alternatives were evaluated through pair-wise comparisons through the decision support software Expert Choice. This software uses the analytic hierarchy process (AHP) method (Saaty, 1980) as an aggregation technique. The pair-wise comparisons were made using the data from several studies like the Environmental Effect Reports (EER)[1] and the independent evaluation studies made by ArupSum.

The main objective of this analysis is to provide a ranking of the alternatives per stakeholder based on their preferences in the first place, rather than looking at an overall ranking for every actor. By introducing the stakeholder dimension, the positive and negative aspects of each alternative can be discussed per stakeholder. This is a very important advantage, since this can lead to a compromise among stakeholders. The real goal of MAMCA is not to provide a ranking to reveal the 'best' alternative, but

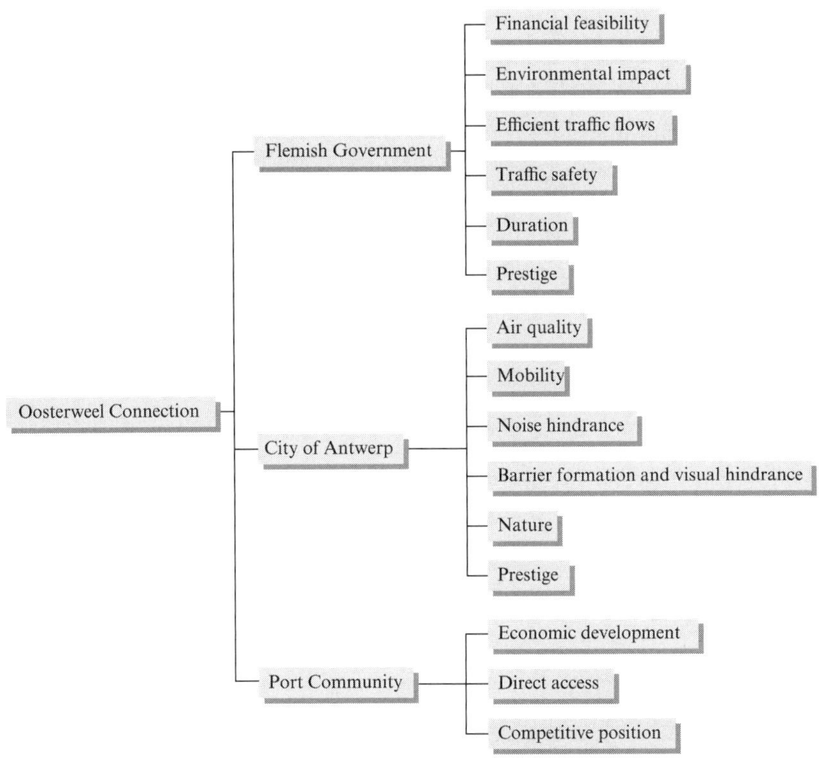

Figure 11.2 Criteria tree of the Oosterweel Connection

to provide insights into the pros and cons of each scenario, and to enhance the discussion between the different stakeholders. The results per stakeholder will be discussed in Section 11.6, together with the results on the multi-actor level. The weight of each stakeholder is initially supposed to be equal in the first analysis, in order to get a first idea of the point of view of each stakeholder and to take them equally into account.

11.6 DISCUSSION

Analysis of the Results

For the Flemish government, the analysis shows the following results (Figure 11.3). The BAM route scores high on account of its high performance on traffic safety and the efficiency of the traffic flows. The latter is a

Table 11.2 Indicator(s) per criterion

Criterion	Indicator(s)
Flemish government	Flemish government
Financial feasibility	Internal rate of return (IRR)
Environmental impact	Particulates (PM2.5), NO_x, decibel
Efficiency traffic flows	Time gains, vehicle kilometres, traffic intensity
Duration	Estimated time to put the measure of the infrastructure in place
Traffic safety	Accidents with personal injuries per year
Prestige	Visual effect
City of Antwerp	City of Antwerp
Air quality	Particulates (PM2.5), NO_x
Mobility	Time gains, vehicle kilometres, traffic intensity
Noise effects	Decibel
Barrier formation and visual hindrance	Height, integration in the city image
Nature	Hectare
Prestige	Visual effect
Port community	Port community
Economic development	Capacity, traffic intensity
Direct access	Number of vehicles per time unit, traffic intensity
Competitive position	Time gains, vehicle kilometres, money

particularly important criterion for this stakeholder. The 'Going Concern' scenario also gets a high score, because it is financially feasible. However, it performs much less well on the other criteria, which indicates that this alternative is not an option for the Flemish government. The AS route shows similar results to the BAM route for the first two criteria, but performs less well on the other criteria. The Kennedy Tunnel performs even better overall than the AS route, but this result is due to a better performance on duration and financial feasibility. The reasoning is similar for the Liefkenshoek Tunnel, which comes right below the AS route in the ranking.

The overall conclusion of the analysis for this stakeholder is that the BAM route provides the best solution for the traffic problems in Antwerp, because it provides better traffic flows on the ring road and it is the safest solution. The environmental impact of the alternative is also limited to a minimum (together with the AS route) compared to the other alternatives and it is also part of the much larger Master Plan.

The analysis for the City of Antwerp shows a very different result (Figure 11.4). The overall classification is a close tie, which indicates why this project was such a tough decision to make for the Antwerp community

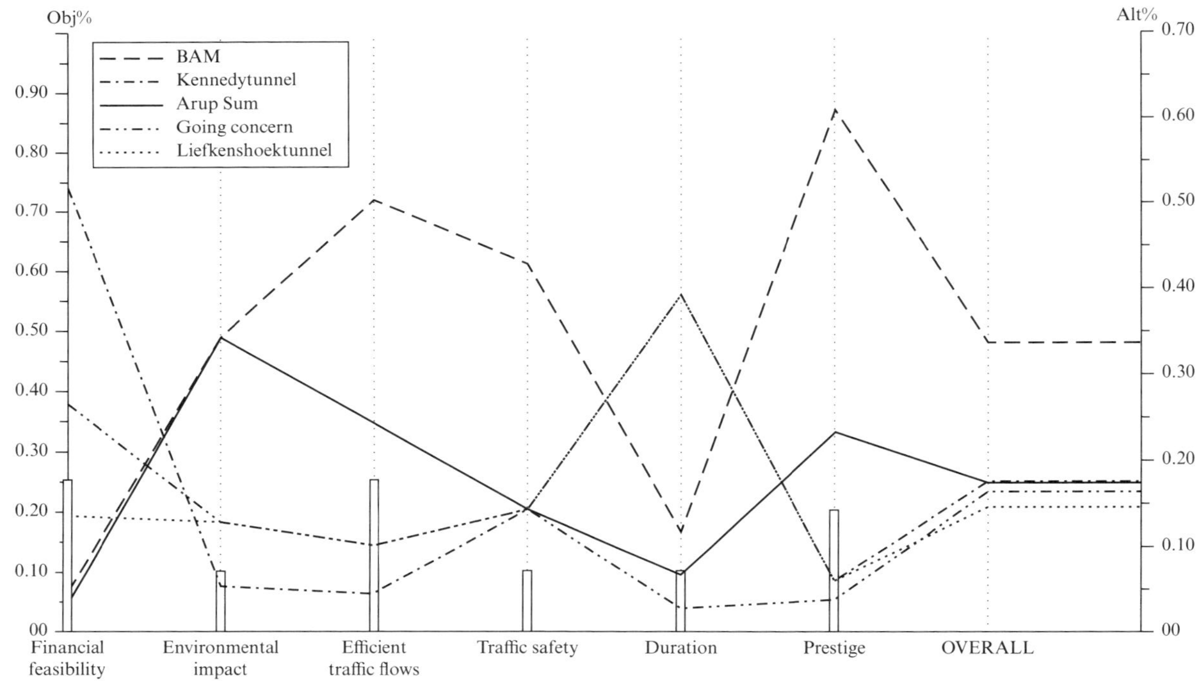

Figure 11.3 Analysis for the Flemish government

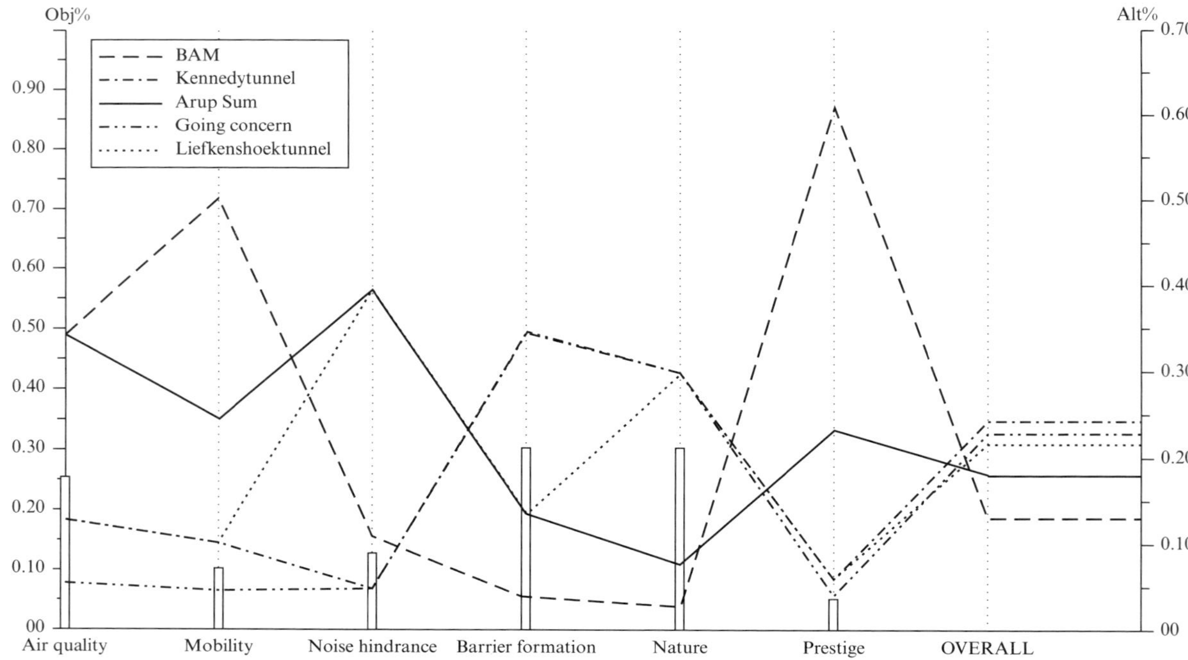

Figure 11.4 Analysis for the City of Antwerp

However, major differences can be seen in the results per criterion between the different scenarios. The BAM route results as the least preferred alternative because of its low performance on barrier formation and nature, even though it provides the best mobility solution. This result shows that the residents of Antwerp have considerable interest in the environmental and town planning effects of the project. These effects were made clear to the community by an intensive communication campaign by action committees and the residents of risk areas such as Deurne and Merksem, for which the BAM route would have very bad effects, which led to a decreasing social support. The trade-off between improved mobility and barrier formation is at the core of the discussion around this decision-making problem. This trade-off will be investigated by performing a sensitivity analysis.

The two short-term proposals, the Kennedy and Liefkenshoek Tunnels, appear to be the best alternatives for the city. The latter performs well on noise effects and nature, while the Kennedy Tunnel has no effect on barrier formation and visual hindrance. This criterion was judged to be the most important, but it is clear that a good performance on mobility and ecological effects (noise and air quality) and a weak performance on barrier formation go hand in hand. This comparison will be discussed in Step 6. The reason why these two short-term alternatives perform well is due to their time perspective. A short-term impact is not of the same magnitude as a long-term impact. These proposals appear to be a part of the overall solution, but nothing more. The ArupSum route provides a solution to minimize noise effects, but reaches a medium result on the rest of the criteria. However, this proposal is far from complete, and needs to be further investigated. The 'Going Concern' performs better than the BAM route, but it performs the worst on mobility, air quality and noise. This alternative is not an option for Antwerp, if the city and the port want to continue to grow.

A very important remark in this analysis is the result of the referendum (October 2009). One-third of the Antwerp population (37.5 per cent attendance rate) voted against the BAM route, making this result difficult to ignore in the decision-making process. In Figure 11.4, the reasons behind this voting behaviour become apparent. For the Port Community, the results are shown in Figure 11.5.

For the port stakeholder group, its competitive position is the most important criterion. Economic development and direct access are equally important. It is clear from this view that the BAM route scores very high on all three criteria.

So, the BAM route is the most preferred one, with the AS route and Liefkenshoek Tunnel coming second and third. This result entirely

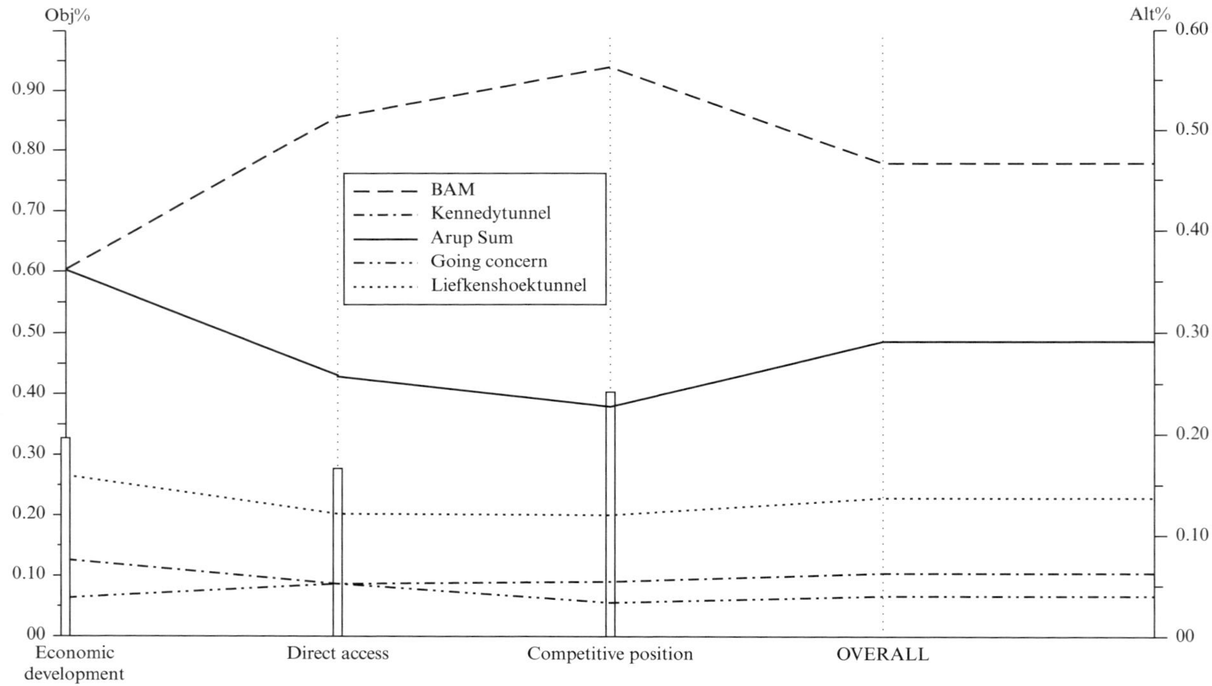

Figure 11.5 Analysis for the Port Community

conforms to reality. This stakeholder always stated that its position towards the Oosterweel Connection was pro the BAM route, because this alternative is the most advanced, and it can be implemented right away (de Tijd, 2009). However, given to the outcome of the referendum, it was clear that this proposal had limited chances for survival.

The results of the Kennedy and Liefkenshoek Tunnels are also in line with expectations. A better connection between the E17 and the Liefkenshoek Tunnel provides better access to the Waasland Port. This again indicates that the Liefkenshoek Tunnel is a part of the solution. The Kennedy Tunnel, however, has no plans to provide better access to and from the port, giving this proposal a weaker score in the overall result.

Finally, the previous analysis can be summarized into one single multi-actor view, which is presented in Figure 11.6. In this figure, the three actors are shown, each with a similar weight to show that their point of view is equally taken into account. The 'OVERALL' axis gives the weighted sum of the opinions of the different stakeholders. However, this should not be seen as the end result of the MAMCA analysis. In this case, we see that the BAM route is ranked first, with a firm lead over the AS route. The two short-term alternatives (Liefkenshoek and Kennedy Tunnels) are respectively third and fourth, and the 'Going Concern' comes last up. However, it is precisely the insights into the reasons behind this point of view that lead to the crucial input for the implementation path. The Flemish government might be willing to implement its BAM route, at least in the first period, being supported by the port, but in reality it is apparent that without taking into account the views of the citizens of Antwerp it is not possible do this.

Implementation

The analysis shows that this project is very complex and difficult to solve. Nonetheless, a decision had to be made, and the Flemish government tried to find a compromise between these two different points of view and opted for a solution that was acceptable for everyone. By the end of March 2010 they decided the following: the BAM route was kept, but instead of a bridge, four tunnels were going to be built, in order to complete the ring road as a full circle (Justaert, 2010). This proposal had three conditions: it had to conform to the European Union's Tunnel Guideline 2004/54/EG; it could not cost more than the original BAM alternative; and it could not take longer to build (ibid.). After a few months of studying this alternative it became clear that it could not achieve those three objectives. The debate came to a dramatic height when eventually the Flemish government made a final decision at the end of September 2010, whereby they kept the

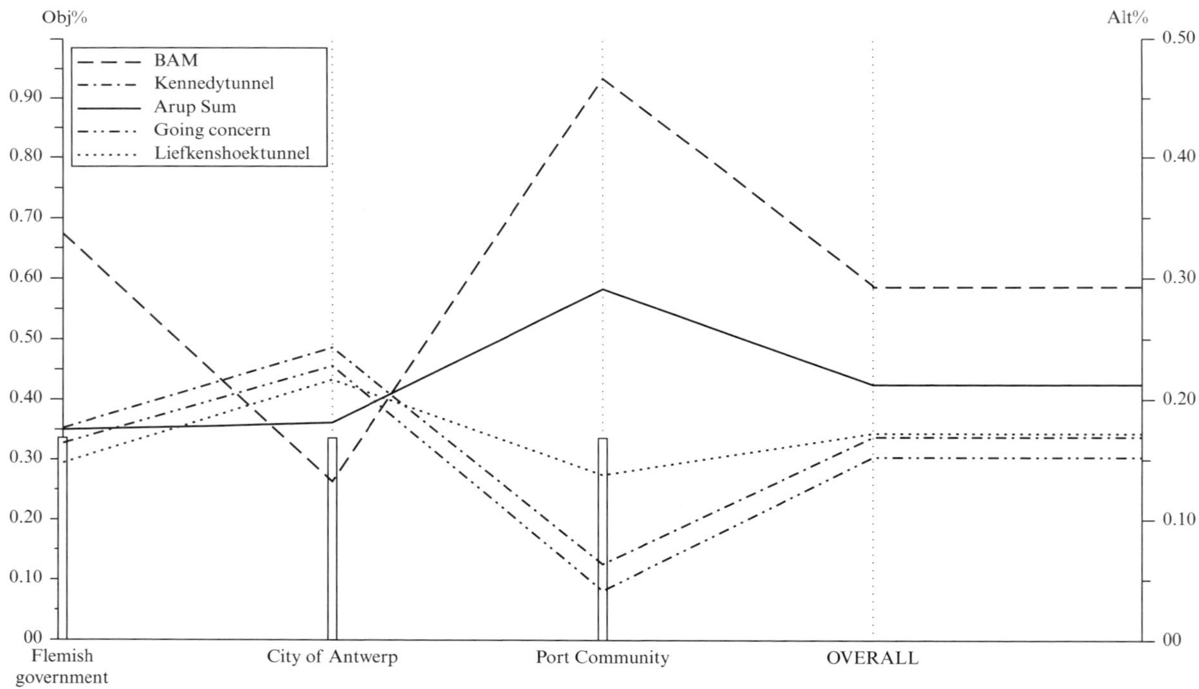

Figure 11.6 Multi-actor view of the Oosterweel Connection

BAM trajectory and replaced the highly contested bridge by a cut & cover tunnel.[2] The extra costs for the project of €352.7 million would be carried by the Port of Antwerp and the city. With this decision, the viability of the Flemish government was ensured and, in the meantime, a solution was formulated, even though it caused many negative reactions.

11.7 CONCLUSIONS

The case of the Oosterweel Connection shows that mega-projects are very difficult to implement because of their great economic, environmental and social impact. The theoretical part of this study demonstrates that there is a need for a formalized framework that can be included in the decision-making process. This chapter started from the assumption that there will always be winners and losers when implementing mega-projects, and that finding a consensus is crucial for their successful implementation.

Multi-actor multi-criteria analysis provides such a multi-actor framework. This evaluation method, which is an extension of the multi-criteria analysis, provides an extra layer in the evaluation process that explicitly includes the stakeholders by letting them determine their objectives and goals for a given project. In this chapter, the Oosterweel Connection was discussed as a case study. To date, this project is the largest and most controversial mega-project in the Flanders. The BAM route, the initial proposal, is a highly contested alternative that faced decreasing social and political support. Most of the opposition came from the fact that a bridge will be built in the centre of Antwerp, causing a lot of disruption.

The MAMCA analysis showed that for the Flemish government and the port the BAM route is the most preferable among the alternatives that were selected, but not for the City of Antwerp. The ignorance of the concerns of the citizens created the difficult debate afterwards.

Since MAMCA was not formally part of the decision-making process, conclusions concerning this decision-making problem should be made with caution. However, this case study shows that the methodology is able to generate a reasonable solution under the given assumptions. This indicates the need for stakeholder involvement and the usefulness of MAMCA as an evaluation tool for policy-makers. It can be perfectly combined with a social cost–benefit analysis, as it provides complementary information on the support for a certain alternative by the concerned actors, and by doing so it gives the necessary information for the development of implementation paths.

NOTES

1. An EER is a mandatory legal report that discusses the environmental impact of a project in order to support decision-making. These reports are prepared by experts in the field of air quality, noise hindrance, ecology, and so on.
2. Cut & cover is a way to construct shallow tunnels where a trench is excavated and roofed over with a support system that is able to support everything that will be built above the tunnel.

LITERATURE

Alvarez-Carillo, P.A., A. Duarte and J.C. Leyva-Lopez (2010), 'A group multicriteria decision support system for ranking a finite set of alternatives', EURO XXIV conference, 11–14 July, Lisbon, Portugal.

BAM (2009), *Masterplan Antwerp: History and Current Situation*, Antwerp: BAM.

Banville, C., M. Landry, J.M. Martel and C. Boulaire (1998), 'A stakeholder approach to MCDA', *System Research*, **15**(1), 15–32.

Belton, V. and T.J. Stewart (2002), *Multiple Criteria Decision Analysis: An Integrated Approach*, London: Kluwer Academic Publishers.

Branco, F.A., P.M. Mendes and M.C. Guerreiro (2000), 'Special studies for Vasco da Gama Bridge', *Journal of Bridge Engineering*, **5**(3), 223–39.

Brans, J.P. (2004), 'The management of the future. Ethics in OR: respect, multicriteria management, happiness', *European Journal of Operational Research*, **153**(2), 466–7.

Bryson, J.M. (2004), 'What to do when stakeholders matter', *Public Management Review*, **6**(1), 21–53.

Buysse, K. and A. Verbeke (2003), 'Proactive environmental strategies: a stakeholder management perspective', *Strategic Management Journal*, **24**(5), 453–70.

Campagnac, E. (2010), 'Mega transport projects planning, appraisal and delivery: a review of case study experiences and research findings, the Millau Viaduct (France)', EURO XXIV conference, 11–15, Lisbon, Portugal.

de Borger, B. and S. Proost (2009), 'De "Oosterweelverbinding" en het ontbrekende alternatief' [The 'Oosterweelverbinding' and the missing alternative], in A. Decoster (ed.), *Leuvense Economische Standpunten* [*Louvain Economic Viewpoints*] 2009/127, KU Leuven University.

de Brucker, K., A. Verbeke and W. Winkelmans (1998), *Sociaal-economische evaluatie van overheidsinvesteringen in transportinfrastructuur* [*Socioeconomic Evaluation of Public Investments in Transport Infrastructure*], Leuven: Garant.

de Tijd (2009), 'Antwerp's port federation behind BAM', 9 October, accessed 18 June 2013 at http://www.tijd.be/nieuws/binnenland/Antwerpse_havenfederatie_achter_BAM.8243232-438.art.

Donaldson, T.J. and L.E. Preston (1995), 'The stakeholder theory of the corporation: concept, evidence and implications', *Academy of Management Review*, **20**(1), 65–91.

Dooms, M. and C. Macharis (2005), 'Introducing the concept of stakeholders in the evaluations of transport infrastructure projects – the DHL-case at Brussels National Airport', paper presented at the 45th Congress of the European Regional Science Association, 23–27 August, Amsterdam, Vrije Universiteit.

Dooms, M., A. Verbeke, C. Macharis and R.S. Jegers (2006), *De zaak DHL: Het regional hub project van DHL in Brussel-Nationaal: een socio-economische en maatschappelijke evaluatie* [*The DHL Case: The Regional Hub Project of DHL in Brussels-National: A Socioeconomic and Societal Evaluation*], Antwerp: Garant.

Erke, A., K. Veisten and R. Elvik (2008), 'Cost–benefit analysis and cost-effectiveness analysis', final deliverable D5.2, IN-SAFETY project EDS & TOI, TOI funded by the Sixth Framework Programme from the European Commission.

Flyvbjerg, B., N. Bruzelius and W. Rothengatter (2003), *Megaprojects and Risk: An Anatomy of Ambition*, Cambridge, UK: Cambridge University Press.
Flyvbjerg, B., M.K. Skamris Holm and S.L. Buhl (2005), 'How (in) accurate are demand forecasts in public works projects?', *Journal of the American Planning Association*, **71**(2), 131–46.
Flyvbjerg, B., M.K. Skamris Holm and S.L. Buhl (2006), 'Inaccuracy in traffic forecasts', *Transport Reviews*, **26**(1), 1–24.
Freeman, R.E. (1984), *Strategic Management: A Stakeholder Approach*, Boston: Pitman.
Gellert, P.K. and B.D. Lynch (2003), 'Mega projects as displacements', *International Social Science Journal*, **54**(175), 15–25.
Hicks, John (1939), 'The foundations of welfare economics', *The Economic Journal*, **49**(196), 696–712.
Justaert, M. (2010), 'A masterplan of 5 billion', *De Morgen*, 3 March.
Kaldor, Nicholas (1939), 'Welfare propositions in economics and interpersonal comparisons of utility', *The Economic Journal*, **49**(195), 549–52.
Kaparos, G. (2010), 'Analysing the case of Rion-Antirrion Bridge through the lenses of a redefined notion of Mega Urban Transport Project (MUTP) success: visions, challenges and lessons', EURO XXIV conference, 11–15 July, Lisbon, Portugal.
Leyva-Lopez, J.C. (2010), 'A consensus model for group decision support based on valued outranking relations', EURO XXIV conference, 11–14 July, Lisbon, Portugal.
Macharis, C. (2000), 'Strategische modellering voor inter-modale terminals: socio-economische evaluatie van de locatie van binnenvaart/weg terminals in Vlaanderen' [Strategic modelling for inter-modal terminals: socioeconomic evaluation of the location of barge/road terminals in Flanders], Brussels: Vrije Universiteit.
Macharis, C. (2004), 'The optimal location of an inter-modal barge terminal', in E.M. Beuthe, V. Himanen, A. Reggiani and L. Zamparini (eds), *Transport Developments and Innovations in a Transforming World*, Berlin: Springer, pp. 211–32.
Macharis, C. (2005), 'The importance of stakeholder analysis in freight transport', *Quarterly Journal of Transport Law, Economics and Engineering*, **8**(25–26), 114–26.
Macharis, C. (2007), 'Multi-criteria analysis as a tool to include stakeholders in project evaluation: the MAMCA method', in E. Haezendonck (ed.), *Transport Project Evaluation: Extending the Social Cost–Benefit Approach*, Cheltenham, UK and Northampton, MA USA: Edward Elgar Publishing, pp. 115–32.
Macharis, C. and B. Boel (2004), 'BRUGARWAT: Brussels garbage by water', in C.J. Ruijgrok and R.H.J. Rodenburg, *Bijdragen vervoerslogistieke werkdagen*, Hoeven: Vervoerslogistieke werkdagen, pp. 229–42.
Macharis, C., A. de Witte and J. Ampe (2009), 'The multi-actor multi-criteria analysis methodology (MAMCA) for the evaluation of transport projects: theory and practice', *Journal of Advanced Transportation*, **43**(2), 183–202.
Macharis, C., A. de Witte and L. Turcksin (2010), 'The multi-actor multi-criteria analysis (MAMCA), application in the Flemish long term decision making process on mobility and logistics', *Transport Policy*, **17**(5), 303–11.
Meeus, T., C. Macharis and M. Dooms (2004), 'Inplanting van tweede HST-terminal te Brussel: scenario Brussel-Nationaal moet verder worden onderzocht' [Addition of a second HST terminal in Brussels: the Brussels-National scenario should be further investigated], Antwerp: De Lloyd, Universiteit en Transport.
Mishan, E.J. and E. Quah (2007), *Cost Benefit Analysis*, London: Routledge.
Nijkamp, P., P. Rietveld and H. Voogd (1991), *Multi-criteria Analysis in Physical Planning*, Amsterdam: Elsevier.
Norman, C. and R. Vickerman (1999), 'Local and regional implications of trans-European transport networks: the Channel Tunnel rail link', *Environment and Planning A*, **31**(4), 705–18.
Priemus, N., B. Flyvbjerg and B. van Wee (2008), *Decision-making on Mega-projects: Cost–Benefit Analysis, Planning and Innovation*, Cheltenham, UK and Northampton, MA, USA: Edward Elgar.

Rothengatter, W. (2008), 'Innovations in the planning of mega-projects', in H. Priemus, B. Flyvbjerg and B. van Wee, *Decision-making on Mega-projects: Cost–Benefit Analysis, Planning and Innovation*, Cheltenham, UK and Northampton MA, USA: Edward Elgar, pp. 1–20.
Saaty, T.L. (1980), *The Analytic Hierarchy Process*, New York: McGraw-Hill.
Saaty, T. (1982), *Decision Making for Leaders*, Wadsworth, Belmont: Lifetime Learning Publications.
Skamris, M.K. and B. Flyvbjerg (1997), 'Inaccuracy of traffic forecasts and cost estimates on large transport projects', *Transport Policy*, **4**(3), 141–6.
Triantaphyllou, E., B. Shu, S. Nieto Sanchez and T. Ray (1998), 'Multi-criteria decision making: an operations research approach', *Encyclopedia of Electrical and Electronics Engineering*, Vol. 15, pp. 175–86.
van Mierlo, J. and C. Macharis (2005), *Goederen – en personenvervoer: Vooruitzichten en breekpunten* [*Freight and Passenger Transport – Perspectives and Breaking Points*], Antwerp: Garant.
Verlinde, S., C. Macharis, W. Debauche, A. Heemeryck, E. van Hoeck and F. Witlox (2009), 'Night-time delivery as a potential option in Belgian urban distribution: a stakeholder approach', *Vervoerslogistieke werkdagen: Bijdragen Deel 1* [*Transport Logistic Workdays: Contributions Part 2*], Deurne: Vervoerslogistieke werkdagen, pp. 153–72.
Walker, W.E. (2000), 'Policy analysis: a systematic approach to supporting policymaking in the public sector', *Journal of Multi-Criteria Decision Analysis*, **9**(1–3), 11–27.
Williamson, O.E. (1991), 'Strategizing, economizing, and economic organization', *Strategic Management Journal*, **12**(2), 75–94.

PART III

COST–BENEFIT ANALYSIS: EX ANTE EVALUATION OF MEGA-PROJECTS

12. CBA: ex ante evaluation of mega-projects

Bert van Wee and Piet Rietveld

12.1 INTRODUCTION[1]

Transport is crucial for society: societies cannot function without transporting people and goods. It enables us to participate in many activities at different locations, such as living, working, education, shopping and visiting relatives and friends. In addition, it allows us to transport goods, from the locations of mining of raw materials, via several production stages, culminating in the shops where people buy products, or even up to the final locations of use, such as houses or offices. On the other hand, transport carries costs, in terms of money, time, effort and the negative impacts on society. In most western countries people spend 10–15 per cent of their income on transport (Schafer and Victor, 1997). On average, and at the aggregate level (e.g., all persons in one country), people travel between 60 and 75 minutes per person per day, in almost all countries worldwide (Szalai, 1972; Zahavi, 1979; Mokhtarian and Chen, 2004). In addition to time and costs, it takes effort to travel. Driving a car, especially over a long distance, demands energy from the drivers, and changing trains, or from a bus to a train, is itself a negative experience for most people, not to mention the time it takes (Wardman, 2001). Cycling takes energy, and the cyclist can get wet, while driving a car over a longer period is tiring for many people. Transport also causes negative impacts on society, mainly due to accidents, emissions of harmful pollutants and CO_2, noise, the barrier effects of infrastructure for people and the fragmentation of nature.

Because of the important role of mega-projects a sound ex ante evaluation of possible new projects is of major importance for the quality of decision-making. Decision-making in transport (including mega-projects) is partly based on considerations related to the pros and cons of candidate policy options. The pros and cons can be related to one or more indicators the decision-maker assumes to be of relevance. Welfare could be an indicator, but there are other options. In addition to national welfare, other more 'political' aspects may play a role, for example, regional equity, such as in Belgium, where transport investments in Flanders and Wallonia need to be in some kind of balance. Prestige can also play a role. Such considerations are often less easy to tackle in indicators.

In most western countries cost–benefit analysis (CBA) is the method used for ex ante evaluations of transport infrastructure projects (Bristow and Nellthorp, 2000; Hayashi and Morisugi, 2000; Grant-Muller et al., 2001). A CBA tries to capture as much as possible the pros and cons of a project, but is limited to those pros and cons that can be included in an economic framework based on welfare. The main feature of CBA is that its valuation of effects is based on the preferences of consumers, that is, on their willingness to pay for the effects. CBA may therefore be interpreted as a market-oriented approach in the public sector, where corrections for market imperfections are applied as much as possible. Thus, CBA provides a summation of the outcomes of a project for all the actors affected where the outcomes are based on how consumers value them. As a result, CBA is not based on political preferences. As we will see this is at the same time both a strength and a weakness. Its strength is that CBA can be characterized as a neutral tool, but this also implies that in cases where the public sector has clear policy objectives that are different from what consumers prefer, CBA may be of little help in the ranking of alternatives.

This chapter aims to introduce the reader to the area of CBA for candidate transport policy options in general, with the emphasis on mega-projects. The focus of this chapter is on western countries, although some of the findings also apply to developing countries. Our chapter focuses on social cost–benefit analysis, which aims to include all impacts that count from a broad welfare perspective, including, for example, environmental and social impacts.

The chapter is organized as follows. Section 12.2 explains what a CBA is. The major strengths of CBA are discussed in Section 12.3. The theoretical and practical weaknesses of current CBAs are presented in Sections 12.4 and 12.5. Section 12.6 summarizes the main conclusions. Several of the strengths and weaknesses not only apply to CBA, but also to multi-criteria analysis (MCA). Our aim is to give a more or less complete overview of the dominant strengths and weaknesses so these have also been included. We also highlight strengths and weaknesses that are applicable to mega-projects in particular.

12.2 WHAT IS A CBA?

A General Introduction

Basically a CBA is an overview of all the pros (benefits) and cons (costs) of a project. These costs and benefits are, as much as possible, quantified and expressed in monetary terms. Benefits are in general based on consumer preferences.[2] Costs and benefits occur in different years within the time horizon of the CBA. To deal with this, they are presented as so-called net present values, implying that, taking interest and inflation into account, it is better to have 1 euro or dollar today than in, for example, 2030. The discount rate is used to express this valuation (see Chapter 14). The final results are often presented in summarizing indicators. The main indicators that are presented are the difference between costs and benefits, the return on investment and the cost–benefit ratio. Almost every handbook on transport economics pays attention to CBA in transport (see, for example, Blauwens et al., 2008; Button, 2010).

For CBA (as well as for other evaluation methods) all non-marginal effects at the network level should be included. The spatial and temporal system boundaries are of crucial importance. If the spatial boundaries used are too tight, relevant effects might occur outside the area under consideration. Deliberately excluding some effects in other areas is common practice if they occur in other (neighbouring) countries – this is legitimated by the fact that it is the tax payer of the country where the project is built who is paying for the project. With respect to temporal boundaries many CBAs include a few decades after the project realization, even though the projects generally last much longer, the main reasons being the increasing uncertainty when the time horizon is extended, and the fact that long-term effects hardly influence results due to discounting (see above). Despite long-term uncertainties some CBAs cover a period of 100 years. Temporal aspects are also relevant, as it is only after the opening of a new infrastructure project that the benefits can be realized, whereas there may be important disbenefits in the form of construction costs, and disbenefits from the building activities during construction of the project. Discounting means that early disbenefits have a relatively strong impact on the CBA results compared to later benefits. Consequently longer construction periods can significantly reduce the benefits of a project. To summarize, it is important that a CBA includes at least two or three decades after the opening of a project.

The use of the term 'effects' of a project implies that a reference case has to be defined, in order to have a clear benchmark. The reference case relates to the world where the project is not carried out. But it is not always exactly the same as doing nothing. First, there may already have been decisions made about related projects that are not in place yet. Such projects need to be included in the reference case. Also, when a project is meant to remove a bottleneck in a certain transport system, the reference case may include some minor low cost changes in the current conditions to reduce the burden of the bottleneck. The exact definition of the reference case can have a substantial influence on the outcomes of a CBA.

Dominant Benefits of Large Infrastructure Projects: Travel Time Gains and Additional Travel

For large infrastructure projects, including mega-projects, two benefit categories dominate: travel time gains and the benefits of additional travel. Travel time gains result from reductions in travel time, transport volumes and the value of time (VOT – see below). Next to travel time savings, additional travel (induced demand) is an important category of benefits for transport infrastructure projects, the benefits of which are generally estimated using the so-called rule of half. This rule can be explained using an example. Let us take a rail project that reduces the travel time between city A and B, for example because a shortcut is made. Person X living in city A commutes to city B by train, both with and without the reduced travel time. All other variables, such as monetary travel costs, safety, and so on, are unaffected by the project. For this person the benefits of the project for each trip consist of the travel time saved multiplied by his (marginal) value of time. Let us now consider person X's neighbour who does not travel between A and B on the old rail line, but does start travelling to city B once the new line is constructed. We do not know at which level of travel time reduction he/she might have made the decision to travel. It might be that even a very small reduction in travel time would have induced the change, but also that the change would only occur if (almost) the full reduction in travel time would have occurred. assuming many persons who start travelling to city B once the new line is constructed, and a linear demand function, the average break-even reduction in travel time is half of the actual reduction in travel time. For the group of new travellers the average travel time reduction benefits are half of the full reduction in travel time of the new rail project, multiplied by the number of trips and the VOT of these persons. As stated before, in transport economics this phenomenon is referred to as the 'rule of half'. In addition, extra benefits may occur due to changes in the time of day. These benefits can also be calculated using the rule of half.

Figure 12.1 visualizes demand with ($Q1$, $GTC1$ – GTC: generalized transport costs, including at least time and money) and without ($Q0$, $GTC0$) a new infrastructure project. A refers to the benefits (increase in consumer surplus) of those people who would travel both with and without the new line, B to the benefits of the extra demand. The surface area of B can easily be calculated as ($Q2 - Q1 * T2 - T1$) * ½, the factor ½ referring to the 'rule of half' as presented above.

As for other infrastructure projects, CBA is applied for mega-projects. This applies at the national level, the cross-border level, and also at the supra-national level, such as projects that are part of the EU TransEuropean Networks.

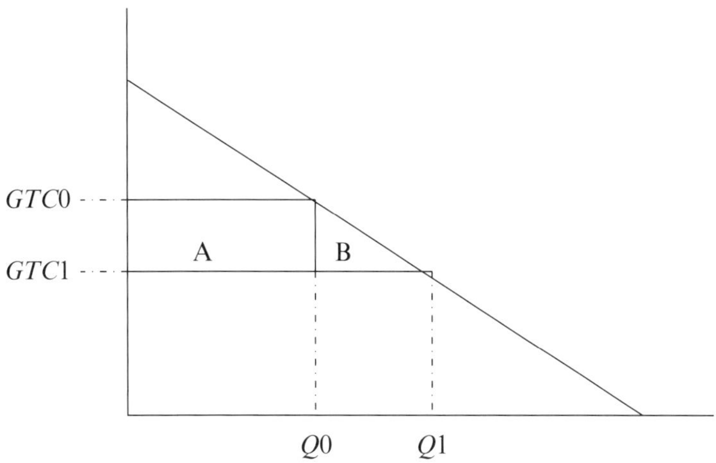

Figure 12.1 *Visualization of the increase in consumer surplus due to a decrease in generalized transport costs*

Models for Demand Forecasts

The overview of CBA-relevant impacts is preferably based on state-of-the-art methods, modelling being the method of preference in most cases. In general two categories of models are used, transport models and impact models, that is, models that address the impacts of transport on external effects such as noise. We have a broad scope of transport models: they include both traditional transport models as well as models for vehicle ownership and characteristics, distribution of traffic over infrastructure classes, and so on.

Transport models are widely available and are used to provide input for CBAs. The output of transport models includes the number of vehicles, wagons, vessels, and so on, as well as their characteristics (age, fuel type, emission class etc.). These numbers and characteristics are in some cases input for CBA. In addition they are often input for traditional transport models. For example, car ownership levels (but not emission characteristics and average fuel costs per kilometre) are needed in a transport model to be able to estimate mode choice and traffic flows. A second output category comes from traditional transport models and covers the origins, destinations, route choice, mode choice and travel distances of people and goods. These data are needed to calculate travel times, traffic volumes and related economic, environmental and social impacts. Third, travel times for both passengers and freight transport are generated by models. These depend on network characteristics, but for road travel also on densities/

congestion levels. As explained above changes in travel times are a major benefit category of infrastructure improvements. Fourth, the characteristics of passengers and freight are an important output of transport models that provide input for a CBA, for example, the value of time for business trips on average is higher than for leisure trips, and the added value of freight transport is often higher in case of high-value goods compared to low-value goods.

Finally, the fifth category of input for CBA based on transport models is a classification of road types. This classification is generally an input for a transport model (a description of network characteristics), rather an output. Data is important because important differences between road types exist with respect to energy use per kilometre, noise emissions and safety impacts. This output highly depends on the impacts that infrastructure changes will have in many ways. First, it influences residential choice and the location choices of firms. These location choices have an impact on mode choice and travel distances. Second, also influences destination choices: the lower the generalized transport costs (time, money, trouble), the easier it becomes to reach destinations at greater distances. Third, infrastructure changes may have an impact on trip frequencies. Fourth, the choice of vehicle types may be influenced by infrastructure changes. For example, the more important the position of motorways in the road network is, the more attractive it becomes to own a big, comfortable, fast car. Fifth, infrastructure has an impact on driving behaviour, which is relevant for safety impacts, emissions and related concentrations of pollutants, and noise. Sixth, route choice and freight routing may be influenced by the quality of infrastructure networks, being relevant for travel times, travel costs, impacts on the environment and safety and congestion levels. These changes interact in a dynamic way and there are many different types of users who will all react differently as individuals and in interaction. Transport models are needed to combine one or more of these responses.

The output of transport models is relevant because it provides results that can be directly included in a CBA, such as travel time changes. Second, the impacts on society and the environment caused by the change in the transport system can be calculated. In other words: transport models provide input for impact models, such as noise, safety and pollution models. Finally, the monetary expression of CBA-relevant output is often obtained using external data, such as the value of time for distinguished modes, motives, income classes and categories of goods. Impact models are manifold. In general they are not directly linked to transport models, but used separately. For CBA purposes the impact models are often not used to estimate local effects, such as noise effects, but rules of thumb are

Table 12.1 Comparison of CBA and MCA

	CBA	MCA
Systematic comparison of alternatives	Yes	Yes
Assessment of the viability of a project	Yes	No
Explicit formulation of weights in trade-offs	Yes	Yes
Basis for weights of various effects	Valuation by consumer	Political valuation
Opportunities for abuse by policy-makers	By manipulation of inputs	By manipulation of inputs and by manipulation of weights
Degree of compensation between various attributes of alternatives	Every unfavourable attribute can in principle be compensated by a favourable outcome for another attribute	Various degrees of compensation are possible by the possibility to incorporate minimum requirements
Risk of double counting	Limited[a]	Yes
Opportunities to take into account attributes that cannot be valued in monetary terms	No	Yes
Possibility to attach weights to the interests of specific actors	Not in the standard form of CBA	Yes

Note: a. It is often stated that the risk of double counting is not present in the case of CBA. This holds true for the case of perfect markets. For imperfect markets where wider economic effects are incorporated, there is a certain risk of double counting.

Source: Rietveld (2013).

used that are often based on impact models. It is beyond the scope of this chapter to go into the different kinds of impact models in further detail.

We conclude that the results of CBA depend on two important elements: (1) the effects of the investment projects generated by means of transport models and wider impact models, and (2) the valuation of these effects. When MCA is used instead of CBA, the first element is still needed. The difference between CBA and MCA is thus less than is sometimes thought, as is also clear from Table 12.1.

12.3 STRENGTHS OF CURRENT CBAs

There are three major explanations for the popularity of CBA in the ex ante evaluation of infrastructure projects and its role in decision-making. These reasons are the main strengths of the method. The first explanation is that most costs and benefits are well known, the second is that models to forecast demand are generally available, and the third is that CBA is a relatively 'neutral' evaluation method. We will discuss these explanations in more detail below.

Costs and Benefits are Known

Most of the costs and benefits are relatively well known, at least theoretically. Investment, maintenance and operation costs can be derived from data from projects constructed in the recent past, or from tenders. The most important benefits are travel time savings, for both travellers and freight transport. Models are generally used to estimate the demand of passengers or volumes of goods transport that will benefit from a new project (see below). In addition, in the case of passengers the travel time savings per trip can easily be estimated by comparing travel times with and without the proposed infrastructure project including changes in network characteristics. Next, the so-called value of time (VOT) is used to express shorter travel times in monetary terms. VOT is higher for business travel and goods transport than for commuting, and leisure travel has the lowest value of time. VOT differs between modes, income classes and some other characteristics of travel and travellers (Gunn, 2001). In the past much more research has been carried out on the VOT for passengers than for goods transport, especially for rail, making VOT estimates for goods transported by rail relatively uncertain. There is far more debate about the wider economic effects (effects additional to the direct effects due to a reduction in generalized transport costs) and environmental effects (see below).

The travel time savings, often being the most important benefits of infrastructure projects, are not fully expressed in GDP. Travel time savings for business trips and goods transport lead to higher productivity and lower costs and have an impact on GDP, but if a commuter can leave home later because commuting times are reduced, or because it takes less time to travel to a relative, GDP is not affected. In CBA it is common to have a broad approach to welfare, implying that all benefits for consumers are included, even if they are not expressed in GDP. This means that the use of cost–benefit analysis is closer to the notion of 'green GDP' than to GDP measured in the traditional way, which only considers goods and services that are sold on markets and ignores elements of welfare such as leisure and a range of quality-of-life aspects. Exactly these elements are incorporated in CBA. One implication is that CBA is less limited in scope than opponents of CBA sometimes think: CBA tries to incorporate all the effects of projects that affect welfare, its main limitation being that it does so from an economic perspective and hence the effects are measured in monetary terms.

Other benefits of rail and tolled road projects might be the gains of the company operating the service or road section. Also relevant in ex ante evaluations are environmental and safety impacts. Changes in safety and the environment might be positive and negative, implying that safety and environmental changes can be listed both under the costs as well as the benefits.

There are Models Available

Section 12.2 explained the use of models to calculate the dominant impacts of mega-projects. Because CBA needs quantitative information on travel time reductions, transport volumes and impacts, it is a major advantage that models are generally available. For cross-border mega-projects the availability of models may be more problematic than for national, regional or local projects, since international transport models are much less often available than national, regional or local models.

The 'Neutral' Character of CBA

The last reason for the popularity of CBA is its often-assumed 'neutral' characteristic as opposed to its main competitor, MCA. Table 12.1 gives a comparison of both methods. As already explained in Section 12.1, the neutral character of CBA stems from its adoption of consumer preferences as the leading valuation principle. In MCA weighting the effects of projects is based on political preferences. It is therefore much easier to manipulate the final outcomes of an MCA compared to a CBA. A CBA is, however, not completely value-free either, for example due to the use of the utilitarian concept, the assumption that price tags should be based on consumer preferences, and because several methodologies exist to obtain these price tags, the choice often having a major impact on the outcomes. In addition, the models to estimate the transport effects can be manipulated (which of course is also true for MCA). Nevertheless, there is a broad consensus that CBA is much more value free than MCA. Another difference between CBA and MCA, not directly related to the neutral character of CBA, is that a CBA explicitly assesses the viability of a project, contrary to MCA.

12.4 WEAKNESSES OF CURRENT CBAs: THEORETICAL ASPECTS

This section concentrates on the main weaknesses and related challenges. Several of them are discussed in more detail in other chapters in this book. We first discuss theoretical aspects, followed by the limitations of the use of CBA in practice, and input related issues.

Difficult to Monetize Effects

A first weakness is that some effects are difficult to monetize, examples being effects on nature or the landscape, and some environmental effects like climate change.[3] Because such impacts can be huge, more research into these impacts is needed. In addition, more research into methods to value these impacts might result in a more equal treatment of them in CBAs. However, we realize that there is still a long way to go before these impacts can be valued. And it is questionable whether methods to value these impacts in a satisfactory way can be developed at all. For such impacts a combination of CBA and MCA might be a better tool to facilitate decision-making than only a CBA with questionable values or PM (pro-memory) estimations.

Distribution Effects

A CBA generally only considers the effects within the area of study, often a country, but ignores distributions within that area, whereas these distributions can be very important for decision-makers. Distributions can relate to welfare effects, accessibility levels, (un)employment, and so on. Mega-projects, more than smaller transport infrastructure projects, may change regional distributions of accessibility, simply because of their size and often the focus on longer distances. The literature mainly discusses distributions over population groups (often by income) and regions. Projects may even aim to distribute welfare more equally over regions and decision-makers may be willing to pay for a more equal distribution. Distributional issues are not systematically explored in a standard cost–benefit analysis. The effects for groups of actors are systematically represented and the final outcome is based on adding the welfare effects for all groups of actors. This implies that actors with high incomes weigh more heavily since their valuation of the effects tends to be higher. This means at the same time that when the objective of a policy is to reduce inequalities, CBA is not very helpful.

Another aspect of distribution effects is that groups that are adversely affected may ask for compensation. A positive result of CBA indeed implies that there is scope for the losers to be compensated by the winners. However, practical implementation may be difficult or costly. Losers may exaggerate their losses in order to receive greater financial compensation, which would then lead to long negotiations. An alternative might be to physically compensate losers, for example by measures dealing with noise nuisance, but such measures may be very costly. Another way of providing compensation is by linking projects, for example if an expressway results in noise in a municipality, this municipality may ask for a compensation, for example in the form of a station along a nearby railway line. Such measures may indeed help to achieve consensus or gain the support of certain actors, but they also may be rather costly.

A possible way to address the compensation problem would be to incorporate distribution effects explicitly in CBA at the phase of selecting the most preferred alternative. As indicated by Rietveld (2003) it is indeed possible to use a social welfare function approach to extend CBA so that it does not only incorporate efficiency effects, but also distributive effects, the latter expressed, for example, by means of a Gini index. This is essentially an extension of the standard CBA approach in the direction of MCA, but staying within the domain of economics. This may help the identification of reasonably efficient alternatives that perform favourably from the distribution point of view.

Long-term Impacts

As explained above, discount rates are used to express the future benefits and costs in the currency of a base year. Discounting reduces the benefits over many decades to almost zero according to the most commonly used discount rates (including risk valuation: often in the order of magnitude of 3–7 per cent). It is questionable whether the effects on future generations are appropriately included in a CBA. One can think of, for example, the effects of climate change, or the depletion of natural resources. (See for further discussion on the discount rate Chapter 14 of this book.) The long-term impacts of mega-projects may be relatively large, at least in absolute terms, because of the size of the project and the fact that they often remain important links in transport infrastructure networks. A regional or local road may be more easily downscaled compared to a major motorway or (high speed) rail link.

Social Exclusion

Mega-projects may have an impact on the level of social exclusion in remote areas. But how should changes in this level be evaluated? CBA takes consumer preferences as a point of departure. But the people most prone to social exclusion are people with low incomes who often do not own cars. Consequently their willingness to pay (WTP) for an increase in opportunities to travel will be low. If the related benefits were based on the WTP of those people a CBA might undervalue the benefits compared to political preferences to reduce levels of social exclusion.

Benefits of Innovations, Image and Prestige

Some projects may be innovative, examples being new infrastructure types such as maglev, or innovative ways of integrating infrastructure within its environment. Innovative projects may have positive spin-offs, for example, because they may reduce the costs of comparable projects in the future due to learning effects, or increase the competitive advantage of companies involved. Such benefits are notoriously difficult to estimate. In addition, projects may increase the image or prestige of a city or even a country. One can think of landmark projects such as beautiful bridges. Measuring and quantifying the positive benefits of such projects is very difficult. CBA in such cases only partially covers the dominant benefits.

12.5 WEAKNESSES OF CURRENT CBAs: PRACTICAL ASPECTS

Wider Economic Effects

The standard approach to project evaluation in CBA is that the economic benefits of a project are measured by means of consumer surplus, based on the demand for transport as already explained in Section 12.3. This means that the benefits of a project are measured exclusively within the transport market and that wider economic benefits are ignored. One might wonder whether this is a valid approach, since the benefits of a project can also be seen in other markets like the labour market (better transport leads to better matches between demand and supply of labour), or the market for consumer good (better transport leads to decreases in prices for the final consumer). An important issue here is the functioning of these related markets: is the decrease in transport costs entirely transferred to the user of the transport service, as would be the case in a perfect market, or do market imperfections play a role? The work of Jara-Diaz (1986) provides an important benchmark. He demonstrates that when markets function perfectly the wider economic effects on other markets are entirely captured by the consumer surplus in the transport market. This would imply that it is a mistake to take into account the benefits of transport investments in other markets. That would lead to double counting. If the markets are functioning properly, then the benefits of lower transport prices and the benefits of the resulting lower prices for consumer goods are identical. This result does not mean that by focusing on demand for transport, other markets can be entirely ignored. An appropriate analysis of demand for transport implies that adjustments in the other markets due to changes in transport costs are taken into account in the derivation of transport demand. Naive methods for analysing transport demand would lead to misleading results. Hence, the result that wider economic benefits in other markets may be ignored in CBA only applies when the demand function has been appropriately derived.

The assumption that markets are perfect is convenient, but is it correct? Market imperfections may, for example, be the result of market power where monopolistic or oligopolistic suppliers apply mark-up strategies, implying that they do not entirely pass on the advantage of price decreases to their clients. Over the last 15 years there has been a growing interest in the question of the extent to which the assumption of perfect markets leads to an underestimation or an overestimation of the total surplus. For example, the SACTRA (1999) report compares the total welfare increases of infrastructure projects with changes in consumer surplus on the transport market and finds that the former is up to 30 per cent higher than the latter (in theory it can even be negative); this analysis is based on a model with monopolistic competition in the context of regional trade. Newbery (1998) finds wider welfare effects of 3–8 per cent in the context of oligopolistic competition. Davies (1999) obtains a wider welfare effect of about 12 per cent in a similar model. Bröcker and Schneider (2002) arrive at wider welfare effects of about 20 per cent by a computable general equilibrium (CGE) model for European regions. Oosterhaven and Elhorst (2003) obtain wider welfare effects ranging from 20 per cent to 80 per cent in a CGE model for Dutch regions. In a monopolistic competition model with localization economies, Venables (2007) finds increases ranging between 60 per cent and 150 per cent. Pilegaard and Fosgerau (2008) find that the welfare gains from transport improvements in the case of labour market search may exceed those computed by the standard CBA by 30 per cent or more. Zhu et al. (2009) find an underestimation of some 10–20 per cent for another model with labour market imperfections.

We conclude that in virtually all cases the standard approach leads to an underestimate of total benefits. Apparently transport improvements tend to reduce the size of the adverse economic effects of market imperfections, implying a positive additional welfare effect. The size of this effect is not easy to determine, however, and the studies cited above have not been applied in a real world context, but rather in an academic setting.

However, we argue that they can provide important information to decision-makers on the socioeconomic impacts, both in terms of overall changes and the re-distribution of welfare, which could be vital for a good CBA. The empirical knowledge on wider economic benefits is limited, making a meta-analysis at this point impractical. On the basis of the above discussion one could expect that wider economic effects are larger when market imperfections are greater, and when land use effects are ignored in the effect studies. Assumed wider economic effects often play an important role in the policy discussion on large infrastructure projects. Therefore, even if they are absent or negligible it is very valuable information to present them explicitly.

The wider economic impact may on average be larger for mega-projects as opposed to smaller transport infrastructure projects, because the generalized transport costs of more origin-destination pairs may be reduced, and reductions in generalized transport costs may be relatively large.

Cross-border Issues

Cross-border projects, especially in case of motorways and (high-speed) rail projects are often mega-projects. Special problems may occur in the case of such cross-border projects. Countries on both sides of the border may use different VOTs, accident risk changes, emissions, health impacts of emissions and noise valuations. These differences may occur due to 'real' differences. For example, income levels may differ, resulting in different VOTs, or population densities near motorways may differ, resulting in differences in the valuation of health impacts equal to the levels of polluting emissions. On the other hand, methodological reasons may explain differences, examples being data collection methods or econometric methods to estimate VOTs. And if so, applying different valuations is cumbersome. In addition to these reasons countries may have different traditions or guidelines for CBA. Consequently, for example, they may use different valuations of discount rates and risks, or have a different focus with respect to social effects (for a comparison of social effects included in the UK versus the Netherlands see Geurs et al., 2009).

The EU HEATCO project (HEATCO, 2006) provides guidelines for cross-border projects with respect to decision criteria, the treatment of non-monetized impacts, the project appraisal evaluation period, the treatment of future risk and uncertainty, discounting, intra-generational equity issues, non-market valuation techniques, value transfer, the treatment of wider socioeconomic effects, marginal costs of public funds, and the producer surplus of transport providers. Next to these general guidelines, it elaborates on the value of time and congestion, the value of changes in accident risks, environmental costs, and costs and wider impacts of infrastructure investments. In order to reduce the amount of ambiguity and uncertainty in cross-border project assessments, guidelines are needed that are internationally consistent, transferable and easily executable. As a first step towards this objective, the HEATCO project proposed a set of internationally harmonized methodological guidelines for project evaluation. These guidelines are based on the state of the art in project evaluation and also include default values where data limitations prohibit the application of comprehensive evaluation methods. Besides, the EU BEACON project focuses on cross-border aspects related to the strategic environmental assessment of transport plans, policies and projects (see http://ec.europa.eu/environment/eia/sea-studies-and-reports/beacon_manuel_en.pdf). For further discussion on cross-border issues we refer to the EU HEATCO project: HEATCO (2006) and http://heatco.ier.uni-stuttgart.de/.

Another feature of cross-border projects is that standard CBA rules imply that when a country invests in a project, the benefits of foreign users have to be ignored. The underlying idea is that foreign users do not contribute to the investment since they do not pay taxes, and therefore their benefits should not be considered. In some cases foreign users do contribute to the investment costs, for example when a project is the result of an initiative of a private international consortium, and user contributions (a fee) are employed to cover all the costs the above argument does not hold, although it is clear that in other cases it will be more difficult for projects with a clear international orientation to pass the standard CBA tests. The obvious way to address this in the context of CBA would be to carry out a sensitivity analysis by redefining a cross-border project as a joint project by two countries. This would shed light on the question of the size of the missing benefits for foreign users. On the basis of such a sensitivity analysis a government could start negotiations with the government in a neighbour country to ask for a contribution corresponding to the benefits flowing to its residents. Another follow-up might be to ask for a contribution from a supra-national body such as the European Commission, as is the case in the EU programme for TransEuropean Networks (for details refer to Rietveld, 2012).

Dynamics

Evaluating candidate policy options for mega-projects is relatively easy if these options in their final form are known. In practice, however, they may change after the CBA has been carried out, for example based on debates on scope or environmental impacts. The same applies to benefits and related variables: these can change over time as well. For example, the benefits of a new rail project may depend on the tariffs. Future changes related to deregulation, liberalization and privatization may lead to changes in tariffs, and consequently in the benefits of the new rail project. And VOTs of projects may change due to future increases in options to use ICT (for work or social reasons) on trains. The benefits of extensions to motorways by adding lanes may decrease if vehicle technology enables cars to drive close to each others, increasing motorway capacity enormously.

The value of a CBA decreases, the more unforeseen (or at least: not included in the CBA) changes occur. Several of the changes may apply to all the choice options at stake, and in a more or less comparable way. Consequently the preferred choice option (in terms of CBA scores) may not necessarily be influenced by these changes, but for a mega-project the preferred option may certainly be influenced by these 'dynamic uncertainties'.

Communication and Impact on Decision-making

In addition to the more 'content-related' topics discussed above, an additional weakness is the communication of results to clients, including decision-makers. CBAs are often not easy to understand for clients, reducing their potential impact. A major challenge is communicating the results to several categories of clients, not only in the form of documents, but also orally or in other ways.

A related topic is the position of CBA in the wider decision-making procedure (see Chapter 13). Politicians may have given their commitment to a mega-project in an early stage, years before the formal decision to build (Cantarelli et al., 2010). In the case of an early commitment, even before the results of a CBA are available, the impact on decision-making will be limited.

Another related topic is the communication of the impacts of a mega-project on accessibility. This applies even if a CBA was not used to ex ante evaluate project alternatives, although in a CBA it is common not to explicitly express accessibility effects. In general the benefits of accessibility changes are included via the valuation of travel time changes – see above. But in addition, clients of a CBA might be interested in having insights into accessibility changes in the form of dedicated accessibility indicators. Then a 'problem' may occur: theoretically 'sound' indicators, such as the so-called logsum indicator expressing the utility of accessibility (e.g., see de Jong et al., 2007) are difficult to communicate, while easy to communicate indicators, such as the geographical indicator 'the number of jobs accessible within 45 minutes from dwellings', are theoretically less sound (Geurs and van Wee, 2004). The correlation between utility-based indicators and geographical indicators seems to be weak, at least for pricing policies (Tillema et al., 2011).

Cost Estimates

Mega-projects often cost much more than assumed at the time of decision-making: by the time the construction is finished the costs are often much higher than at the time of the formal decision to build. It is also very likely that the extent of the cost overruns as found in the international literature is greatly underestimated – if we took the point of no return in decision-making for the estimate of the costs, cost overruns would probably be much larger – see Cantarelli et al. (2010) who use the term 'lock-in': before the formal decision to build it is possible that decision-makers have already given their commitment to a project, and there is no way back anymore (see Chapter 15).

Dealing with Uncertainty

Because a CBA (as well as its competitors, including MCA) ex ante evaluates candidate policy options, such as options for mega-projects, assumptions with respect to future developments need to be made, key examples being assumptions in the areas of demography, the economy, spatial developments and oil prices. The scenario methodology is generally used to deal with combinations of (often related) developments. A mega-project will be evaluated more positively if one assumes high population and income growth, and a concentration of activities (dwellings, offices, etc.) near related stations or motorway exits. Properly dealing with uncertainties is inherently difficult because the future is unknown. The best one can do is to develop 'valid' scenarios expressing the dominant uncertainties. Because of the importance of assumptions with respect to demography, the economy and other areas the development and selection of scenarios used gives opportunities to manipulate the outcomes of a CBA (see also 'the neutral character of CBA' above and 'demand forecasts' below).

Demand Forecasts

Another weakness is the quality of the demand forecasts. Based on a review of the scarce literature in this area van Wee (2007) concludes that demand is often overestimated, for rail even more than for road projects. In the USA this theme has been addressed by Pickrell (1989) and Button

(2010). The diagnosis is that the overestimates are not only due to wrong inputs in transport models such as future values of GDP and energy prices, but also due to the poor quality of some of the models, the ways the models are used and the interpretation of model output in the planning process. Thus, manipulation of interest groups (or, formulated in a less negative way, strategic behaviour) is a critical issue. Quality assurance of CBA use is therefore strongly recommended. The good news is that Button (2010) finds that in the USA overestimates in more recent studies are considerably lower than they used to be.

There is another element of demand forecasts that is important in the case of mega-projects. Many mega-projects – at least in the context of a continent such as Europe with its many countries – are cross-border in nature. As a result, there is a need for demand analysis that appropriately takes into account the effects of borders on cross-border transport. Rietveld (2012) provides a review of this area. Although the creation and expansion of the EU has led to a reduction of border-related barriers to transport in Europe, these barriers still exist and continue to be of a considerable size. There are still great differences in language, culture, institutions, preferences and public sector regulation. Depending on the type of infrastructure and transport mode we find that there are still substantial border effects, implying a decrease in demand for transport of some 30 to 70 per cent when a trip crosses a border compared with a similar trip that does not cross a border. It is clear that such border effects have a downward influence on demand for border crossing trips which implies that for cross-border infrastructure projects it is more difficult to pass CBA tests than for similar projects that do not cross a border.

12.6 CONCLUSION AND DISCUSSION

The most important conclusions of this chapter are listed below:

- A CBA is an overview of all the pros (benefits) and cons (costs) of a project. As much as possible these costs and benefits are quantified and expressed in monetary terms. Benefits are in general based on consumer preferences.
- CBA is a very popular method to ex ante evaluate candidate options for mega-projects.
- There are three major explanations for the popularity of CBA in the ex ante evaluation of infrastructure projects and its role in decision-making – these reasons are the main strengths of the method. The first explanation is that most costs and benefits are well known, the

second is that models to forecast demand are generally available, and the third is that CBA is a relatively 'neutral' evaluation method. The first two reasons are also helpful if an MCA is used for the ex ante evaluation, but because CBA relies more heavily on quantitative inputs than MCA, these explanations are even more relevant for CBA than for MCA.

- Despite its popularity CBA has several weaknesses. These relate to the quality of cost estimates and demand forecasts, uncertainties about wider economic effects, cross-border issues, difficult to monetize effects such as effects on nature and the landscape, benefits of innovations, image and prestige, distribution effects, long-term effects, the lack of explicit information that the decision-maker may consider to be relevant, in particular accessibility effects and effects on social exclusion. In addition, it is difficult to apply CBA when there are strong uncertainties related to the dynamics of a project. An additional challenge is communicating a CBA in a way that the clients appreciate.

The above list of weaknesses is long and could therefore be interpreted as a reason to reject CBA, at least for mega-projects.[4] But we should be careful about being too negative. If one takes the perspective (as we do) that for the quality of public decision-making it is important that decision-makers are well informed, one can assume that the quality of decision-making is greater if the decision-makers make the choice they would have made (1) if they had have all (from their perspective) potentially relevant choice options available, (2) if they were fully informed, and (3) if they were able to evaluate different choice options (i.e., weigh the pros and cons of choice options). This is perhaps a valid rule of thumb for a high level of democracy. Then the question becomes: which methodology for ex ante evaluations of transport projects and policies is 'best'? One could argue that it is important to analyse the pros and cons of relevant choice options, but that a valuation of these pros and cons is not needed. In that case, a simple scorecard could do the job. (According to Table 12.1 a major advantage of CBA and MCA is that a list of important pros and cons is presented in both methods.) In some cases, this may be true. But in many other cases this is at least risky, mainly because the pros and cons are probably not all equally important, either from the decision-maker's point of view, or for relevant actors in the field, or from a broad welfare perspective. Some form of analysis is then useful, the two main methods being CBA and MCA. The choice between the two methods should be based on the pros and cons of the options in a specific case (ex ante evaluation of competing options for mega-projects). The main pro of an MCA is that it allows the explicit inclusion of actor preferences in weighting relevant outcomes of interest. This also is its main weakness: setting the weights is highly subjective, and can easily (at least: more easily than in the case of a CBA) lead to manipulations. If there are several impacts of policy options that cannot be monetized well, an MCA may be a 'richer' approach than a CBA. The dominant pros and cons of a CBA are opposite to those of an MCA: a CBA gives less room for specific preferences, but because of its emphasis on (mainly) consumer preferences (expressed in monetary terms), it is more neutral. For important difficult-to-monetize effects the method can be 'poorer' than an MCA.

NOTES

1. Some parts of this chapter are based on van Wee and Tavasszy (2008).
2. In some cases, such as CO_2 emissions, benefits are not based on consumer preferences.
3. In practice price tags for CO_2 emissions are often used based on the so-called 'distance to target' method. Nevertheless, major uncertainty about future climate change and its valuation remains. Targets can also be changed, which may greatly influence the price tags for CO_2 emissions if based on the distance to target method. It is beyond the scope of this chapter to further discuss pricing CO_2 emissions.
4. This paragraph is drawn from van Wee (2011).

LITERATURE

Blauwens, G., P. de Baere and E. van de Voorde (2008), *Transport Economics*, Antwerp: De Boeck.

Bristow, A. and J. Nellthorp (2000), 'Transport project appraisal in the European Union', *Transport Policy*, **7**(1), 51–60.

Bröcker, J. and M. Schneider (2002), 'How does economic development in Eastern Europe affect Austria's regions? A multiregional general equilibrium framework', *Journal of Regional Science*, **42**(2), 257–85.

Button, K.J. (2010), *Transport Economics*, 3rd edition, Cheltenham, UK and Northampton, MA, USA: Edward Elgar.

Cantarelli, C.C., B. Flyvbjerg, B. van Wee and E.J.E. Molin (2010), 'Lock-in and its influence on the project performance of large-scale transportation infrastructure projects: investigating the way in which lock-in can emerge and affect cost overruns', *Environment and Planning B: Planning and Design*, **37**(5), 792–807.

Davies, S. (1999), *Review of the Evidence of the Incidence of Imperfect Competition in the UK*, Report to the UK Standing Advisory Committee on Trunk Road Assessment (SACTRA).

de Jong, G., A. Daly, M. Pieters and T. van der Hoorn (2007), 'The logsum as an evaluation measure: review of the literature and new results', *Transportation Research Part A: Policy and Practice*, **41**(9), 874–89.

Geurs, K.T., W. Boon and B. van Wee (2009), 'Social impacts of transport: literature review and the state of the practice of transport appraisal in the Netherlands and the United Kingdom', *Transport Reviews*, **29**(1), 69–90.

Geurs, K.T. and B. van Wee (2004), 'Accessibility evaluation of land-use and transport strategies: review and research directions', *Journal of Transport Geography*, **12**(2), 127–40.

Grant-Muller, S.M., P. MacKie, J. Nellthorp and A. Pearman (2001), 'Economic appraisal of European transport projects: the state-of-the-art revisited', *Transport Reviews*, **21**(2), 237–61.
Gunn, H. (2001), 'Spatial and temporal transferability of relationships between travel demand, trip cost and travel time', *Transportation Research E*, **37**(2–3), 163–89.
Hayashi, Y. and H. Morisugi (2000), 'International comparison of background concept and methodology of transportation project appraisal', *Transport Policy*, **7**(1) 73–88.
HEATCO (2006), *Proposal for Harmonised Guidelines. Developing Harmonised European Approaches for Transport Costing and Project Assessment and Other Deliverables*, Brussels: European Commission.
Jara-Diaz, S.R. (1986), 'On the relation between users' benefits and the economic effects of transportation activities', *Journal of Regional Science*, **26**(2), 379–91.
Mokhtarian, P. and C. Chen (2004), 'TTB or not TTB that is the question: a review and analysis of the empirical literature on travel time (and money) budgets', *Transportation Research Part A*, **38**(9–10), 643–75.
Newbery, D. (1998), *Efficiency Benefits of Transport Costs Reductions*, report prepared for SACTRA, Department of Applied Economics, Cambridge University.
Oosterhaven, J. and J.P. Elhorst (2003), 'Modelling interactions between the economy, the environment and transportation at the local and regional level, with an application to Dutch maglev projects', paper presented at the TRIP Research Conference on the Economic and Environmental Consequences of Regulating Traffic, Copenhagen, February.
Pickrell, D.H. (1989), *Urban Rail Transit Projects: Forecast Versus Actual Ridership and Costs*, Washington, DC: US Department of Transportation.
Pilegaard, N. and M. Fosgerau (2008), 'Cost benefit analysis of a transport improvement in the case of search unemployment', *Journal of Transport Economics and Policy*, **42**(1), 1–20.
Rietveld, P. (2003), 'Winners and losers in transport policy: on efficiency, equity, and compensation', in D.A. Hensher and K.J. Button (eds), *Handbook of Transport and the Environment*, Amsterdam: Elsevier, pp. 585–602.
Rietveld, P. (2012), 'Barrier effects of borders: implications for border-crossing infrastructures', *European Journal of Transport Infrastructure Research*, **12**(2), 150.
Rietveld, P. (2013), 'Appraisal methods for transport policy', in B. van Wee, J.A. Annema and D. Banister (eds), *The Transport System and Transport Policy. An Introduction*, Cheltenham, UK and Northampton, MA, USA: Edward Elgar, pp. 329–52.
SACTRA (1999), *Transport and the Economy*, Standing Advisory Committee on Trunk Road Assessment, London: SACTRA.
Schafer, A. and D. Victor (1997), 'The past and future of global mobility', *Scientific American*, **227**(4), 36–9.
Szalai, A. (ed.) (1972), *The Use of Time: Daily Activities of Urban and Suburban Populations in Twelve Countries*, The Hague: Mouton.
Tillema, T., E. Verhoef, B. van Wee and D. van Amelsfort (2011), 'Evaluating the effects of urban congestion pricing: geographical accessibility versus social surplus', *Transportation Planning and Technology*, **34**(7), 669–89.
van Wee, B. (2007), 'Large infrastructure projects: a review of the quality of demand forecasts and cost estimations', *Environment and Planning B*, **34**(4), 611–25.
van Wee, B. (2011), *Transport and Ethics. Ethics and the Evaluation of Transport Policies and Pojects*, Cheltenham, UK and Northampton, MA, USA: Edward Elgar.
van Wee, B. and L.A. Tavasszy (2008), 'Ex ante evaluation of mega-projects: methodological issues and cost–benefit analysis', in H. Priemus, B. Flyvbjerg and B. van Wee (eds), *Decision-making on Mega-projects. Cost–Benefit Analysis, Planning and Innovation*, Cheltenham, UK and Northampton, MA, USA: Edward Elgar.
Venables, A.J. (2007), 'Evaluating urban transport improvements: cost–benefit analysis in the presence of agglomeration and income taxation', *Journal of Transport Economics and Policy*, **41**(2), 173–88.

Wardman, M. (2001), 'A review of British evidence on time and service quality valuations', *Transportation Research Part E*, **37**(2–3), 107–28.
Zahavi, Y. (1979), *The UMOT-Project, US Department of Transportation*, Report DOT-RSPA-DPB-2-79-3, Washington, DC: US Department of Transportation.
Zhu, X., J.N. van Ommeren and P. Rietveld (2009), 'Indirect benefits of infrastructure improvement in the case of an imperfect labor market', *Transportation Research Part B*, **43**(1), 57–72.

13. The use of CBA in decision-making on mega-projects: empirical evidence

Jan Anne Annema

13.1 INTRODUCTION

Worldwide, cost–benefit analysis (CBA) is often applied as a tool to support political decision-making in the transport sector. This chapter aims to answer two main questions. First, are CBAs actually used by the decision-makers in the practice of ex ante mega-project evaluation? Second, which suggestions for improvements can be made from the analysis of the actual use of CBA? These two questions are mainly answered using literature study and case studies. The literature study contains empirical evidence of actual CBA use from many different countries. The case studies are confined to mega-projects from the Netherlands because the author of this chapter knows cases from this country in depth. In Section 13.2 the context of the use of CBA in mega-project planning worldwide is explained. An overview of literature on the role of CBA in decision-making on mega-projects worldwide is given in Section 13.3. Section 13.4 discusses 16 Netherlands mega-project case studies. The discussion focuses on the role of CBA in the decision-making and on the role of the Netherlands CBA guidelines in the decision-making process. Barriers for the application of CBA in mega-project planning by decision-makers are identified in Section 13.5. In Section 13.6 several suggestions are made for improved CBA practice. Some conclusions are given in Section 13.7.

13.2 THE CONTEXT: CBA REQUIREMENTS AND STANDARDIZATION

CBAs are used for supporting new mega-project decision-making all over the world (Willis et al., 1998; Hayashi and Morisugi, 2000; Lee, 2000; Nakamura, 2000; Odgaard et al., 2005; Annema et al., 2007; Mackie and Kelly, 2007; World Bank, 2010). Most countries and international bodies such as the World Bank and the European Union also apply some kind of CBA standardization in order to state clearly for which projects CBAs are required and in order to improve the quality of the CBA. Nakamura (2000) points at a two-volume instruction manual for Japanese transport project evaluation, not only covering conventional CBA but also aspects such as distributional weighting of effects for the reduction of regional disparity, and multi-criteria analysis for further comprehensive evaluation. English written examples of CBA requirements and recommendations are the UK *New Approach to Appraisal* (NATA, more details to be found on http://www.dft.gov.uk/webtag/), the Netherlands *Guide for Cost–Benefit Analysis* (Eijgenraam et al., 2000) and the *Guide to Cost–Benefit Analysis of Investment Projects* (EC Directorate General Regional Policy, 2008). Detailed information on CBA requirements and standardization for Europe can be found in the so-called HEATCO project (HEATCO, 2006). HEATCO stands for 'Developing Harmonised European Approaches for Transport Costing and Project Assessment' (all deliverables can be downloaded from http://heatco.ier.uni-stuttgart.de/).

Civil servants and experts may produce and use CBA requirements, manuals and guidelines and apply CBA to new mega-projects accordingly, but the question remains: 'Has this practice any impact on decision-making?' Or, in other words: 'Do the real decision-makers – the politicians – actually use the CBA results or do they take them for granted and decide on other grounds'?

Even if the politicians ignore CBA results completely but civil servants use CBA in the design phase or in the initial screening phase, then CBA still plays its role. With the second question – 'Do the politicians actually use CBA?' – we aim to find evidence of CBA use in the final political stage of decision-making. In the next section some answers to the questions posed will be given based on an international literature review. Later, in Section 13.6, we will deal with the third key question: 'Which suggestions for improvements can be drawn from the analysis of the actual use of CBA?'

13.3 ACTUAL CBA USE IN MEGA-PROJECT PLANNING: A LITERATURE REVIEW

Some research has been carried out on actual CBA use in mega-project planning. 'Use' is somewhat vague. In this chapter 'use' means that there are indications that in the decision-making process CBA outcomes have influenced the decision in some way.

Table 13.1 summarizes the main findings of relatively recent studies (published since 1998). There are some older studies such as McFadden

Table 13.1 Overview of CBA use based on a wide range of international studies since 1998

Study	Aimed At	Method	Main Results
Nyborg (1998)	Analysing, among others, CBA use by Norwegian parliamentarians related to transport projects	In-person interviews with 16 Norwegian Members of Parliament	None of the respondents appeared to use the cost–benefit ratio as a 'final answer'. Eleven respondents appeared to interpret the cost–benefit ratio as an indicator to sort out projects that deserve a closer look. Indications of conflict seemed to be used much more extensively as a screening device than the cost–benefit ratio, however
Nellthorp and Mackie (2000)	Reproducing the pattern of decision-making on 68 UK road schemes	Modelling based on the so-called Appraisal Summary Table (APT)	The APT gave the scheme performance against the government's five objectives – environment, safety, economy, accessibility and integration. In the APT, among others, the net present value (NPV) and the benefit-to-cost ratio (BCR) were presented to the decision-makers. The researchers were unable to find any statistical evidence that the pattern of decision-making was systematically related to NPVs or BCRs. Their preferred model showed that decision-makers use other appraisal factors that are not valued in monetary terms such as the scheme's impact on noise, landscape, heritage, reliability and regeneration
Sager and Ravlum (2005)	Analysing, among others, CBA use by Norwegian parliamentarians	Members of the Norwegian national assembly's Standing Committee on Transport and Communications were interviewed	The majority (all except the Socialist Left Party) shared the belief that the CBA is an important part of clarifying the economic impacts of transport projects on society. Nevertheless, the main result from the study is that the parliamentarians make little use of the CBAs in decision-making

Table 13.1 (continued)

Study	Aimed At	Method	Main Results
Bax et al. (2009)	Analysis of the barriers to the utilization of knowledge from economic analysis in road safety policy	Interviewed: 83 European leading decision-makers influencing road safety policy	A quarter to half of the respondents mention technical barriers to the use of cost–benefit analysis. Most mentioned the barrier (48; N = 83): 'cost–benefit analysis may be impossible because the effects of the measures are not known or not trusted'
Proost et al. (2010, 2011)	To do, among others, an efficiency test on 11 European Union TransEuropean Transport Network (TEN-T) cases	Document analysis, amongst others	The EU TEN-T cases comprised four high-speed rail projects, two freight transportation infrastructure projects and another five in more detail. Proost et al. conclude that often for these TEN-T projects no good documentation is available. Despite the help of the European Commission services it was impossible to obtain a cost–benefit analysis for most projects. Proost et al. (2010) remark that this constitutes an important finding in itself
World Bank (2010)	Evaluating CBA use in World Bank projects appraisal	Document analysis	Bank policy states that cost–benefit analysis should be conducted for all project appraisals. However, projects with CBA or cost-effectiveness analysis (CEA) dropped from 70 per cent to 25 per cent between the early 1970s and the early 2000s. In the relatively high-CBA World Bank sectors (transport is included in this sector) the CBA or CEA share dropped from approximately 90 per cent in the early 1970s to just over 50 per cent in the 2000s

Table 13.1 (continued)

Study	Aimed At	Method	Main Results
Shapiro (2010)	To give some reflections on CBA use in United States regulatory policy	Writing an essay-like paper	Shapiro tells about CBA being the centre of intense controversy over the past 30 years. However, in his view CBA is now firmly entrenched in the regulatory process in the USA and few predict that this will change in the decades ahead. 'The emerging questions involve not whether to adopt CBA, but how; we should now be turning to those questions'
Odeck (2010)	To examine which factors in the Impact Assessment (IA) sheet determined the rankings of road projects by Norwegian decision-makers. The dataset comprised a pool of 1121 independent road projects, of which 184 were selected for investment	Odeck hypothesized different models that may explain decision-making using a multinomial logit model	An IA sheet involves the assessment of all net impacts, whether monetized or not. Ideally, the IA will contain both monetized impacts (such as cost–benefit ratio) and non-monetized net impacts (such as landscape intrusion and many other environmental impacts). One conclusion that Odeck draws is that BCAs per se do not matter for decision-making, but that their components are taken into account in non-monetary units or partially rather than in a composite cost–benefit ratio or NPV. His work reiterates (as he remarks himself) the finding of Nellthorp and Mackie (2000) who used a different model
Eliasson and Lundberg (2012)	To study how CBA results were used in the process of shaping the Swedish National Transport Investment Plan 2011–21.	Document analysis and interview	They find that planners use CBA results primarily as a screening tool to avoid investment with negative net benefits. They also conclude that politicians select investment essentially at random, from a pure CBA perspective. Their impression is that the planners responsible for prioritizing among investments saw CBA as a useful tool, and evidently, CBA results played an important role in the selection process. It is also evident from their research, however, that the selection was not based on CBA results alone

(1976), but it is assumed that the relatively recent studies selected better represent the current mega-project planning practices in the world. The studies selected focus on economic analysis in mega-project planning but some studies have a somewhat broader approach such as World Bank (2010) (not only transport infrastructure projects), Shapiro (2010) (regulatory policies not only aimed at the transport sector) and Bax et al. (2009) (road safety policy). These studies are also included in the overview because some valuable lessons can be learned from them.

The overall picture from Table 13.1 is clear: politicians appear not to use CBA's main outcome such as the net present value (NPV) or benefit-to-cost ratio (BCR) as an important source to support their decision. Two studies indicate that they use appraisal factors in non-monetized units in their decision-making (Nellthorp and Mackie, 2000; Odeck, 2010). Eliasson and Lundberg (2012) conclude that planners in Sweden (civil servants who prepare the decision-making) indeed use CBA as a screening device. Another observation from Table 13.1 is that CBAs are not always judged as indispensable or required by decision-makers. The World Bank (2010, p. ix) analysis is most striking in this respect. Cost–benefit analysis used to be one of the World Bank's signature issues, so the report (ibid.) states. Nevertheless, the CBA application in the World Bank dropped considerably in the past decades (Table 13.1). Also, the European Union practice related to mega-project planning is clear: apparently political decisions could be made without support from CBA results (Proost et al., 2010).

13.4 DUTCH EXPERIENCE WITH CBAs IN MEGA-PROJECT PLANNING

Section 13.3 shows that politicians hardly seem to use main CBA results (BCR or NPV) in transport investment decision-making. In this section we analyse the Netherlands CBA practice for mega-projects planning in the period 2000 to 2011 by looking at 16 cases. By analysing these different Netherlands cases it is aimed to add to the insights of the empirics of CBA application by decision-makers as described in Section 13.3. In the selection of cases we took 500 million euros as the minimum investment cost level to define 'large' or 'mega'-projects (based on an assumption by van Wee, 2007). First, we analyse the CBA impact on the Netherlands decision-making processes for the 16 mega-projects. Hereafter, the experience with the Dutch CBA guide (Eijgenraam et al., 2000) in the decision-making processes will be discussed.

CBA Impact on Dutch Mega-project Decision-making

Table 13.2 presents the investment costs estimated, the NPV and the political decision for the 16 mega-projects that were debated in the period 2000 to 2011. The 16 mega-projects represent the total population of mega-projects debated in the Netherlands in this period. For some infrastructure projects the investment costs vary (Table 13.2) as in these cases different project variants were studied.

The first observation from Table 13.2 is that for all mega-projects in this period a CBA (sometimes even more than one) was made, except for the project last mentioned (Case 16), the original decision to build the so-called North/South subway in Amsterdam. This high CBA score is in contrast with the World Bank development and the EU TEN-T projects (see previous section) and is related to the decision by the Dutch government in 1998 to make an inventory of the knowledge of economic effects of infrastructural projects. The ministries were moved to start this research programme after the observation that the economic effects of major Dutch investments plans were, before 1998, often estimated using diverse methods. The 1998 research programme (the Dutch acronym is the 'OEI' programme) concluded that 'not only was the assessment before 1998 characterized by diverse research methodologies, but many intense, and not always very lucid, discussions about the appropriateness and applicability of these methodologies arise' (Eijgenraam et al., 2000, p. 1). The most important report in the OEI programme (Eijgenraam et al., 2000) proposed CBA as the preferred method to support large infrastructure decision-making in the Netherlands and contained a set of guidelines for applying CBA. In 2000 the Dutch government decided that this CBA guide should be applied to all major transport infrastructure plans (Annema et al., 2007).

The final decision in 2002 by the Amsterdam council to build the North/South subway line in Amsterdam is not supported by a publicly available CBA because the prime responsibility for this project was with the municipality instead of the national government. In any case, around 2008 the Amsterdam subway project ran into big trouble because during construction of the first kilometres and underground stations it turned out that the risks and complexity of the project were to a large extent underestimated in the original decision. It became apparent that to finish the line would cost twice as much as expected at the time of the original decision-making in 2002 and the project would be finished in 2017 instead of in 2011 as originally agreed upon. A committee was appointed in 2009 to advise on the question to go ahead or to stop the subway project (Commissie Veerman, 2009). This committee used CBA to underpin their view. It is this CBA that is included in Table 13.2.

Table 13.2 Decision-making on 16 Dutch transport mega-projects 2000–11

	Investment (billion euros)	NPV (billion euros)	Decision
1 High speed rail Amsterdam–Germany	1.4–2.6	−1.4 to −3.1	No go; CBA played a role to decide on improved utilization of the existing tracks instead of building new tracks
2 New rail line Lelystad–Zwolle	± 0.6	−0.06	Go
3 Schiphol Amsterdam Airport extension	0.3–0.8	0.2 to −9.1	No go
4 Improved freight rail between Rotterdam and Belgium	0.9–1.0	−0.5 to −0.2	No go; CBA was used to design 'best' track and to possibly build the project in phases. However, final decision was 'no go'
5 New railroad between the four Dutch large cities	4.3–8.2	−0.6 to −5.5	No go; high costs compared to 'added value' was used as argument in a official policy document to decide negatively on this project
6 Transport and urban development Amsterdam South (Zuidas)	1.1–2.7	−0.5 to −1	Go
7 High speed rail Amsterdam–Groningen	3.5–7.9	−3.2 to −8.5	No go
8 Botlek road tunnel Rotterdam area	0.3–0.9	−0.6 to −2.2	Go; CBA argument was used for selection. The tunnel variant with the higher NPV compared to the selected one was selected
9 New highway between Delft and Schiedam	0.12–0.62	0.04 to −0.6	Go
10 New and extended highways between Schiphol and Almere	1.3–3.1	−2.1 to −0.9	Go. CBA, Environmental Impact Assessment and local protests influenced highway design

Table 13.2 (continued)

	Investment (billion euros)	NPV (billion euros)	Decision
11 Rotterdam port extension	>1	−0.2 to −0.8	Go, CBA played a role in the decision to build the extension of the port in phases
12 Second lock Terneuzen	0.8–1.8	0.6 to −1.0	Go
13 Improving sea lock IJmuiden (near Amsterdam port)	0.52	−0.25	No go. However, after some years of this decision, the decision process was re-opened. Decision is currently pending
14 Nationwide road pricing (flat rate variants: 3.4 or 5.7 €ct/km[a])	± 4	14 to 17	No go
15 New public transport between Amsterdam and Almere	1.2–1.9	−1.7 to −3.2	Discussion process still open. New (cheaper) variant has been proposed
16 Finishing the construction of the complete so-called North/South line subway in Amsterdam	±1.8–2 to finish the project	0.8 to 0	Go

Note: a. €ct/km = Eurocents per kilometre driven.

Sources: Besseling et al. (2005); Annema et al. (2007); Rienstra (2008); CommissieVeerman (2009); Rienstra and Visser (2010); Koopmans (2010).

Table 13.2 shows that in four cases a clear negative NPV resulted in a 'no go' and in two cases a clear positive net balance resulted in a 'go'. Here, 'clear' means that the whole range of a CBA's NPV as estimated for a particular project is positive or negative. In two cases a positive net balance was followed with a 'no go'. In three cases a negative net balance resulted in a 'go'. In two cases the decision is still pending while the CBAs showed a negative NPV. Three cases showed a net CBA balance that ranged from negative to positive. In two of these 'unclear' cases it was decided to go ahead with the project and in one case it was not. Thus, for Dutch politicians there are also clearly more and/or other reasons to go ahead or stop a mega-project than the efficiency criterion alone. On the other hand, the outcomes are not too bad from a CBA utilization perspective either. Koopmans (2010) is actually rather positive about the impact of CBA in decision-making for large infrastructure projects in the Netherlands, based on an analysis of more or less the same projects. We take a more cautious position in this chapter. We think that there are only clues that CBAs or parts of a CBA have had impact on some of the political decisions. Here, the word 'clues' is used on purpose because it is hard to prove that CBA results were used in the final political decision for a project. One reason for this it that in policy documents or in parliamtentary minutes CBA results are often not or not clearly mentioned as an argument pro or contra. This does not mean that the CBAs' outcomes did not play a role at all in the decision-making process, but it does mean that their role is rather vague. Another reason is that we cannot know if some of the decisions would not have been the same in a situation without performing CBAs (the pre-2000 period) but with the support of other ex ante impact reports.

An important clue that CBAs influenced the political decision-making process can be seen from the fact that in some Dutch mega-projects the original proposals were adapted ('High speed rail Amsterdam – Germany' (Case 1), 'New and extended highways between Schiphol and Almere' (Case 10), 'Freight rail improvements between Rotterdam and Antwerp' (Case 4), 'Rotterdam port extension', Case 11) or economic arguments were used to choose a particular variant ('Botlek Tunnel', Case 8) or to postpone a decision to look for better (e.g., cheaper) options ('New public transport between Almere and Amsterdam', Case 15) (Table 13.2). However, we should be careful with this observation, since – once again – it is not known what would have happened if decision-making in these cases had been supported in the pre-CBA fashion. Nevertheless, in the explanations for a particular design choice in these cases economic reasons were often mentioned. Thus, at least it seems reasonable to assume that the new Netherlands CBA thinking since 2000 has had an impact on decision-making related to design choices.

The Role of the Netherlands CBA Guide

We may conclude that in the Netherlands the application of CBA since 2000 has had some impact on political decision-making for mega-projects. The Dutch practice can be considered a standardized approach as it is obligatory to use a CBA guide (see above). In this part of Section 13.4 we formulate the question: 'What is the impact of this guide on the decision-making process on infrastructure projects?'

The impact of a CBA guide on decision-making is indirect because the aim of a guide is primarily to improve the quality of the CBAs applied. Naturally, the idea is that by improving the quality of CBAs the decision-making process also improves but – as shown in Section 13.3 and above for the Netherlands cases – political decision-makers do not per se use CBAs even if their quality is high. Thus, the role of a CBA guide in decision-making processes can be best determined by evaluating the quality of the CBAs made. Annema et al. (2007) analysed in depth the CBAs applied to 13 Netherlands transport infrastructure projects in the period 2000–06 (nine cases were the same as depicted in Table 13.2). On the positive side, they distinguished methodological improvements as a result of the standardized CBA practice. First, an improvement in the evaluation practice they noticed is that all impacts of a project are estimated using the same future scenarios. Second, thanks to the guide, policy-makers can base their decisions on fairly complete information on the effects of a project. Nevertheless, their main conclusion was not very positive: according to them, applying a standardized CBA approach in the Netherlands had not as yet fulfilled its potential. Seven CBAs analysed had weaknesses or even major weaknesses with respect to methods and assumptions, according to the authors. Furthermore, Annema et al. (2007) found the transparency generally poor in most cases of Dutch CBA practice.

The Dutch guide can be regarded as a living document because since 2004 diverse addenda have been included. For example, addenda have been written on the improved treatment of risks and ecological effects. Annema et al. (2007) could identify that the supplement on improved treatment of risks is actually used in practice, and indeed improved the quality of CBAs. In the supplement on improved treatment of ecological effects addendum, it was proposed to always present physical effects in the main summarizing CBA table as well as the monetary values. This was proposed in order to improve CBAs' transparency for the political decision-makers. However, this practice has been applied to only a limited extent. These authors analysed, amongst others, 54 transport CBAs, applied in the period 2000 to 2011. They found that physical effects were included in 5 per cent of the CBA reports before 2005 and 14 per cent after

2005. Thus, the addendum to the guidelines has had some impact, but after 2005 still only a minority of the CBAs have published present physical impacts clearly.

An interesting role related to the guide is played by the Netherlands Bureau for Economic Policy Analysis (CPB, the Dutch acronym, an independent economic research institute funded by national government). CPB was a main author of the guide and the institute plays a major role in reviewing CBAs in order to evaluate if the CBAs carried out fulfil the requirements and advice of the guide. Rienstra (2008) concludes that only in two cases out of the 13 he analysed was the CPB review negative. This seems to indicate that most CBAs are of good quality in themselves. However, Koopmans (2010) thinks that it is more probable that a critical CPB increased the discipline among the Dutch CBA experts. CPB more or less forms a deterrent to consultants from producing bad quality or 'political' CBAs. Their reputation and future turnover may be at risk if they should often receive a negative CPB review.

13.5 EXPLAINING THE LIMITED USE OF CBAs IN DECISION-MAKING ON MEGA-PROJECTS

Why are CBAs used in transport infrastructure decision-making to a limited extent? The answer to this question is important in order to be able to reflect on recommendations for an improved use of CBA (next section). In answering the 'why' question, it should be realized that the application of knowledge by decision-makers is limited in general. There is a huge knowledge base on this topic (e.g., Landry et al., 2001; Kasemir et al., 2003; Bax, 2011) that shows, amongst others, that knowledge based, for example, on social aspects, road safety and climate change science, is used only to a limited extent by political decision-makers. In the academic literature many barriers are explained for this limited use. We distinguish five barriers that may explain the limited use of CBA decision-making on mega-projects:

Barrier Related to Information Overload

One barrier for limited use is related to a CBA often being just one part of a considerable amount of information about projects (Sager and Ravlum, 2005). For example, in the Netherlands there is a famous photo of a parliamentarian who poses next to the huge number of documents he received during the decision-making process of a mega-project (a dedicated freight rail line from Rotterdam to Germany, the so-called Betuweroute; see

Priemus, 2007). This seems representative for most mega-project planning. It is plausible to assume that some decision-makers just miss the CBA information, forget about it when the time of final decision-making arrives or simply do not have the time to really scrutinize the CBA information received.

Barrier Related to Lack of Understanding

Another barrier for politicians to use CBAs is possibly a lack of understanding (mentioned in Nyborg, 1998 and van Wee, 2007). Nyborg (1998) could not identify in her study any respondents who had clearly misunderstood major features of the method. On the other hand, van Wee (2007) and also the author of this chapter have the impression that not all features of CBAs are deeply understood by most Dutch decision-makers. Combined with the first reason for limited use (the overload of information and the lack of time to really scrutinize all information) it seems plausible that some politicians will simply ignore the relatively complicated CBA as their main source of information in the decision-making process. Beukers et al. (2012) found, based on focus group sessions and 22 open in-depth interviews with Dutch CBA professionals (consultants, civil servants who prepare the decision, scientists), that, in particular, non-economists often experience CBA as a black box. Beukers et al. (2012) conclude that plan owners (the civil servants who are responsible for preparing a new plan) are anxious if their plan is assessed with CBA and this anxiety is increased if they do not exactly understand the calculation methods being used.

Barrier Related to Not Accepting Certain Premises, and Mistrust

A third family of barriers is related to acceptance and trust. Politicians – even the ones who actually understand the CBA – may not accept some normative premises of the technique or they may not trust the effects estimated (Sager and Ravlum, 2005; Bax et al., 2009). The research by Bax et al. (2009) on the application of economic analysis in road safety policy even suggests that mistrust in the possibility of good-quality effect estimates is the most important explanation for the limited CBA application in road safety policies (see Table 13.1). Mouter et al. (2013) also found this barrier important. They interviewed 86 Dutch CBA experts and users (in this case the users are almost all civil servants who prepare final decision-making but who do not make the decision) on their perception of the important substantive problems with CBA for transportation and spatial projects. Their research showed that the majority of substantive problems with CBA that were mentioned in the interviews are related to estimates of effects. From the 634 unique perceptions on CBA problems that were mentioned in this study by the experts and users, 52 per cent could be assigned to the 'problems with estimating non-monetized effects' category. If the Dutch experts and users (the civil servants preparing the political decision) doubt or even mistrust effect estimates used in CBAs it seems plausible that some final decision-makers will have some severe reservations about actually using the instrument in all cases. In Beukers et al. (2012) (see above) the mistrust of CBA seems especially related to non-economists in the decision-making process (e.g., the spatial planners) who fear that their values, like the increase in liveability, do not get the same attention as those effects that economists do understand, such as less travel time.

Political Barrier

A broad fourth barrier category can be denoted as 'political'. On the basis of suggestions in the literature we distinguish three kinds of political reasons that might explain limited CBA utilization. First, some politicians may just think that expert technique should not provide the final answer (Sager and Ravlum, 2005). Second, politicians may take only the sentiments of the regional or local community into account when making a decision on building new infrastructure or, sometimes, may just have to comply with the promises given by the other party members during election campaigns (ibid.). There is some empirical proof of the importance of local sentiments. Knight (2003) tested the so-called 'common pool incentive' in US transportation decision-making. By this Knight means that local public goods, such as roads, financed from a national tax base (as in the US Congressional votes for transportation projects), provide concentrated benefits to recipient jurisdiction but disperse costs, creating incentives for legislators to increase own-district spending but to restrain aggregate spending and the associated tax costs. Knight (ibid.) analysed 1998 Congressional votes over transportation funding. His empirical results indeed provide evidence that US legislators respond to common pool incentives: the probability of supporting tax proposals increases when the money is spent in their own districts and decreases for tax proposals where the money will be spent on a aggregate spatial level. In those circumstances, expert information on efficiency or even effectiveness may totally be ignored or may not be very influential. Nakamura (2000, p. 3) identifies for the Japanese case one of the reasons that full economic evaluation has rarely been applied during the process of decision-making on transport infrastructure projects: 'Politicians, particularly local politicians, have sought to increase their influence on investments in transport infrastructure which they claim will have economic benefits for their constituencies and, therefore, are reluctant to accept highly objective evaluation techniques and to utilize the results of analysis'. Finally, in the European Union, local (in this case national) sentiments seem very important in infrastructure decision-making. Proost et al. (2010 and 2011) speculate that the EU decision-making process is such that European investment money needs to be spread out over an adequate number of countries and regions to obtain a sufficient majority in the European Parliament. Consequently, only a portfolio of projects would pass the majority threshold, irrespective of the individual economic efficiency of each project. The World Bank (2010, p. xi) sees as an underlying cause for the decreased use of CBAs for World Bank projects (even if it is obligatory to draft them), 'A decision-making process under which decisions are made before cost–benefit evidence is provided, and that provides few institutional checks to counteract the influence of advocacy for projects that undermines rigor in project appraisal, including cost–benefit analysis'. In this 'advocacy for projects' one can perhaps see once again signs of the common pool incentive as defined by Knight (2003).

The third kind of political reason is inspired by the hypothesis by Proost et al. (2010) that many EU transport infrastructure investments have been accepted on the basis of the general transport policy that advocated a strong expansion of rail passenger and rail freight to address road congestion and environmental objectives including greenhouse gas (GHG) emissions. Thus, in this view politicians seem to emphasize the objective of mega-projects in their decision-making. Politics is about framing and selling simple messages. 'Rail line X is the sustainable solution'. 'The port is of high strategic importance and needs to be expanded'. 'We need the new road to make region Y better accessible to beat the high unemployment there'. In order to sell these messages, they might more or less ignore the costs required to meet the objective (let alone the question of whether a mega-project will result in meeting a particular objective anyway). Naturally, this political position forms a barrier to actually using CBA information. Politicians may behave like this due to the common pool incentive mentioned above but also because they may tend to be far too optimistic or just careless about mega-projects' costs and risks. The reasons for this might be psychological ('optimism bias') and/or intended ('strategic misrepresentation') (Flyvbjerg et al., 2003; Flyvbjerg, 2008).

Combined Barriers

Naturally, it seems logical to assume that the four barriers mentioned reinforce each other, resulting in a fifth 'reinforcing' barrier. As far as we know the existence of a combined barrier has never been investigated, so we can only speculate. The speculation would be to assume that CBA will hardly be used in a situation where politicians are not very interested in knowing the efficiency of mega-projects (but mainly focus on one effect that they find important), where the efficiency is calculated with a rather complicated tool, where other reports to support the decision-making are available with easier and perhaps more popular messages (from the political viewpoint of the decision-maker) and where the politician is surrounded by civil servants who doubt or mistrust some of the CBA results. Perhaps it is a miracle that CBA information has been used in some mega-project cases at all.

13.6 SUGGESTIONS FOR IMPROVED USE OF CBAs IN MEGA-PROJECT DECISION-MAKING

At first glance, this section may seem redundant as there are apparently many barriers to utilization. So, why bother to make suggestions for improvement? We think, however, that this general position is too strong. First, the 16 Dutch mega-project cases and some of the literature reviewed still showed some CBA impact on decision-making. Second, in our view we think that CBA information is highly useful decision-making information (compared with other information) that should be available in a mega-project decision-making process anyway. A clear position on the importance of CBA information is taken by Sunstein who is a fervent advocate of CBA (Shapiro, 2010). Sunstein was appointed by President Obama as the Administrator of the Office of Information and Regulatory Affairs (OIRA). Sunstein drew on the relatively new field of behavioural economics to justify CBA. He thought that behavioural economics has shown that individuals often rely on biases and heuristics to assist in decision-making (the political barriers for CBA utilization mentioned in the previous section support this observation). These biases and heuristics often lead individuals to make decisions that are not in their own interest, so he claimed. Sunstein's viewed CBA as a corrective for this: 'Cost–benefit analysis . . . is most plausibly justified on cognitive grounds – as a way of counteracting predictable problems in individual and social cognition' (in Shapiro, 2010, p. 8).

In order to play a corrective role this chapter indicates that some improvements to general current CBA practice could be made. If these suggestions lead only to some very modest increase in CBA application perhaps some inefficient mega-projects worldwide will be abandoned, postponed or changed (e.g., down-sized), which is already a major societal gain.

The following suggestions are based on ideas expressed in Nyborg (1998), Short and Kopp (2005), Rienstra (2008), World Bank (2010), Shapiro (2010), Eliasson and Lundberg (2012) and on our own ideas:

Suggestions for Improvements Related to Barriers Such as a Lack of Trust and Transparency

In order to make CBAs more trustworthy and transparent it seems paramount to use clear guidelines and to install formal procedures. These guidelines and procedures should not only comprise notions on how to perform transparent CBAs, but also describe how to carry out an obligatory problem analysis before a CBA is made and how to perform obligatory independent reviews. This idea of the importance of more formal settings of CBA can also be found in Shapiro (2010) who evaluated 30 years of CBA experience in US regulatory policies: 'Examination of CBA will turn to its institutional setting within the regulatory process. Questions about the independence of those conducting the analyses will dominate the debate and the resolution of these questions may result in institutional structures that further cement CBA as part of the regulatory process' (p. 19).

The role of the Dutch CBA guidelines is evaluated as positive in Section 13.4 with regard to some aspects (e.g., completeness), but in some other aspects (transparency, quality as regards content) the Dutch practice did not fulfil expectations. That is the reason why we think that it is important not only to make guidelines but also to accompany guidelines with formal procedures concerning an independent review. The Dutch practice shows positive experience with independent reviews. These reviews should not only focus on improving the substantive quality but also the transparency of CBAs. For example, in CBA guidelines it could be clearly stated that mega-project impacts should also be provided in physical unit information, such as the average number of minutes saved by daily commuters or the extra tons of carbon dioxide (CO_2) as a consequence of realizing a mega-project. As Nyborg (1998) suggests, this information may give a better intuitive understanding of the performance of a project than reporting all effects solely in monetary units. The World Bank (2010) report suggests also that formal rules for disclosure could be a further method to reinforce the objectivity of a CBA. Currently, within the World Bank it is impossible to replicate the CBA (World Bank, 2010). We think that this poor practice is representative of most CBA practices worldwide. Rules for disclosing the spreadsheet used (to the independent reviewers anyway) could help resolve this problem, particularly if – as suggested by the World Bank – the data were to be disclosed in a way that highlighted key assumptions and parameters of the cost–benefit exercise.

Another way of improving the trust in CBAs is performing ex post analyses: 'Ex-post evaluations should have a central role in improving the process of infrastructure planning', according to Short and Kopp (2005, p. 363). In our experience it is currently very hard for most mega-project planners worldwide to find ex post information. Sometimes even the final political decision, including the motivations to accept or reject a project, can hardly be found (as in the Dutch situation). It seems useful from a CBA learning perspective to gather systematically in a country or in an organization such as the World Bank, ex ante information for mega-projects and compare this information with ex post results.

Suggestions for Improvements Related to Political Barriers

The highest probability of a CBA having influence on decision-making seems to be in the very early stages of project development. For example, in Eliasson and Lundberg (2012) CBA played a role as a screening device in the early planning phase to select projects and to force investments designs to be more cost-effective. This influence in the very early stages seems in accordance with the political barriers of CBA utilization as mentioned in the previous section. The moment a mega-project is born it may have 'completely' stolen the hearts and minds of politicians, resulting in them being more and less deaf to the efficiency criterion. This is the reason why we suggest also including an obligatory problem analysis in CBA guidelines (including an independent review on this; see Section 13.4). A problem analysis has to be conducted in the very early stage of a project. In this stage questions such as: 'What is the problem the mega-project actually has to solve?' and, 'Which solutions are foreseeable to solve the problem?' are required. Thus, in this early stage of project development it may become clear that the alternatives may indeed comprise a mega-project, but also a down-sized mega-project or even solutions that are not related to improving transport infrastructure. Rienstra (2008) suggests performing the CBA in the problem analysis phase. In his view, by doing so, the role of a CBA changes from 'evaluator' to 'improver'. By carrying out CBA on the mega-project, the down-sized mega-project and non-infrastructure solutions (perhaps more solutions are foreseeable) it can be shown to decision-makers which of the solutions performs best with regard to the efficiency criterion. The Dutch mega-project cases (Section 13.4) suggest that CBA can indeed play an 'improver' role because some original schemes were changed after the production of a CBA.

The previous suggestions for improvements are not intended to state that CBA results should be the only basis on which the political decision is made. Perhaps the fear of CBA determining the decision is an important reason for politicians to ignore it. An improvement could be to position CBA clearly as just one of the many relevant policy information documents. The instrument is mainly very strong in evaluating classic economic efficiency of mega-projects. The CBA framework, on the other hand, is less often used for addressing the distributional impacts of the mega-project or the broader aspects of sustainability (e.g., related to intergenerational justice because ex ante long-term impacts are per definition low in standard CBA as a consequence of discounting; see van Wee, 2011). Additionally, van Wee (2011), in a study based on an extensive literature review, points out that the philosophical basis of CBA, namely utilitarianism, is not undisputed either. So, one way of improvement could be to extend the standard CBA reports with all kinds of extra analyses on distributional impacts, sustainability issues and ethical discussions. However, this may make the CBA even less transparent than is often currently experienced. Therefore, it may be better to create different concise, transparent and independent review reports containing CBA results, sustainability impacts, distributional consequences of mega-projects, and so forth. These reports should be strong in analysing their main objective but also make clear that they perform partial analyses. In order to avoid information overload the main results of these reports could be summarized for politicians in impact assessment sheets or 'Appraisal Summary Tables' (see Table 13.1). The underpinning – for politicians and advisers who are interested – can be found in the reports.

Other Suggestions for Improvement

Naturally, far more suggestions for improvements could be made regarding all kinds of CBA issues: improving the estimates of effects of mega-projects, improving methods to put monetary values on effects, improving the standard numbers for monetary values such as for the value of time (VOT) or the value of a statistical life (VSL), planning process improvements and so forth. It is outside the scope of this chapter to be more specific on these issues. These improvements are mentioned here briefly because these 'normal' CBA improvements also seem to be important to overcoming some of the barriers of CBA application in decision-making. They should not be neglected.

13.7 CONCLUSIONS

The main conclusion is that the use of CBA in mega-projects is limited at best. The Dutch case studies show some impact on 'go/no go' decisions and on changing original project proposals. In a Swedish study CBA results were used as a screening device in the early planning phase to select projects and to force investments designs to be more cost-effective. In this chapter, some possible ways are identified to improve the utilization of CBAs in mega-project planning. These include a more formal setting for CBA in the planning process (using guidelines and independent reviews) and to perform CBA at an early stage in the planning process. By doing so, the instrument can be used as an 'improver'. Nevertheless, perhaps the role of CBA or even any other tool in the planning of mega-projects will always be modest, even after implementing the improvements suggested. To paraphrase Sager and Ravlum (2005), 'It might simply not be the destiny of a planning tool to be the main course of the politicians' meal'.

LITERATURE

Annema, J.A., C. Koopmans and B. van Wee (2007), 'Evaluating transport infrastructure investments: the Dutch experience with a standardized approach', *Transport Reviews*, **27**(2), 125–50.

Bax, C. (2011), 'Processes and patterns. The utilization of knowledge in Dutch road policy', thesis, Nijmegen: Radboud University and Leidschendam: SWOV (Institute for Road Safety Research).

Bax, C., R. Elvik and K. Veisten (2009), 'Knowledge utilisation in road safety policy: barriers to the use of knowledge from economic analysis', *Knowledge, Technology & Policy*, **22**(4), 275–85.

Besseling, P., W. Groot and R. Lebouille (2005), *Economische analyse van verschillende vormen van prijsbeleid voor het wegverkeer* [*Economic Analysis of Different Road Transport Pricing Schemes*], CPB Document No. 87, The Hague: Centraal Planbureau [in Dutch].

Beukers, E., L. Bertolini and M. Te Brömmelstroet (2012), 'Why cost benefit analysis is perceived as a problematic tool for assessment of transport plans: a process perspective', *Transportation Research Part A: Policy and Practice*, **46**(1), 68–78.

Commissie Veerman (2009), *Bouwen aan verbinding, Advies van de onafhankelijke Commissie Veerman over de toekomst van de Noord/Zuidlijn te Amsterdam* [*Constructing a Relation. Advice of the Independent Committee Veerman on the Future of the North South Amsterdam Subway*], accessed 20 June 2013 at http://www.geonet.nl/upload/documents/dossiers/bouwputten/bouwenaanverbinding.pdf, in Dutch.

EC (European Commission) Directorate General Regional Policy (2008), *Guide to Cost–Benefit Analysis of Investment Projects*, Brussels: DG Regional Policy, European Commission, accessed 20 June 2013 at http://ec.europa.eu/regional_policy/sources/docgener/guides/cost/guide2008_en.pdf.

Eijgenraam, C.J.J., C.C. Koopmans, P.J.G. Tang and A.C.P. Verster (2000), *Evaluation of Infrastructural Projects: Guide for Cost–Benefit Analysis*, accessed 20 June 2013 at http://www.rws.nl/en/images/Guide per cent20for per cent20Cost–benefit per cent20Analysis per cent20I_tcm224-324078.pdf.

Eliasson, J. and M. Lundberg (2012), 'Do cost–benefit analyses influence transport investments decisions? Experiences from the Swedish Transport Investments Plan 2011–21', *Transport Reviews*, **32**(1), 30–48.

Flyvbjerg, B. (2008), 'Curbing optimism bias and strategic misrepresentation in planning: reference class forecasting in practice', *European Planning Studies*, **16**(1), 3–21.

Flyvbjerg, B., N. Bruzelius and W. Rothengatter (2003), *Mega-projects and Risk: An Anatomy of Ambition*, Cambridge, UK: Cambridge University Press.

Hayashi, Y. and H. Morisugi (2000), 'International comparison of background concept and methodology of transportation project appraisal', *Transport Policy*, **7**(1), 73–88.

HEATCO (2006), *Proposal for Harmonised Guidelines. Developing Harmonised European Approaches for Transport Costing and Project Assessment and Other Deliverables*, Brussels: European Commission.

Kasemir, B., J. Jaeger, C.C. Jaeger and M.T. Gardner (2003), *Public Participation in Sustainability Science. A Handbook*, Cambridge, UK: Cambridge University Press.

Knight, B. (2003), 'Parochial interests and the centralized provision of local public goods: evidence from congressional voting on transportation projects', NBER Working Paper Series, No. 9748, pp. 1–23.

Koopmans, C. (2010), 'Kosten en baten van het Centraal Planbureau: verleden, heden en toekomst' [Costs and benefits of the CPB Netherlands Bureau for Economic Policy Analysis: past, current and future], *TPEdigitaal*, **4**(3), 19–30.

Landry, R., N. Amara and M. Lamari (2001), 'Utilization of social science research knowledge in Canada', *Research Policy*, **30**(2), 333–49.

Lee, D.B. (2000), 'Methods for evaluation of transportation projects in the USA', *Transport Policy*, **7**(1), 41–50.

Mackie, P. and C. Kelly (2007), *Transport Appraisal in Other Countries: Lessons for the NATA Refresh – Specification*, report produced for Department for Transport, University of Leeds.

McFadden, D. (1976), 'The revealed preference of a government bureaucracy: empirical evidence', *The Bell Journal of Economics*, **7**(1), 55–72.

Mouter, N., J.A. Annema and G.P. van Wee (2013), 'Ranking the substantive problems in the Dutch cost benefit analysis practice', *Transportation Research Part A: Policy and Practice*, **49**(C), 241–55.

Nakamura, H. (2000), 'The economic evaluation of transport infrastructure: needs for international comparisons', *Transport Policy*, **7**(1), 3–6.

Nellthorp, J. and P.J. Mackie (2000), 'The UK Roads Review – a hedonic model of decision making', *Transport Policy*, **7**(1), 127–38.

Nyborg, K. (1998), 'Some Norwegian politicians' use of cost–benefit analysis', *Public Choice*, **95**(3–4), 381–401.

Odeck, J. (2010), 'What determines decision-makers' preferences for road investments? Evidence from the Norwegian road sector, *Transport Reviews*, **30**(4), 473–94.

Odgaard, T., C. Kelly and J. Laird (2005), *HEATCO Work Package 3: Current Practice in Project Appraisal in Europe, HEATCO (Developing Harmonized European Approaches for Transport Costing and Project Assessment)*, Deliverable 1/Vol. 1, Kongens Lyngby: COWI A/S, Denmark.

Priemus, H. (2007), 'Development and design of large infrastructure projects: disregarded alternatives and issues of spatial planning', *Environment and Planning B: Planning and Design*, **34**(4), 626–44.

Proost, S., F. Dunkerley, B. de Borger, A. Günhneman, P. Koskenoja, P. Mackie and S. van der Loo (2011), 'When are subsidies to TransEuropean Network projects justified?', *Transportation Research A, Policy and Practice*, **45**(3), 161–70.

Proost, S., F. Dunkerley, S. van der Loo, N. Adler, J. Bröcker and A. Korzhenevych (2010), 'Do the selected TransEuropean transport investments pass the cost benefit test', CES – Discussion Paper Series 10.02, KU-Leuven CES, pp. 1–22.

Rienstra, S. (2008), *De rol van kosten-batenanalyse in de besluitvorming* [*The Role of Cost–Benefit Analysis in the Decision-making Process*], The Hague: The Netherlands Institute for Transport Policy Analysis (KiM) (in Dutch).

Rienstra, S. and J. Visser (2010), *Infrastructuur en economische structuurversterking. De relatie met de kosten-batenanalyse* [*Infrastructure and Strengthening the Economic Structure. The Relation with Cost–Benefit Analysis*], The Hague: the Netherlands Institute for Transport Policy Analysis (KiM) (in Dutch).

Sager, T. and I-A. Ravlum (2005), 'The political relevance of planners' analysis: the case of a parliamentary standing committee', *Planning Theory*, **4**(33), 33–65.
Shapiro, S. (2010), 'The evolution of cost–benefit analysis in U.S. regulatory decision making', Jerusalem Papers in Regulation & Governance, Working Paper No. 5, Jerusalem: The Hebrew University Mount Scopus.
Short, J. and A. Kopp (2005), 'Transport infrastructure: investment and planning. Policy and research aspects', *Transport Policy*, **12**(4), 360–67.
Tweede Kamer (2004), *Reconstructie Betuweroute: de besluitvorming uitvergroot* [*Reconstructing the Betuwe Line: the decision-making process scrutinized*], Tweede Kamer der Staten-Generaal, Vergaderjaar 2004–2005, Document 29283, The Hague (in Dutch).
van Wee, B. (2007), 'Large infrastructure projects: a review of the quality of demand forecasts and cost estimation', *Environment and Planning B: Planning and Design*, **34**(4), 611–25.
van Wee, B. (2011), *Transport and Ethics. Ethics and the Evaluation of Transport Policies and Projects*, Cheltenham, UK and Northampton MA, USA: Edward Elgar.
Willis, K.G., G.D. Garrod and D.R. Harvey (1998), 'A review of cost–benefit analysis as applied to the evaluation of new road proposals in the UK', *Transportation Research-D*, **3**(3), 141–56.
World Bank (2010), *Cost–Benefit Analysis in World Bank Projects*, Washington, DC: The International Bank for Reconstruction and Development/The World Bank.

14. Long-term impacts of mega-projects: the discount rate

Carl Koopmans and Piet Rietveld

14.1 INTRODUCTION

In social cost–benefit analysis (SCBA), discount rates are used to convert costs and benefits that occur at different points in time, to present values that can be added and subtracted. Especially if important costs and benefits occur in the long term (more than say 30 years), the discount rate may have a large impact on the SCBA outcomes. As an example, Figure 14.1 shows that applying a 4 per cent discount rate[1] strongly reduces the weight of long-term benefits and costs. A 1 per cent discount rate leads to much higher weights for long-term impacts.[2]

Mega-projects are often aimed at the long term. After they have been built, their existence is usually taken for granted over a very long period. New roads and railroads often remain in place for 100 years or more. Flood barriers continue to protect the land behind them over very long periods. The wind farms being built in many places may also exist for a very long time. Over these long periods, mega-projects continue to provide benefits. However, there may also be extensive costs: maintenance,

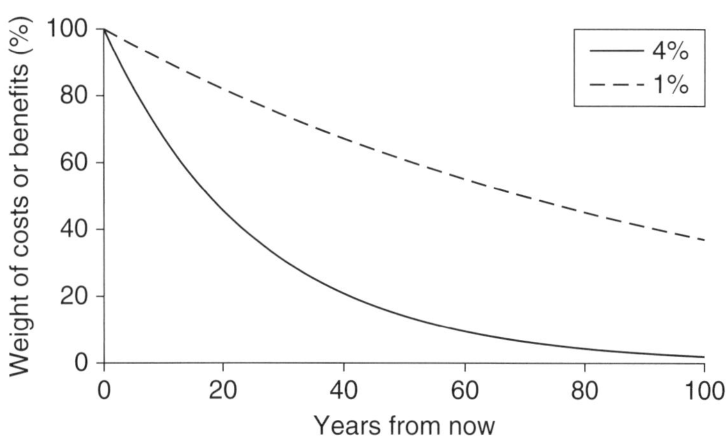

Figure 14.1 The level of the discount rate has strong consequences

reinvestment and opportunity costs of the land used. Given these long-term costs and benefits, the choice of the discount rate is especially important in the context of mega-projects.

In the literature there is a fierce debate on appropriate discount rates, in particular for climate change policies. High and low discounted rates, respectively, are defended using strong arguments and strong words. In this chapter we summarize the main arguments in the debate (Section 14.2), analyse which arguments apply to different types of mega-projects (14.3), and show which reasons are behind the discount rates used in the practice of project appraisal (14.4). Finally, we draw conclusions that provide guidance in choosing discount rates for mega-projects (14.5).

14.2 APPROACHES IN THE LITERATURE

In the environmental economics literature, the question of which discount rate is appropriate has received much attention (Pearce et al., 2006). Although the literature contains many different strands, we may discern two main approaches, following Arrow et al. (1996). First we present the so-called descriptive approach. For this approach, we show the effects of including different types of risk. Then we describe the second, so-called prescriptive approach. Next, the question is raised whether different effects may be discounted at different rates. Finally, we discuss other issues and draw conclusions.

Descriptive Approach

The first approach is deriving discount rates from market behaviour, in particular capital markets. In capital markets, actors trade future and present costs and benefits. To receive money now, actors have to promise a larger repayment in the future, including interest, dividend and/or increases in stock values. Therefore, the interest rates or profit rates in these markets reflect the willingness to pay of economic actors for having costs or benefits now instead of in the future. As willingness to pay is the basic measure of all costs and benefits in SCBA, it can also be applied to discounting.

The problem with this approach is that due to market imperfections there may be a substantial gap between the rate of time preference of consumers and the rate of return on investments achieved by firms. The former can, for example, be measured by means of the interest rate on government bonds (where the risk of default is low, at least in most countries).

The rate of return on investments in the private sector is usually much higher. The reason for this gap is that the returns on private investments are taxed, first through corporate tax on profits, then through income tax and (if applicable) through consumption or value-added tax.

Therefore, Lind (1982) proposes distinguishing between the social rate of time preference (SRTP), which pertains to consumption in different periods, and the social discount rate, which also includes the opportunity costs of private investments that are replaced by public investments. These opportunity costs relate to the taxes mentioned above. Lind (ibid.) shows that, in social cost–benefit analysis, the opportunity costs of private investments may alternatively be included by making adjustments in the benefits and costs rather than in the social discount rate. Throughout this chapter it is assumed that these adjustments are included in the benefits and costs. This implies that the discount rate only pertains to comparing consumption (including environmental effects on consumption) over time.[3]

An important assumption in the descriptive approach is that discount rates derived from financial decisions on a time scale of at most a few decades may be applied to benefits and costs that occur over (much) longer periods, affecting future generations. Bradford (1999) defends this approach by assuming that welfare can be freely (re)distributed among generations within a country. For instance, if the present generation builds dikes to protect low-lying areas from sea level rise, the present generation might reduce its endowments to future generations in other respects.

The impact of time preference on discounting is expressed in the Ramsey (1928) equation:

$$r = \delta + \eta g \tag{14.1}$$

where:
r = discount rate;
δ = pure rate of time preference;
η = minus the consumption elasticity of marginal utility of consumption;
g = annual consumption growth.

This equation contains, apart from a pure rate of time preference (δ), an additional term that reflects the impact of consumption growth (g). If future generations consume more than the present generation, this would be a rationale to count their consumption for less. Or in other words, in this case more consumption by the present generation (and therefore less by future generations) would spread consumption more evenly over time. As marginal utility of consumption falls with increasing consumption, a more even distribution would increase total utility.

The long-term discount rates that follow from the descriptive approach are (for developed countries) mostly around 5 to 6 per cent per year (Arrow et al., 1996, Table 4.1). Nordhaus (2007) assumes a time preference of 1.5 per cent with a consumption elasticity of 2, arriving at a discount rate of 5.5 per cent (this implies that consumption grows by 2 per cent per year). In his empirical work, Nordhaus (ibid.) often uses 6 per cent. Weitzman (2007) indicates that for many projects outside the climate domain a 'trio of twos': values of $\delta = 2$ per cent, $g = 2$ per cent and $\eta = 2$ would be reasonable in the Ramsey equation. This would yield a discount rate of 6 per cent. Using these discount rates, long-term benefits and costs do not count for much. This reduces the value of investments with long-term benefits. Moreover, such discount rates do not discourage investments with long-term costs, because these are discounted strongly.

Including Different Types of Risk

Interest rates in capital markets are higher if more financial risk is involved. If there is a substantial probability that the loan will not be repaid (e.g., current Greek state bonds), the interest rate needed to persuade investors is higher. The risk premium not only reflects the expected probability that the loan will not be repaid, but also risk aversion on the part of investors.

In SCBA of investments in infrastructure, an important risk is that the net benefits will be smaller than expected. However, even if the expected value of the net benefits has been estimated correctly, there will be both the possibility of higher and lower net benefits than expected, and the expected value of these deviations will be zero. Under this condition, if there are many government investments with uncorrelated outcomes, the gains and losses will cancel each other out given the law of large numbers. Moreover, the financial effect will be spread out over many taxpayers, making the risk for each individual tax payer very small. Under these assumptions, Arrow and Lind (1970) show that government investment should use risk-free interest rates (i.e., the rate of state bonds of financially stable countries).

However, these assumptions may not be valid in practice. The benefits of most infrastructure investments are positively correlated with GDP,[4] and therefore with each other. In other words, if one infrastructure project has higher (or lower) benefits than expected, it is likely that this will be the case for other projects as well. Therefore, investing in infrastructure usually adds to the total risk of the 'investment portfolio'. The value of this risk can be subtracted from the benefits (Little and Mirrlees, 1994), but it may also be reflected by adding a risk premium to the discount rate. The costs of infrastructure may also be positively correlated to GDP growth, because if growth is high many firms will invest in construction, possibly increasing prices.[5]

For mega-projects the law of large numbers may not apply. If a mega-project forms a substantial part of total government investments in infrastructure, the risk of higher or lower costs or benefits from the mega-project may not cancel out against other much smaller projects. Moreover, for very large mega-projects that cost many billions of dollars, the financial impact for individual taxpayers will not necessarily be small. And finally, the effects of – often unique – mega-projects may be more uncertain than the impacts of standard, run-of-the-mill investments. Therefore, an additional risk premium in the discount rate may be appropriate for mega-projects in particular.

Many environmental effects of mega-projects, climate change impacts in particular, occur in the very long term. Over such periods, much is uncertain about the environmental impacts, but also about the appropriate discount rate. Weitzman (1998) shows that in case of uncertainty about the discount rate, the lowest possible rate is the most appropriate. We illustrate this with an example (adapted from de Zeeuw et al., 2008) in Table 14.1. The example assumes three equally probable discount rates, with an average of 4 per cent. However, if we compute the discount factors (the factors with which costs and benefits are multiplied) for different time scales, and then take the average discount factor, we see that this goes towards the lowest of the three discount rates (1 per cent) if the time scale is very long.

In another article, Weitzman (2009a) shows that combining market rates of interest with a small risk of very large climate risks is equivalent to using a discount rate that declines over time. In an example he arrives

Table 14.1 Uncertain discount rate causes falling discount rate over time

Discount rate (r)	Probability	Years From Now (t)			
		0	10	100	1000
		Discount factors ($1/(1 + r)^t$)			
1%	1/3	1.000	0.905	0.370	0.000048
4%	1/3	1.000	0.676	0.020	0.000000
7%	1/3	1.000	0.508	0.001	0.000000
Average		1.000	0.696	0.130	0.000016
	Discount rates equivalent to average discount factors				
		4%	3.68%	2.06%	1.11%

at a rate of 1 per cent for effects that occur after 50 years and 0.3 per cent effects that occur after 1000 years. Weitzman (2009b) shows that long-term climate risks are very hard to assess, but that they are potentially so large that they may have a stronger impact than discounting using capital market rates. We note that including such large risks in the discount rate would lead to a negative discount rate.

Prescriptive Approach

Sustainability is considered by many people as an important principle in making choices with long-term consequences. The general idea is that human activities and the natural environment should develop harmoniously. This has been translated into many different definitions of sustainability. The best-known definition is from the 'Brundtland Report' (World Commission on Environment and Development, 1987, Chapter 2), 'Development that meets the needs of the present without compromising the ability of future generations to meet their own needs'. As the concept of 'needs' is clearly subjective, this definition is not very useful for economic analysis. In environmental economics, sustainability is sometimes interpreted as a zero rate of pure time preference with respect to present versus future consumption, because other positions would be 'ethically indefensible' (Cline, 1999).

An important example of applying the prescriptive sustainability approach is the Stern Review (Stern, 2006), an extensive study on climate change policy in the United Kingdom. In the Ramsey equation (14.1), Stern (2006) used the following values:

δ = 0.1 per cent. This value reflects a small risk of human extinction (e.g., through a large asteroid). Otherwise the rate of time preference is zero, reflecting the principle of sustainability.
g = 1.3 per cent. The assumed long-term annual rate of consumption growth includes negative effects from environmental problems, which may reduce future growth.
η = 1. If consumption, for example, grows by 1 per cent, the marginal utility of consumption falls by 1 per cent. This corresponds to a logarithmic utility function.

Together, these values imply a discount rate r of 1.4 per cent per year.

Gowdy et al. (2010) argue that a reduction of the stock of natural capital should be included in the growth rate g, and that this may cause g (and possibly r) to become negative. Moreover, they see future growth as including not only consumption. They assert that psychological and aesthetic benefits linked to external effects on, for example, biodiversity are not captured in market prices. This illustrates the normative nature of the prescriptive sustainability approach.

The environmental approach has been attacked by Nordhaus (2007), who argues that a near-zero discount rate is inconsistent with market rates of interest and savings rates. He writes (p. 700): 'The [Stern] Review seems to have become lost in the discounting trees and failed to see the capital market forest by overlooking the constraints'.

The discount rate derived in the Stern Review is typical of studies that use the Ramsey equation starting from sustainability or equal treatment of generations ($\delta = 0$ per cent or very small). The discount rates found are often around 1 to 2 per cent (e.g., Cline, 1999). Using such discount rates, policies that aim at long-term effects become much more attractive than using discount rates derived from capital markets.

Different Discount Rates for Different Impacts?

An alternative approach towards the theme of environmental or ecological discounting is to explicitly consider a differentiated discounting procedure to financial costs and benefits (F) on the one hand, and environmental costs and benefits (E) on the other hand. The intuition behind this is that in the future the scarcity in the environmental domain is probably stronger than in the financial domain.

Malinvaud (1953) was probably the first to propose the use of differentiated discount rates. For the environmental effects E it would imply the transformation of effects at times t into the immediate ($t = 0$) equivalent environmental impact. When the standard discount rate rf is used for financial effects, this approach leads to an adjusted account rate re for environmental effects, where in general rf is higher than re since the growth potential for environmental quality is in general lower than for financial assets. When the financial and environmental effects (expressed in money terms) of a project at time t are denoted as F_t and E_t, respectively, the net present value (NPV) of a project is given by:

$$NPV = \Sigma_t F_t/(1 + rf)^t + \Sigma_t E_t/(1 + re)^t \qquad (14.2)$$

This expression is used, for example, by Almansa and Martinez-Paz (2011) in an analysis of NPV sensitivity to various discounting alternatives, taking $rf = 5.5$ per cent as a reference value, based on values often used in the EU. In a more refined model, taking into account substitutability between financial and environmental goods in the context of intertemporal utility maximization, Gollier (2010) arrives at reference values of 3.2 per cent for rf and 1.5 per cent for re.

There is still another approach to deal with this issue of different scarcities for financial and environmental resources: when environmental resources will be scarcer in the future, their relative price may be expected to increase. For the NPV this would imply that future effects E would deserve a higher weight. Thus, assuming that E_t in (14.2) is based on constant prices for the environmental good, then with an expected real price rise per year of p for environmental goods, an alternative expression for NPV would be:

$$NPV = \Sigma_t F_t/(1 + rf)^t + \Sigma_t(1 + p)^t E_t/(1 + rf)^t \qquad (14.3)$$

This may well be a more attractive approach to dealing with differences in scarcity between the two types of goods since it has the advantage that it is easier to explain to laypersons. The difference between the two approaches should not be exaggerated, however. Gollier (ibid.) indicates that the two approaches are essentially equivalent under some simplifying conditions, in particular when uncertainty does not play a role.

This approach has been thoroughly examined by Hoel and Sterner (2007). In their model, the composition of the basket of financial and environmental goods may gradually change in the course of time, which makes the rf and p parameters essentially non-constant. This provides another link with the discussion on non-constant, or declining discount rates. Another result from their analysis is that – depending on the scarcity of environmental goods and substitution possibilities between environmental and financial goods – one may well arrive at the conclusion that the annual price increase of environmental goods p is higher than the discount rate rf. This would essentially imply a negative discount rate, a case that was also already found in the preceding section. This would of course provide a strong case in favour of projects with minimum adverse effects on the environment.

The models on which these future values of scarce environmental qualities are based are rather stylized. Future research in this field should therefore not just address the present valuation of the environment, but also the possible future values. An important question in this context is whether the income elasticity of environmental goods is higher than 1. The environment is usually considered to be such a 'luxury good' (Baumol and Oates, 1988, p. 241). If this is the case,[6] we will want to consume relatively more of these goods in a future with higher incomes. This increase in demand may cause the value of environmental goods to rise, which could be equivalent to a lower discount rate.

Also, preferences may shift over time, causing utility functions to give more (or less) value to the environment. Goodin (1982) therefore considers discounting as a questionable approach. Bromley (1989) describes the preferences of future generations as a 'missing market': the demand of future generations for environmental services is not, or insufficiently, reflected in the preferences of the present generation.

In the practice of social cost–benefit analysis, a higher valuation of environmental costs and benefits would shift the problem of choosing an appropriate discount rate to choosing appropriate corrections for the future value of cost and benefits. This is exceedingly difficult in practice, as the preferences of future generations are hard to predict (ibid.). Accordingly, the choice of an adapted discount rate is difficult as well. The alternative approach of correcting valuations does not solve the problem of taking account of long-term effects: it only puts it outside of the domain of the discount rate.

Discussion and Conclusions

Using discount rates that reduce future costs and benefits may be inconsistent with the way distribution effects at any given point in time are often treated in social cost–benefit analysis. For effects for different actors at one point in time, usually no weighting is applied. That is, a euro or dollar of willingness to pay (WTP) of, say, low-income groups, has an equal weight to a euro or dollar that high-income groups are willing to pay. However, in CBAs the WTP of future generations has a much lower weight than the WTP of the present generation, as a consequence of discounting. The question seems to be what kind of consistency we want to sacrifice: consistency with capital markets or consistency with equal weights for the willingness to pay of different people?

The overall tendency of the last decades is that discount rates used in social cost–benefit analysis have declined (see Section 14.4). This is not related to declining inflation since the recommended discount rates are formulated in real terms. Nevertheless, also with lower discount rates it is clear that long-term effects get a low weight in decisions. This has raised the concern that environmental effects that often have a long-term character receive insufficient weight in policy analysis. For example, a natural area that is used for an infrastructure project is not available any more for all future generations.

A rather obvious way to address this point would be to recommend even lower discount rates. There is also a downside to low discount rates, however. A lower discount rate would indeed lead to a higher weight for long-term effects, but this is not necessarily good for the environment. The point is that with a very low discount rate one may expect a very large number of projects to pass cost–benefit tests since the large majority of investment projects have negative net benefits during the construction period and positive net benefits during the period the investment is used productively. An increase in the volume of investment projects could have an adverse effect on environmental quality. Markandya and Pearce (1988) indicate that it is not easy to determine the balance of the two countervailing forces (a low interest rate implies more projects, but per project a smaller long-run burden on the environment). In the world of real decision-making probably the latter factor will be more relevant than the former because social cost–benefit analysis will not be the only factor that determines investment volumes at the macro level. Limitations on public sector budgets will also certainly play a role. Nevertheless we may conclude that just making discount rates lower in order to prevent long-term environmental degradation is an overly simple way to address long-term concerns.

The issue of uncertainty is important here. As already explained in Section 14.2, a common way to address uncertainty in private investments is to apply a risk premium on top of the social rate of discount. An undifferentiated application of this rule would obviously increase the discount rate applied, but it may well have unintended environmental effects in specific cases. Consider an investment project with a strong toxic component leading to high costs at the end of its lifecycle (for example, a nuclear power plant). Then adding a standard risk premium to the discount rate might increase the net present value of the project. This might push the choice of power plant technology into an environmentally unfriendly direction. A more refined way to address uncertainties would be the application of a certainty equivalence approach that explicitly addresses the valuation of uncertainty related to specific costs and benefits of a project (Markandya and Pearce, 1988).

We conclude that the debate on discounting is complicated and still inconclusive. In order to provide good information it seems necessary that the CBA should at least show the impact of the discount rate, through a sensitivity analysis with different discount rates. This seems especially important for mega-projects with relatively high long-term environmental impacts.

14.3 APPLICATION TO MEGA-PROJECTS

Mega-projects have many different dimensions (Priemus et al., 2008; Chapter 1 in this book). A practical definition may be projects that involve an investment of at least 1 billion euros. Given their size they may well have a broad range of intended and unintended side-effects. Typical examples of mega-projects in the transport domain are airports, seaports, high-speed railway lines, tunnels and bridges. In a broader domain of projects they may incorporate nuclear power plants, exploration for natural resources, large flood protection projects, large spatial development programmes such as new towns, and large events such as the Olympic Games and the accompanying infrastructures. In this section we first discuss the long-term effects of mega-projects. Next, the question is raised whether special discount rates for mega-projects would be appropriate.

Long-term Effects

The time span of mega-projects may be considerable, both in terms of preparation, actual construction and of course their effects once they start being used. Preparation may take up to ten to 20 years, actual construction may be up to ten years, the actual life time is in many cases at least 40 to 100 years or more. Taking into account retrofitting the lifetime may well be 100 up to 200 years, and apart from actual use, the effects may last considerably longer.

Most of the literature on mega-projects is on recent projects so that it is difficult to assess how long the effects may continue to make themselves felt. Therefore, it may be illuminating to consider mega-projects in history. Pyramids – at least some of them – have a long lifetime and unforeseen effects such as the attraction of tourist flows millennia later. The same holds true for many ambitious projects from the Roman period such as large amphitheatres and temples. These projects ended in cultural heritage that is highly valued in present day times. It is fair to say of course that most of the large projects built in the past just ended in ruins and dust due to earthquakes and the relentless ravages of time.

More recent mega-projects such as the construction of national railway systems built about 150 years ago continue to function in many countries, although of course now incorporating much newer technologies. At the same time, most of the large investments in canal systems that took place some 150 to 200 years ago at best only remain functioning for recreational purposes. There is a large variety here: the Canal de Midi project connecting the Atlantic Ocean with the Mediterranean was built around 1680 and still exists but without any commercial transport function. The Suez Canal built around 1870 connecting the Mediterranean with the Indian Ocean has maintained its position as a critical link in global freight transport. The same goes for the Panama Canal, opened in 1914. Other mega-projects of the twentieth century include port areas that may sometimes still function as ports, although after substantial adjustments. National highway systems built some 30 to 80 years ago are – with the necessary maintenance and retrofitting – still functioning well and have become the backbone of medium-distance transport networks in almost all countries. Their long-run effect may be considerably longer since they have affected the spatial development in countries (see, for example, Fernald, 1999). Power plants have a much vaguer spatial footprint in this respect, with the exception of ill-fated projects such as the Chernobyl and Fukushima plants that will have lasting effects on the spatial development in the regions involved.

This inevitably anecdotal review makes clear that mega-projects may indeed have very long-lasting effects, sometimes in a way that is very different from what was expected at the time of construction. At the same time, some projects never were successful or only were so for a very short period. And a considerable number of the projects have a long lifetime owing to large refurbishing investments in the course of time. In many cases one can be pretty sure that possible refurbishments did not play a key role in the go/no-go decision on construction.

In terms of broader economic impacts, one may claim that large investments in transport networks sometimes have lasting effects on urban development (see, for example, Koopmans et al., 2012 for the case of investments in rail infrastructure). Also, mega-projects such as the Suez Canal and the Panama Canal will have had lasting effects on trade patterns and the competitive position of ports on various competing routes.

Special Discount Rates for Mega-projects?

An important question is whether the sheer size of mega-projects has implications for the discount rates to be applied. For example, the size of mega-projects may extend the period during which effects are relevant. That is a good reason to pay special attention to the discount factor for mega-projects. We will therefore discuss some special features of mega-projects that potentially have implications for discounting.

First, most mega-projects are meant to contribute to economic development in the short to medium run (up to some 30 to 40 years). If the longer run is important for mega-projects (say longer than 50 years) the immediate question to be asked would be whether postponing the project would not be a preferable alternative. However, there may be special cases. For example, mitigation policies may have to be imposed now to avoid large potential damage of climate change in say 50 years when the costs of mitigation would be much higher when it would be postponed. Thus, for mega-projects in the domain of climate change mitigation, long-run effects are of special relevance. And this implies that the discount rate is of utmost importance, a conclusion that also follows from the discussion on the Stern Review (Stern, 2006) described in Section 14.2.

Somewhat related to this point is that mega-projects such as the construction of a large airport may have large environmental effects that are relevant for long-term themes such as climate change. This statement is correct as such, although it does not necessarily mean that these effects are substantially different from the sum of a number of smaller-scale airport expansion projects implying the same aggregate investment. Then, when the long-run climate effects would be relevant for the large new airport, they would be of equal relevance for the set of smaller airport projects.

Another possible distinguishing feature is that mega-projects probably have larger long-run effects on spatial economic development. The construction of an individual small- or medium-sized link in a network will probably not have a notable structuring effect on spatial development. But a completely new network or the construction of a major missing link in a network (such as the Suez and Panama Canals) may well have a lasting effect. There are two reasons why the relevance of these long-run structuring effects is not as big as one might think. First, even revolutionary new networks such as the railway network in the nineteenth century did not have the overwhelming effects that are sometimes claimed (see Fogel, 1964 for a detailed study on the USA). And second, the long-term structuring effects even when they are large are difficult to predict so that they are surrounded by a large degree of uncertainty. It makes little sense to attach a large weight to very uncertain side-effects in the long run when the primary aim of a project would be to generate net gains in the short to medium term.

Still another property of mega-projects that may be relevant for discounting is that even in the short run their effects may be more difficult to assess than the effects of small projects. The point is that large projects by definition are not carried out that often so that their effects may be rather unique and unexpected. For example, the construction of the Channel Tunnel linking the UK with France was a unique project and its effects appeared difficult to predict. The main uncertainty was not so much related to the behaviour of the users of the tunnel, but to the competing suppliers (Rietveld and Bruinsma, 1998; Anguera, 2006). In particular, ferry operators reacted strongly to the opening of the tunnel, leading to faster and more competitive services. This increased the attractiveness of existing alternatives of the tunnel so that its commercial success was much smaller than expected.

Finally, mega-projects may be so large that their failure or success would be noted in macroeconomic terms, whereas in the case of smaller projects their effects may be expected to cancel each other out. Thus, mega-projects would increase the variance in the macroeconomic performance of an economy and that would call for an extra risk premium. This reasoning is correct in theory, but for the large majority of mega-projects, however large they may be, their size in terms of investment, and also in terms of benefits will be limited relative to the national economy. Maybe it is only in the case of evident failure of a mega-project such as the breakdown of the Fukushima nuclear reactors in Japan in 2011 followed by the closure of other nuclear reactors in the country, combined with the lack of network infrastructure to import electricity from other countries, that this project had a notable effect on the national economy.

Our conclusion is that mega-projects because of their sheer size deserve even more intensive ex ante policy analysis than smaller projects. Mega-projects that are carried out in the context of long-run climate change mitigation by definition deserve special attention with regard to discounting, and the same holds true for mega-projects that have adverse effects on climate change in the long run. But this reasoning equally applies to smaller projects. Thus, discounting is an issue that has to be addressed anyhow for all projects that may affect climate change. We do find that mega-projects may have long-run economic effects on spatial structures and urbanization patterns, but our understanding of these effects is not sufficient to make this a serious point for cost–benefit analysis, hence the discount factor theme is not so relevant here. Finally, in exceptional cases mega-projects may show up adversely in macroeconomic performance when they collapse, and this implies that the issue of risks in case of failure has to be addressed, possibly leading to a risk premium for such projects.

14.4 DISCOUNT RATES USED IN PRACTICE

Discount rates used in cost–benefit analysis differ between countries. Just before the year 2000, the discount rates used for transport projects in EU countries, Japan, the USA and Germany varied between 3 and 8 per cent (Bristow and Nellthorp, 2000; Hayashi and Morisugi, 2000). Also, there is a pattern of falling discount rates after about 1990 (see Table 14.2). The discount rate in the United Kingdom was reduced from 6 to 3.5 per cent in 2003 (UK Treasury, 2003); Germany reduced its social discount rate from 4 to 3 per cent in 2004; and France reduced its rate from 8 to 4 per cent in 2005.[7] This reflects falling interest rates, as most countries use the rate at which they borrow money as the basis for calculating discount rates (Berechman, 2009). The capital market approach described in Section 14.2 appears to be dominant. For the 2007–13 period, the European Commission has suggested using two benchmark social discount rates: 5.5 per cent for relatively poor countries (countries eligible for the Cohesion Fund) and 3.5 per cent for rich countries (European Commission, 2008).

Although the discount rates used in practice are usually not based on

Table 14.2 Discount rates used in different countries

Country	Nominal Discount Rate
Australia	8% (1991) Current: annually reviewed
Canada	10% (1995)
China	8% for short- and medium-term projects (1995) Lower than 8% for long-term projects (1995)
France	8% (1985) (real discount rate) 4% (2005) (real discount rate)
Germany	4% (1999) 3% (2004)
India	12% (1995)
Italy	5% (1995)
Netherlands	4% (1998) (real discount rate) 7% (2004) (real discount rate; includes 3% risk premium) 5.5% (2006) (real discount rate; includes 3% risk premium)
New Zealand	10% (1995) (whenever there is no other agreed sector discount rate)
Norway	7% (1978) 3.5% (1998)
Pakistan	12% (1995)
Spain	6% (1995) (transport) 4% (1995) (water)
United Kingdom	5% (1978) 6% (1989) 3.5% (2003) Different rates lower than 3.5% for long-term projects over 30 years (1995)
United States	10% (before 1992) (Office of Management and Budget) 7% (after 1992) (Office of Management and Budget) 2–3% (1995) (intragenerational) (Environmental Protection Agency) 0% (1995) (intergenerational) (Environmental Protection Agency)

Sources: Netherlands: this chapter; other countries: Zhuang et al. (2007).

prescriptive sustainability considerations but on the descriptive approach based on capital markets, several countries apply discount rates that decrease over time. This corresponds to incorporating risk. In the United Kingdom, the discount rate falls from 3.5 per cent in the first 30 years to 1.0 per cent for effects that occur after more than 300 years (UK Treasury, 2003, p. 99). In the HEATCO proposal for guidelines for transport project evaluation, the value of future CO_2 emissions is computed using a falling discount rate (HEATCO, 2006, p. 117).

In the USA, OMB (2003) recommends the use of a discount rate of 7 per cent for projects and regulations where public policies affect the mix of private and public investments; this level is based on the opportunity costs of capital, following from the descriptive (capital market) approach. A second discount rate recommended by OMB is 3 per cent for projects or regulations mainly affecting private consumption. This level is based on the social rate of time preference as described in Section 14.2. Further, a sensitivity analysis is recommended where both levels are used. OMB is not the only authority in the USA issuing discount rate recommendations. In practice other discount levels may also be used depending on the policy domain and the level of government (federal versus state).

In the Netherlands a real discount rate of 2.5 per cent is used, to which a risk premium of 3 per cent is added. However, for irreversible environmental effects the risk premium is only 1.5 per cent (Aalbers, 2009) (see Box 14.1).

In most CBAs of mega-projects, standard discount rates are used. For instance, Kay et al. (1989) used a 5 per cent discount rate in a cost–benefit analysis of the Channel Tunnel. Total investment costs were estimated at £4.9 billion ($8 billion) in 1989, while the tunnel was expected to open in 1993. In an ex post evaluation, Anguera (2006) showed that the costs have been higher and the benefits lower than expected. Despite a lower discount rate of 3.5 per cent he computes a negative net present value of more than £9 billion. As another example, de Rus and Inglada (1997) estimate ex post costs and benefits of high-speed rail built between Madrid and Seville, with investment costs of 500 billion pesetas ($4 billion) of 1996. Using a 6 per cent social discount rate, they show that the costs exceed the benefits.

14.5 CONCLUSIONS

The choice of the rate of discount has a strong influence on the outcome of cost–benefit analysis. We discuss two main approaches to this choice. The first one is descriptive and bases the discount rate on the interest rate on capital markets, which may include a compensation for risk. This approach can be extended by taking into account long-term uncertainties. In this case it appears that the discount rate is not constant but declining. The second approach is prescriptive and uses the concept of sustainability. Generally, the first approach leads to higher discount rates than the second, especially for the first decades.

A refinement in another direction is that different discount rates are

BOX 14.1 DISCOUNTING IN THE NETHERLANDS

The prescribed discount rate for social cost–benefit analysis in the Netherlands is 5.5 per cent. It consists of a risk-free discount rate of 2.5 per cent based on state bonds, plus a risk premium of 3 per cent based on average covariances between costs and benefits on the one hand and GDP on the other hand[a]. Only for irreversible external effects is a 4 per cent rate is used, to correct for long-term environmental risk. We may see this as based on the prescriptive (capital market) approach of Section 14.2 (which would imply 5.5 per cent for all effects), including environmental risks as described in Section 14.2 (which would probably lead to lower values than 4 per cent for long-term environmental effects).

Analysis of 72 CBAs of transport improvements and spatial projects shows that the standard discount rates were applied in almost all cases (Annema and Koopmans, 2012). There was only one CBA in which sensitivity analysis took place with a 2.5 per cent discount rate for all costs and benefits. As a result, the long-term benefits for nature increase in importance.

Another survey, aimed at analysts who carry out CBAs of involving environmental effects, confirms that the prescribed discount rates are used by most of these analysts (Koetse et al., 2011). However, some analysts mention 2.5 per cent (apparently they do not include the risk premium), and in one case 1 per cent is mentioned. These are possibly sensitivity analyses carried out in addition to standard CBAs using 5.5 per cent/4 per cent. Eight out of 18 respondents say that they think climate mitigation (which reduces irreversible changes) and climate adaptation (which only reduces the costs of climate change) should be evaluated using different discount rates.[a]

[a] The risk premium may take other values between 0 and 6%, depending on the covariance of the costs and benefits involved. However, in practice the risk premium used is almost always 3%.

used for different impacts. We find that there are good reasons for such an approach since it is plausible that scarcity for environmental goods in the future will be higher than for standard consumption goods. This means essentially that the price of environmental effects will increase faster than of the other effects.

This discussion makes clear that the choice of the discount rate is to some extent a normative-political one. It is therefore not surprising to see that countries vary considerably in their choice of discount rates for social cost–benefit analysis. A general tendency can be observed that the discount rates decrease during the course of time. Given the strong impact of the discount rate on outcomes of cost–benefit analysis, sensitivity analyses are recommended.

When we consider mega-projects, their size as such does not mean that different discount rates have to be applied compared with small projects. More important is the nature of the effects. When mega-projects have strong long-term effects, positive in the case of mitigation of climate change, or negative because of aggravation of climate problems, this provides a good reason to consider choosing low discount rates for these effects.

NOTES

1. All discount rates in this chapter are in real terms (i.e., corrected for inflation), unless mentioned otherwise.
2. Another example is given by Olsson et al. (2012). They show that using discount rates from different countries in a cost–benefit analysis of a Norwegian rail project strongly influences the results.
3. It might, however, be that variations in the discount rates used in different countries presented later in this chapter follow from different ways to deal with this issue.
4. The benefits of infrastructure depend on the demand for transport, energy, and so on. Demand grows stronger if GDP grows fast.
5. A much larger risk on the cost side seems to be systematic underestimation of costs (Pickrell, 1992; Flyvbjerg et al., 2003), but this is probably not correlated to GDP growth.
6. This point is not beyond dispute: Kristrom and Riera (1996) review empirical studies in which elasticities lower than 1 are also found.
7. In a recent study, Olsson et al. (2012) report discount rates from 2 to 8 per cent for seven Western European countries. However, the 8 per cent figure used for France appears not to be up to date. If we correct for this, the range would be 2 to 6 per cent.

LITERATURE

Aalbers, R. (2009), 'Discounting investments in mitigation and adaptation', Discussion Paper No. 126, The Hague: CPB Netherlands Bureau for Economic Policy Analysis.

Almansa, C. and J.M. Martinez-Paz (2011), 'What weight should be assigned to future environmental impacts? A probabilistic cost benefit analysis using recent advances on discounting', *Science of the Total Environment*, **409**(7), 1305–14.

Anguera, R. (2006), 'The Channel Tunnel – an ex post economic evaluation', *Transportation Research A*, **40**(4), 291–315.

Annema, J.A. and C.C. Koopmans (2012), 'De leefomgeving in maatschappelijke kosten-batenanalyses van transportprojecten' [The living environment in social cost–benefit analyses of transport projects], *Tijdschrift Vervoerswetenschap*, **48**(2), 51–67 (in Dutch).

Arrow, K.J. and R.C. Lind (1970), 'Uncertainty and the evaluation of public investment decisions', *American Economic Review*, **60**(3), 364–78.

Arrow, K.J., W.R. Cline, K.G. Maler, M. Munasinghe, R. Squitieri and J.E. Stiglitz (1996), 'Intertemporal equity, discounting, and economic efficiency', in J.P. Bruce, H. Lee and E.F. Haites, *Climate Change 1995 – Economic and Social Dimensions of Climate Change*, Cambridge, UK: Cambridge University Press.

Baumol, W.J. and W.E. Oates (1988), *The Theory of Environmental Policy*, 2nd edition, Cambridge, UK: Cambridge University Press.

Berechman, J. (2009), *The Evaluation of Transportation Investment Projects*, London: Routledge.

Bradford, D.F. (1999), 'On the uses of benefit–cost reasoning in choosing policy toward global climate change', in P.R. Portney and J.P. Weyant (eds), *Discounting and Intergenerational Equity*, Washington, DC: Resources for the Future.

Bristow, A.L. and J. Nellthorp (2000), 'Transport project appraisal in the European Union', *Transport Policy*, **7**(1), 51–60.

Bromley, D.W. (1989), 'Entitlements, missing markets, and environmental uncertainty', *Journal of Environmental Economics and Management*, **17**(2), 181–94.

Cline, W.R. (1999), 'Discounting for the very long term', in P.R. Portney and J.P. Weyant (eds), *Discounting and Intergenerational Equity*, Washington, DC: Resources for the Future.

de Rus, G. and V. Inglada (1997), 'Cost–benefit analysis of the high-speed train in Spain', *Annals of Regional Science*, **31**(2), 175–88.

de Zeeuw, A., R. in 't Veld and D. van Soest (2008), *Social Cost Benefit Analysis for Environmental Policy-Making*, The Hague: RMNO (Advisory Council for Spatial Planning, Nature and the Environment).

European Commission (2008), *Guide to Cost–Benefit Analysis of Investment Projects*, Brussels: European Commission.

Fernald, J.G. (1999), 'Roads to prosperity? Assessing the link between public capital and productivity', *American Economic Review*, **89**(3), 619–38.

Flyvbjerg, B., N. Bruzelius and W. Rothengatter (2003), *Megaprojects and Risk: An Anatomy of Ambition*, Cambridge, UK: Cambridge University Press.

Fogel, R.W. (1964), *Railroads and American Economic Growth: Essays in Econometric History*, Baltimore, MD: Johns Hopkins University Press.

Gollier, C. (2010), 'Ecological discounting', *Journal of Economic Theory*, **145**(2), 812–29.

Goodin, R.E. (1982), 'Discounting discounting', *Journal of Public Policy*, **2**(1), 53–71.

Gowdy, J., R.B. Howarth and C. Tisdell (2010), 'Discounting, ethics, and options for maintaining biodiversity and ecosystem integrity', in P. Kumar (ed.), *The Economics of Ecosystems and Biodiversity: Ecological and Economic Foundations*, London and Washington, DC: Earthscan.

Hayashi, Y. and H. Morisugi (2000), 'International comparison of background concept and methodology of transportation project appraisal', *Transport Policy*, **7**(1), 73–88.

HEATCO (2006), *Proposal for Harmonised Guidelines. Developing Harmonised European Approaches for Transport Costing and Project Assessment and other Deliverables*, Brussels: European Commission.

Hoel, M. and T. Sterner (2007), 'Discounting and relative prices', *Climatic Change*, **84**(3–4), 265–80.

Kay, J., A. Manning and S. Szymanski (1989), 'The economic benefits of the Channel Tunnel', *Economic Policy*, **4**(8), 211–28.

Koetse, M.J., E. Koomen, C.C. Koopmans, P. Rietveld and W. Verhagen (2011), *Klimaatverandering en klimaatonzekerheid in MKBA's* [*Climate Change and Climate Uncertainty in Social CBAs*], Amsterdam: Vrije Universiteit (in Dutch).

Koopmans, C., P. Rietveld and A. Huijg (2012), 'An accessibility approach to railways and municipal population growth, 1840–1930', *Journal of Transport Geography*, **25**, 98–104.

Kristrom, B. and P. Riera (1996), 'Is the income elasticity of environmental improvements less than one?' *Environmental and Resource Economics*, **7**(1), 45–55.

Lind, R.C. (1982), 'A primer on the major issues relating to the discount rate for evaluating national energy options', in R.C. Lind (ed.), *Discounting for Time and Risk in Energy Policy*, Washington, DC: Resources for the Future.
Little, I.M.D. and J.A. Mirrlees (1994), 'The costs and benefits of analysis: project appraisal and planning twenty years on', in R. Layard and S. Glaister (eds), *Cost–Benefit Analysis*, 2nd edition, Cambridge, UK: Cambridge University Press.
Malinvaud, E. (1953), 'Capital accumulation and efficient allocation of resources', *Econometrica*, **21**(2), 233–68.
Markandya, A. and D. Pearce (1988), 'Natural environments and the social rate of discount', *Project Appraisal*, **3**(1), 2–12.
Nordhaus, W.D. (2007), 'A review of the Stern Review on the economics of climate change', *Journal of Economic Literature*, **45**(3), 686–702.
Olsson, N.O.E., A. Okland and S.B. Halvorsen (2012), 'Consequences of differences in cost–benefit methodology in railway infrastructure appraisal – a comparison between selected countries', *Transport Policy*, **22**(C) 29–35.
OMB (2003), *Circular A-4, 'Regulatory Analysis'*, Washington, DC: Office of Management and Budget.
Pearce, D., G. Atkinson and S. Mourato (2006), *Cost–Benefit Analysis and the Environment*, Paris: Organisation for Economic Co-operation and Development.
Pickrell, D.H. (1992), 'A desire named streetcar. Fantasy and fact in rail transit planning', *Journal of the American Planning Association*, **58**(2), 158–76.
Priemus, H., B. Flyvbjerg and B. van Wee (2008), *Decision-making on Mega-projects. Cost–Benefit Analysis, Planning and Innovation*, Cheltenham, UK and Northampton MA, USA: Edward Elgar.
Ramsey, F.P. (1928), 'A mathematical theory of saving', *Economic Journal*, **38**(152), 543–59.
Rietveld, P. and F. Bruinsma (1998), *Is Transport Infrastructure Effective?*, Berlin: Springer.
Stern, N. (2006), *The Economics of Climate Change: The Stern Review*, Cambridge, UK: Cambridge University Press.
UK Treasury (2003), *The Green Book. Appraisal and Evaluation in Central Government*, London: TSO.
Weitzman, M.L. (1998), 'Why the far-distant future should be discounted at its lowest possible rate', *Journal of Environmental Economics and Management*, **36**(3), 201–8.
Weitzman, M.L. (2007), 'A review of the Stern Review on the economics of climate change', *Journal of Economic Literature*, **45**(3), 703–24.
Weitzman, M.L. (2009a), 'Risk-adjusted gamma discounting', Working Paper No. 15588, Cambridge, MA: NBER.
Weitzman, M.L. (2009b), 'On modeling and interpreting the economics of catastrophic climate change', *Review of Economics and Statistics*, **91**(1), 1–19.
World Commission on Environment and Development (1987), *Our Common Future*, New York: Oxford University Press.
Zhuang, J., Z. Liang, T. Lin and F. de Guzman (2007), 'Theory and practice in the choice of social discount rate for cost–benefit analysis: a survey', Economics Working Paper No. 94, Manila, Philippines: Asian Development Bank.

15. Mega-projects' cost performance and lock-in: problems and solutions

Chantal C. Cantarelli and Bent Flyvbjerg

15.1 INTRODUCTION

A major problem in the planning of mega-projects is the high level of misinformation about costs (and benefits) that decision-makers face in deciding whether to build and the high risks such misinformation generates. The inaccuracy of construction cost estimates is typically measured as the size of cost overrun. There are many well-known mega-projects with major cost overruns. One of the most famous 'project disasters' in this respect is the Channel Tunnel. This undersea rail tunnel linking the United Kingdom and France is the longest of its kind in Europe with a length of about 50 km. Construction costs increased from £2600 million to £4650 million (1985 prices), which is 80 per cent higher than the forecasted costs (Flyvbjerg et al., 2003a). Another well-known mega-project failure is the Central Artery/Tunnel project in Boston, USA, also known as the 'Big Dig' or Big Dug' due to persistent tunnel leaks. This large and complex underground highway project suffered a cost overrun of US $11 billion or 275 per cent (Flyvbjerg, 2007). Bangkok's underground subway was 67 per cent over budget. Many other examples of projects with cost overruns exist, for example, the Great Belt link in Denmark (54 per cent overrun), the Humber Bridge in the UK (175 per cent overrun) and the Paris Nord TGV in France (25 per cent overrun) (Flyvbjerg et al., 2003a). Cost overruns appear to be a global phenomenon, existing across 20 nations on five continents (Flyvbjerg et al., 2003b).

Several studies have focused on cost overruns, for example, Merewitz (1973); Morris (1990); Pickrell (1990, 1992); Riksrevisionsverket [Auditor General of Sweden] (1994); Nijkamp and Ubbels (1999); Bordat et al. (2004); Odeck (2004); Dantata et al. (2006); Ellis et al. (2007) and Lee (2008). All of these studies show that cost overruns are more common than cost underruns, with frequencies ranging between 52 per cent and 95 per cent. Conversely, the magnitude of the cost overruns differs between the studies. The studies by Nijkamp and Ubbels (1999), Odeck (2004), Bordat et al. (2004) and Ellis et al. (2007) found rather small cost overruns – up to 20 per cent – whereas Morris (1990) and the Riksrevisionsverket (1994 in

Odeck, 2004) found enormous average cost overruns of 164 per cent and 86 per cent respectively. As for the differences in average cost overruns between the various studies, the following main explanations can be given. First of all, the main reason for the differences in the average cost overrun between studies is the difference in the use of nominal and real prices (Flyvbjerg, 2007, 2008). Second, the way data are handled can explain the differences in the extent of cost overruns between studies (see for a more extensive elaboration Flyvbjerg et al., 2003b). Studies use different baselines from which cost overrun is calculated and hence the extent of overrun differs between studies. Third, differences can also be related to the variation in sample size. If the sample size is small, outliers may have a large influence on the results. Fourth, the differences can be explained by the differences in the geographical area that is covered (different economies), and the project types that are included (different project dynamics and complexity).

This chapter addresses the cost performance of mega-projects in more detail by presenting the results of a worldwide study into cost overruns. Although the study was carried out in 2002 it is still the largest statistical study in this research area. Furthermore, specific attention is paid to the phenomenon of lock-in. Lock-in influences the decision-making process and strongly impacts the outcomes of projects' cost performance. Besides describing these two major problems in decision-making on large-scale projects, we also provide various solutions to deal with them. The chapter finishes with some conclusions and implications.

15.2 INACCURACY OF COST ESTIMATES[1]

Inaccuracy in construction cost forecasts is measured as actual costs minus forecasted costs as a percentage of forecasted costs. An inaccuracy of zero means that the forecasted cost for the project was correct and thus equalled actual costs. Actual costs are defined as real accounted construction costs determined at the time of project completion. Estimated costs are defined as budgeted or forecasted construction costs determined at the time of formal decision to build. This is also called the 'decision date', 'the time of the decision to proceed', the 'go decision' (Flyvbjerg et al., 2003a). At that moment, cost estimates were often available as data for decision-makers to make an informed decision. Although the project planning process varies with project type, country and time, it is typically possible for any given project to identify a specific point in the process as the time of decision to build. Usually a cost estimate was available at this point in time for the decision-makers. If not, then the closest available estimate was used, typically a later estimate resulting in a conservative bias in the measure for inaccuracy. This method is the international standard for measuring inaccuracy of cost estimates (Fouracre et al., 1990; Pickrell, 1990; National Audit Office and Department of Transport, 1992; Walmsley and Pickett, 1992; Leavitt et al., 1993; World Bank, 1994 in Flyvbjerg et al., 2002; Nijkamp and Ubbels, 1999).

Why Are Cost Overruns a Problem?

Cost overruns are considered problematic for the following four reasons (Flyvbjerg 2007, p. 582). First of all, 'they lead to a Pareto-inefficient allocation of resources – that is, waste'. Cost forecasts are often inaccurate but the large standard deviations show that the margin by which costs are 'wrong' differs across projects. As a consequence, the ranking of projects is affected and 'decision makers are likely to implement inferior projects'. Additional budget is required as projects become more expensive than was initially estimated. The budget for other projects can therefore be affected, particularly as the total budget for infrastructure investments is often fixed in a given period. Cost overruns thus result in financial wastage and in fewer infrastructure projects being realized than planned. Second, cost overruns can 'lead to delays and further cost overruns' (ibid.). When confronted with cost overruns, attempts must be made to secure additional funding and projects must often be renegotiated or reapproved. This inevitably takes time and cost overruns increase with each additional year before implementation (Flyvbjerg et al., 2004). Third, cost overruns 'destabilize policy, planning, implementation, and operations of projects'. Cost overruns can lead to continuous re-approval and unrest in the project organization and parliament. Fourth, 'the problem is getting bigger because projects get bigger' (Flyvbjerg, 2007, p. 582). When projects become more and more expensive and still involve cost overruns, the financial consequences can become so large that they may even destabilize the finances of a whole country or region. This occurred when the billion-dollar cost overrun on the 2004 Athens Olympics affected the credit rating of Greece and when benefit shortfalls hit Hong Kong's new US$20 billion Chek Lap Kok airport after it opened in 1998 (Flyvbjerg, 2007, p. 583).

The Size of Cost Overruns

One of the largest quantitative studies on cost overruns is by Flyvbjerg et al. (2002, 2003a, 2003b, 2004). The study includes 258 (land-based) transport infrastructure projects with comparable data for forecasted and actual construction costs. The projects were located in 20 nations on five continents, including both developed and developing nations. Projects for the sample were selected on the basis of data availability. Although

Table 15.1 Average cost overrun for rail, fixed links and roads

Type of Project	Number of Cases (N)	Average Cost Overrun (%)	Standard Deviation (s.d.)	Level of Significance, *p*
Rail	58	44.7	38.4	<0.001
Fixed links	33	33.8	62.4	<0.004
Road	167	20.4	29.9	<0.001

Source: Adjusted from Flyvbjerg (2008, p. 127).

there are several reasons why the projects with available data may not be representative (Flyvbjerg et al., 2003b), using these projects will only result in a conservative bias of cost overruns. Table 15.1 shows the average cost overrun for rail, fixed links (bridges and tunnels) and roads. Rail projects incur the highest difference between actual and estimated costs, with an average of no less than 44.7 per cent, followed by fixed-link projects (bridges and tunnels) averaging 33.8 per cent and roads at 20.4 per cent. An F-test failed to support the null hypothesis with a very high level of statistical significance that type of project has no effect on percentage cost escalation ($p < 0.001$).

The following main findings pertain to cost overruns in transport infrastructure projects:

- Cost escalation happens in almost nine out of ten projects. For a randomly selected project, the likelihood of actual costs being larger than forecast costs is 86 per cent. The likelihood of actual costs being lower than or equal to forecast cost is 14 per cent.
- We reject with overwhelming significance the thesis that the error of overestimating costs is as common as the error of underestimating costs ($p < 0.001$; two-sided test, using the binomial distribution).
- Forecast costs are biased and the bias is caused by systematic underestimation.
- We reject with overwhelming significance the thesis that the numerical size of the error of underestimating costs is the same as the numerical size of the error of overestimating costs ($p < 0.001$; non-parametric Mann-Whitney U-test). Costs are not only underestimated much more often than they are overestimated or correct, costs that have been underestimated are also wrong by a substantially larger margin than costs that have been overestimated.
- Dividing fixed links into tunnels and bridges it is concluded that cost overruns for tunnels are larger (48 per cent) than for bridges (30 per cent) but the difference is not statistically significant.

- High-speed rail links have the highest average cost overrun (52 per cent) followed by urban rail links (45 per cent) and conventional rail links (30 per cent) but the difference is not statistically significant.
- Overrun is constant for the 70-year period covered in the study – estimates have not improved over time.

15.3 EXPLANATIONS

Three main types of explanations exist that claim to account for inaccuracy in forecasts of costs: technical, psychological and political-economic explanations. Technical explanations are the most common type of explanation of inaccuracy in forecasts (Ascher, 1978; Morris and Hough, 1987; Wachs, 1990; Flyvbjerg et al., 2002, 2005). They account for cost overruns in terms of imperfect forecasting techniques, inadequate data, honest mistakes, inherent problems in predicting the future, lack of experience on the part of forecasters, and so on. There are different underlying causes that attribute to these technical explanations. For example, price rises are often argued to be a main cause for cost overruns. These price rises can typically be seen as the result of problems with predicting the future. Furthermore, a poor project design usually results in many project changes and consequently higher costs. The poor project design may have been the consequence of a lack of experience on the part of forecasters.

Psychological explanations account for cost overruns in terms of planning fallacy and optimism bias (developed by Kahneman and Tversky, 1979; Kahneman and Lovallo, 1993; Lovallo and Kahneman, 2003). The planning fallacy is the tendency to underestimate the time, costs and risks of future action and at the same time overestimate the benefits of the same actions. Optimism bias is the systematic tendency for people to be overly optimistic about the outcome of planned actions. This over-optimism can be traced to the cognitive bias in people's minds – the errors in the way the mind processes information – when making decisions. This 'error' is, in the case of cost forecasting, the inability to estimate costs independent of context. People are optimistic about the performance of their project and forecast costs low. When the real costs at project completion are revealed, these are typically much higher (Fouracre et al., 1990, p. 10; Walmsley and Pickett, 1992, p. 11; World Bank, 1994, p. 86; Flyvbjerg et al., 2002, p. 288; Mackie and Preston, 1998).

Political-economic explanations describe cost overruns as the result of the deliberate underestimation of costs by planners and promoters. This is also sometimes referred to as strategic misrepresentation. Wachs (1989, 1990) refers to manipulation of forecasts. Whether it is deliberate underestimation, strategic misrepresentation or manipulation of cost forecasts, they all incur the underestimation of costs to increase the likelihood of project approval and funding. Planners are aware that in order for projects to be selected for implementation, forecasts of outcomes have to be highly favourable. This shows the strategic behaviour that underlies the underestimation of costs in project planning. The so-called asymmetric information between decision-makers and forecasters allows this strategic behaviour. Decision-makers typically have less information compared to forecasters when making a decision about a project and they therefore have to rely on forecasters for cost estimates. This dependency creates opportunities for forecasters to misrepresent the cost estimates to their benefit. Besides asymmetric information, political and organization pressures give reason to strategic misrepresentation. For instance, costs are underestimated due to competition for scarce funds or jockeying for position. Optimism bias and strategic misrepresentation both involve deception, but where the latter is intentional, that is lying, the first is not. Optimism bias is self-deception.

How Valid are Explanations?

Although technical explanations are widely accepted, sample sizes were too small to statistically test its validity. By the data of the large-sample study described in the previous section this became possible; technical explanations are rejected as a main reason of forecasting inaccuracy. There are two main reasons for rejecting technical explanations of forecasting errors (Flyvbjerg et al., 2002, p. 286). First, if misleading forecasts were truly caused by technical inadequacies, simple mistakes and inherent problems with predicting the future, we would expect an even distribution of errors in cost estimates around zero, but this is not the case. Second, if imperfect techniques, inadequate data and lack of experience were main explanations of the underestimations, an improvement in forecasting accuracy over time would be expected, since errors and their sources would be recognized and addressed through the refinement of data collection, forecasting methods, and so on. Despite substantial expenditures on improving data and methods, it has no effect on forecasting accuracy. It is not forecasting errors that need explaining but the fact that for a large majority of cases costs are underestimated. Although it is impossible to predict for individual projects exactly which geological and safety problems will occur it is possible to predict the risk, based on experience from other projects, that some problems will occur in a project and that one can and should account for these risks in forecasting costs.

Psychological explanations better fit the data. An optimistic cost estimate is a low one and if appraisal optimism is a cause of cost overrun, the actual costs would be higher than the estimated costs. Consequently, the existence of appraisal optimism would be able to account for the systematic underestimation of the costs. Optimism bias would be an important and credible explanation of underestimated costs in infrastructure forecasting if estimates were produced by inexperienced forecasters, that is, persons who were estimating costs for the first or second time and who were thus unknowing about the realities of infrastructure building and were not drawing on the knowledge and skills of more experienced colleagues. This may explain individual cases but it is unlikely that the whole profession would make these kinds of mistakes. People learn from their mistakes and this would reduce or eliminate optimism bias, hence estimates would become more accurate over time. However, the data show that this has not happened and this leads us to reject optimism bias as a primary reason for cost underestimation.

Political-economic explanations account the best for the systematic underestimation of costs found in the data. A strategic estimate of costs would be low, resulting in cost overrun. For legal, economic, moral and other reasons, if promoters and planners have intentionally misrepresented cost estimates to get a project started, they are unlikely to formally tell researchers or others that this is the case. This makes it particularly difficult to demonstrate this strategic behaviour but two studies succeeded. First, the study by Flyvbjerg and COWI (2004) showed that there are strong interests and incentives at the approval stage to present projects as favourably as possible, that is, with underestimated costs. Second, the study by Wachs (1990) concluded that forecasts of costs are presented to the public as instruments for deciding whether or not a project is to be undertaken, but they are actually instruments for getting public funds committed to a favourable project. Both studies falsify the notion that in situations with high political and organizational pressure the lowballing of costs is caused by unintentional technical error or optimism bias.

15.4 LOCK-IN AND PROJECT COST PERFORMANCE[2]

Besides the above-mentioned explanations, the phenomenon of lock-in plays an important role in the understanding of cost overruns (see also Cantarelli et al., 2010). It addresses the problem of inaccurate cost forecasts from a wider decision-making perspective, from initial idea to project implementation.

Lock-in is usually used in a technical context (see e.g., Paul David's article,

1985, on the QWERTY keyboard) but here we consider the institutional or behavioural form. We define lock-in as the over-commitment of decision-makers to an ineffective course of action (for example, a decision or project). A distinction between over-commitment and early commitment is essential. Early commitment is in itself not necessarily negative and could even be advantageous to the decision-making process as it could force a decision and thereby avoid delay. Over-commitment, on the other hand, has by definition a negative influence on project performance. It refers to the style of psychological coping associated with the inability to withdraw from obligations (Vrijkotte et al., 2004). As the commitment goes on and on and eventually escalates, people continue with a certain decision path, where they should have re-evaluated it.

Lock-in and Cost Overruns

Lock-in affects the project cost performance in two distinctive ways. First, lock-in affects the decision-making and hence outcome; this is called lock-in at the decision-making level. Due to lock-in, decision-makers may have committed themselves to the project before the actual 'go decision' is taken. This decision-making moment can be called the 'real decision to build' as opposed to the 'formal decision to build' ('go decision'). Since cost estimates usually become more accurate over time and the real decision to build precedes the formal decision to build, the estimated costs at the real decision to build will often be lower than those at the formal decision to build. Consequently, using the estimated costs at the real decision to build as a baseline for calculating cost overruns would result in higher overruns.

Second, lock-in affects the project features and hence the outcome; this is called lock-in at the project level. So, after the decision to build a project is made, decision-makers may be committed to certain project features and are unable to revise the decision regarding these features. As they hold on to inefficient project choices suboptimal outcomes are reached and funding is wasted.

To conclude, lock-in can be distinguished at two different levels, the decision-making level and the project level. We specify the definition of lock-in as: the over-commitment of parties to an inefficient project before the formal decision to build is taken, and to the inefficient specifications of the project after the formal decision to build has been taken.

How Can Lock-in Occur?

In order to get a better understanding of the mechanisms in the decision-making process that lead to lock-in four indicators for lock-in can be identified. First, escalating commitment is an indicator for lock-in. There are different causes of escalating commitment, such as strategic behaviour and political vulnerability. Strategic behaviour was already addressed in the previous section with respect to the deliberate underestimation of costs to get projects approved. As a consequence of this strategic behaviour decision-makers hold on to certain projects longer than desired because these projects are projected as promising to them. Political vulnerability similarly makes people more committed to a certain decision or project but this is caused by power and interests that are at stake. Two other factors that may result in escalating commitment are agreements between parties, and a narrowly defined decision-making process that focuses on a specific solution rather than on a broad problem-setting.

Second, inflexibility and closure of alternatives is considered an indicator of lock-in. We treat inflexibility and closure of alternatives as one indicator because they have the same roots: they follow from path dependency. Path dependency is relevant in the context of project cost performance because the outcome depends on the start and the specific development of the decision-making process in time. In other words, decisions to be made in the future are often dependent on the outcomes of decisions that were made in the past, which can no longer be reversed to reach another outcome. Lock-in is created as a consequence of path dependency when suboptimal policies are used even though a better alternative is present (Woerdman, 2004).

The third indicator is sunk costs: the irretrievable costs in terms of money or time. Wilson and Zhang (1997, p. 289) illustrate the relationship between sunk costs and lock-in as follows: 'Individuals show a greater tendency to continue an endeavour once an investment in funds, effort or time, has been made'. Thus the commitment to the project or decision increases concurrently with the amount of time and money invested in the decision-making process, creating lock-in. At the project level, sunk costs in money may create lock-in. Once money is spent on certain project specifications, that money is no longer available for other project requirements. Revising the decision regarding specific project features becomes impossible. From a behavioural economic perspective the relationship between sunk costs and lock-in can be described by the concept of loss aversion: the tendency to have a strong preference for avoiding losses over acquiring gains. There is an apparent asymmetry in the way in which individuals value gains and losses, with losses having a greater impact than equivalent-sized gains. This finding was proposed by Nobel-prize winner Kahneman and Lovallo (1993). Sunk costs can in this context result in lock-in via loss aversion as follows: once an investment in time or money is made, individuals prefer to continue with the decision/project as there is still a possible chance of success as opposed to a sure loss of the investment when they decide to quit.

Last, the fourth indicator of lock-in is the need for justification. Brockner et al. (1986, p. 110) argue that 'decision-makers show evidence of entrapment whenever they escalate their commitment to ineffective policies, products, services or strategies in order to justify previous allocations or resources to those objectives'. The need for justification is derived from the theories of self-justification and dissonance, which describe how individuals search for confirmation of their rational behaviour (Staw, 1981; Wilson and Zhang, 1997). This need arises from social pressures and mechanisms like 'face-saving'. Face-saving was described by Whyte (1986, p. 311) as a situation wherein 'people try to rationalize their actions or psychologically defend themselves against an apparent error in judgment'. The involvement of interest groups and organizational pushes and pulls can also introduce pressures into the decision-making process, threatening the position of the decision-makers, who may feel pressure to continue with a (failing) project in order to avoid publicly admitting what they may see as a personal failure (McElhinney, 2005). A decision is likely to be influenced by the need for justification when the support for a decision is sustained despite contradicting information and social pressures.

Types of Lock-in

Different types of lock-in can be distinguished depending upon whether or not one is aware that one becomes 'locked-in' (conscious versus unconscious lock-in) and whether or not one intentionally creates lock-in (intentional versus unintentional lock-in). Let us consider the difference between the various types of lock-in in more detail by considering the four indicators of lock-in.

With conscious lock-in, decision-makers are aware of their tendency to continue with a decision or project despite possible negative messages instead of evaluating them critically. With unconscious lock-in, the decision-makers are not aware of such behaviour.

Conscious lock-in can be caused by sunk costs in terms of money. People are often well aware of the amount of money they invest in projects and once they invest more and more in a project, their commitment becomes stronger and they may not evaluate the project's potential objectively anymore. Unconscious lock-in is more likely to be the result of sunk costs in terms of time. Commitment to a project evolves over time, without knowing the exact amount of time one has invested. Moreover, it is difficult to manage the time one spends on the decision-making of a project, which further contributes to the ignorance of lock-in. In general, indicators of lock-in that can be managed to a certain extent are likely to result in conscious lock-in and indicators that cannot be managed are more prone to unconscious lock-in. Consider, for example, the closure of alternatives, an indicator that can easily be managed. Decision-makers are well aware whether one project or solution is considered or whether there is a wide variety of alternative solutions being examined.

With the distinction between intentional and unintentional lock-in, the main difference is the behaviour on the part of a decision-maker. When this behaviour is led by the aim to ensure the implementation of a project anyway, it is referred to as intentional lock-in. The importance of such kind of lock-in is presented by Walby (2003), who argues that an important role is played by social and political institutions that lock in certain paths of development, by shaping power, opportunity and knowledge (David, 1985; Arthur, 1989; North, 1990; Nee and Cao, 1999; Mahoney, 2000; Pierson, 2000a, 2000b, 2001).

Evidence of Lock-in

The real decision to build is often taken informally and within a fuzzy environment (Teisman, 1995; Flyvbjerg et al., 2003a). This makes it difficult to identify this moment in the decision-making process and hence to establish the actual impact of lock-in on project cost performance. Furthermore, as we have seen from the previous section, people are often either unaware of lock-in or intentionally create lock-in. It is therefore unlikely that they can or will admit that they have committed themselves to the project before the formal decision to build was taken. In order to disclose the real decision to build, interviewing techniques therefore seem inappropriate. Rather, case studies seem the most suitable method in this respect. These case studies allow considering the presence or absence of the indicators of lock-in and their impact on the decision-making process. This will reveal the extent to which lock-in has taken place and how it occurred. Moreover, the point of no return – the moment in the decision-making process where it was no longer possible to reverse the decision – can be identified. This moment is typically seen as the real decision to build. In the remainder of this section we will describe the findings of a case study into lock-in. The case study concerns the Betuweroute and the focus lies on lock-in at the decision-making level. This project was chosen because it has been implemented recently and is well documented.

The Betuweroute is a dedicated freight-transport railway line of about 160 km, between the port of Rotterdam and the European hinterland. As long ago as the early 1980s the construction of a new railway line was proposed to deal with the unsatisfactory rail connections of the 'mainport' Rotterdam. However, it was not until 1996 that the formal decision to build was taken.

During this period from initiation to formal decision to build, there were several key decision-making moments that point to lock-in: the publication in 1990 of the SVVII (Second Transport Structure Plan), the project memorandum in 1991, the introduction of the New Track Act in 1992, the start of the PKB procedure in 1992, the Agreement of Warnemünde in 1992 (agreement between the Netherlands and Germany about the connection of the Betuweroute to the German network of railway lines), and the consideration of the project in 1994.

With the publication of the SVVII, the Betuweroute project was included in the policy plans to solve the problem of insufficient railway capacity (TCI, 2004). This shows a strong focus on the 'solution' early on in the decision-making phase. By taking the project as the starting point, decision-makers may have become excessively committed to the project (De Gelderlander, 1995 in Roscam Abbing et al., 1999, p. 13; Priemus, 2007, p. 630). In the project memorandum of 1991, the Dutch Railway Company investigated the Betuweroute project but failed to consider other possible solutions. In general, the problem analysis focused solely on railway connections and it failed to include solutions of alternative modalities such as inland waterway transport. Beside this closure of alternatives, escalating commitment was identified as an indicator of lock-in in the Betuweroute case study by the various agreements that were made. Especially the Agreement of Warnemünde marks an escalating commitment. Due to the various agreements the decision to construct the railway line became formalized. Furthermore, due to social pressures as a consequence of the continuous criticism of the project, the cabinet decided to follow a two-track policy. This policy included on the one hand the publication of the PKB1 (Key Planning Decisions, Part 1, design track decision), while on the other hand conducting additional research into the justification of the intention to implement the Betuweroute. By this two-track policy, one could proceed with the development of the Betuweroute project (further locking themselves into the project) despite the lack of proof of the desirability and necessity of the project.

Arguments to support the decision to implement the project were poorly founded but this was no reason to reconsider the decision to implement the Betuweroute project (Ministerie van Verkeer en Waterstaat, 1996–2007; TCI, 2004). Even when new insights regarding the desirability and necessity of the project became available, political parties were unwilling to change their opinions regarding the decision to implement the Betuweroute project. This indicates the inflexibility of the decision-making process as well as the different mechanisms of face-saving on the part of the decision-makers.

Considering these different moments during the decision-making, the point of no return is the start of the PKB procedure in 1992. Before this moment, when the SVVII and the project memorandum were published no formal agreements had yet been made and it was still possible to reconsider the decision. However, when the PKB started, the first steps into project implementation had already been taken. This made it impossible to reopen the discussion regarding the decision to build. This was clearly demonstrated by the rejection to reconsider the project when new insights became available. Withdrawing was no longer an option; decision-makers were obliged to build the project.

To summarize, due to lock-in, the real decision to build was taken before the formal decision to build. With estimated costs being lower at the earlier phase in the decision-making process, cost overruns calculated in connection with the real decision to build were about five times larger than the cost overruns calculated in connection with the formal decision to build. Due to lock-in, the actual extent of cost overruns has been misrepresented.

15.5 SOLUTIONS

As became clear from the above, inaccurate cost forecasts are not the only problem in the decision-making of mega-projects – lock-in is a serious problem threatening project cost performance as well. In this section we will provide a set of solutions to deal with these problems.

Measures to Deal with Lock-in

When formulating measures to deal with lock-in, it is of the utmost importance to take the different types of lock-in into account, whether conscious/unconscious lock-in and intentional/unintentional lock-in. Since it is easier to deal with lock-in when one is aware that lock-in takes place, in the case of unconscious lock-in, it is necessary to create this level of awareness. Only then can measures be essentially effective. A possible way to increase this awareness is to introduce so-called review stages into the decision-making phase. During these stages, the possible presence or threat of lock-in is evaluated. Guidelines about the indicators of lock-in may be used to test for the presence of lock-in and strategies may be formulated to deal with lock-in that has actually taken place. Consider, for example, the indicator inflexibility and the closure of alternatives. In the review stage, parties have to reach an agreement about the amount and type of alternatives that have been considered in order to proceed to the next stage of the decision-making process. If such an agreement cannot be reached, they have to go back to the stage of problem analyses. In this way they make sure that no feasible alternatives are left out of the decision-making process and thus eliminate the chance of lock-in.

Beside the difference in conscious and unconscious lock-in, it makes a great difference whether one is dealing with intentional or unintentional lock-in. With intentional lock-in decision-makers are not likely to cooperate in finding a solution and this requires a different set of measures than those in a situation where decision-makers do cooperate. The introduction of a review stage into the decision-making process and a set of guidelines for indicators of lock-in might be sufficient to deal with unintentional lock-in. This will, however, not work in the case of intentional lock-in, and therefore, an independent process supervisor or third party reviewer is suggested to deal with this type of lock-in.

One way in which it is possible to determine whether lock-in was present and whether it influenced the decision-making process is by considering the outcomes of cost–benefit analyses. Cost–benefit analyses (CBAs) are often used for the ex ante evaluation of projects to support decision-making. However, since the outcomes of these CBAs are not necessarily binding, a negative cost–benefit outcome does not imply that the project will be rejected. Some projects are politically desirable despite their negative CBA outcome and are implemented regardless. However, the large amount of projects with a negative CBA outcome that is held on to instead of blown off is at least remarkable (see Chapters 12 and 13 in this book and Annema et al., 2007 who show that in the Netherlands there is a tendency to postpone decisions of projects rather than to reject projects altogether). It is unlikely that all of these projects are politically desirable. This tendency to hold on to projects can be explained by lock-in as a consequence of escalating commitment and the need for justification. By delaying the project decision, decision-makers have more time to find ways to promote the project and in this way increase the chance of project selection.

To the extent that lock-in is caused by escalating commitment, decision-makers themselves can avoid lock-in, for example by avoiding commitment when the cost–benefit analysis is not yet solid or when cost estimates are not yet sound. When lock-in is caused by the need for justification, decision-makers are less able to control or eliminate lock-in. In that case, independent authorities or reviewers may be brought into the decision-making to check upon the role of the cost–benefit analyses in the decision-making process. They would have to pay more attention to the outcomes of these cost–benefit analyses, especially for those projects that are still to be deliberated upon but have, at first sight, a negative cost–benefit outcome.

Measures to Deal with Inaccurate Cost Forecasts

When considering solutions for inaccurate forecasts of costs, two fundamentally different situations need to be distinguished: (1) planners and promoters consider it important to get forecasts of costs right, and (2) planners and promoters do not consider it important to get forecasts of costs right, because optimistic forecasts are considered necessary to get projects started. In the first situation better forecasting methods can result in improved accuracy. In the second situation, better methods will not help because promoters and planners will find another way to misrepresent the forecasts. Misrepresentation can be moderated by measures of accountability and improved incentive structures are therefore recommended.

Improved Methods

If planners genuinely consider it important to get forecasts right, we recommend they use the forecasting method called 'reference class forecasting' to reduce inaccuracy and bias. This method was originally developed to compensate for the type of cognitive bias in human forecasting that Princeton psychologist Daniel Kahneman found in his Nobel prize-winning work on bias in economic forecasting (Kahneman and Tversky, 1979; Kahneman, 1994). Reference class forecasting has proven more accurate than conventional forecasting.

Reference class forecasting consists in taking a so-called 'outside view' on the particular project being forecast. The outside view is established on the basis of information from a class of similar projects. The outside view does not try to forecast the specific uncertain events that will affect the particular project, but instead places the project in a statistical distribution of outcomes from this class of reference projects. Reference class forecasting requires the following three steps for the individual project:

1. Identifying a relevant reference class of past projects. The class must be broad enough to be statistically meaningful but narrow enough to be truly comparable with the specific project.
2. Establishing a probability distribution for the selected reference class. This requires access to credible, empirical data for a sufficient number

of projects within the reference class to make statistically meaningful conclusions.

3. Comparing the specific project with the reference class distribution in order to establish the most likely outcome for the specific project.

The contrast between inside and outside views has been confirmed by systematic research (Gilovich et al., 2002). The research shows that when people are asked simple questions requiring them to take an outside view, their forecasts become significantly more accurate. However, most individuals and organizations are inclined to adopt the inside view in planning major initiatives. This is the conventional and intuitive approach. The traditional way to think about a complex project is to focus on the project itself and its details, to bring to bear what one knows about it, paying special attention to its unique or unusual features, trying to predict the events that will influence its future. The thought of going out and gathering simple statistics about related cases seldom enters a planner's mind. This is the case in general, according to Lovallo and Kahneman (2003, pp. 61–2).

While understandable, planners' preference for the inside over the outside view is unfortunate. When both forecasting methods are applied with equal skill, the outside view is much more likely to produce a realistic estimate. That is because it bypasses cognitive and organizational biases such as appraisal optimism and strategic misrepresentation, and cuts directly to outcomes. In the outside view, planners and forecasters are not required to make scenarios, imagine events, or gauge their own and others' levels of ability and control, so they cannot get all these things wrong. Surely the outside view, being based on historical precedent, may fail to predict extreme outcomes, that is, those that lie outside all historical precedents. But for most projects, the outside view will produce more accurate results. In contrast, a focus on inside details is the road to inaccuracy.

The comparative advantage of the outside view is most pronounced for non-routine projects, understood as projects that planners and decision-makers in a certain locale have never attempted before, such as building an urban rail system in a city for the first time, or a new major bridge or tunnel where none existed before. It is in the planning of such new efforts that the biases toward optimism and strategic misrepresentation are likely to be large. To be sure, choosing the right reference class of comparative past projects becomes more difficult when planners are forecasting initiatives for which precedents are not easily found, for instance the introduction of new and unfamiliar technologies. However, most mega-projects are both non-routine locally and use well-known technologies. Such projects are, therefore, particularly likely to benefit from the outside view and reference class forecasting.

Improved Incentives: Public Sector and Private Sector Accountability[3]

The problem of misinformation is an issue of power and profit and must be dealt with as such, using the mechanisms of transparency and accountability that are commonly used in liberal democracies to mitigate rent-seeking behaviour and the misuse of power (Flyvbjerg et al., 2005). Two basic types of accountability define liberal democracies: (1) public sector accountability through transparency and public control, and (2) private sector accountability via competition and market control.

In order to achieve public sector accountability through transparency and public control, the following would be required as practices embedded in the relevant institutions:

- National-level government should not offer discretionary grants to local infrastructure agencies for the sole purpose of building a specific type of infrastructure, for instance rail. Such grants create perverse incentives. Instead, national government should simply offer 'infrastructure grants' or 'transportation grants' to local governments and let local political officials spend the funds however they choose, but ensure that every dollar they spend on one type of infrastructure reduces their ability to fund another.
- Forecasts should be made subject to independent peer review. Where large amounts of taxpayers' money are at stake, such review may be carried out by national or state accounting and auditing offices, like the General Accounting Office in the USA or the National Audit Office in the UK, who have the independence and expertise to produce such reviews. Other types of independent review bodies may be established, for instance within national departments of finance or with relevant professional bodies.
- Forecasts should be benchmarked against comparable forecasts, for instance using reference class forecasting as described in the previous section.
- Forecasts, peer reviews, and benchmarkings should be made available to the public as they are produced, including all relevant documentation.
- Public hearings, citizen juries, and the like should be organized to allow stakeholders and civil society to voice criticism and support of forecasts. Knowledge generated in this way should be integrated in planning and decision-making.

- Scientific and professional conferences should be organized where forecasters would present and defend their forecasts in the face of colleagues' scrutiny and criticism.
- Projects with inflated cost–benefit ratios should be reconsidered and stopped if recalculated costs and benefits do not warrant implementation. Projects with realistic estimates of benefits and costs should be rewarded.
- Professional and occasionally even criminal penalties should be enforced for planners and forecasters who consistently and foreseeably produce deceptive forecasts.

An example of a professional penalty would be the exclusion from one's professional organization for violating its code of ethics. An example of a criminal penalty would be punishment as the result of prosecution before a court or similar legal body, for instance where deceptive forecasts have led to substantial mismanagement of public funds (Garett and Wachs, 1996). Malpractice in planning should be taken as seriously as it is in other professions. Failure to do this amounts to not taking the profession of planning seriously.

In order to achieve private sector accountability in forecasting via competition and market control, the following would be required, again as practices that are both embedded in and enforced by the relevant institutions:

- The decision to go ahead with a project should, where at all possible, be made contingent on the willingness of private financiers to participate without a sovereign guarantee for at least one-third of the total capital needs. This should be required whether projects pass the market test or not; that is, whether projects are subsidized or not or provided for reasons of social justice or not. Private lenders, shareholders and stock market analysts would produce their own forecasts or would critically monitor existing ones. If they were wrong about the forecasts, they and their organizations could be hurt. The result would be more realistic forecasts and reduced risk.
- Full public financing or full financing with a sovereign guarantee should be avoided.
- Forecasters and their organizations must share financial responsibility for covering benefit shortfalls (and cost overruns) resulting from misrepresentation and bias in forecasting.
- The participation of risk capital should not mean that government gives up or reduces control of the project. On the contrary, it

means that government can more effectively play the role it should be playing, namely as the ordinary citizen's guarantor of safety, environmental quality, risk management and a proper use of public funds. If the institutions with responsibility for developing and building mega-projects would effectively implement, embed and enforce such measures of accountability, then the misrepresentation in transportation forecasting, which is widespread today, might be mitigated. If this is not done, misrepresentation is likely to continue, and the allocation of funds for transportation investments is likely to be wasteful.

15.6 CONCLUSIONS

This chapter has shown that cost overruns are a severe problem in mega-projects. Psychological or political-economic explanations mainly account for the inaccuracy of cost forecasts. Besides, lock-in seems to play an important role in the project's costs performance. In terms of explanations, lock-in relates both to psychological and political-economic explanations. By sunk costs in terms of time, the cognitive bias in people's minds influences the way in which they take decisions. Similarly, the need for justification could be traced back to psychological processes because people would prefer to continue with a project with the chance to turn it into a success rather than to accept its failure. On the other hand, the need for justification could also have its origin in political-economic causes when decision-makers act strategically to pursue a decision that is favourable to them.

The phenomenon of lock-in thus contributes to a large extent to the understanding of cost overruns. Moreover, it also contributes to determining the cost performance. Because of lock-in the real decision to build has been taken before the formal decision to build, at a moment when the estimated costs are much lower, which consequently will reveal a higher cost overrun when measuring the project performance. Cost overruns are expected to be underestimated because the cost increases between the real decision to build and the formal decision to build are not included. Ideally, cost overruns should therefore be measured based on the estimated costs at the moment of the real decision to build. There are, however, two caveats with measuring cost performance based on the real decision to build. First, although we have shown how lock-in can occur and how it can affect the cost performance, more data are needed to test that the real decision to build preceded the formal decision to build and the degree at which these decision-making moments differ. Moreover, evidence as to the extent to which cost overruns based on the real decision to build differ from cost overruns based on the formal decision to build is essential. Second, it is difficult to actually determine the real decision to build. Although it is theoretically possible to retrieve the real decision to build of a project, in practice it is extremely difficult to obtain this information from decision-makers themselves. Decision-makers might not want to reveal this information or they are not aware that they made a decision earlier than the formal decision to build (caused by unconscious lock-in as shown above). Further research into these areas is recommended.

Beside these research implications, there are also policy implications. The large and persistent cost overruns stress the importance of governments to pay more attention to cost forecasts in the decision-making process. The inaccuracy of cost forecasts is not only caused by inadequate forecasting methods; it is rather the result of psychological and political-economic factors like optimism bias and strategic misrepresentation. This requires policy-makers to implement different measures besides better forecasting methods, for example, better measures regarding accountability. Furthermore, when dealing with cost overruns policy-makers need to be aware that it is not only the inaccuracy of cost forecasts that is a problem, but it is also the over-commitment to inefficient decisions early in the decision-making process that causes trouble. For this, changes in the decision-making process itself are required that allow decision-makers to recognize lock-in and deal with it. Also the involvement of independent review committees to prevent lock-in created intentionally is recommended.

Last, there are certainly ways to improve in cost performance of mega-projects. One way is improving the accuracy of cost forecasts, another is preventing lock-in. Without pretending that lock-in can be removed altogether, there are certainly ways to avoid lock-in, as demonstrated above. The type of lock-in should thereby be taken into account. Unintentional lock-in may be prevented by introducing a specific set of guidelines in the decision-making process. For intentional lock-in this might not be sufficient and in this situation independent reviews of the decision-making process are suggested.

NOTES

1. This section draws on Flyvbjerg et al. (2003b) and Flyvbjerg (2007).
2. This section mainly draws on Cantarelli et al. (2010).
3. These solutions of improved incentives are drawn from Flyvbjerg et al. (2002).

LITERATURE

Annema, J.A., C. Koopmans and B. van Wee (2007), 'Evaluating transport infrastructure investments: the Dutch experience with a standardized approach', *Transport Reviews*, **27**(2), 125–50.

Arthur, W.B. (1989), 'Competing technologies, increasing returns and lock-in by historical events', *The Economic Journal*, **99**(394), 116–31.

Ascher, W. (1978), *Forecasting: An Appraisal for Policy-Makers and Planners*, Baltimore, MD: Johns Hopkins University Press.

Bordat, C., B.G. McCullouch, S. Labi and K.C. Sinha (2004), *An Analysis of Cost Overruns and Time Delays of INDOT Projects*, Publication No. FHWA/IN/JTRP-2004/7, SPR-2811, Washington, DC: Transportation Research Board.

Brockner, J., R. Houser, G. Birnbaum, K. Lloyd, J. Deitcher, S. Nathanson and J.Z. Rubin (1986), 'Escalation of commitment to an ineffective course of action: the effect of feedback having negative implications for self-identity', *Administrative Science Quarterly*, **31**(1), 109–26.

Cantarelli, C.C., B. Flyvbjerg, B. van Wee and E.J.E. Molin (2010), 'Lock-in and its influence on the project performance of large-scale transportation infrastructure projects: investigating the way in which lock-in can emerge and affect cost overruns', *Environment and Planning B*, **37**(5), 792–807.

Dantata, N.A., A. Touran and D.C. Schneck (2006), *Trends in U.S. Rail Transit Project Cost Overrun*, Washington, DC: Transportation Research Board 2006 Annual Meeting CD-ROM.

David, P. (1985), 'Clio and the economics of QWERTY', *American Economic Review*, **75**(2), 332–7.

Ellis, R., J.H. Pyeon, Z. Herbsman, E. Minchin and K. Molenaer (2007), *Evaluation of Alternative Contracting Techniques on FDOT Construction Projects*, Tallahassee: Florida Department of Transportation.

Flyvbjerg, B. (2007), 'Policy and planning for large-infrastructure projects: problems, causes, cures', *Environment and Planning B: Planning and Design*, **34**(4), 578–97.

Flyvbjerg, B. (2008), 'Public planning of mega-projects: overestimation of demand and underestimation of costs', in H. Priemus, B. Flyvbjerg and B. van Wee (eds), *Decision-making on Mega-projects. Cost–Benefit Analysis, Planning and Innovation*, Cheltenham, UK and Northampton, MA, USA: Edward Elgar, pp. 120–44.

Flyvbjerg, B. and COWI (2004), *Procedures for Dealing with Optimism Bias*, Transport Planning: Guidance Document, London: UK Department for Transport.

Flyvbjerg, B., N. Bruzelius and W. Rothengatter (2003a), *Megaprojects and Risk: An Anatomy of Ambition*, Cambridge, UK: Cambridge University Press.

Flyvbjerg, B., M.K.S. Holm and S.L. Buhl (2002), 'Underestimating cost in public works, error or lie?', *Journal of the American Planning Association*, **68**(3), 279–95.

Flyvbjerg, B., M.K. Holm and S.L. Buhl (2003b), 'How common and how large are cost overruns in transport infrastructure projects?', *Transport Reviews*, **23**(1), 71–88.

Flyvbjerg, B., M.K.S. Holm and S.L. Buhl (2004), 'What causes cost overrun in transport infrastructure projects?', *Transport Reviews*, **24**(1), 3–18.

Flyvbjerg, B., M.K.S. Holm and S.L. Buhl (2005), 'How (In)accurate are demand forecasts in public works projects? The case of transportation', *Journal of the American Planning Association*, **71**(2), 131–46.

Fouracre, P.R., R.J. Allport and J.M. Thomson (1990), 'The performance and impact of rail mass transit in developing countries', TRRL Research Report No. 278, Crowthorne, UK: Transport and Road Research Laboratory.

Garett, M. and M. Wachs (1996), *Transportation Planning on Trial: The Clean Air Act and Travel Forecasting*, Thousand Oaks, CA: Sage.

Gilovich, T., D. Griffin and D. Kahneman (eds) (2002), *Heuristics and Biases: The Psychology of Intuitive Judgment*, Cambridge, UK: Cambridge University Press.

Kahneman, D. (1994), 'New challenges to the rationality assumption', *Journal of Institutional and Theoretical Economics*, **150**(1), 18–36.

Kahneman, D. and D. Lovallo (1993), 'Timid choices and bold forecasts: a cognitive perspective on risk taking', *Management Science*, **39**(1), 17–31.
Kahneman, D. and A. Tversky (1979), 'Prospect theory: an analysis of decisions under risk', *Econometrica*, **47**(2), 313–27.
Leavitt, D., S. Ennis and P. McGovern (1993), 'The cost escalation of rail projects: using previous experience to re-evaluate the CalSpeed estimates', Working Paper No. 567, Berkeley, CA: Institute of Urban and Regional Development, University of California.
Lee, J.K. (2008), 'Cost overrun and cause in Korean social overhead capital projects: roads, rails, airports, and ports', *Journal of Urban Planning and Development*, **134**(2), 59–62.
Lovallo, D. and D. Kahneman (2003), 'Delusions of success: how optimism undermines executives' decisions', *Harvard Business Review*, **81**, 56–63.
Mackie, P. and J. Preston (1998), 'Twenty-one sources of error and bias in transport project appraisal', *Transport Policy*, **5**(1), 1–7.
Mahoney, J. (2000), 'Path dependency in historical sociology', *Theory and Society*, **29**(4), 507–48.
McElhinney, D. (2005), 'Concept of entrapment and decision-making', *Management Decision*, **43**(2), 189–202.
Merewitz, L. (1973), *How Do Urban Rapid Transit Projects Compare in Cost Estimating Experience?*, Berkeley, CA: Institute of Urban and Regional Development, University of California.
Ministerie van Verkeer en Waterstaat (1996–2007), *Voortgangsrapporten 1–22, Betuweroute* [*Progress Reports 1–22, Betuwe Rail Line*], The Hague: Ministerie van Verkeer en Waterstaat (in Dutch).
Morris, S. (1990), 'Cost and time overruns in public sector projects', *Economic and Political Weekly*, **15**(47), 154–68.
Morris, P.W.G. and G.H. Hough (1987), *The Anatomy of Major Projects: A Study of the Reality of Project Management*, New York: John Wiley.
National Audit Office, Department of Transport (1992), *Contracting for Roads*, London: National Audit Office.
Nee, V. and Y. Cao (1999), 'Path dependent societal transformation: stratification in hybrid mixed economies', *Theory and Society*, **28**(6), 799–834.
Nijkamp, P. and B. Ubbels (1999), 'How reliable are estimates of infrastructure costs? A comparative analysis', *International Journal of Transport Economics*, **26**(1), 23–53.
North, D.C. (1990), *Institutions, Institutional Change and Economic Performance*, Cambridge, UK: Cambridge University Press.
Odeck, J. (2004), 'Cost overruns in road construction – what are their sizes and determinants?', *Transport Policy*, **11**(1), 43–53.
Pickrell, D.H. (1990), *Urban Rail Transit Projects: Forecasts Versus Actual Ridership and Cost*, Washington, DC: US Department of Transportation.
Pickrell, D.H. (1992), 'A desire named streetcar: fantasy and fact in rail transit planning', *Journal of the American Planning Association*, **58**(2), 158–76.
Pierson, P. (2000a), 'Increasing returns, path dependence, and the study of politics', *American Political Science Review*, **94**(2), 251–68.
Pierson, P. (2000b), 'Not just what, but when: timing and sequence in political processes', *Studies in American Political Development*, **14**(1), 72–92.
Pierson, P. (2001), *The New Politics of the Welfare State*, Oxford: Oxford University Press.
Priemus, H. (2007), 'Development and design of large infrastructure projects: disregarded alternatives and issues of spatial planning', *Environment and Planning B: Planning and Design*, **34**(4), 626–44.
Riksrevisionsverket (Auditor General of Sweden) (1994), *Infrastrukurinvestingar: En Kostnadsjamorelse Mellan Poan of Utyfall i 15 Storre Prosjekt InnomVagverket of Banverket* [*Infrastructure investments: a comparison of costs of plan and actual outcome in 15 large projects within Vägverket and Banverket*], Stockholm: Auditor General of Sweden [in Swedish].
Roscam Abbing, M.R., A.A.J. Pols and M. Bierman (1999), *Hoe Spoort Het Water?*

Ontspoorde Besluitvorming Betuwelijn: een Analyse van Genegeerde Alternatieven [*How Does Watertransport Rail: Derailed Decision-making of the Betuwelijn: An Analysis of Ignored Alternatives*], Delft: Technische Universiteit Delft (in Dutch).

Staw, B.M. (1981), 'The escalation of commitment to a course of action', *Academy of Management Review*, **6**(4), 577–87.

Teisman, G. (1995), *Complexe Besluitvorming, een Pluricentrisch Perspectief op Besluitvorming over Ruimtelijke Investeringen* [*Complex Decision Making, a Pluricentric Perspective on the Decision Making on Spatial Investments*], The Hague: VUGA (in Dutch).

Tijdelijke Commissie Infrastructuurprojectenb (TCI) (2004), *Onderzoek naar Infrastructuurprojecten. Reconstructie Betuweroute, de Besluitvorming uitvergroot* [*Study into Infrastructure Projects. Reconstruction of the Betuweroute Decision-making Enlarged*], TK 2004–2005, 29 283, No. 7, Tijdelijke Commissie Infrastructuurprojecten, Tweede Kamer der Staten-Generaal, The Hague: Sdu Uitgevers (in Dutch).

Vrijkotte, J.G.M., L.J.P. van Doornen and E.J.C. de Geus (2004), 'Overcommitment to work is associated with changes in cardiac sympathetic regulation', *Psychosomatic Medicine*, **66**(5), 656–63.

Wachs, M. (1989), 'When planners lie with numbers', *Journal of the American Planning Association*, **55**(4), 476–79.

Wachs, M. (1990), 'Ethics and advocacy in forecasting for public policy', *Business and Professional Ethics Journal*, **9**(1–2), 141–57.

Walby, S. (2003), 'Complexity theory, globalisation and diversity', Conference of the British Sociological Association, University of New York, accessed 23 June 2013 at http://www.lancs.ac.uk/fass/sociology/research/publications/papers/walby-complexity globalisationdiversity.pdf.

Walmsley, D.A. and M.W. Pickett (1992), 'The cost and patronage of rapid transit systems compared with forecasts', Research Report No. 352, Crowthorne, UK: Transport Research Laboratory.

Whyte, G. (1986), 'Escalating commitment to a course of action: a reinterpretation', *Academy of Management Review*, **11**(2), 311–21.

Wilson, R.M.S. and A. Zhang (1997), 'Entrapment and escalating commitment in investment decision making: a review', *British Accounting Review*, **29**(3), 277–305.

Woerdman, E. (2004), *Politiek en politicologie* [*Politics and Political Science*], Groningen: Wolters-Noordhoff (in Dutch).

World Bank (1994), *World Development Report 1994: Infrastructure for Development*, Oxford: Oxford University Press.

16. Ethics and the ex ante evaluation of mega-projects[1]

Bert van Wee

16.1 INTRODUCTION

Policy-making in general, and also therefore transport policy-making, implies making choices. For infrastructure-related policies examples are budget allocations for infrastructure in general, and choosing between alternatives for a new road or railway line. Because of all the choices to be made, there is a huge need for ex ante evaluation of the choice options. An important question therefore is: how can potential options for future transport projects and policies be evaluated? In many countries nowadays (social) cost–benefit analysis (CBA) is a very popular ex ante evaluation method (Bristow and Nellthorp, 2000; Hayashi and Morisugi, 2000; Grant-Muller et al., 2001). A CBA is basically an overview of all the pros (benefits) and cons (costs) of a project or policy option. These costs and benefits are quantified as far as possible and expressed in monetary terms. Costs and benefits that occur in different years are discounted and presented as so-called net present values. Final results are often presented in summarizing indicators, such as the difference between costs and benefits, the return on investment and the cost–benefit ratio. See Chapter 12 for more information on CBAs for mega-projects. Research into the use of ex ante evaluation frameworks shows that CBA is used at least in some stage of the evaluation (Odgaard et al., 2005; Thomopoulos et al., 2009; Chapter 13 in this book).

Despite its popularity, CBA has often been criticized for several reasons (see, for example, Sagoff, 1988; Grant-Muller et al., 2001; Gardiner, 2006; Thomopoulos et al., 2009), most of them related to the utilitarian perspective and related ethical considerations. This chapter aims to discuss the ethically relevant criticism of CBA. It is mainly based on literature in the area of ethics, but also on literature from disciplines such as economics and geography (van Wee, 2011). Because of the focus of this book the chapter mainly discusses criticism relevant to transport mega-projects. The criticism is not unique to CBAs of mega-projects, but is also applicable to CBAs for other transport infrastructure projects, for policy options like road pricing, and in some cases also to CBAs in areas other than transport. At certain points in this chapter I explicitly emphasize the importance of topics for mega-projects in particular. The topic of cost overruns, and the importance of strategic behaviour are topics that are particularly relevant for mega-projects – discussed in Chapter 15 of this handbook. For a literature review on this topic: see van Wee (2007).

Section 16.2 gives an overview of ethically relevant criticism on CBA. Section 16.3 discusses the question of whether a multi-criteria analysis (MCA) is an alternative for CBA. Section 16.4 focuses on the implications of the criticism of Section 16.2. Section 16.5 presents a checklist for including ethics in the ex ante evaluation of mega-projects. Section 16.6 discusses the question of how useful a CBA is for the ex ante evaluation of transport policy options.

16.2 OVERVIEW AND DISCUSSION OF CRITICISM

Utilitarianism is the most popular theory in a family of ethical theories called consequentialism. Utilitarianism is a theory within the wider family of consequentialism. Consequentialism 'is the view that normative properties depend only on consequences' (*Stanford Encyclopedia of Philosophy* – http://plato.stanford.edu/). Utilitarianism, or more specifically 'act consequentialism', 'is the claim that an act is morally right if, and only if, that act maximizes the good, that is if, and only if, the total amount of good for all, minus the total amount of bad for all, is greater than this net amount for any incompatible act available to the agent on that occasion' (*Stanford Encyclopedia of Philosophy*). Utilitarianism provides an ethical foundation for CBA: a CBA compares policy options from the perspective of utility (mainly based on the willingness to pay of consumers). Utilitarianism is an extremely powerful ethical view, particularly when one is concerned with issues of public policy, because it makes ethical questions a matter of a straightforward calculation (Hausman and McPherson, 2006). Nevertheless, several challenges can be made to utilitarianism. This chapter discusses the following points of criticism:

1. Utilitarianism could be useful for some evaluative purposes, but not for all. In other words, the area of application is limited.
2. The selection of indicator to be maximized is not without dispute. It could be welfare, but other alternatives exist.
3. Distribution effects are ignored.
4. Some effects are difficult to monetize.
5. There is more than utilitarianism. Other – in some cases, competitive – theories exist.

6. There is more to be evaluated than welfare. Other values may also be relevant.
7. Not only humans matter.
8. Poor people count less than rich people.
9. Choices of people are not always based on reason.
10. CBA evaluates changes in welfare and ignores absolute levels.
11. Not only the outcomes of choice options matter, but also the process of selecting/defining/designing options.

These points of criticism are discussed below.

1 The limited area of application

Utilitarianism might be a useful theory for evaluating some choice options, but not all. For example, for a question such as how to think about euthanasia, slavery or abortion, utilitarianism is probably not the most helpful theory – in the area of applied ethics philosophers generally use other theories to discuss such topics. In the case of the ex ante evaluation of transport mega-projects it is questionable whether such moral dimensions should be put into the equation. If the ex ante evaluation considers the choice options for major road or rail extensions the criticism is of limited relevance, although if it is proposed that mega-projects are to reduce social exclusion it might become relevant. Mega-projects are often politically legitimated because they integrate weak regions into the wider economy, the TransEuropean Networks being an example. One can also think of the building of new roads or rail projects to decrease levels of social exclusion in remote areas. A major problem with social exclusion is that the willingness to pay (WTP) of some groups of citizens is very low, for example children in remote areas going to school or very low-income people who simply cannot afford to own (and use) a car. If policy-makers want to introduce social exclusion-related policies to encourage such people to participate more in society, utilitarianism might be cumbersome.

Another category of ex ante evaluations for which utilitarianism can be problematic is if budget allocations play a major role, as a result of which quite 'incomparable' allocations of a Ministry of Transport have to be compared. One can think of the competition between budgets for mega-projects such as high speed rail extensions and local or regional projects that aim to improve accessibility at that level, partly motivated by social inclusion motives. Though such infrastructure projects may implicitly compete because Ministries of Transport generally have more or less fixed budgets, ex ante evaluations that compare mega-projects and local or regional projects are very scarce, to the best of my knowledge. In practice

CBA is not or hardly used for such comparisons. So the limitations of CBA for such ex ante evaluations are probably more interesting in theory than in practice, even though the choice of budget allocations is highly relevant from an ethical point of view.

2 The indicator to be maximized

CBA assumes what welfare should be maximized (or optimized in one way or another, e.g., by maximizing benefits minus costs, or optimizing the cost–benefit ratio). Several authors have stated that it is questionable whether all ex ante evaluations should focus on maximizing an indicator, and if that is the case, which indicator. Influential philosophers like Rawls and Sen have proposed alternatives, such as 'primary social goods', capabilities, or the welfare or well-being of the least advantaged. See, for example, Rawls (1971) and Sen (2009). According to Rawls (1971, 1982), primary social goods include:

- basic liberties, including freedom of association, liberty, and so on;
- freedom of movement and choice of occupation;
- powers and prerogatives of offices and positions of responsibility;
- income and wealth;
- the social basis of self-respect.

Rawls discussed the use of the optimization of primary social goods as an alternative for optimizing welfare.

Sen (2009) disagrees with Rawls. He argues that it is not the provision of certain kinds of 'primary social goods' that should be equalized (not welfare), but what he calls 'capabilities', which lie between goods and welfare. Sen argues that the fit between a person's primary goods and the substantive freedoms that that person can in fact enjoy, can be very imperfect due to a person's actual capabilities. It is beyond the scope of this chapter to discuss indicators further – this is more a general discussion than that specifically related to transport (mega-projects). The main message is that there may be more than welfare to be optimized and evaluated.

In the field of transport it is important to decide which trips or activities will be considered as primary social goods. It is beyond the ambitions of this chapter to reach a 'final' proposal, but a certain level of access to schools, jobs, shops, family or friends, and health care facilities can be considered more likely to be included in a list of primary social goods than access to luxury holiday destinations or helicopter access to business parks for captains of industry. Of course, a huge element of subjectivity may arise, as does paternalism. I do not want to suggest that certain categories of activities and related access to them should not count, rather that the option exists to label some as primary social goods. I think doing so strongly relates to the concepts of access and accessibility, and exploring ways to include these concepts in ex ante evaluations of transport policy options could be of interest.

In the case of capabilities as proposed by Sen it also could be an option to include levels of accessibility in the evaluation because accessibility strongly relates to the capabilities of performing activities at certain locations. Major questions then become: whose accessibility? Who to compare? Again I do not aim to reach a 'final' proposal, but it is worth exploring the accessibility of groups like disabled persons (in several categories), low-income groups, or people who do not have a car at their disposal.

A third option could be to focus on the least advantaged. This could be done by evaluating their welfare in the traditional way as is done in CBA. Alternatives could relate to accessibility levels (and related indicators) of the least advantaged as described above, or to apply income-dependent weight factors for utility (see below).

A fourth option could be to focus on quality-of-life-related indicators, happiness often being used in research (e.g., Easterlin, 1973, 1974; Veenhoven, 1991), although not often in the area of transport (exceptions being Spinney et al., 2009; Bergstad et al., 2011; and Ettema et al., 2011).

Considering these options a general statement with respect to transport mega-projects can be made. Such projects are generally not proposed to improve accessibility to basic destinations ('basic social goods') or for the least advantaged, nor do they have major impacts on related indicators. Consequently it can be concluded that if policy choices were based on such indicators that a shift in decision-making would occur away from transport mega-projects.

3 Distribution effects and equity are ignored

CBA is often criticized for ignoring distribution effects and indeed, many applications of CBA are guilty of this (e.g., Rietveld et al., 2007; Thomopoulos et al., 2009). However, it is important to realize that CBA does not exclude reporting distribution effects, for example, over income classes or regions. So the criticism mainly relates to the use of CBA in practice.

From a utilitarian perspective the value of each benefit for each person counts equally. But for decision-making it may be important who benefits and to what extent, and who loses and to what extent. Based on a literature review Thomopoulos et al. (2009) give an overview of equity

Table 16.1 Equity types and principles found in literature

Equity Types	Features
Horizontal equity	Comparable individuals, groups or regions should be treated in a comparable way
Vertical equity	Disadvantaged individuals, groups or regions deserve protection. People should be burdened according to their ability to contribute, and this may lead to schemes where taxes may be progressive
Territorial equity	Results from the notion of individual equity when it is projected onto relatively homogeneous regions in need of similar funds for (public) transport
Territorial cohesion	Refers to balanced development of human activities across the EU
Level playing field	Transport sectors should be treated in similar ways according to taxation, payment for the use of infrastructure, etc.
Transport users should pay their way	This concept is usually interpreted in terms of average costs, implying that the collective of all transport users pays for the aggregate costs
Individuals negatively affected by policies need to be compensated	This principle has its starting point in the status quo situation and implies that winners have to compensate losers
Egalitarianism	All individuals are treated equally, making the same contribution, regardless of their financial (or other) ability
Spatial equity	Refers to the geographical location of an individual, group or region affected by a transport infrastructure project
Social equity	Refers to the impacts on personal, economic or social characteristics of an individual, group or region
Solidarity	It is anticipated that an increased focus on solidarity issues will be facilitated by setting the EU transport policy in the context of the wider EU cohesion policy

Source: Thomopoulos et al. (2009).

categories that could matter in ex ante evaluations of transport policies, projects and plans, as well as considerations from an equity point of view – see Table 16.1. Such considerations and the way to use them are political choices.

Probably the two most important distinctions that are made from a distribution or equity perspective are the distinctions between income classes and regions. This may be ethically and politically relevant, especially if low-income categories or poor regions 'lose' and high-income categories or regions 'win'. In the case of transport mega-projects regional differences between winners and losers can easily occur because impacts of such projects can differ between regions.

In addition there is a lot of debate in the literature on the ethics related to temporal distribution effects – this is the area of intergenerational justice (e.g., Tremmel, 2006; Gosseries and Meyer, 2009). Due to the practice of discounting (see above), the implications of mega-projects for the long-term future (over more than 30 years) have hardly any impact on the outcomes of a CBA. But is this fair to future generations? It is often expected that mega-projects will last for much longer, often more than a century. For further discussion of the relevance of the concept of intergenerational justice for transport see van Wee (2011).

4 Some effects are difficult to monetize

CBA aims to express all effects in monetary terms. However, some effects, such as construction costs, or travel time savings, are easier to express in monetary terms than others, such as nature, aesthetics, or social cohesion. Even if generally accepted methods exist to monetize effects, there is still a debate whether this is acceptable, an example being pricing human lives, or at least pricing changes in risks (leading to the indicator 'value of a statistical life' – VOSL).

5 Other theories

In addition to utilitarianism several other ethical theories can be used as a point of departure to evaluate (in our case) transport options. Below I discuss two dominant theories: deontology and rule based ethics.

Deontology – the concept of duties The concept of duties as proposed by deontologists could be relevant for the evaluation of potential transport policy options. For example, one could argue that society has the duty to provide a certain level of access to activity destinations to most – if not all – members of society. The consequence could be that ex ante evaluations should include at least some kind of evaluation of accessibility levels. The options as described above could be helpful. In addition, the government might have made promises in the past, for example to a specific region to build a railway line connecting the region to the national railway network. An example is the so-called Zuiderzee Line in the Netherlands. This possible new rail line connecting the weak economy of the north of the country to the strong economy of the western part of the country was promised to the north by politicians. The two CBAs showed that for all alternatives costs would greatly exceed benefits, and consequently the politicians decided not to build the line. The promise had been made, however, so the north was compensated financially. To put it more generally, if promises are at stake, an explicit evaluation of when the promises are kept could be included in an ex ante evaluation.

Deontology – rule-based ethics Rule-based ethics holds that the primary task of ethics is to provide the right rules of action. One of the oldest rule views is based on the Ten Commandments. The eighteenth-century philosopher Immanuel Kant developed the principle of the 'categorical imperative'. Several formulations of the categorical imperative exist. A relatively easy-to-understand formulation is: act in such a way that you always treat humanity, whether in your own person or in the person of any other, never simply as a means, but always at the same time as an end (Audi, 2007). This implies that we always treat persons not merely as a means, but also as ends in themselves. This applies to oneself as well as to others. Everyone matters and matters equally.

Here I limit the discussion to Kantianism. The idea that people should never be used as a means could be interpreted that it is immoral that people lose in order for others to win. This interpretation links Kantianism to the Pareto optimum, probably the most often cited optimum for welfare, which states that the optimum is reached when nobody can increase his or her welfare without someone else's welfare decreasing. However, a big problem occurs in many practices, including transport mega-projects: it is almost impossible to do anything in the transport system without having losers. Let us use the example of building a motorway to replace a regional road that crosses several towns in order to reduce noise and air pollution and to increase safety levels in those towns. However, it is highly likely that people living on the outskirts of the towns will face increased noise levels due to the motorway. Does a Pareto optimum then imply that the new motorway should not be built? This is questionable, because due to increased car ownership and car use levels, people living along the current regional road will be losers anyway. So, there are losers anyway. Or consider any policy that costs money: the tax payer is then always the loser. So I would argue, as have many others before me (e.g., Hausman and McPherson, 2006; Rietveld et al., 2007), that in real-world transport cases, the Pareto principle is of limited value, and that deontology is very difficult to apply. 'Solutions' to this problem include the use of the well-known Hicks-Kaldor (Hicks, 1939; Kaldor, 1939) principle This principle says that a project has net positive welfare effects if the benefits are such that the winners compensate the losers. This implies hypothetical compensation. In theory, such compensation would indeed make everybody better off, but implementation can easily lead to a wide range of problems involving high transaction costs and asymmetric information.

6 Values matter

A utilitarian approach may be too limited if specific values are also taken into account, freedom probably being one of the most important values. Hausman and McPherson (2006) reflect on the issue of freedom of choice. They argue that from a libertarian point of view not only the outcome matters, but also the process. In other words, 'one does not respect freedom by forcing people to do what they would have chosen to do, and one does not respect rights by forcing on people risks that they would voluntarily have chosen to impose upon themselves' (Hausman and McPherson, 2006, p. 267). To give an example: a woman could decide to accept a job an hour away from home. It could make a big difference whether she has voluntarily chosen this job, compared to a situation where this job is the only job available to her. In the latter case there is no freedom of choice. The same applies to many other choices for activities and related destinations. The concept of freedom in ex ante evaluations could be included by evaluating policy options via accessibility indicators (see Geurs and van Wee, 2004) such as the accessibility of activity destinations of several kinds of activities within certain time limits, or weighted by travel time or generalized transport costs for the trips to be made, or via person-based indicators. Another option is to use the output of discrete choice models, such as generalized costs functions or log-sum-based accessibility indicators (see for the log-sum-based approach, de Jong et al., 2007), or indicators derived from activity-based models (e.g., Shiftan, 2008).

In addition, more values exist. Audi (2007) presents what he calls 'basic values': these are, for example: hedonic values, moral values, intellectual values, aesthetic values, spiritual and religious values, social values, emotional values and athletic values. 'Basic' means that it cannot be reduced to any other value or to combinations of others, nor that its realization can be combined with that of others. If we took the values of Audi (2007) as a point of departure, an ex ante evaluation could explicitly check if other values are at stake. Social values are probably the most relevant for transport and are to some extent probably strongly related to accessibility. But social values can include more, such as forced relocation due to new transport infrastructure (mega-projects and other), cultural diversity and safety impacts. For an overview of social effects and the impact of transport, and the way they can be and are assessed in the UK and the Netherlands, I refer to Geurs et al. (2009).

7 Not only humans matter

CBA takes human beings as a point of departure. Impacts on other species and nature are included from a human perspective. For example, the willingness to pay for nature conservation can be and sometimes is included in CBAs. But one can debate whether this is all that matters. Several philosophers have argued that there is an ethical dimension that could be relevant, in addition to the human dimension – see, for example, Jamieson (2003). One could argue that even if human beings became extinct it matters whether the planet is in its current state compared to a state of great pollution, complete deforestation and huge levels of erosion.

8 Rich people versus poor people

This point is related to point 3 on distribution effects, but adds to that by discussing elements of weighting between categories of people. Taking changes in utility as the main indicator for evaluations CBA is an undemocratic evaluation method, in the sense that the principle of 'one man one vote' does not apply. Rich persons – ceteris paribus – have per person more influence on the outcomes of a CBA than poor people. For example, in the evaluation of transport mega-projects the 'value of time' (VOT) of higher-income groups is higher than the VOT of low-income groups. The use of different VOTs for different income categories is an ethically relevant issue (Grant-Muller et al., 2001). As a result, higher-income groups score generally better in a CBA, and certainly in the case of mega-projects (see below), than lower-income groups (e.g., Mackie et al., 2003). As a reaction the so-called 'equity value of time' was introduced in virtually all cost–benefit analyses used in the USA and abroad. The equity value of time is based on an average income level (Morisugi and Hayashi, 2000 cited in Martens, 2006). It is important to realize that mega-projects may be particularly attractive for business travellers and high-income groups travelling fast over larger distances. Another ethical problem with respect to WTP for travel time savings is that it implicitly holds that the life of a high-income person (with a high WTP for travel time savings) is worth more than the life of a low-income person. The same problem occurs with respect to the WTP for lower risks: high-income people then are worth more than low-income people.

In addition, another problem occurs with a straightforward summing up of WTP for individuals, which is that the marginal utility of one monetary unit decreases with wealth. In other words, for a person on a minimum wage, an increase of – for example – 100 euros per month adds more to this person's utility (and probably well-being) than for a person earning 1 million euros per year. Hausman and McPherson (2006) cite Bradford DeLong who explains that a policy of maximizing net benefits coincides with a utilitarian policy if and only if each individual's utility is weighted inversely proportionally to each individual's marginal utility of wealth.

9 Choices and reason

People not only base their choices and behaviour on reason, but also on passion and impulse. People may, for example, over-eat and over-drink. Sen (2009) refers to the 'weakness of will'. If this is the case, then it can be questionable whether behaviour is a useful expression of utility, welfare, or well-being. Sen argues that these departures from rational choice do not, in themselves, suggest that the idea of rationality should be modified. In addition, it is questionable whether this subject is relevant for the ex ante evaluation of mega-projects. Psychologists have argued that car use to some extent could be considered an addictive behaviour. The same could apply to travel behaviour in general. But to the best of my knowledge such ideas have not been widely discussed in the academic literature, so the scientific basis for this point of view probably is weak. Choices and reason are therefore at this time an interesting subject of academic research, but currently not a reason to criticize current CBA practice in the area of transportation.

10 Absolute levels are ignored

It is important to realize that a CBA evaluates the changes due to policy options, not the absolute levels that result from policy options. This contradicts the use of welfare indicators that need absolute levels of indicators. For example, if one is interested in the number of people with an income below a certain level, or with access to opportunities below a certain level the changes do not matter. Of course it is possible to report the number of people below such levels, in addition to a CBA. Then the combination of a CBA and MCA might result.

11 The process matters

In line with the ideas of Sen (2009) my recommendation is not to substitute public deliberation for a CBA. A CBA is helpful, but also deliberation, or more generally, the process, matters because preferences can be influenced by arguments and deliberation. Deliberation, for example, can make people aware of the value of, for example, providing access to remote areas or specific groups of people, or to the effects on nature or the landscape, two effect categories that often apply to mega-projects. Second, people may value their role in decision-making, regardless of the outcomes. Therefore, Sen argues that not only the result of choice matters, but also the process of choice. Sen refers to what he calls social realizations. Social realizations are much more inclusive than the outcomes, and can include a broad view of the realizations, including the nature of the agencies involved, the processes used, and people's relationships (ibid.). In other words, people may value being involved in the process, regardless of the outcomes and this involvement may make the final decision more acceptable. Utilitarian ethics is in this sense restrictive.

16.3 MULTI-CRITERIA ANALYSIS (MCA) AS AN ALTERNATIVE, OR COMBINING CBA AND MCA

If transport policy options have important (ethically or non-ethically relevant) effects that are difficult to monetize (e.g., nature effects, aesthetics, specific social effects, distribution effects) need to be evaluated MCA may be an alternative. MCA addresses problems with variables that are difficult to value by making use of weights to solve the problem. An alternative could be a hybrid methodology combining CBA and MCA (e.g., Grant-Muller et al., 2001; Beuthe, 2002; Macharis et al., 2010). Monetary values could be used for some (quantitative) variables that are relatively easy to monetize in a generally accepted way. For other variables weighting is needed according to MCA practice, and it may be even needed in order to combine both categories of variables (see, for an example, Shiftan et al., 2002). Not surprisingly, MCA has been particularly used to assess project impacts if environmental or social effects are important (Lahdelma et al., 2000), or if explicit attention needs to be paid to the perspectives of distinguished stakeholders (Thomopoulos et al., 2009; Macharis et al., 2010). MCA is often criticized as well, mainly because of the subjectivity of the weights to be used, possibilities for manipulation and lack of robustness (e.g., Eijgenraam et al., 2000; Thomopoulos et al., 2009). Although manipulations in MCA might occur more easily than in CBA it is also possible in CBA, for example, by prescribing or selecting unit values (such as for the value of time or the VOSL), by providing manipulated cost estimates (e.g., Flyvbjerg et al., 2003), or by strategically selecting scenario assumptions or models. It is beyond the scope of this chapter to further discuss the pros and cons of MCA.

16.4 IMPLICATIONS OF ETHICALLY BASED CRITICISM OF CBA

What are the possible implications of ethically relevant criticism of CBA? First of all it is important to discuss whether, for a particular context, a

CBA is useful at all. I agree with Hausman and McPherson (2006) who conclude that a CBA might provide a reasonable basis for decision-making in cases where the winners and losers are more or less equal in their ability to pay (or at least when it is clear who the winners and losers are, and to what extent they win and lose), where uncertainty about dominant consequences is limited, and where the kinds of reasons recommending different policies are widely understood. This implies that the usefulness of CBA is greater if the alternatives to be evaluated are more or less comparable. This will often be the case when more or less comparable options for mega-projects are to be compared, such as different alternatives for high-speed rail, or major road extensions. Applying CBA for comparisons of, for example, investments in road versus on-demand bus or taxi transport for isolated regions can be more risky, and requires at least a check on ethical dimensions.

A second conclusion is that proponents of CBA do not claim that the outcomes of a CBA should be the only basis for decision-making and thus that the 'best' option should be chosen. This is because political preferences may occur, as a result of which some may value certain outcomes higher than would be assumed by the price tags. For example, a green party may value changes in CO_2 emissions higher than assumed in the CBA. In addition, politicians may include in their decision many other aspects – see Section 16.2– such as some form of equity or distribution effects (e.g., by region), or inequality of income, or absolute levels of accessibility. Third, specific groups in society could be linked to political parties, and winners and losers might be unequally distributed amongst those groups. As a result, democratic decision-making does not have to lead to choosing the 'best' option according to the outcomes of a CBA.

Third, and this is more a methodological issue: CBA can generate more than one outcome. Suppose there are two choice options for a new motorway, A and B. A is more expensive and has more benefits than B. A has a bigger absolute difference in benefits minus costs, whereas B has a higher return on investment or benefits-to-cost ratio. Which option should be chosen? Choices like these are also influenced by general concerns about government budgets and deficits, or the opportunity costs of other policies (projects and others) that could have been financed by the money that is not spent if B is chosen instead of A. To support such choices techniques exist for comparing projects on the basis of an optimization of the use of a given budget (see, for instance, Pearce and Nash, 1981).

Fourth, a very fundamental conclusion is that it is not only the outcome of the CBA that matters, but also many process-related issues. Process matters in itself, regardless of its impact on the outcomes. In addition, the process could have an impact on the outcomes, for example because of the selection of policy options, or their specifications.

If a CBA is to be used at all for an ex ante evaluation of transport mega-projects, this chapter has shown that several challenges exist for improvements from an ethical perspective. The most important ones, especially for mega-projects, I think, come next.

First, the recommendation is to consider reporting distributive effects. Who are the winners and – probably more important – the losers? As explained above, regional distribution effects can easily occur in mega-projects. Reporting this is relevant in itself and if issues concerning distribution are raised, distributive weights can be applied, either based on income-dependent decreased marginal utility, or on political preferences. The researcher can vary quantitative weights and check the impact on the outcomes of the CBA.

Second, several of the insights of ethical theories can be interpreted as a plea for the inclusion of specific accessibility indicators, for example, for specific groups of population or regions. Mega-projects can create important changes in accessibility. An important question then becomes: how can the scores for such criteria be evaluated? Should an evaluation be expressed in monetary terms and included in a CBA? At least two answers can be given. One is that accessibility can be expressed elegantly in monetary terms using the so-called log-sum of utility-based discrete choice transport models – see, for example, de Jong et al. (2007). But this ignores several points of criticism underlying the plea for the inclusion of these indicators – see above. Another answer could be that the scores on the accessibility indicators are presented separately. I think the latter option is the best one. This is not a plea against the utility-based accessibility indicators. These indicators are a very elegant way of expressing accessibility in monetary terms, in a way consistent with the valuation of other indicators generally included in a CBA framework. I would argue that these indicators are of great use as far as the valuation of accessibility from a utilitarian perspective is needed. However, for specific evaluations based on the ethical theories described above, including the evaluation of social exclusion policy options, their value – if they have any value – is much less.

Third, an explicit check on the values and duties that are at stake for a specific ex ante evaluation of transport policy options is recommended, promises for mega-projects made to regions being an example. In addition to these challenges that are particularly important for mega-projects, more challenges exist that have a more general nature.

Fourth, it is recommended that the addition of indicators for evaluation related to the utility, welfare or well-being of the least advantaged, or other specific groups is at least considered. Fifth, a check on insights from theories other than utilitarianism could be made, as explained above. Sixth, related to the lack of democratic equality of a CBA, one could check what the outcomes of the evaluation of policy options would be for a democracy, according to the 'one man one vote' principle. This seems straightforward but is not, as, for example, data on individual persons (how many, would they win or lose?) are often not available. In addition, it is overly simplistic to assume that people would only vote based on their own direct interests. For example, a person who does not benefit from the policies him- or herself – say, a bus service – might value living in a society that provides that option for others. Also, there is the problem of who to include. Take, for example, a mega-project of regional importance. A democratic evaluation including all inhabitants of the country would almost certainly lead to a negative decision, because many tax payers would lose a small amount of money, whereas only a small minority, that is, the people who live in the region under consideration, or regular visitors, would benefit. It may be better to include the general preference for regional projects: all regions would benefit from a certain amount of money spent on regional projects. But this is too general to be of use for specific projects. The conclusion is that some checks on the level of democracy may be of interest, but could be difficult to make.

16.5 CHECKLIST TO INCLUDE ETHICS IN THE EX ANTE EVALUATION OF MEGA-PROJECTS

If a CBA is to be used at all, this chapter has shown that several challenges exist in order to better include ethics in the ex ante evaluations of mega-projects (and other candidate transport policy options). Based on these challenges, van Wee (2011) derived a checklist that could be used to link the ideas of this chapter to ex ante evaluations in the transport sector. The checklist can be applied where a CBA provides the evaluation framework, but also in the case of another evaluation method (such as MCA), as well as for at least some of the ex ante evaluation of the individual effects that are included in such an evaluation method. Below is a summary of the checklist. The first three questions and question 6 are general, and are specifically related to the inclusion of ethics in ex ante evaluations.

Checklist to include ethics in ex ante evaluations of transport mega-projects and other candidate transport policy options:

1. What is the problem or the challenge?
2. What are the choice options?
3. What are all the important pros and cons of the choice options?

4. Who are the winners and losers?
5. Can losers be compensated, and will they be compensated?
6. Do particular trade-offs exist?
7. Do irreplaceable things exist or not?
8. Should outcomes be maximized or not?
9. Does closed partiality occur?
10. Are additional values affected, and if so: which, for whom, and in which way?
11. Do (additional) considerations with respect to equity, justice or equality exist?
12. Are commitments or duties at stake?
13. Is a choice needed?

Below I briefly discuss the items in the checklist. For additional information see van Wee (2011).

1 What is the problem or the challenge?

A first question to be answered is: what is the problem or challenge? In the case of transport mega-projects, problems or challenges often relate to accessibility (in its many forms – see Geurs and van Wee, 2004), reducing travel times, or to the reliability of travel times, to an increase of transport choice options, and to increased (regional) economic growth.

2 What are the choice options?

A second important question to be answered is: what are the choice options that could be made? A problem might occur if, in an early stage, the list of choice options is too limited, as a result of which potentially interesting options are excluded. This could easily happen with transport mega-projects, because the discussions often start with the proposal of one 'solution'. An example is the Dutch Betuweroute, a dedicated rail freight line connecting Rotterdam harbour to the hinterland (including the German Ruhrgebiet). No alternatives were included in the discussion, and the 'solution', the Betuweroute' was not the outcome of a problem analysis.

In an early stage, it might even be of value to include 'bad' options, if there are potential supporters of such an option, in order to make clear that it is a 'bad' option. In this early stage of decision-making, it is important to include potential actors that might have an opinion on what could be potentially interesting choice options, for at least three reasons. First, these actors may come with potentially interesting choice options. Second, it is not only the outcome that matters, but also the process (see above). From a broad democratic point of view (see above), public deliberation is important in itself. Third, not all policy decisions can be implemented in practice. Actors or institutions that are against a specific solution might follow legal procedures to avoid implementation. Involving important actors in the process might reduce future problems related to implementation. I assume decision-makers would like to reduce such problems.

3 What are all the important pros and cons of the choice options?

Third, I assume a decision-maker (as well as other actors involved) wants to know what the important pros and cons are of choice options. I assume they want insights into effects in real terms, as well as expressed in monetary terms, if (in their eyes) appropriate and generally acceptable methods exist to do so.

4 Who are the winners and losers?

Next, I assume the decision-maker wants to have insights into who are the winners and losers, and how much they win or lose (distribution effects). As explained above, mega-projects can change accessibility levels over regions, resulting in regions that win and others that lose. And high-income groups benefit relatively more from new motorways and (high-speed) inter-urban rail lines. This question aims to explicitly include equity and distribution effects. The question of who are the winners and losers is more often related to the specific roles or activities of people, than to the persons themselves. Take the example of a new major motorway that benefits car users at the cost of the people living close by. A person can both drive his or her car on that road, but also live close to the road and experience noise nuisance.

5 Can losers be compensated and will they be compensated?

The decision-makers might be interested in knowing if losers can, and will, be compensated. Furthermore, if they are compensated, do they feel compensated in a satisfactory way?

6 Are there particular trade-offs?

In the case of some choices, specific trade-offs might occur. For example, some choice options could have approximately equal outcomes of interest, except for a trade-off between travel time savings and expected accidents. If so, the decision-maker might be interested in the occurrence of these trade-offs, as well as in the specific details of them.

7 Irreplaceable things or not?

The decision-maker might be interested in knowing if there are any 'irreplaceable things' involved in the choice options, such as the areas of nature that would be affected. Because of their size mega-projects, such as new motorways and new inter-urban (high-speed) rail lines, can have irreversible effects on nature.

8 Maximization or not?

The next question to be answered concerns the matter of whether one wants to maximize any variable. Again, if yes, then what variable? See Section 16.2 for a discussion.

9 Does closed partiality occur?

To evaluate the ethical dimensions of a decision, it may be valuable to reflect on what an impartial person would think about decision options. In the case of closed impartiality, the procedure of making impartial judgements only invokes the members of a given society or nation. In the case of open impartiality, the procedure of making impartial assessments can (and in some cases, must) invoke judgements, among others, from outside the focal group, to avoid a parochial bias.

10 Are additional values affected and if so, which, for whom and in which way?

It is also necessary to consider possible insights into any values that might be relevant to the choice being made in addition to those evaluated by answering the questions above. See Section 16.2 for a discussion.

11 Do (additional) considerations with respect to equity, justice or equality exist?

One of the value categories is equity/justice. This category is strongly related to equality – see the egalitarian theories as discussed above. For this category of values, specific questions to be answered could be of value. A first question is whether one wants to equalize something at all (as assumed in egalitarian theories). If the answer is yes, the question is: which variable? Options again could be welfare, primary social goods, or capabilities.

12 Are commitment or duties at stake?

Commitment can imply choices to be made that one (a person, a government, an organization) would not have made without commitment. I assume that a decision-maker wants to know explicitly if any commitment or duties could play a role in the decision to be made. In the case of transport mega-projects, these can be political commitments, or duties such as promises to groups of people or regions. Commitments could also relate to the programme of the political party to which the decision-maker belongs, or the government coalition.

13 Is a choice needed?
Above, a distinction is made between voluntary and non-voluntary (forced) choices. This is especially significant if important values are negatively affected, for example, if there are people that 'lose' in an ethically speaking (for the decision-maker) unacceptable way, the desired option might be to reject the choice. Whether this is possible depends on knowing whether a choice needs to be made at all.

The 'Best' Policy

Now that we have discussed the checklist above, an important question of course is: what is the 'best' policy? It is important to recognize the three generally recognized criteria required to answer the question: effectiveness, efficiency and equity (e.g., Young and Tilley, 2006). Effectiveness relates to the question of whether the policy leads to an improvement. For example, if a policy aims to reduce road fatalities, the first criterion is to test whether the policy indeed leads to a reduction in fatalities. The second criterion, efficiency, relates to the question of what costs are incurred in order to make the improvement. For example, a particular road safety policy might result in a reduction in fatalities, but the price to be paid could be, for example, 40 million euros per reduced fatality, whereas another policy costing 400000 euros per reduced fatality had not been implemented. So, in terms of cost-effectiveness the policy is not efficient. The third criterion, equity, is related to the question of whether the policy is 'fair'. Maybe a cost-effective way to reduce road fatalities is to increase the age at which people can get a drivers' licence to 30 years old. But is this fair? The checklist above mainly relates to equity issues. This, of course, is not surprising, because ethics to a large extent deal with questions of equity and fairness.

16.6 DISCUSSION: HOW USEFUL IS CBA FOR THE EX ANTE EVALUATION OF TRANSPORT POLICY OPTIONS?[2]

Considering the above criticisms the major question is: how useful is CBA for the ex ante evaluation of transport policy projects and policies in general, and for transport mega-projects in particular? This chapter could easily give the impression that from an ethical perspective CBA is not considered to be of use for such purposes. However, we should be careful about being too negative. If one takes the perspective (as I do) that to ensure the quality of public decision-making it is important that decision-makers are well informed, the question becomes: which methodology for ex ante evaluations of transport projects and policies is 'best'? The choice between CBA and MCA should be based on the pros and cons of the options for a specific case. The main pro of an MCA is that it enables the actor preferences to be weighted, providing relevant outcomes of interest. This is also its main weakness: setting the weights is highly subjective, and therefore susceptible (at least, more so than for a CBA) to manipulation. The dominant pros and cons of CBA are opposite to those of an MCA: it gives less room for specific preferences, but because of its emphasis on (mainly) consumer preferences (expressed in monetary terms) is more neutral. When choice options are more or less comparable, the balance of pros and cons of MCA versus CBA supports the use of CBA. But even then I recommend an explicit check on ethical aspects, as explained above. If the choice options are less comparable, or if important ethical aspects are at stake, a hybrid methodology of CBA and MCA might be preferred, or an MCA. Another general recommendation is that if ethical issues might be important for the ex ante evaluation of transport projects and policies, it is recommended that at least a sensitivity analysis is added to standard questions addressing CBA such as: how would policy options be evaluated using other (additional or alternative) assumptions on the indicator(s) to be considered other than utility? What impact would adding different assumptions have on valuing distribution effects? What if the value of CO_2 increased according to the discount rate? What if one used an equity-based value of time? What if the value of a statistical life was income independent?

Would it be an option to not try to evaluate ex ante the pros and cons of alternative choice options at all? I think the answer is 'no'. We need such an evaluation to ensure the quality of decision-making. Not having a systematic assessment of the dominant pros and cons of a project has – at least in the Netherlands – led to decision-making that caused a lot of frustration among politicians, partly because of major inconsistencies in partial evaluations and highly debatable assumptions made in the related research (see Annema et al., 2007; de Jong and van Wee, 2007).

16.7 CONCLUSION

The main conclusion from this chapter is that the methodology of CBA for transport mega-projects has several limitations if the ethical implications of candidate policy options for these mega-projects are at stake. Some of the ethical implications, but not all, relate to the utilitarian perspective of CBA. The limitations are not exclusively related to mega-projects, but also apply to other transport infrastructure projects. Nevertheless, some limitations are more relevant for mega-projects than for other transport infrastructure projects. These limitations occur, for example, in the areas of regional distribution effects, income-related distribution effects, promises made to specific regions and the impacts of mega-projects on nature and landscape.

To check whether ethical implications are at stake a checklist is provided in Section 16.5. The checklist is not only limited to ethical implications, but also to more general considerations if candidate policy options are to be selected to reduce a problem or face a challenge.

Despite the criticism for CBA from an ethical perspective I do not reject CBA – in many cases it is still the preferred methodology if candidate options for transport mega-projects are to be evaluated ex ante. In some other cases the combination of CBA and MCA does the job.

NOTES

1. This chapter is based on van Wee (2011, 2012).
2. This section is a summary of a similar discussion in Chapter 12, now focused on criticism from the perspective of ethics. For further discussion on the usefulness of CBA I refer to Chapter 12.

LITERATURE

Annema, J.A., C. Koopmans and B. van Wee (2007), 'Evaluating transport infrastructure investments: the Dutch experience with a standardized approach', *Transport Reviews*, **27**(2), 25–150.

Audi, R. (2007), *Moral Value and Human Diversity*, Oxford and New York: Oxford University Press.

Bergstad, C.J., A. Gamble, T. Gärling, O. Hagman, M. Polk, D. Ettema, M. Friman and L.E. Olsson (2011), 'Subjective well-being related to satisfaction with daily travel', *Transportation*, **38**(1), 1–15.

Beuthe, M. (2002), 'Transport evaluation methods: from cost–benefit analysis to multicriteria analysis and the decision framework', in L. Giorgi and A. Pearman (eds), *Project and Policy Evaluation in Transport*, Aldershot, UK and Burlington, VT, USA: Ashgate Publishing Ltd, pp. 209–41.

Bristow, A. and J. Nellthorp (2000), 'Transport project appraisal in the European Union', *Transport Policy*, **7**(1), 51–60.

de Jong, W.M. and G.P. van Wee (2007), 'A new guideline for "ex ante" evaluation of large infrastructure projects in the Netherlands', in E. Haezendonck (ed.), *Transport Project Evaluation*, Cheltenham, UK and Northampton, MA, USA: Edward Elgar.

De Jong, G., A. Daly, M. Pieters and T. van der Hoorn (2007), 'The logsum as an evaluation measure: Review of the literature and new results', *Transportation Research Part A*, **41**(9), 874–89.

Easterlin, R.A. (1973), 'Does money buy happiness?', *Public Interest*, **30**(30), 3–10.

Easterlin, R.A. (1974), 'Does economic growth improve the human lot?' in P.A. David and

W.E. Melvin (eds), *Nations and Households in Economic Growth*, Palo Alto, CA: Stanford University Press, pp. 98–125.
Eijgenraam, C.J.J., C.C. Koopmans, P.J.G. Tang and A.C.P. Verster (2000), *Evaluation of Infrastructural Projects: Guide for Cost–Benefit Analysis, Sections I and II*, The Hague: CPB/Rotterdam: NEI (now ECORYS).
Ettema, D., T. Gärling, L. Eriksson, M. Friman, L.E. Olsson and S. Fujii (2011), 'Satisfaction with travel and subjective well-being: development and test of a measurement tool', *Transportation Research Part F: Traffic Psychology and Behaviour*, **14**(3), 167–75.
Flyvbjerg, B., N. Bruzelius and W. Rothengatter (2003), *Mega-projects and Risk: An Anatomy of Ambition*, Cambridge, UK: Cambridge University Press.
Gardiner, S.M. (2006), 'Protecting future generations: intergenerational buck-passing, theoretical aptitude and a brief for a global core precautionary principle', in J.C. Tremmel (ed.), *Handbook of Intergenerational Justice*, Cheltenham, UK and Northampton, MA, USA: Edward Elgar.
Geurs, K.T., W. Boon and B. van Wee (2009), 'Social impacts of transport: literature review and the state of the practice of transport appraisal in the Netherlands and the United Kingdom', *Transport Reviews*, **29**(1), 69–90.
Geurs, K.T. and B. van Wee (2004), 'Accessibility evaluation of land-use and transport strategies: review and research directions', *Transport Geography*, **12**, 127–40.
Gosseries, A. and L.H. Meyer (eds) (2009), *Intergenerational Justice*, Oxford: Oxford University Press.
Grant-Muller, S.M., P. MacKie, J. Nellthorp and A. Pearman (2001), 'Economic appraisal of European transport projects: the state-of-the-art revisited', *Transport Reviews*, **21**(2), 237–61.
Hausman, D.M. and M.S. McPherson (2006), *Economic Analysis, Moral Philosophy, and Public Policy*, 2nd edition, Cambridge, UK: Cambridge University Press.
Hayashi, Y. and H. Morisugi (2000), 'International comparison of background concept and methodology of transportation project appraisal', *Transport Policy*, **7**(1), 73–88.
Hicks, J. (1939), 'The foundations of welfare economics', *Economic Journal*, **49**(196), 696–712.
Jamieson, D. (2003), 'Values in nature', in R.G. Frey and G. Heath Wellman (eds), *A Companion to Applied Ethics*, Malden, MA and Oxford: Blackwell Publishing Ltd.
Kaldor, N. (1939), 'Welfare propositions in economics and interpersonal comparisons of utility', *Economic Journal*, **49**(195), 549–52.
Lahdelma, R., P. Salkminen and J. Hokkanen (2000), 'Using multicriteria methods in environmental planning and management', *Environmental Management*, **26**(6), 595–605.
Macharis, C., E. van Hoeck, E. Perkin and T. van Lier (2010), 'A decision analysis framework for intermodal transport: comparing fuel price increases and the internalisation of external costs', *Transportation Research Part A*, **44**(7), 550–61.
Mackie, P.J., M. Wardman, A.S. Fowkes, G.A. Whelan, J. Nellthorp and J.J. Bates (2003), 'Values of travel time savings in the UK', Working Paper prepared for the Department for Transport, Leeds: University of Leeds/John Bastes Services, Institute for Transport Studies.
Martens, K. (2006), 'Basing transport planning on principles of social justice', *Berkeley Planning Journal*, **19**(1), 1–17.
Morisugi, H. and Y. Hayashi (2000), 'Editorial', *Transport Policy*, **7**(1), 1–2.
Odgaard, T., C. Kelly and J. Laird (2005), *Current Practice in Project Appraisal in Europe, HEATCO Research Project* (Harmonised European Approaches for Transport Costing and Project Assessment), Leeds: University of Leeds, Institute of Transport Studies.
Pearce, D.W. and C.A. Nash (1981), *The Social Appraisal of Projects – A Text in Cost Benefit Analysis*, London: Macmillan.
Rawls, J. (1971), *A Theory of Justice*, Boston, MA: Harvard University Press.
Rawls, H. (1982), 'Social unity and primary goods', in A. Sen and B. Williams (eds), *Utilitarianism and Beyond*, Cambridge, UK: Cambridge University Press.
Rietveld, P., J. Rouwendal and A.J. van der Vlist (2007), 'Equity issues in the evaluation

of transport policies and transport infrastructure projects', in M. van Geenhuizen, A. Reggiani and P. Rietveld (eds), *Policy Analysis of Transport Networks*, Aldershot: Ashgate, pp. 19–36.
Sagoff, M. (1988), *The Economy of the Earth*, New York: Cambridge University Press.
Sen, A. (2009), *The Idea of Justice*, London: Allen Lane.
Shiftan, Y. (2008), 'The use of activity-based modeling to analyze the effect of land-use policies on travel behavior', *Annals of the Regional Science*, **42**(1), 79–97.
Shiftan, Y., M. Ben-Akiva, G. de Jong, S. Hakkert and D. Simmonds (2002), 'Evaluation of externalities in transport projects', *EJTIR*, **2**(3–4), 285–304.
Spinney, J.E.L., D.M. Scott and K.B. Newbold (2009), 'Transport mobility benefits and quality of life: a time-use perspective of elderly Canadians', *Transport Policy*, **16**(1), 1–11.
Thomopoulos, N., S. Grant-Muller and M.R. Tight (2009), 'Incorporating equity considerations in transport infrastructure evaluation: current practice and a proposed methodology', *Evaluation and Program Planning*, **32**(4), 351–9.
Tremmel, J.C. (ed.) (2006), *Handbook of Intergenerational Justice*, Cheltenham, UK and Northampton MA, USA: Edward Elgar.
van Wee, B. (2007), 'Large infrastructure projects: a review of the quality of demand forecasts and cost estimations', *Environment and Planning B*, **34**(4), 611–25.
van Wee, B. (2011), *Transport and Ethics. Ethics and the Evaluation of Transport Policies and Projects*, Cheltenham, UK and Northampton, MA, USA: Edward Elgar.
van Wee, B. (2012), 'How suitable is CBA for the ex ante evaluation of transport projects and policies? A discussion from the perspective of ethics', *Transport Policy*, **19**(1), 1–7.
Veenhoven, R. (1991), 'Is happiness relative?', *Social Indicators Research*, **24**(1), 1–34.
Young, W. and F. Tilley (2006), 'Can businesses move beyond efficiency? The shift toward effectiveness and equity in the corporate sustainability debate', *Business Strategy and the Environment*, **15**(6), 402–15.

PART IV

WIDER IMPACTS: REGIONAL GROWTH AND SUSTAINABILITY

17. The wider economic impacts of mega-projects in transport

Roger Vickerman

17.1 INTRODUCTION

Mega-projects in transport are frequently justified on the basis of the wider impacts they will have on the economy. Often these wider impacts are specified rather vaguely in terms of being essential for the competitiveness of the city or country in question. This argument has been used in the context of the expansion of hub airports (Frontier Economics, 2011), the development of high-speed rail networks (Department for Transport, 2012), major metropolitan rail network developments (Crossrail, 2005) or road developments such as Boston's 'Big Dig' (Altshuler and Luberoff, 2003). Although the argument has been growing in importance as a justification for these projects, it is not a new one. The US Inter-State Highway Programme of the 1950s used an economic argument (Mohring and Harwitz, 1962) and this was reiterated in the development of the TransEuropean Transport Networks (TEN-T) in Europe (CEC, 2009).

The economic justification for these arguments is typically some combination of reduced transport costs and agglomeration effects beyond those conventionally captured in a traditional transport cost–benefit analysis (Gramlich, 1994). This has been bolstered by the insights of the New Economic Geography (NEG) approach (Fujita et al., 1999; Fujita and Thisse, 2002), which gives a more rigorous basis to the argument that these impacts can be self-sustaining and cumulative, although with the often ignored warning that the impacts could be negative as well as positive and that positive impacts in some areas could well have negative repercussions in others (SACTRA, 1999).

Whilst the theoretical case may be made for there being such impacts, albeit under specific conditions, providing empirical evidence to substantiate whether it applies in a particular case has proved to be difficult. Incorporating such impacts into an appraisal methodology has proved even more problematic. In this chapter we examine the theoretical and empirical case for considering the wider impacts of transport mega-projects leading to suggestions for ways of incorporating these into appraisal practice. While much of the argument is a familiar one, the key issue is whether and how mega-projects differ from any other transport project. Is it just a question of scale in which larger projects will have larger impacts and thus need additional evidence? Or does the scale of a project lead to a fundamental difference in the nature of those impacts? In the next section we rehearse the theoretical basis of the argument. In the third section we consider ways of modelling these impacts. The fourth section is concerned with a review of what we can learn from the empirical evidence from both ex ante and ex post studies of such projects. The final main section develops an approach to appraisal based on the Economic Impact Report concept suggested in SACTRA (1999). Much of the discussion is based on recent experience in the UK where the explicit recognition of wider economic impacts has been incorporated into the formal appraisal process more fully than in other regimes.

17.2 THE THEORETICAL BASIS OF WIDER IMPACTS

This is not the place to provide a full review of the theory behind the existence of wider impacts from transport investments (see Lafourcade and Thisse, 2011 for a recent review). This section picks out the main insights from the theoretical developments.

The traditional approach to measuring the impact of transport improvements assumed that the markets served by transport were essentially perfectly competitive. This would mean that prices in those markets would reflect marginal costs and hence if transport costs fell as a result of the improvement there would be downward pressure on those prices. Since the effect on prices exactly reflects the fall in transport costs, these should not be included as an additional benefit as that would imply double counting. Whilst this is clear for transport used in the production of goods it is also relevant to passenger transport since the fall in, for example, commuting costs would also be reflected in wages in competitive labour markets. The direct benefits to the transport user would thus exactly and completely measure the benefits from the transport improvement and there would be no case for adding any wider impacts.

If, however, the transport-using markets were imperfectly competitive, such that prices were not equal to marginal costs, but instead involved a mark-up over such costs, this direct connection between the change in transport costs and the prices of the activities using transport would no longer hold (Vickerman, 2007). Moreover, such markets are more likely to involve increasing returns to scale rather than the constant returns (and hence constant marginal cost) of the perfectly competitive market. Thus, any increase in the level of output reduces unit costs. This increases the disconnection between the cost of transport and the price in the market for the transport-using activity. Since prices in imperfectly competitive markets will be above marginal cost, any fall in transport costs implies an increase in mark-up. Whether this is passed on, in whole or part, to the consumer in reduced prices or retained by the producer (equivalent effects can be identified for commuters) it implies that there will be an impact that is additional to the change in the cost of transport. The size of this impact is not immediately determinate.

Unlike the perfect competition case firms in imperfect competition may have different costs, depending for example on the extent of any returns to scale already realized. Thus, firms in larger markets will generally have lower costs than firms in smaller markets. This will enable them to exploit any change in the costs of transport more easily and grow their markets even further (with a consequent reduction in unit costs). Thus, there is the potential for a continuing growth in the larger market at the expense of the smaller market and these agglomeration effects are a further additional impact. Transport changes can thus be seen to have impacts that are similar to exogenous productivity changes leading to endogenous growth effects (see Lafourcade and Thisse, 2011).

This is revealed in a growth of output (GDP), but by having an impact on prices the changes in costs will also have an equivalent impact on consumer welfare; the GDP effect and the welfare effect are two ways of measuring the same impact and will be broadly (allowing for measurement errors) equivalent (see, for example, Department for Transport, 2005).

Embedded in this theoretical account are three key elements that relate to the claims made for transport improvements: that they will enhance the rate of economic growth; that they will redress imbalances in prosperity and promote convergence; that they will enhance the welfare of non-users in ways that are not captured by conventional cost–benefit analysis. It will be immediately clear that these claims overlap with each other and are probably not consistent with each other. We turn in the following section to ways of measuring these impacts in a way that can be used in appraisal.

17.3 MODELLING WIDER IMPACTS

The key question here is whether modelling wider impacts requires large-scale models to capture all the impacts. Because the idea of wider impacts implies an economy-wide approach in which allowance needs to be made for imperfect competition, the simple assumption that the transport model, however complex, will capture all the impacts is likely to be inadequate. The reigniting of interest in wider impacts has coincided with the development of more complex and sophisticated land-use transport interaction (LUTI) models and in particular the growth in the use of spatial computable general equilibrium (SCGE) models. Although arguably LUTI and SCGE models have very similar underpinnings, LUTI models tend to maintain a fairly conventional view of the economic relationships, while the growth of SCGE approaches has paralleled the theoretical developments of NEG with the emphasis on increasing returns and imperfect competition. Both, however, suffer from the problem of using inputs from static input–output matrices, which may not allow for the types of dynamic response likely to be invoked by mega-projects involving large changes in the cost of transport inputs. Both also rely on an equilibrium, market clearing approach to calibration.

Nevertheless, large-scale models can be useful in demonstrating the way in which the effects of transport changes can work through an economy, although care may need to be taken in interpreting the results. This depends on the transport component of inputs to each sector. The problem is that we have generally poor and incomplete information on the way transport is used by sector. The transport input component generally only refers to the direct purchase of transport services by firms; it may therefore underestimate the cost of transport provided by the firm on its own account, the time costs of employees travelling on the firm's account and the cost of commuting by the firm's employees.

SCGE models (see Bröcker and Mercenier, 2011 for a comprehensive review) start with a closed perfectly competitive economy that typically has a production sector, a household sector, a government sector and an investment function. Assuming perfect competition and equilibrium so that all the sectors balance and savings equals investment the models can generate a general equilibrium in which all the quantities and their associated relative prices can be derived as the solution to a set of non-linear equations. Basic elasticities of substitution are typically imported from outside the model but sensitivity tests can check their robustness. The next step is to introduce increasing returns and imperfect competition. Increasing returns affects assumptions about the number and size of firms; imperfect competition implies that firms are not price-takers and this requires assumptions about the nature of competition. The simplifying assumption usually made is that firms produce differentiated products and each firm only produces one differentiated product. Once we move from a single-region closed model to a multi-region model, trade has to be allowed for. Products are now distinguished not only by their differentiation from other products, but also by their origin. This has the advantage that the model can replicate the empirical observation that similar products are traded (cross-hauled) between regions.

In most applications of SCGE models there is not much interest in transport. Where allowance needs to be made for trade costs the simplest assumption is that of so-called 'iceberg' transport costs in which a certain proportion of the output of a good in one region is used up in transporting it to another region. This tends to assume fixed transport costs per unit of distance, although these can vary between products, and does not allow for the variations in levels of competition between different transport sectors. Refinements that model the transport sector more effectively start by allowing for the generalized cost of transport including time costs, which also leads to the need to model the time input to activities in the household sector. This is useful as it links to a more realistic modelling of the labour supply function linked to commuting. It also enables allowance to be made for congestion costs, which provides a valuable link to the transport supply function. There are similar adjustments to the production sector as firms also buy personal transport for their employees in the course of business as well as freight transport for both inputs and outputs. In both cases time and congestion are relevant, not least in terms of ensuring delivery on time.

As will be clear from this very brief overview SCGE models are large, complex and potentially expensive in terms of data and computer time. Simplified versions can be used for the numerical simulation of problems using assumed values of key parameters. These may be useful in demonstrating the sort of wider impacts that can be expected. Full computation will typically require data that may only be available on a national basis in most countries, for example that on underlying production and household consumption functions. Attempts to apply these in a local context may thus lead to a lack of precision when combined with specific local data on the transport system and labour market. This would particularly affect projects in relatively small regions but even in large metropolitan regions the structure of production and consumption may be unrepresentative of the country as a whole.

SCGE models remain essentially aggregate models in which the objective is to ensure equilibrium in a series of markets. What they do not do is identify the way in which changes in transport provision can change spatial patterns of behaviour and location. LUTI models that are founded in spatial interaction models can provide a way of building in more specific location effects, particularly a residential location element (see Wegener, 2011, for a useful review of alternative approaches to these models). Since most LUTI models have been developed to deal with urban planning situations they focus on the residential location/commuting issues and thus are often much less well adapted to dealing with goods transport. Some models also use a link to an external transport model rather than trying to build in an interaction between the transport and location elements in the same model. Like SCGE models, LUTI models suffer from a potential 'black box' problem that much of the detail is hidden from the user and is therefore dependent on the assumptions made by the model developer. Critical here will be the assumptions about the way markets react and interact. Most models use an assumption of market clearing in order to balance supply and demand in each market – this is particularly critical with respect to the labour market. Since most models also use an input–output framework to capture the interaction between sectors this provides a potentially static structure to the approach.

This presents a conundrum in which a complex model is used to capture the interactions between the transport systems and the wider economy it serves, but the relationships in the model cannot respond to the changes in transport provision except through a set of constant parameters. Moreover, these parameters typically relate to marginal responses to components of the generalized cost of transport, but applying them in situations where the changes are non-marginal and where critical thresholds of time and cost may change significantly may perpetuate inaccuracies. The problem is that we do not know a priori whether this will lead to under- or over-estimation of the likely response and the associated wider benefit or cost of this response. This may suggest that models that are less aggregated could be more useful in that they allow the user to understand more closely the sources of possible change and be aware of the various limitations.

The key element in mega-projects in metropolitan areas is likely to be the impact on labour markets. The effect of opening a new metro line or a major tunnel or bridge within a metropolitan area is to reduce commuting costs, widen the labour market catchment area for firms within the city and raise the real wage of workers (Venables, 2007). Faced with a wider catchment, firms can potentially overcome labour market constraints that push up labour costs, thus increasing their competitiveness. Better matching of skills can be achieved in a larger labour market, which can increase productivity. Labour itself benefits from shorter journey time, which widens job search, potentially increases participation (and even hours of work) and enhances productivity through the reduction in stress and so on associated with long commutes. Recent work by Graham (2007) has modelled these effects by examining the way changing accessibility increases the effective density of the labour market facing individual firms in given locations. Effective density is a measure of aggregate accessibility to workers given by:

$$U_i = \frac{E_i}{\sqrt{\frac{A_i}{\pi}}} + \sum_{j}^{i \neq j} \left[\frac{E_j}{d_{ij}} \right] \tag{17.1}$$

where U_i is the total effective density of employment that is accessible to any firm located in area i, E_i is total employment in area i, A_i is its area, E_j is total employment in area j, and d_{ij} is the distance between i and j. Increases in effective density produce agglomeration economies that are treated as a technology component that shifts a firm's production or cost function:

$$Y = g(U)f(X) \tag{17.2}$$

where Y is the output level of the firm, $\mathbf{X}$ is a vector of factor inputs, and $\mathbf{g(U)}$ is a vector of influences on production that arise from agglomeration economies. Firm-level data can then be used to estimate a translog production function, which identifies implicit elasticities.

The advantage of the effective density model is that it enables a direct link to be made between a specific transport improvement and the locations of its main users. Being sufficiently disaggregated it therefore enables this specific change to be directly related to potential agglomeration and output effects. However, the major missing element is still how a major change in transport provision will change the behaviour of users. The assumption in all is that users respond to generalized costs, so as long as the change in generalized costs is calculated accurately we can infer behaviour assuming that users continue to respond at the observed marginal rate.

17.4 EMPIRICAL EVIDENCE: A REVIEW OF SOME STUDIES

Banister and Thurstain-Goodwin (2011) have used the typology of macro, meso and micro, which had been used to classify the wider impacts of transport in an OECD-ITF (2008) report (see also Vickerman, 2008b, 2010). Within this typology Banister and Thurstain-Goodwin have reviewed three UK case studies as indicative of the arguments supporting the developments based on the three types of approach. They use the Channel Tunnel Rail Link as an example of a project justified on the highest level of macroeconomic impacts on growth; the Crossrail project as one based on meso-level arguments about agglomeration economies; and the Jubilee Line Extension in London as one with largely micro-impacts on property markets and land use. While it is true that the arguments used to justify projects often focus on particular characteristics of a project and, although each of these projects individually is large enough to be classified as a mega-project, the geographical scale of the impact varies from the national to the regional to the more local and there are elements of each scale in each project. All large-scale projects will impact on the national economy and potentially affect the rate of growth. All projects will have an impact on labour markets, productivity and agglomeration. And all projects will have local impacts on land use and property markets.

To a large extent the nature of the arguments used to justify projects will condition the amount of effort that goes into providing evidence to support that justification. We have seen that modelling is complex and potentially expensive and that reliable data is frequently only available at a national level. This tends to reinforce the view that the modelling of wider impacts is something that should only be carried out on large projects that are seen to be more likely to have national impacts. However, the size of a project cannot be taken as an indicator of its impact. As SACTRA (1999) noted, even quite small projects that have the effect of unlocking the potential development of land could have disproportional impacts while large projects may have much less impact. For example, the Crossrail project, the case for which the work reported by Graham (2007) originally contributed, was shown to have very significant wider impacts that were critical in achieving a satisfactory cost–benefit ratio for the project. In part this was because of the large agglomeration effects that could be identified for certain sectors, particularly financial services, highly clustered in London and that have a wider effect on the UK economy as a whole. The HS2 proposal to build a high-speed rail line from London, initially to Birmingham but subsequently to Manchester and Leeds as part of a core North–South link, despite being much larger in both geographical and financial terms, appears to generate much less significant wider economic impacts relative to its cost. It is worth examining these two cases in more detail to identify the reasons for this.

Crossrail (see Crossrail, 2005 and Banister and Thurstain-Goodwin, 2011, for more detail) is a project to construct a new rail link across Central London from west to east in a 21 km tunnel. This will provide the first link between commuter services to the west and east of London and provide direct links from the west (including Heathrow Airport) to employment centres in the City and Docklands financial districts and from the east to the commercial districts of the West End. Given the complexity of tunnelling and the need to construct a number of new major interchanges with London Underground (metro) lines the estimated cost of the project is of the order of £16 billion (€19.4 billion, $25.5 billion). By providing new direct links between outer suburban locations and Central London substantial travel time savings could be made for existing travellers, leading also to newly generated trips and benefits to travellers at the traditional terminus stations facing less congestion. These direct user benefits amount to around £12 billion producing a cost–benefit ratio (CBR) significantly less than unity.

Campaigners for new cross-London rail links had pointed out for many years the relatively poor quality of rail links in London, compared, for example, with those in Paris following the creation of the RER regional express network. This was argued to be a direct cause of the apparent lower productivity of London compared with Paris (CEBR and OEIL, 1997). This belief, generated by aggregate observations of productivity levels and overall network densities, supported the view that there must be benefits of such cross-city links that were simply not captured in the direct user benefits measured by willingness to pay and the value of travel time savings. SACTRA (1999) had argued that in the presence of increasing returns to scale and imperfect competition there may be such impacts, in addition to those directly measured as user benefits, but that these could be negative in certain circumstances. As we have seen above, the problem is how to measure such benefits objectively and accurately so they can be incorporated in an extended cost–benefit analysis. In the Crossrail case this led to the work reported in Graham (2007), which was instrumental in the Department for Transport's reappraisal of the case (Department for Transport, 2005).

Using the agglomeration and labour market efficiency estimates provided by Graham's work, based on disaggregated data at firm level and thus including detailed locational information, additional benefits of the order of £7 billion were identified. This raised the CBR to around 1.2 and was used to justify the go-ahead for the project. Interestingly the identification of the expected wider benefits of the project were also used to raise funding for the projects from the private sector and to justify additional tax levies on development in the areas expected to benefit. These are justified on the basis that the productivity benefits do accrue to identifiable groups, but that these cannot be captured through user charges in the same way as direct user benefits. Furthermore, private sector developers were given the opportunity to develop a small number of additional stations on the route. Taking on the development risk of the site they could expect to recoup this through the development gains from businesses locating to a site with prime accessibility. This demonstrates the view that although the supposed wider benefits have some characteristics of a public good, it may still be possible to charge expected groups of beneficiaries rather than funding the provision of these benefits out of general taxation.

In contrast to the Crossrail case, wider impacts have not featured so strongly in the analysis of HS2, the proposed high-speed rail line from London to the Midlands and North. This is a significantly larger project involving ultimately the construction of a high-speed rail network linking London with Birmingham, Manchester and Leeds and providing for accelerated services to other major cities including Liverpool, Glasgow and Edinburgh at a total cost of £36 billion. This is despite popular arguments about its contribution to the UK economy and to redressing regional imbalance in the UK economy, including statements by the UK government in its policy paper announcing the go-ahead for the project (Department for Transport, 2012). The interesting point here is that the appraisal of HS2 demonstrated an initial favourable CBR on the basis of user benefits alone so that, although wider benefits were calculated in essentially the same way as for Crossrail, any potential wider benefits have not been seen as critical to the decision and so can be left as an assumed understatement of such effects.

The problem with using the Crossrail method for HS2 is that the former is very clearly a metropolitan project within a single labour market area. The benefits can be seen as deriving from extending that labour market area and improving the accessibility of all within the area so that effective density increases and this drives the ensuing agglomeration effects. But is the same methodology valid for an inter-urban link? Arguably the link enhances the effective density of the labour market areas of each of the main centres and this produces the expected gains identified. But, as more recent work by Graham et al. (2009) has shown, the distance decay on effective density is in practice very steep and hence we would not expect to see agglomeration effects proportional to the scale of the project. This raises the question as to whether a rather different method is required for such inter-metropolitan projects. The informal argument is that improving connectivity in a national context must be good for the national economy so treating it as a set of independent local labour markets is inappropriate. The analytical question is what happens when we join this set of independent labour markets together? Here the effects of competition between the labour markets may outweigh the effects of increased effective density within them. The effects of this competition may be either to bias the benefits to one or other of the labour markets (the core-periphery effect) or to enhance the combined agglomeration effects of the joint labour market in which firms can reallocate themselves, or their activities, between the cities effectively treating them as a single mega-city.

The evidence on this is mixed. In an ex ante study of a proposed high-speed maglev link between Amsterdam and the northern Netherlands using an SCGE model Oosterhaven and Elhorst (2003) and Elhorst et al. (2004) found rather limited labour market effects, but ones that were generally centralizing. Ex post studies of French TGV links based largely on survey methods found no strong tendency towards centralization or decentralization to or from Paris, but a degree of internal reorganization within firms to relocate particular activities to generate greater scale economies while using the improved transport links to foster intra-firm communication. In an additional study for HS2 Graham and de Melo (2010) identified the potential for some very limited additional benefits arising from a rather strict interpretation of these inter-metropolitan effects.

What is missing in almost all of these studies is a serious attempt to understand the behavioural changes that a non-marginal change in transport provision may cause. The general inaccuracy of demand forecasts for major infrastructures, evidenced in particular by the work of Flyvbjerg et al. (2006), but also in official studies such as by the UK National Audit Office (2012), demonstrates that the principal problem for the evaluation of wider impacts stems from basic problems of demand forecasting. If demand forecasts do not allow adequately for induced effects or are based excessively on parameters from other projects it will not be possible to derive accurate forecasts of user benefits, nor to have a strong basis for evaluating any wider impacts.

17.5 TOWARDS EFFECTIVE APPRAISAL

In this section we move from the more theoretical and abstract discussion to outline a method of appraisal for individual projects based on the evidence from the examples above. As an example this draws heavily on the UK approach, which is one of the more comprehensive (see www.dft.gov.uk/webtag for full details). The underlying objective is to develop a more theoretically correct cost–benefit analysis, recognizing externalities and imperfect competition. As we have already seen, using SCGE models may be precluded on cost grounds for all but the largest projects. Although data may be available at the national level, most transport projects will have data requirements at a more detailed level than typical in SCGE studies. It is not clear that available LUTI models are sufficient to measure possible employment change effects arising from major projects.

The Webtag methodology identifies five major objectives for inclusion in transport appraisal. These cover environment, economy, safety, accessibility and integration. The economy objective itself has five elements: value for money; improvement of transport economic efficiency for business;

improvement of transport economic efficiency for consumers; reliability; beneficial wider impacts through productivity and wider welfare gains and to support the regeneration of an area. It is this final wider impacts area on which we concentrate here although it is important to understand where these wider impacts fit in the overall picture.

The wider impacts embrace four elements: agglomeration; output change in imperfectly competitive markets; labour supply impacts; moves to more or less productive jobs. The guidance suggests that output change and labour supply impacts should be assessed for all schemes greater than £20 million; the agglomeration impacts are assessed if the investment increases accessibility in an area close to an economic centre or large employment centre (defined on the basis of Functional Urban Regions); employment relocation is only assessed where such relocation is shown to be likely on the basis of a detailed LUTI model.

The labour supply impact has three components. First, the change in commuting costs affects the benefit individuals obtain from working, equivalent to a change in the net wage. This results in a change in labour supply based on applying an elasticity to the net wage change. This produces additional productivity, which is calculated by multiplying the change in number of people working by the average economic contribution (GDP) of a new worker.

The output change in imperfectly competitive markets is measured by the difference between the (higher) willingness of consumers to pay for increased output and the (lower) cost of the extra production. This is estimated in a fairly arbitrary way by uplifting the estimate of conventional travel time and travel cost benefits to business users and to freight (the current uplift factor is 10 per cent).

Agglomeration is measured on the basis of an effective density indicator similar to that discussed above. The effective density for scenario *S*, depends on the generalized costs, *g*, for mode *m*, and the rate of distance decay, α, for sector *k*, given total employment *E* in area *j*:

$$d_i^{s,k,f} = \sum_{j,m} \frac{E_j^{s,f}}{\left(g_{i,j}^{s,m,f}\right)^{\alpha^k}} \tag{17.3}$$

This uses generalized costs to produce a change in the cost of access from a given change in transport provision. Each fractional change in agglomeration is estimated to lead to a change in productivity:

$$WI1_i^{k,f} = \left[\left(\frac{d_i^{A,k,f}}{d_i^{B,k,f}}\right)^{\rho^k} - 1\right] GDPW_i^{b,k,f} E_i^{B,k,f} \tag{17.4}$$

This measures wider impacts in terms of changes in density d_i, given GDP per worker $GDPW_i$ and employment E_i, for each area i, each sector k, for each forecast year f, given the elasticity of productivity with respect to density, ρ^k, in sector k, comparing the effects of scheme A with the base case B.

Additional consideration is given to impacts on Regeneration Areas (RAs), measured as the change in the number of RA residents in employment (plus the change in the number of jobs in the RA). This is concerned only with impacts within the RA and the surrounding region, it is not necessary to demonstrate whether any new jobs generated by a transport scheme would otherwise have gone somewhere else in the country.

Whilst this methodology provides a reasonably robust means of assessing a range of wider impacts, and is applicable to all modes, it is still dependent on the issue of standard parameters that are not sensitive to different industrial structures in different locations. As we have seen in the examples used in the previous section there may be significant differences between urban and inter-urban situations in terms of the way agglomeration effects are realized and with which a standard methodology finds it difficult to deal.

Dealing with wider impacts has also led to another layer of complexity on top of the problem of forecasting user benefits that are directly dependent on traffic forecasts. Effective appraisal depends on both a comprehensive treatment of all elements of benefits and costs and sufficient transparency to allow all stakeholders in a project to be able to participate fully in any consultation.

17.6 SOME IMPLICATIONS

The starting point for this discussion was essentially that the application of simple rules of appraisal for mega-projects could be dangerous. Assuming that any project is bound to be good for a local economy is unwarranted and investment in transport can seriously damage the economic health of an area. But failure to invest in transport can damage it too if potential benefits fail to be realized. Appraisal rules need to be comprehensive, but transparent, so that decisions are robust, and clearly understood by all stakeholders.

Sometimes the level of decision-making may be inappropriate for a project such that spillovers between jurisdictions are ignored. These spillovers could be either positive or negative. There is the further danger that policy refraction may occur (Vickerman, 2008a). Hence an authority may fail to include the potential wider benefits to a neighbouring region's economy from an improvement in its own transport provision; or to include the potential costs such as the environmental costs from induced traffic. This is particularly likely in the case of multi-level governments where the higher level may set the overall policy framework but expect a lower level to implement that policy through the planning of individual projects. In some cases the higher-level authority may provide some or all of the finance but expect the lower-level authority to undertake the detailed planning procedures and contribute some or all of the finance. A good example of this is the European Union's TransEuropean Networks programme.

Jurisdictional competition could therefore lead to either over- or under-investment in infrastructure. The desire to secure the supposed benefits could lead to neighbouring regions investing in competing infrastructures; this is particularly seen in the desire for regions to have their own airport. On the other hand the failure to count the benefits accruing to a neighbour could lead to a lack of investment. In part this arises because there are rarely mechanisms to compensate other regions for received benefits (or imposed costs).

The debate on wider benefits seems to have gone full circle from an initial view that 'transport is critical' to a more circumspect view of the need to 'beware double counting' arising from the use of a narrow cost–benefit approach to a new belief that 'wider benefits are the key' informed by the new theoretical and empirical literature. But we should beware of all simple rules in transport appraisal; the fact that we can identify the existence of wider impacts does not mean they always exist, or are always positive. And although there seems to be some evidence that where identified such benefits often fall within a fairly common range of around 10 per cent to 20 per cent of direct user benefits, this does not imply that a simple uplift can be applied.

There remains much on the research agenda. Imperfect competition and the productivity gains from transport have been the focus of much recent research, but more studies using firm-level data are needed to provide a more robust basis for future decisions. The failure to derive reliable forecasts for mega-projects that result in a step change in transport provision and thus can render the use of previously derived parameters of models redundant implies more work is needed on deriving evidence from micro-behavioural studies. Since most appraisal tends to be carried out on individual links in a network, there is a gap between these and possible wider network effects that current appraisal methods find more difficult to handle. The existence of spillovers from projects and the potential for jurisdictional competition also requires careful definition of projects and more guidance on how wide an area needs to be included to get reliable results. Finally, too little resources have been put into the development of a robust methodology for ex post studies to examine whether transport investments have really made the difference claimed.

17.7 CONCLUSIONS

This chapter starts with the assumption that there are impacts from transportation projects that are not captured by traditional appraisal methods. This is based on the premise that in a world of imperfect competition and increasing returns to scale, the change in transportation costs will not reflect exactly the total change in output or welfare that results. Prices of activities using transport may thus change more or less than the change in transport costs and this implies that there could be benefits that are greater (or in some cases smaller) than those measured by conventional cost–benefit analysis. In addition there is a second round effect that arises because of agglomeration forces that this process sets in motion. Firms and individuals move towards the now more favoured locations and this increased density of activity has the effect of raising productivity in that location. But this is not a simple relocation of activity as in a zero-sum game; productivity, output and welfare in the favoured locations will typically be raised by more than any reductions in less-favoured locations.

In a theoretical model this is relatively easy to demonstrate, but moving from a theoretical to an empirical model has proved more challenging. Recent advances in LUTI and SCGE models have shown the possibilities, but these are expensive to develop and implement and will tend only to be used for the largest projects. More precise models based on the idea of effective density may be able to generate good estimates of the agglomeration elasticities that lie at the heart of these effects, and we have reviewed how these have been used effectively for mega-projects in the UK.

However, it is clear from this discussion that we cannot assume that there will always be positive wider impacts (benefits) from such projects, nor that they will have a clearly defined relationship with direct user benefits. This will remain an empirical question, but one we have identified that needs further research on a number of dimensions.

LITERATURE

Altshuler, A. and D. Luberoff (2003), *Mega Projects: The Changing Politics of Urban Public Investment*, Washington, DC: The Brookings Institution.

Banister, D. and M. Thurstain-Goodwin (2011), 'Quantification of the non-transport benefits resulting from rail investment', *Journal of Transport Geography*, **19**(2), 212–23.
Bröcker, J. and J. Mercenier (2011), 'General equilibrium models for transportation economics', in A. de Palma, R. Lindsey, E. Quinet and R. Vickerman (eds), *A Handbook of Transport Economics*, Cheltenham, UK and Northampton, MA, USA: Edward Elgar.
CEBR (Centre for Economics and Business Research) and OEIL (Observatoire de l'Economie et des Institutions Locales) (1997), *Two Great Cities: A Comparison of the Economies of London and Paris*, London: Corporation of London.
CEC (Commission of the European Communities) (2009), *TEN-T: A Policy Review. Towards a Better Integrated TransEuropean Transport Network at the Service of the Common Transport Policy*, COM (2009) 44, Brussels: Commission of the European Communities.
Crossrail (2005), 'Crossrail: socio-economic technical report', London: Cross London Rail Links Ltd, accessed 27 June 2013 at http://www.crossrail.co.uk/railway/getting-approval/crossrail-bill-supporting-documents/specialist-technical-reports/.
Department for Transport (2005), 'Transport, wider economic benefits and impacts on GDP', Technical Paper, London: Department for Transport.
Department for Transport (2012), *High Speed Rail: Investing in Britain's Future – Decisions and Next Steps*, Cm 8247, London: The Stationery Office.
Elhorst, J.P., J. Oosterhaven and A.E. Romp (2004), 'Integral cost–benefit analysis of maglev technology under market imperfections', SOM Research Report, University of Groningen, accessed 26 June 2013 at http://irs.ub.rug.nl/ppn/268887764.
Flyvbjerg, B., M. Skamris Holm and S.L. Buhl (2006), 'Inaccuracy in traffic forecasts', *Transport Reviews*, **26**(1), 1–24.
Frontier Economics (2011), *The Role of Britain's Hub Airport in Economic Recovery: A Report Prepared for Heathrow*, London: Frontier Economics Ltd.
Fujita, M. and J.F. Thisse (2002), *Economics of Agglomeration*, Cambridge, UK: Cambridge University Press.
Fujita, M., P. Krugman and A.J. Venables (1999), *The Spatial Economy: Cities, Regions and International Trade*, Cambridge, MA: MIT Press.
Graham, D.J. (2007), 'Agglomeration, productivity and transport investment', *Journal of Transport Economics and Policy*, **41**(3), 317–43.
Graham, D.J. and P. de Melo (2010), *Advice on the Assessment of Wider Economic Impacts: A Report for HS2*, London: Department for Transport.
Graham, D.J., S. Gibbons and R. Martin (2009), 'Transport investments and the distance decay of agglomeration benefits', Working Paper, London: Imperial College of London.
Gramlich, E. (1994), 'Infrastructure investment: a review essay', *Journal of Economic Literature*, **32**(3), 1176–96.
Lafourcade, M. and J-F. Thisse (2011), 'New Economic Geography: the role of transport costs', in A. de Palma, R. Lindsey, E. Quinet and R. Vickerman (eds), *A Handbook of Transport Economics*, Cheltenham, UK and Northampton, MA, USA: Edward Elgar.
Mohring, H. and M. Harwitz (1962), *Highway Benefits: An Analytical Framework*, Evanston, IL: Transportation Center, Northwestern University.
National Audit Office (2012), *The Completion and Sale of High Speed 1*, Report by the Comptroller and Auditor General, HC 1834 Session 2010–2012, 28 March 2012, London: The Stationery Office.
OECD/International Transport Forum (2008), *The Wider Economic Benefits of Transport: Macro-, Meso and Micro-economic Transport Planning and Investment Tools*, Round Table 140 Economic Research Centre, Paris: OECD.
Oosterhaven, J. and J.P. Elhorst (2003), 'Indirect economic benefits of transport infrastructure investments', in W. Dullaert, B. Jourquin and J.B. Polak (eds), *Across the Border: Building on a Quarter Century of Transport Research in the Benelux*, Antwerp: De Boeck.
SACTRA (1999), *Transport and the Economy, Standard Advisory Committee on Trunk Road Assessment*, London: The Stationery Office.

Venables, A.J. (2007), 'Evaluating urban transport improvements: cost–benefit analysis in the presence of agglomeration and income taxation', *Journal of Transport Economics and Policy*, **41**(2), 173–88.
Vickerman, R.W. (2007), 'Cost–benefit analysis and large-scale infrastructure projects: state of the art and challenges', *Environment & Planning B*, **34**(4), 598–610.
Vickerman, R.W. (2008a), 'Multi-level policy-making in transport: the problems for border regions', *International Journal of Public Policy*, **3**(3/4), 228–45.
Vickerman, R.W. (2008b), 'Recent evolution of research into the wider economic benefits of transport infrastructure investments', in OECD/International Transport Forum, *The Wider Economic Benefits of Transport: Macro-, Meso and Micro-economic Transport Planning and Investment Tools*, Round Table 140 Economic Research Centre, Paris: OECD, pp. 31–49.
Vickerman, R.W. (2010), 'Myth and reality in the search for the wider benefits of transport', in E. van de Voorde and T. Vanelslander (eds), *Applied Transport Economics: A Management and Policy Perspective*, Antwerp: De Boeck, pp. 379–96.
Wegener, M. (2011), 'Transport in spatial models of economic development', in A. de Palma, R. Lindsey, E. Quinet and R. Vickerman (eds), *A Handbook of Transport Economics*, Cheltenham, UK and Northampton, MA, USA: Edward Elgar.

18. Mega-projects: new challenges to cope with climate change and energy transition

Jan Anne Annema and Hugo Priemus

18.1 INTRODUCTION

This chapter discusses what climate change and energy transition may imply for transport mega-infrastructure planning. Two main research questions are put forward in this chapter. (1) How strong are the arguments for taking possible climate change and energy transition impacts into account when planning new transport mega-infrastructure? These issues are sometimes already considered when realizing new mega-projects. An example is the extension of the Port of Rotterdam in the Netherlands. In this 2.9 billion euro land reclamation project, the design is partly based on the expectation that due to climate change, in 50 years from now the sea level may rise by 50 cm (KB, 2008). Therefore, a somewhat higher dyke around the new port is being built and a more elevated road from the new port to the hinterland is being developed. (2) The second main question in this chapter is how can the potential consequences of climate change and energy transition be considered in decision-making for transport mega-projects? For new transport mega-projects it is often far more difficult to decide on a sensible decision-making strategy that includes climate change and energy transition than in the case of the port extension of Rotterdam. The main reason for this – as this chapter will show – is the huge uncertainties related to the consequences of climate change and energy transition in transport and on mega-projects. If these uncertainties are not properly considered, there are risks of over-investment or under-investment in the measures for adapting transport mega-projects to future climate change and energy transition impacts.

For infrastructure in general, climate change and energy transition are relevant. For the decision-making on mega-projects these factors are even more crucial for a number of reasons:

- the high costs of mega-projects and the difficulties in changing projects during the decision-making processes;
- the length of the decision-making process and the life time of mega-projects, which decreases flexibility and increases the uncertainties;

- the direct functions of mega-projects for coping with climate change and energy transition (evacuation function, multi-functionality of road/rail as a dike preventing flooding);
- complementarity of mega-projects with energy consumption and emission of vehicles.

When we speak of mega-project planning in this chapter, we have in mind not only the planning of large transportation infrastructure projects, which includes completely new infrastructure projects but also large-scale asset management or reconstruction projects of existing transportation infrastructures.

Section 18.2 describes the potential consequences of climate change and energy transition for transport mega-projects. Section 18.3 analyses a possible strategy in four steps to deal with the highly uncertain impacts in decision-making on mega-projects. Sections 18.4 and 18.5 present a final discussion and conclusions.

18.2 POTENTIAL IMPACTS OF CLIMATE CHANGE AND ENERGY TRANSITION

Potential Impacts of Climate Change on Mega-project Planning

This section will show that there are arguments for considering climate change impacts when planning for new mega-infrastructure projects. However, at the same time, the chapter will show that knowing what to do with the insights on climate change impacts when planning new mega-infrastructure is not straightforward because of uncertainties.

We start with the observation from the Intergovernmental Panel on Climate Change (IPCC, 2012, pp. 9 and 11) that:

> projected changes in climate extremes under different emission scenarios generally do not strongly diverge in the coming two to three decades, but these signals are relatively small compared to natural climate variability over this time frame. Even the sign of projected changes in some climate extremes over this time frame is uncertain. For projected changes by the end of the 21st century, either model uncertainty or uncertainties associated with emission scenarios used becomes dominant, depending on the extreme.

Thus, climate change impacts could be negligible for infrastructure designed to last less than 30 years, and – perhaps – of more importance for more durable infrastructure. New mega-infrastructure projects (e.g., large ports, national roads and rail, new subways) are designed to be used for many decades to come, which means that it would seem wise to include possible (and highly uncertain) long-term climate change impacts when planning them – especially the mega-projects. Although the climate change conclusions from the IPCC are severely criticized by some politicians and scientists, we take these observations by the IPCC as the mainstream scientific view on climate change at the time of writing this chapter.

In order to conclude if further future changes in the global climate system changes might affect transportation mega-infrastructure, knowledge is needed on the likelihood of changes in climate and weather relevant to mega-projects in transportation. This body of knowledge is increasing. For example, the likelihood of changes in climate and weather most relevant for US transport are estimated in Transportation Research Board (2008). According to this report, almost certain future changes relevant for the US transport system are: decreases in the number of very cold days, increases in Arctic temperatures, later onset of seasonal freeze, earlier onset of seasonal thaw and sea level rise. Here, it is already important to note that the observations made by Transportation Research Board (2008) are formulated in a qualitative way. Koetse and Rietveld (2009) remark in their overview of empirical findings on the impact of climate change and changing weather conditions on transport that the level of uncertainty increases substantially when quantitative effects of climate change on transportation are considered. In fact, Koetse and Rietveld (ibid.) observe that many of the climate change and weather effects on the transport system are ambiguous, both in terms of magnitude and even direction.

Based on the literature overview presented by Koetse and Rietveld (ibid.), Table 18.1 summarizes all potential effects – positive and negative – of climate change on transportation and infrastructure. Two kinds of core potential impacts of climate change related to transport mega-infrastructure planning can be distinguished in the table. First, the number of extreme events may increase, leading to more infrastructure damage than previously expected. The other core impact is that weather changes might result in a different transport demand for transport mega-infrastructure compared to expectations in business-as-usual (BAU) scenarios. With BAU scenarios we mean here any kinds of scenarios about expected transport demand for the new transportation mega-infrastructure used in the decision-making phase that ignore any possible climate change impacts. Table 18.1 presents a general overview. We emphasize that climate change has weather and sea level rise impacts that are different for different regions in the world. Even within one large country, significant differences in impact can occur (Christensen et al., 2007). This implies that when decision-makers for new mega-projects want

Table 18.1 Consequences of climate change for transport infrastructure and mobility

Consequences of Climate Change	Potential Impacts for Infrastructure and Mobility
Increase of extreme events: sea level rise, storm surge, hurricanes and flooding	All kinds of transportation infrastructure (roads, rails, ports) can be affected by extreme events, especially in coastal areas An obvious impact is that the infrastructure can be severely damaged, or perhaps even completely ruined Next to these damage costs, the change in extreme events can also lead to indirect network costs such as costs due to delays, detours and trip cancellation
Temperature and precipitation changes	Changes in patterns of global tourism can result in an increase or decrease in passenger transport demand in certain regions during certain periods Changes in global freight patterns, for example, due to changes in places where food is produced (from south to north on a global scale). These changes could result in an increase or decrease in freight transport demand in certain regions Changes in bicycle use Reduced ice cover on rivers, lakes and seas could open possibilities for increased transport by water and, perhaps, the adoption of new routes (e.g., using the Northwest Passage near the North Pole some months per year) Increased number of periods with low water levels in rivers may affect the inland shipping sector negatively
Changes in weather conditions (high temperatures, ice, storms, lightning, changes in wind force and wind direction)	Changes in the number of failures in rail infrastructure and, consequently, changes in rail transport demand and modal shift Changes in the frequency and severity of road accidents Changes in road congestion, travel time and time reliability and, consequently, changes in road transport demand and modal shift Air transport: changes in delays, cancellations and accidents (especially due to changed wind conditions) and, consequently, changes in air transport demand and modal shift

Source: Koetse and Rietveld (2009).

to take potential climate change impacts into account they should aim for a region-specific impact assessment.

The keyword in Table 18.1 is 'change'. Current practices all over the world show that mega-infrastructure projects such as motorways, airports and high-speed rail networks can function with sufficient quality in all kinds of climates and weather conditions – even in extreme conditions and even in regions with relatively high risks of flooding. When new mega-projects are developed using only BAU scenarios this could lead to under-estimation or overestimation of damage risks and/or future transport demand. These underestimations and overestimations of future 'changed' circumstances might result in severe societal costs (including missed opportunities for benefits). For example, Grenzeback and Lukmann (2007) report infrastructure damage costs (they have only included readily available costs) of 1.1 billion dollars caused by the Hurricanes Katrina and Rita in the United States. Floods from January 1987 to July 2011 in the United States caused a total monetary loss of 39 billion dollars (Warner and Tissot, 2012). These damage cost estimates illustrate that when it is expected that hurricanes and flooding will take place more often in a region it could make sense to prepare for these future changed circum-stances in mega-infrastructure planning in that region because by doing so, large monetary costs might be completely avoided or at least reduced.

Potential Impacts of Energy Transitions on Mega-project Planning

This section will show that there are also arguments for considering energy transition in the planning for new mega-infrastructures, in spite of the high uncertainties.

Oil is currently the main fuel for transport worldwide. The transport sector is responsible for almost 70 per cent of oil consumption in OECD countries (IEA, 2012), and in most BAU scenarios it is expected that the high oil dependency of transport will continue in the future. However, this high dependency might change, which could have impacts on mega-project planning.

One reason for an energy transition from oil to renewable resources is that some scientists think that world oil supply will begin to fall during the next few years (for example, Gilbert and Perl, 2010). This vision is also referred to as 'peak oil' which means the time at which the world reaches its maximum oil production and then declines. Some people believe that this time will be reached soon. Other scientists are less convinced of peak oil and state that sufficient oil for this century probably exists because the oil reserves-to-production ratio (R/P) remains rather constant at around 40 (e.g., Lior, 2012). Benes et al. (2012) discuss two diametrically opposed views concerning the future of world oil production and prices. The geological view expects that physical constraints will dominate the future evolution of oil output and prices. The technological view of oil expects that higher oil prices must eventually have a decisive effect on oil output by encouraging technological solutions. Based on a new model aimed at reconciling the geological and technological view, Benes et al. (ibid.) forecast nearly a doubling of the real price of oil between 2010 and 2020. However, they add to this forecast that 'the error bands are wide, and reflect sharply differing judgments on ultimately recoverable reserves and on future price elasticities of oil demand and supply' (p. 1). This debate shows at least that continuing upward oil prices are likely in the future. And these price increases could potentially be very high in a relatively short time span. The possible impact of the large-scale production of shale gas on oil prices is still unclear.

Another reason for an energy transition is policy pressure to make transport, or more generally the economy, less dependent on oil because of carbon dioxide (CO_2) emission reduction goals and for geopolitical reasons. For example, the European Union White Paper (EC, 2011) aims at phasing out conventionally fuelled cars from cities by 2050 and a 50 per cent shift in middle-distance passenger and longer-distance freight journeys from road to other modes of transport by the same time. They pursue these goals to achieve a 60 per cent reduction in CO_2 emissions and comparable reduction in oil dependency.

Thus, non-policy-related reasons (falling oil supply), policy reasons or both reasons at the same time could result in impacts for mobility in the future compared to BAU. A first impact is changed transport demand due to far higher oil prices compared to expectations in BAU scenarios. Fuel price elasticity literature shows that passenger and freight transport demand are fuel price sensitive, although in most cases not to a great extent (e.g., Hanly et al., 2002; Goodwin et al., 2004; Small and van Dender, 2007; Brons et al., 2008; Barla et al., 2009; Geilenkirchen et al., 2009; VTPI, 2011; Dahl, 2012). Long-term fuel price elasticity for car use ranges between –0.3 to –0.5; for road freight diesel demand, indicative fuel price elasticities are in the range of between –0.05 (short term) and –0.6 (long term). Some air travel segments are price elastic, especially the leisure segments (Gillen et al., 2004). The elasticities are based on model and empirical studies with relatively limited fuel price changes. It is highly uncertain whether these elasticities are also valid should oil prices suddenly start to rise to a very high level.

A second impact of falling oil supply and stringent policies to stimulate an energy transition could be the emergence of complete new vehicle technology. Current expectations with respect to electric cars are high, not only for environmental reasons[1] but also because of the expected depletion of fossil fuels (van Wee et al., 2012). Sierzchula et al. (2012) show that the number of companies producing models of electric vehicle (EVs) has substantially increased since 2004. However, whether EVs become the new technology of the future is still uncertain (e.g., Dijk et al., 2013; Wells and Nieuwenhuis, 2012 on technological change trajectories in transportation).

The realization of a network for powering EVs by changing or powering batteries (in addition to the network of gasoline stations) is a mega-project in itself. An emerging new vehicle technology could also have implications for the planning of classic mega-projects such as roads, ports and rails. The emergence of new technology could have no impact on the infrastructure, as in the case of battery powered vehicles, biofuels or fuel cells, when other vehicle propulsion technologies are still used that still need 'normal' roads, waterways and airports. But the emergence of new vehicle technology could have a substantial impact in other cases, such as with grid-based electric vehicles (Gilbert and Perl, 2010). In that case, new conventional transport infrastructures will be needed less in the future and will have to be substituted by grid infrastructures.

It is clear that the potential impacts of future energy transitions are highly uncertain. There is a risk of over-investment or under-investment in new mega-projects if the possibilities of very high oil prices and the emergence of new technologies are completely ignored when planning for them.

18.3 DEALING WITH CLIMATE CHANGE AND ENERGY TRANSITION IN MEGA-PROJECT PLANNING

Next to mitigation measures (greenhouse gas [GHG] emission reduction measures) there is increasing policy attention to adaptation to climate change (e.g., Eisenack et al., 2012 for a review on transport adaptation). According to IPCC, adaptation to climate change refers to adjustments in natural and human systems (such as mega-infrastructure projects) in response to actual or expected climate change impacts, which moderate, harm or exploit beneficial opportunities. A number of EU Member States have adopted national adaptation strategies or are in the process of doing so (Prutsch et al., 2010; Greiving and Fleischhauer, 2012).

Should new or existing mega-projects also be adapted to climate change and to an energy transition away from oil? An answer based on current knowledge (Section 18.2) seems to be: yes, if it is part of a 'no regret' policy. A 'regret' adaptation policy would be to invest in an adaption measure with very high costs, which is only beneficial if there is only one possible future scenario and when this future scenario does not come true. A 'no regret' policy would be taking an adaptation measure that has a positive benefit-to-cost ratio in all possible futures. As this position is too farfetched (nobody can foresee all possible futures), it is perhaps better to aim for an 'as little regret as possible' policy, in which adaptation measures are taken that have positive benefit-to-cost ratios in more foreseeable futures.

Dealing with uncertainty in ex ante infrastructure or transport policy planning is not new. The most common approach is the use of different future scenarios in the ex ante evaluation. By designing different future scenarios, researchers map possible futures. Here, it is very important to note the term 'possible'. In fact, the future is unknown and is largely determined by non-predictable developments (Taleb, 2007). Climate change and energy transition might happen in the near future but the speed, the extent and the exact impacts are largely unknown, as Section 18.2 shows. Many scientists have thought about policy strategies that take high future uncertainty into account. The key idea of these scientists is not to develop precise plans for one precise future (the 'regret' policy as mentioned), but rather to construct policies that are flexible, adaptable and devised not to be optimal for a 'best estimate' future, but robust across a range of plausible futures (Walker et al., 2001; Makridakis and Taleb, 2009; Wright and Goodwin, 2009; see also Priemus et al., Chapter 5 of this book).

Thus, in mega-transport planning, it seems worthwhile looking for possibilities for designing flexible or adaptable mega-projects. Table 18.2 maps some possibilities.

Robustness Test

The possibilities mentioned in Table 18.2 go hand in hand with extra costs, sometimes low, sometimes very high. Therefore, it seems worthwhile not only to look for adaptable options but also to estimate the costs and benefits of these possibilities in very different futures (a 'robustness' test). Based on ideas in van Ierland et al. (2012) and own ideas, a three-step approach is proposed in this chapter to find potential efficient adaptation measures in transport mega-project planning. The core of the approach is to analyse adaptation measures in conventional BAU scenarios and in more unconventional scenarios including climate change and energy transition impacts using classic cost–benefit analysis. This approach is novel and has added value because in current CBA practice – as far as we know – these unconventional climate change and energy transition scenarios are not considered (based on an analysis of examples of

Table 18.2 Possible adaptation measures for mega-projects

Adaptation Measures	Remark on Initial Costs
Climate change	
Adaptation (the 'soft' measures): – Improve weather forecasts and information (before people decide to travel but also during travel) – Improve ICT so that people can work at home easily (e.g., have access to work-related servers) in case of the temporary failing of road and rail infrastructure, or so they can travel less due to very high oil prices – Improve evacuation plans for airports, ports, railways stations and undergrounds in case of emergency – Make spatial reservations (for new airports on elevated areas, for example)	Mostly low-cost measures. Improving information, evacuation plans and ICT are perhaps 'no regret' measures: even in futures without large climate change or energy transition impacts, these measures could be beneficial. By making spatial reservations, flexibility is created to allow for waiting for more information on the possible climate change and energy transition impacts. Of course, this idea comes with a cost as the reserved space cannot be used for anything else during the waiting time but these costs can be far lower compared to a situation where something else has been built on an elevated area that needs to be demolished because, due to climate change impacts, the elevated area is now an ideal place for the construction of a mega-project
Adaptation of road infrastructure technology: – The use of different materials – Other parameter settings (e.g., to improve complex constructions that deal better with heat or freezing stress. A complex construction is, for example, the connection of a road with a bridge or a tunnel) – Increase drainage capacity	Low to somewhat higher costs (e.g., in the case of increasing drainage capacity for tunnels or aqueducts). Also, some of these measures could be 'no regret' as they could also be beneficial in futures without or with limited climate change impacts. Furthermore, these adaptations can be taken, especially when a new transport infrastructure is built, but also when maintenance or reconstruction projects need to be carried out
Adaptation of rail infrastructure technology: – Proper maintenance of track and track bed – Proper setting of the stress-free rail temperature	Low to somewhat higher costs. As in the adaptation of road infrastructure technology these measures could also be 'no regret' and can be taken when maintenance or reconstruction of existing tracks is needed. However,

Table 18.2 (continued)

Adaptation Measures	Remark on Initial Costs
Climate change	
– Install less switches or remove switches (less chance of freezing, less chance of lightning disturbances)	installing less switches, especially, could result in high costs as less switches result in a less flexible rail network (there is less redundancy in the rail network – see below), whereas, in contrast, building more redundancy in a network is seen as a potentially good adaptation measure
Adaptation of infrastructure design to sea level rise: – Higher dikes to be built around seaports – Roads and rails to be built along elevated tracks (which could also function as secondary dykes) – Compartmentalization of large dyke rings – Enhancing capacity of locks and weirs – Avoiding new developments in high-risk areas – Building more redundancy into the system	Relatively high to very high costs. It could be very costly to build more redundancy into the transport system, for example. The idea is that different transport infrastructures (e.g., rail and road) are developed in such a way that if one kind of infrastructure fails in a region (e.g., due to extreme weather or flooding), the other still functions. Therefore, they might have to be unbundled spatially
Adaptation to higher river levels: – Canalization of waterways at specific bottlenecks – Increased height of bridges – Enhancing capacity of locks and weirs – Development of retention areas	Relatively high to very high costs
Adaptation to changed demand and modal choice: – Building large infrastructure in phases – Building new mega-infrastructure in such a way that there is room for adaptation in the future	Relatively high to very high costs. An example of building new infrastructure in an 'adaptive' way is by starting with building a new road or railway with only a limited number of lanes but then constructing tunnels and viaducts in such a way that there is already room for more lanes or tracks if needed in future

Table 18.2 (continued)

Adaptation Measures	Remark on Initial Costs
Energy transition changes	
Adaptation to changed demand and modal choice: – Building large infrastructure in phases – Building new infrastructure in such a way that there is room for change in the future	Relatively high to very high costs – see above
Adaptation to changed technology: – Keeping different technology options open – Using existing technology (e.g., petrol stations where batteries can also be charged or you can fill up with hydrogen) – Building grid-like infrastructure in phases and in such a way that there is room for change in the future	Building grid infrastructure is very costly (see above). Also, developing and stimulating different technologies come with a cost. However, it is potentially far more expensive and risky to put all bets on one new oil-free technology right now (e.g., biofuels, hydrogen fuel cells, electric vehicles, grid technology) as all of these new technologies are currently in development and all still have large disadvantages as well as their advantages (e.g., high costs, technical issues and in the case of biofuels, land use competition issues). So, a flexible and adaptive policy approach seems wise to stimulate the new technologies using instruments such as R&D support for all technologies, carrying out small-scale experiments and niche management

Source: TRB (2008); de Bruin et al. (2009); Eichhorst (2009); Priemus, 2009; Koetse and Rietveld (2012).

CBA requirements and recommendations written in English: NATA. More details can be found on http://www.dft.gov.uk/webtag/; *Guide for Cost–Benefit Analysis* (Eijgenraam et al., 2000); the *Guide to Cost Benefit Analysis of Investment Projects* (EC Directorate General Regional Policy, 2008); and the HEATCO project. HEATCO stands for 'Developing Harmonised European Approaches for Transport Costing and Project Assessment'. All deliverables can be downloaded from http://heatco.ier.uni-stuttgart.de/).

Step 1: Identify the possible impacts of climate change and of energy transition

In the first step the possible impacts of climate change (e.g., expected sea level rise, change in temperature, more or less extreme weather conditions or change in precipitation patterns) and energy transition (e.g., changed demand) on the specific new or existing[2] mega-infrastructure should be studied. Climate change impacts are region specific and can even be negative for a mega-project in one region (decreased demand, increased risk of flooding) yet offer opportunities in another region (new or increased tourist travel demand). Also, energy transition impacts may be region or country specific. One reason for this is that in some countries far more active low-carbon transport policies might be pursued compared to others, resulting perhaps in earlier or later transport energy transitions. Another reason is that due to high fuel levies and a relative high amount of public transport, as is the case in most European countries, the impacts of possibly very high fuel prices in the near future might be different compared to other countries with far lower levies and less public transport supply (such as in North America). So, it is paramount to include a regional, perhaps even a local, perspective in the impact analyses.

Step 2: Construction of two unconventional future scenarios

Based on Step 1, two unconventional future scenarios can be constructed (next to conventional BAU scenarios): one including the possible climate change impacts on the new infrastructure and one including the energy transition impacts. In the BAU scenarios the decision-maker is informed about what might happen in the future with transport demand, congestion, technology, prices, environmental impacts and so forth, if the already existing policies continue to be pursued and if no unconventional changes in economy, society or natural circumstances take place. BAU scenarios are based on continuity in the nature of things and in the speed and direction of changes (van der Duin et al., 2006). For example, in BAU scenarios all kinds of future conventional changes are possible (e.g., related to economic changes, demographical developments, technical progress, nature) but in most cases neither complete new developments nor abrupt or relatively large changes are assumed. It is important to emphasize that we suggest still using different BAU scenarios in mega-project planning because conventional changes are also uncertain and this uncertainty should also be taken into consideration when deciding on new mega-projects. Van Cranenburgh et al. (2012) suggest constructing additional (unconventional) scenarios on potentially profound substantial changes[3] in the transport system in order to test the robustness of future transport policies. They clearly state that 'we do not suggest constructing all kinds of "wild" scenarios and disposing of the business-as-usual scenarios'. They propose a more conservative approach in which 'conventional scenario studies are complemented with scenarios that include potential future substantial change' (van Cranenburgh et al., 2012, p. 594). This approach determines Step 2.

Step 3: Cost–benefit analysis using all scenarios, identifying possible adaptation approaches

In Step 3, possible adaptation approaches (Table 18.2 gives examples) are designed or chosen and subsequently tested with regard to their efficiency. First, it is proposed to carry out cost–benefit analyses for the new mega-project or for the large-scale reconstruction or asset management in both the conventional scenarios as well as in the 'impacts of climate change' scenario and the 'impacts of energy transitions' scenario.

Three main outcomes are possible in this first estimate, which require different subsequent adaptation analyses:

- The outcome could be that in both the conventional and the two unconventional scenarios the net present value (NPV) of the project is negative. The conclusion is that the new or reconstructed mega-project is not a profitable investment from a societal point of view. The societal benefits of the projects do not outweigh the societal costs in any possible future studied. Perhaps, in the 'impacts climate change scenario' extra transport demand is generated compared to the conventional scenarios but, apparently, even with this extra demand the benefits of the project do not outweigh the costs. Perhaps, risk of flooding for the new mega-project (and thus, increased future repair costs) increases in the unconventional scenario compared to business-as-usual; or future demand will be far lower compared to business-as-usual because of the very high oil prices assumed. However, these outcomes do not matter, for it is not worthwhile realizing the project from a societal point of view anyway.
- The outcome could be that in both the conventional and the two unconventional scenarios the NPV is positive. The new mega-project investment (including reconstruction and asset management) seems to be robust in many foreseeable futures even without taking any adaptation measure and so it could be developed. However, in this case, it is still worthwhile studying the adaptation measures that could be taken related to the new mega-project (Table 18.2). Cost–benefit analyses in the unconventional scenarios can be carried out for these measures to evaluate if the benefits of these measures

outweigh the costs. If the answer is yes, these measures improve the mega-project from a societal point of view if the more unconventional futures come true. Naturally, these measures will, per definition, worsen the project's NPV in the conventional scenarios as there will only be costs and no benefits. Nevertheless, if the NPVs decrease only slightly in these more conventional futures and keep being positive, the decision-maker could still decide to implement the adaptation measure(s). If the NPVs of adaptation measures in the unconventional scenario are not positive, adaptation measures could be better ignored or postponed.

- A third possible outcome is that in some scenarios the NPV of a mega-project (including reconstruction or asset management) is positive and in others negative. In this case, adaption measures (e.g., the ones mentioned in Table 18.2) could be selected to evaluate if they (or just one of these) make investing in the mega-project more robust. Does the number of scenarios with a positive NPV increase by including one or more of these measures? An example could be that a port extension is profitable in the conventional scenarios but not in the climate change scenario due to higher risks of flooding. In that case, it could be 'no regret' to already build some higher dykes around the extension. This will result in extra investment costs but perhaps they are so low that the NPV stays positive in the conventional scenarios and the NPV in 'the impacts of climate change' scenario turns from negative to positive. Another example: it is conceivable that a mega-project has a positive NPV in the high economic growth BAU scenario but not in the two unconventional scenarios. A reason could be that in these unconventional scenarios future transport demand for the new infrastructure is relatively low due to climate change impacts or a very high oil price. In this case, an idea could be to design the original mega-project so that it is smaller (see Table 18.2, 'Adaptation to changed demand and modal choice') and thus, initially cheaper. However, at the same time the new infrastructure could be built in such a way that it is relatively easy and cheap to expand it if, in the future, when more knowledge becomes available, it will turn out that the climate change impacts or energy transition impacts are far lower compared to the expectations in the unconventional scenarios. Another idea in this case could be to postpone the final decision to actually build the mega-project but to start finalizing all kinds of procedural and legal matters (political decision procedure, acquiring land, and so forth). If, in the future, for example, the lower demand due to climate change and energy transitions does not become a reality (or perhaps later in time than expected in the unconventional scenarios), the mega-project could still be built relatively early. If in the future the disappointing demand due to climate change and energy transitions comes true, the space reserved can be used for another purpose. It is clear that to deal with high future uncertainty the keywords are flexibility, adaptive capacity and postponing decisions in order to wait for more information. Based on the real options approach, Koetse and Rietveld (2012) also point to the potential importance of postponing investments when the probability of change increases, in which case the opportunity costs of suboptimal investments become larger.

In addition, it can be recommended that private parties are involved in the analysis in Steps 1 to 3. By doing so, private partners may not only become actively involved in developing and realizing new mega-infrastructure projects but also in research and development and the search for better and innovative adaptation technologies compared to the examples given in Table 18.2 (see also Agrawala and Fankhauser, 2008).

18.4 DISCUSSION

The analysis using unconventional scenarios suggested in the previous section is rather straightforward and might help decision-makers to decide on the need for taking adaptation measures, but the analysis has one obvious severe drawback. The analysis tests a mega-project investment only on the usefulness of considering adaptation measures against potential large impacts due to climate change and energy transition. However, far more 'surprising' natural developments or unconventional societal changes might happen, which might impact the future prospects of mega-infrastructures. These 'unknowns' are, in general, not taken into account. Van Cranenburgh et al. (2012, p. 594) observe in their paper on past substantial changes in transport that, at first sight, their findings do not cause grave concern: 'if the next 40 years see similar substantial changes in trends of order of magnitudes and directions as we have seen during the last 40 years, then our findings suggest that scenario studies based on business-as-usual scenario will do a fairly reasonable job'. Annema and de Jong (2011) showed, after having examined 42 BAU scenarios for future transport and traffic development in the Netherlands in the period 1970–2000, that in most of the important transport BAU scenario results in the past in the Netherlands, such as future car use and transport emissions, the policy-makers were not misled. However, both van Cranenbergh et al.

(2012) and Annema and de Jong (2011) emphasize that developments in the past are not a guarantee that the same developments will take place in the future. Van Cranenbergh et al. (2012, p. 570) even point out the changing issues of this chapter by remarking: 'Especially if we take into consideration the challenges faced by society today, such as oil depletion and climate change, the absence of more drastic substantial changes in the next 40 year seems relatively unlikely'. Perhaps, if in the future more knowledge becomes available about other unconventional potentially high impact issues, these can be included in the analysis. In that case the current two could be removed or included in the 'normal' business-as-usual scenarios.

In the analyses proposed, attention has only been given to adaptation policies (Table 18.2). However, adaptation is not a goal in itself. The aim of adaptation is to change the new mega-infrastructure in such a way that future damage costs are avoided or reduced. It is possible that with GHG emission mitigation measures (in or outside the transport sector) these costs could be avoided against lower costs compared to taking adaptation measures. With current knowledge and climate modelling, it is impossible to estimate these 'avoided costs' of a mitigation measure for a specific mega-project case. Therefore, in the pragmatic approach of Section 18.3 this possibility is ignored. However, in the future, knowledge and modelling might improve so that it indeed becomes possible to estimate the costs that were avoided. Then it is useful to also include mitigation options as ways of making a new mega-project more resilient for the future.

Many reports and articles stress the importance of spatial planning in adaptation to climate change impacts (Priemus and Rietveld, 2009). Should cities and activities in general still be built or expanded in areas with high flooding risks, for example? Should new dwellings be built in rural areas or in expansive cities (urban sprawl), which makes electricity grid-based transport (trams, trains) less feasible, while this might be needed in a future with very high oil prices? Thus, choices in spatial planning are paramount when considering developing new mega-projects. The decision about where to build or expand a mega-project is highly dependent on the decision on where to build or expand cities and industrial activities. Therefore, in the decision-making process for these spatial projects it may also be useful to carry out the 'three-step analysis' as proposed. Anyway, it seems preferable from a climate change and energy transition point of view to integrate decision-making on spatial and infrastructure projects (area development) as much as possible.

Vellinga et al. (2012, p. 466) remark in their paper on adaptation for climate change that 'as long as the climate changes incrementally and taking into account the lock-ins and path dependency, adaptation will most probably be an incremental process'. Also, our approach will most probably result, primarily, in incremental changes. The current scientific evidence on climate change and energy transition makes it plausible to make unconventional scenarios (compared to BAU), which are perhaps a bit 'wild' compared to BAU but not 'very wild'. An example of this evidence is a recent report for the Dutch government; based on the latest insights it concludes that, with the current pace of change, the impacts of climate change are manageable (van Minnen and Ligtvoet, 2012). In fact, the implicit assumption in the Steps 1 to 3 proposed is that both changes will take place incrementally, making it unappealing to take very expensive measures, which will only have large future benefits if sudden radical changes in oil price or weather conditions take place, for example. However, the relatively cautious approach taken in this chapter might have to be reconsidered when new dramatic events take place related to climate change and energy transition or when more scientific knowledge becomes available.

18.5 CONCLUSION

Two main questions are dealt with in this chapter. First, how strong are the arguments for taking possible climate change and energy transition impacts into account when planning for new mega-transport infrastructure or for restructuring existing mega-transport infrastructure? The answer is that the current scientific evidence is ambiguous: the extent and the direction of the impacts are highly uncertain and region-specific. Still, the impacts could be so severe that is seems wise to include these impacts in the ex ante evaluation. Second, how can the potential consequences of climate change and energy transition be considered in up-front decision-making for mega-projects? The answer given in this chapter is a cautious three-step approach based on considering flexible adaptation measures and on including unconventional climate change and energy transition future scenarios next to conventional BAU scenarios in the ex ante decision-making. By using these scenarios – conventional and unconventional – in standard cost–benefit analysis the decision-maker can evaluate the robustness of taking possible adaptation measures. Do certain chosen adaptation measures lead to positive or more positive NPVs compared to not taking these measures? If the answer is yes, the decision-maker could decide to take these measures.

NOTES

1. The extent of electric vehicles being more environmentally friendly compared to fossil fuel-based vehicles is dependent, amongst others, on the way the electricity is generated. It is beyond the scope of this chapter to discuss this theme further. An overview of issues on this theme can be found in Hawkins et al. (2012).
2. When reconstruction or asset management is considered.
3. A substantial change is an unconventional change that directly or indirectly causes an enduring change in at least one principal indicator of mobility (for example, transport demand) of at least 5 per cent on a supranational scale (van Cranenburgh et al., 2012).

LITERATURE

Agrawala, S. and S. Fankhauser (eds) (2008), *Economic Aspects of Adaptation to Climate Change: Costs, Benefits and Policy Instruments*, Paris: Organisation for Economic Co-operation and Development (OECD).

Annema, J.A. and M. de Jong (2011), 'The history of the transport future – evaluating Dutch transport scenarios of the past', *Transport Reviews*, **31**(3), 341–56.

Barla, P., B. Lamonde, L.F. Miranda Morena and N. Boucher (2009), 'Travelled distance, stock and fuel efficiency of private vehicles in Canada: price elasticities and rebound effect', *Transportation*, **36**(4), 389–402.

Benes, J., M. Chauvet, O. Kamenik, M. Kumhof, D. Laxton, S. Mursula and J. Selody (2012), 'The future of oil: geology versus technology', IMF Working Paper No. WP/12/109, Washington, DC: International Monetary Fund.

Brons, M., P. Nijkamp, E. Pels and P. Rietveld (2008), 'A meta-analysis of the price elasticity of gasoline demand. A SUR approach', *Energy Economics*, **30**(5), 2105–22.

Christensen, J.H., B. Hewitson, A. Busuioc, A. Chen, X. Gao, I. Held, R. Jones, R.K. Kolli, W.-T. Kwon, R. Laprise, V. Magaa Rueda, L. Mearns, C.G. Menndez, J. Risnen, A. Rinke, A. Sarr and P. Whetton (2007), 'Regional climate projections', in S. Solomon, D. Qin, M. Manning, Z. Chen, M. Marquis, K.B. Avery, M. Tignor and H.L. Miller (eds), *Climate Change 2007: The Physical Science Basis. Contribution of Working Group I to the Fourth Assessment Report of the Intergovernmental Panel on Climate Change*, Cambridge, UK and New York: Cambridge University Press.

Dahl, C.A. (2012), 'Measuring global gasoline and diesel price elasticities', *Energy Policy*, **41**(C), 2–13.

de Bruin, K., R.B. Dellink, A. Ruijs, L. Bolwindt, A. van Buuren, J. Graveland, R.S. de Groot, P.J. Kuikman, S. Reinhard, R.P. Roetter, V.C. Tassone, A. Verhagen and E.C. van Ierland (2009), 'Adaptation to climate change in the Netherlands: an inventory of climate adaptation options and ranking of alternatives', *Climate Change*, **95**(1/2), 23–45.

Dijk, M., R.J. Orsato and R. Kemp (2013), 'The emergence of an electric mobility trajectory', *Energy Policy*, **52**(C), 135–45.

EC (European Commission) Directorate General Regional Policy (2008), *Guide to Cost–Benefit Analysis of Investment Projects*, Brussels: DG Regional Policy, European Commission.

EC (2011), *White Paper on Transport. Roadmap to a Single European Transport Area – Towards a Competitive and Resource-efficient Transport System*, COM (2011), 144, 28 March, Brussels: European Commission.

Eichhorst, U. (2009), *Adapting Transport in Developing Cities to Climate Change*, Eschborn: Deutsche Gesellschaft für Technische Zusammenarbeit (GTZ).

Eijgenraam, C.J.J., C.C. Koopmans, P.J.G. Tang and A.C.P. Verster (2000), *Evaluation of Infrastructural Projects: Guide for Cost–Benefit Analysis*, accessed 27 June 2013 at http://

www.rws.nl/en/images/Guide%20for%20Cost–benefit%20Analysis%20I_tcm224-324078.pdf.

Eisenack, K., R. Stecker, D. Reckien and E. Hoffmann (2012), 'Adaptation to climate change in the transport sector: a review of actions and actors', *Mitigation and Adaptation Strategies for Global Change*, **17**(5), 451–69.

Geilenkirchen, G.P., K.T. Geurs, H.P. van Essen, A. Schroten and B. Boon (2009), *Effecten van prijsbeleid in verkeer en vervoer* [*Pricing Policies Impacts on Traffic and Transportation*], Bilthoven: Planbureau voor de Leefomgeving/Delft: CE, in Dutch.

Gilbert, R. and A. Perl (2010), *Transport Revolutions: Moving People and Freight Without Oil*, 2nd edition, Gabriola Island, British Colombia: New Society Publishers.

Gillen, D.W., W.G. Morrison and C. Stewart (2004), 'Air travel demand elasticities: concepts, issues, and measurement', accessed 26 June 2013 at http://www.fin.gc.ca/consultresp/airtravel/airtravstdy_-eng.asp.

Goodwin, P., J. Dargay and M. Hanly (2004), 'Elasticities of road traffic and fuel consumption with respect to price and income: a review', *Transport Reviews*, **24**(3), 275–92.

Greiving, S. and M. Fleischhauer (2012), 'National climate change adaptation strategies of European states from a spatial planning and developments perspective', *European Planning Studies*, **20**(1), 27–48.

Grenzeback, L.R. and A.T. Lukmann (2007), 'Case study of the transportation sector's response to and recovery from Hurricanes Katrina and Rita', Cambridge Systematics, Cambridge, MA.

Hanly, M., J. Dargay and P. Goodwin (2002), *Review of Income and Price Elasticities in the Demand for Road Traffic*, ESRC TSU Publication 2002/13, ESRC Transport Studies Unit Centre for Transport Studies, University College, London.

Hawkins. T.R., O.M. Gausen and A.H. Strømann (2012), 'Environmental impacts of hybrid and electric vehicles – a review', *Journal of Life Cycle Assessment*, **17**(8), 997–1014.

IEA (2012), *World Energy Outlook 2011*, Paris: International Energy Agency.

IPCC (2012), 'Summary for policymakers', in C.B. Field, V. Barros, T.F. Stocker, D. Qin, D.J. Dokken, K.L. Ebi, M.D. Mastrandea, K.J. Mach, G-K, Plattner, S.K. Allen, M. Tignor and P.M. Midgley (eds), *Managing the Risks of Extreme Events and Disasters to Advance Climate Change Adaptation, A Special Report of Working Groups I and II of the Intergovernmental Panel on Climate Change*, Cambridge, UK and New York: Cambridge University Press, pp. 1–19.

KB (2008), *Besluit van 23 mei 2008, nr. 08.001524 houdende verlening van concessie aan het Havenbedrijf Rotterdam N.V. te Rotterdam houdende bepalingen omtrent het ondernemen van droogmakerijen en indijkingen ten behoeve van de landaanwinning voor de Maasvlakte* [*Decision of May 23, 2008 to Give Concession to the Rotterdam Port Authority for Land Reclamations in Order to Realize Maasvlakte 2*], The Hague: Sdu Uitgevers, in Dutch.

Koetse, M.J. and P. Rietveld (2009), 'The impact of climate change and weather on transport: an overview of empirical findings', *Transportation Research Part D*, **14**(3), 205–21.

Koetse, M.J. and P. Rietveld (2012), 'Adaptation to climate change in the transport sector', *Transport Reviews*, **32**(3), 267–86.

Lior, N. (2012), 'Sustainable energy development: the present (2011) situation and possible paths to the future', *Energy*, **43**, 174–91.

Makridakis, S. and N. Taleb (2009), 'Decision making and planning under low levels of predictability', *International Journal of Forecasting*, **25**(4), 716–33.

Priemus, H. (2009), 'Sea level rise and spatial planning in the Dutch Randstad', paper for the AESOP 2009 Congress 'Why Can't the Future be More Like the Past?', Liverpool, 15–18 July.

Priemus, H. and P. Rietveld (eds) (2009), 'Climate change, flood risk and spatial planning', Special Issue, *Built Environment*, **35**(4), 425–592.

Prutsch, A., T. Grothmann, I. Schauser, S. Otto and S. McCallum (2010), 'Guiding principles for adaptation to climate change in Europe', ETC/ACC Technical Paper No. 2010/6 November.

Sierzchula, W., S. Bakker, K. Maat and B. van Wee (2012), 'The competitive environment of electric vehicles: an analysis of prototype and production models', *Environmental Innovation and Societal Transitions*, **2**, 49–65.
Small, K.A. and K. van Dender (2007), 'Fuel efficiency and motor vehicle travel: the declining rebound effect', *Energy Journal*, **28**(1), 25–51.
Taleb, N.N. (2007), *The Black Swan: The Impact of the Highly Improbable*, New York: Random House.
Transportation Research Board (TRB) (2008), *Potential Impacts of Climate Change on U.S. Transportation*, TRB Special Report No. 290, Washington, DC: Transportation Research Board.
van Cranenburgh, S., C. Chorus and B. van Wee (2012), 'Substantial changes and their impact on mobility: a typology and an overview of the literature', *Transport Reviews*, **32**(5), 569–97.
van der Duin, P., C. Hazeu, P. Rademakers and J. Schoonenboom (2006), 'The future revisited: looking back at *The Next 25 Years* by the Netherlands Scientific Council for Government Policy (WRR)', *Futures*, **38**, 235–45.
van Ierland, E. (ed.) (2012), *Decision Support Tools, Mid-term Review Report Knowledge for Climate Theme 8*, National Research Programme Knowledge for Climate/Nationaal Onderszoekprogramma Kennis voor Klimaat (KvK), Wageningen, by Ekko van Ierland Consortium leader with contributions of work package leaders, names not mentioned.
van Minnen, J. and W. Ligtvoet (2012), *Effecten van klimaatverandering in Nederland: 2012* [*Climate Change Impacts for the Netherlands: 2012*], The Hague: Planbureau voor de Leefomgeving (in Dutch).
van Wee, B., K. Maat and C. de Bont (2012), 'Improving sustainability in urban areas: discussing the potential for transforming conventional car-based travel into electric mobility', *European Planning Studies*, **20**(1), 95–110.
Vellinga, P., N. Marinova and J. van Loon-Steensma (2012), 'Adaptation to climate change. A framework for analysis with examples from the Netherlands', *Built Environment*, **35**(4), 452–70.
VTPI Victoria Transport Policy Institute (2011), *Transportation Cost and Benefit Analysis II, Congestion Costs*, site accessed 26 June 2013 at www.vtpi.org.
Walker, W.E., S.A. Rahman and J. Cave (2001), 'Adaptive policies, policy analysis and policy-making', *European Journal of Operational Research*, **128**(12), 282–9.
Warner, N.N. and P.E. Tissot (2012), 'Storm flooding sensitivity to sea level rise for Galveston Bay, Texas', *Ocean Engineering*, **44**(0), 23–32.
Wells, P. and P. Nieuwenhuis (2012), 'Transition failure: understanding continuity in the automotive industry', *Technological Forecasting and Social Change*, **79**(9), 1681–92.
Wright, G. and P. Goodwin (2009), 'Decision making and planning under low levels of predictability: enhancing the scenario method', *International Journal of Forecasting*, **25**(4), 813–25.

19. Road vehicle automation: elephant in the infrastructure room

Richard Gilbert

19.1 EXPLANATIONS, DEFINITIONS AND SCOPE

The idiom 'elephant in the room' refers to an obvious truth, problem, challenge or risk that is being ignored. In this chapter's title, the elephant is the progressive automation of the control of road vehicles. The 'infrastructure room' is the metaphorical space that contains academic and other discourse about transport infrastructure including mega-projects, discourse that has mostly not addressed the potential impacts of road vehicle automation. There is no discussion of such impacts, for example, in these reports on the future of transport:

- the European Commission's White Paper *Roadmap to a Single European Transport Area* (EC, 2011);
- the World Energy Council's *Global Transport Scenarios* (WEC, 2011);
- the Organisation for Economic Co-operation and Development's *Strategic Transport Infrastructure Needs to 2030* (OECD, 2012);
- the International Transport Forum's *Transport Outlook 2012* (ITF, 2012);
- the World Bank and the Asian Development Bank's *Urban Mass Transport Infrastructure in Medium and Large Cities in Developing Countries* (Vandycke and Wright, 2012).

This chapter concerns what may be the widespread deployment over the next few decades of autonomous road vehicles (ARVs) and the implications of this deployment, particularly for infrastructure planning. ARVs have or are expected to have sufficient on-board sensing and computing resources to travel safely and reliably on regular streets and expressways (motorways) without human intervention. The information ARVs receive from their sensors can be augmented by information conveyed by wireless communication, including vehicle-to-vehicle (V2V) and vehicle-to-infrastructure (V2I) connections. ARVs can also receive directions in this way as to destination and other matters. Dual-mode ARVs allow control by a human operator as well as or instead of on-board computer systems.

ARVs may be propelled by internal combustion engines or electric motors. If ARVs' traction is electric, energy may be provided by on-board batteries that can be recharged or replaced automatically. If appropriate infrastructure is available, electrically propelled ARVs can be energized from the electric grid while in motion.

ARVs that could replace today's personal vehicles are also called driverless cars (Benenson et al., 2008), autonomous cars (Marks, 2012), robocars (Templeton, 2012a), and cybercars (Nashashibi et al., 2012). ('Automobile' is rarely used for road vehicles that do not require a human operator.) Autonomous taxicabs (ATs) are ARVs managed in fleets to provide taxicab services without drivers. The term 'shared autonomous taxi' has also been used (Ford, 2012).

Personal rapid transit (PRT) comprises on-demand, origin-to-destination passenger (and sometimes freight) service in small, automated vehicles mostly moving on a network of guideways with off-line stations (Carnegie and Hoffman, 2007, pp. 18–19). PRT essentially consists of small ARVs moving on elevated or ground-level guideways rather than roads.

Autonomous local delivery vehicles (ALDVs) are ARVs managed in fleets to provide local delivery of goods between automated collection and delivery points. The terms 'robotruck' and 'deliverbot' are also used (Templeton, 2012a). Autonomous heavy-duty vehicles (AHDVs) are large ARVs used primarily for long-distance travel on expressways. They can be propelled by diesel engines, as heavy-duty trucks (lorries) are now. They are unlikely to be electrically powered unless energy can be provided from the electrical grid while in motion, likely via overhead wires (catenaries).

This chapter discusses all of the above, proceeding on the assumption that ARVs could well become widely deployed during the next two decades. This is a debatable assumption, as is almost any prediction. It is an assumption worth making because of the evidence and opinions set out below. It is worth making too because it stimulates exploration of the revolutionary implications of such deployment, and raises important questions to be addressed by transport infrastructure planners.

More general matters addressed in this chapter include the potential impacts of deployment of ARVs, mostly as ATs, on car ownership and use and on the evolution of public transport. Also addressed are freight movement, energy consumption for transport and the electrification of transport. Implications for infrastructure planning, including mega-projects, are noted at several points in the chapter and brought together in the final section, which also touches on how the deployment of ARVs as ATs might unfold.

19.2 PROSPECTS FOR ARVs

This and the next section build on several reviews and overviews of the development of and prospects for ARVs including Dickmanns (2002); Sun et al. (2006); Benenson et al. (2008); Campbell et al. (2010); Berger and Rumpe (2012); and Silberg and Wallace (2012). These two sections also build on several more popular but nevertheless substantial discussions including those by Anon (2012a); Folsom (2012); Vanderbilt (2012a, 2012b); and two websites: Templeton (2012a) and DCMW (2012).

Parts of the road vehicle manufacturing industry appear to be embracing ARVs, as supporters of academic research teams and separately. The German company BMW AG sees automation as a way of making car ownership more attractive. 'You may have the option to drive or not. Sit back, relax, do other things', said a company official (Proudfoot, 2012). An official of General Motors Company of Detroit, Michigan, said that 'self-driving cars could be in showrooms by the end of the decade' and that vehicles that 'partially drive themselves' may debut by the middle of the decade (Lienert, 2011).

The Swedish Volvo Car Corporation (a wholly owned subsidiary of a Chinese company) is said to be 'staking its future on . . . [producing] an accident-free vehicle within seven years' (Duxbury and Stoll, 2012). This means, in effect, producing a marketable ARV, although Volvo has said it would like humans to remain in control most of the time. A Volvo official has said, 'The car of the future will be like the farmer's horse. The farmer can steer the horse and carriage but if he falls asleep the horse will refuse to walk into a tree or off a cliff' (Joseph, 2012). The Japanese company Toyota appears to be similarly cautious (Lavrinc, 2013).

Other automakers engaged in ARV development include the German companies Audi and Volkswagen (Squatriglia, 2012), and Mercedes-Benz (Vijayenthiran, 2011). Work of companies outside the regular auto industry is relevant including, for example, that of Autonomous Solutions Inc. of Petersboro, Utah, which produces autonomous off-road vehicles for military purposes.

The pacesetter in driverless technology appears to be Google Inc. of Mountain View, California, working through Stanford University's Artificial Intelligence Laboratory. Google has a fleet of more than a dozen ARVs that by August 2012 had completed some 500 000 kilometres of testing. 'They've covered a wide range of traffic conditions, and there hasn't been a single accident under computer control', explained Google's official blog (Google, 2012).

Google's interest in transport in a sense antedates its primary interest in search engines. During his May 2009 Commencement Address at the University of Michigan, Google co-founder Larry Page said:

> When I was here . . . I wanted to build a personal rapid transit system on campus to replace the buses. It was a futuristic way of solving our transportation problem. I still think a lot about transportation – you never lose a dream, it just incubates as a hobby. Many things that people labor hard to do now, like cooking, cleaning, and driving, will require much less human time in the future. (Page, 2009)

In 1993, Page was an undergraduate member of the University of Michigan's Solar Car team. He met Sergey Brin, Google's other co-founder, while they were graduate students at Stanford University. At the September 2012 signing of the State of California's bill concerning autonomous vehicles at Google's headquarters, Brin said the company 'will have autonomous cars available for the general public within five years' (Tam, 2012).

The Japanese government has set the goal of having ARVs on the road during the early 2020s (Hornyak, 2012). Members of the authoritative Institute of Electrical and Electronics Engineers (IEEE) anticipate that ARVs will account for up to 75 per cent of cars on the road by 2040 (IEEE, 2012).

Sebastian Thrun, the leader of Google's ARV project, has noted that current ARVs have not quite reached the performance level of an attentive human driver (DCMW, 2012). He would want millions of kilometres completed without a crash before Google could be considered to have a marketable product (Mosher, 2012).

Across such a testing period, there would be the challenge of bringing down the cost of ARVs. The hardware required for full automation now costs several tens of thousands of dollars per vehicle (Fountain, 2012). With refinement and mass production, this cost is expected to fall to about $3000 (Anon, 2012a; Yvkoff, 2012). The extra purchase cost could be more than offset by reduced insurance costs (because vehicles and roads will be safer), reduced operating costs (because autonomous vehicles will drive more uniformly, using less fuel and wearing out the vehicle less), and reduced vehicle manufacture costs (because autonomous vehicles will need fewer human-operated controls and fewer safety features).

Led by Nevada, there has been authorization of deployment of ARVs or moves towards deployment in several US states (Florida, California, Hawaii, Oklahoma and Arizona), with more jurisdictions in the USA being approached by Google and other interested parties. Road testing is also occurring in several European countries, and much relevant work is under way in Japan and China. There has been opposition to these moves.

Table 19.1 Results of a survey of attitudes of 1000 UK drivers to driverless cars

	Percentage Agreeing	
	Under 35	Over 55
Would feel unsafe being a passenger in a driverless car	32%	65%
Would not consider buying a driverless car	48%	85%
Would enjoy a driverless car as much as driving themselves	51%	12%

During a race for the Republican nomination as a candidate for a seat in Florida's Senate in the November 2012 election, one contestant attacked a rival's support for ARVs, resulting in the headline, 'Florida political ad suggests that self-driving cars will be the death of grandma' (Wolford, 2012). The supporter of ARVs won the nomination and then the Senate seat.

Surveys on attitudes towards ARVs in North America and Europe suggest an age divide: young people welcome them; older people do not. Table 19.1 presents results from a survey of 1000 UK motorists conducted during 2012 for Robert Bosch GmbH, a maker of automotive parts headquartered in Germany (Anon, 2012b).

In spite of their relatively strong opposition to ARVs, older people reported welcoming automatic safety features in driven automobiles almost as much as younger people (63 vs 71 per cent).

JD Power and Associates, a California-based information services company, surveyed 17400 US vehicle owners early in 2012 and found a similar divide: a third of those under 38 years would buy an ARV even if it cost $3000 more, but less than 9 per cent of respondents over 56 years would buy one (Yvkoff, 2012).

Accenture, a global management consulting, technology services and outsourcing company headquartered in Ireland, surveyed just over 1000 adults in both the USA and the UK early in 2011 and found a similar amount of discomfort with riding in an ARV to that found by Bosch (Accenture, 2011). In both countries, 51 per cent said they would not feel comfortable in an ARV; Bosch found that an overall 53 per cent would feel unsafe. Accenture went further and asked what might reduce the discomfort. In both countries the main considerations would be: (1) ability to take control over the vehicle if needed; (2) a record of 100 per cent reliability; (3) evidence that deployment of ARVs actually reduces accidents.

Puls, a German market research firm, interviewed 1002 German drivers and confirmed another result of the Bosch survey. There were higher levels of positive regard for specific safety features and driving aids than for the prospects of widespread deployment of ARVs (Wagner and Mendle, 2012).

The reported level of acceptance of ARVs, especially among younger people, complements the general optimism of developers that ARVs will be a feature of road traffic within a decade and a predominant feature not long afterwards. The optimism is reinforced by understanding that what needs to be improved in function and cost-effectiveness are no more than electronics and software, and that results in similar areas – such as autopilots and drones in aviation – provide encouragement.

19.3 DRIVING THE MOVE TOWARDS ARVs

Vanderbilt (2012b) noted: ‘The idea of autonomous vehicles gained widespread public exposure at General Motors’ Futurama exhibit at the 1939 World’s Fair, where the automaker envisioned “abundant sunshine, fresh air [and] fine green parkways” upon which cars would drive themselves’. The cars were not seen as ARVs but rather as freeing drivers through ‘a collaborative partnership between the car and the highway’ (Gelertner, 1995, p. 35).

Research along these lines continued in the USA and Japan until the 1970s, when more ‘intelligence’ began to be located in the vehicle. Progress became substantial during the 1990s with the massive expansion of computing power per unit volume, which is continuing (Tsugawa, 2008), and much progress in sensor technology.

A major boost to the development of ARVs came in 2001 when the US Congress mandated that one-third of military aircraft were to be unmanned by 2010 and one-third of ground combat vehicles by 2015. Aviation regulators have been asked by the US Congress to integrate unmanned aircraft into the air-traffic control system by 2015 (Anon, 2012c).

For ground vehicles, implementation of the 2001 mandate was spearheaded by the Defense Advanced Research Projects Agency (Luettel et al., 2012). DARPA is the successor to ARPA (Advanced Research Projects Agency) whose Arpanet, operational in 1969, was the progenitor of the Internet, developed to provide a communications system that could survive a nuclear attack. Military interest remains prominent in vehicle automation, not only in the US. Military universities in China and Germany serve as centres of research on this topic. However, car manufacturers are automating road vehicle operations today chiefly to provide safer driving.

In richer countries, injuries requiring hospitalization and deaths resulting from road traffic collisions have fallen steeply. In Canada, they fell by much more than half per capita between 1990 and 2009 (Transport Canada, 2011). Nevertheless, road crashes remained the leading cause of death for persons aged 15–24 (PHAC, 2012).

The fall in serious injuries and deaths from crashes on Canadian roads is typical of richer countries, as is the prominence of road crashes as a major cause of death among young people. Poorer countries, which are rapidly motorizing often with inferior vehicles and infrastructure, mostly show an increasing rate of road traffic-related serious injuries and fatalities, described as a 'major global public health crisis' (Sharma, 2008). On a per capita basis their average rate passed that of richer countries around the year 2000 and is expected to be more than double that of richer countries by 2020 (Peden et al., 2004).

A key result of detailed analyses of crashes is that the overwhelming cause is driver error. In its June 2008 report to the US Congress, the National Highway Traffic Safety Administration described analysis of 5471 road crashes (NHTSA, 2008). Of the 5361 for which a critical reason for the crash could be determined, 95 per cent were attributable to drivers, and 5 per cent to vehicles or road conditions. Of the driver-related critical reasons, 41 per cent were recognition errors (inattention, internal and external distractions, and inadequate surveillance); 34 per cent were decision errors (travelling too fast for conditions, making false assumptions about others' actions, and illegal manoeuvres); 10 per cent were performance errors (overcompensation and poor directional control).

Automobiles sold in richer countries have some or all of these automated safety features: antilock brake system, emergency brake assist, forward-collision warning, traction-control system, blind-spot detector, lane-departure warning, lane-departure prevention, electronic stability control, adaptive cruise control, and drunk-driving prevention. Also available in high-cost vehicles are automatic braking, back-over detection, traffic sign recognition and automatic pedestrian recognition (Ashley, 2008). Other automatic features are less related to safety, including self-parking systems (Kane, 2011). Most of these features are elements of control systems for ARVs.

Particularly with Google's eminence in relevant research and development, interest has returned to the early considerations of convenient and productive travel. In a late 2012 interview, Google chief executive Larry Page justified the company's work on development of ARVs as helping to improve quality of transport and access to employment, reduce wasted labour, and reduce the need for parking facilities (Helft, 2012).

Noted earlier was the motivation of German car manufacturer BMW, which sees automation as a way of adding to the appeal of its products.

BMW recognizes that car sales may fall, perhaps more because 'young people have learned that life without a car is still a life'. Thus the appeal is to younger people for whom BMW sees interactivity as the key: 'The car may say to its driver on the way into Munich, "Stop, take the train," because of information it has received regarding conditions within the city' (Proudfoot, 2012).

19.4 LIABILITY CONCERNS POSED BY ARVs

Technology relevant to ARVs seems to be currently ahead of the law (Brandom, 2012), which mostly requires one or more operators to be in a car even though it is driven by a computer, and which does not yet address who would be responsible if an ARV entirely under computer control were indeed to cause the death of a grandmother.

Consideration of liability issues seems no more intense than in California, where the Law School of Santa Clara University, in the Silicon Valley region, is a focus of discussions. In January 2012, Santa Clara Law held a symposium entitled 'Driving the Future: The Legal Implications of Autonomous Vehicles'. Papers from the event are available, notably those by Beiker (2012); Douma and Palodichuk (2012); Marchant and Lindor (2012) and Peterson (2012).

The considerations are complex. Some are specific to California law and practice, including those to do with vehicle insurance, about which Peterson (2012, p. 1395) noted, 'the drafters of Proposition 103, and the voters convinced to follow their lead, embedded in California a regulatory system ill-suited to insuring self-driving automobiles that are controlled by new and fast developing technology'. The more general issue was summarized by Marchant and Lindor (2012, p. 1339), 'Autonomous vehicles will increase the safety of vehicle travel by reducing vehicle collisions. Ironically, autonomous vehicles are likely to increase the liability exposure of vehicle manufacturers. Autonomous vehicles will shift the responsibility for avoiding accidents from the driver to the vehicle manufacturer'.

Manufacturers could reduce their liability by selling ARVs only to fleet operators, who may be more willing than individual owners to assume some of the liability. Fleet operators could in turn rent to individual users or, perhaps more likely, use the ARVs to provide an autonomous taxicab (AT) service.

Google has hinted that it may see car-sharing as the primary business model for its ARV technology (DCMW, 2012). The above-noted statement by IEEE members observes that 'autonomous vehicles will make car sharing programs more prevalent'. A car-sharing service using ARVs and a taxicab service using ARVs amount to essentially the same thing.

19.5 AUTONOMOUS TAXICABS (ATs)

This section builds on previous characterizations of possible AT services, notably those by Mitchell et al. (2010); Ford (2012); Grush (2012); Kornhauser (2012); and Templeton (2012a).

A client would order an AT by smartphone or computer, specifying destination, number of passengers and amount of baggage, negotiating exact pick-up and set-down locations with the dispatch computer and the time of pick-up. An ARV of an appropriate size would arrive at the agreed time and take the client and companions to the destination. When passengers and baggage have been unloaded, the vehicle will be available for a new assignment. For large loads, whether passengers or baggage, two ATs might arrive, linked electronically to travel together to the destination.

An AT could be shared by strangers if they agreed. Sharers would benefit from lower hire rates, although their rides would usually take a little longer. One proponent has made sharing a central feature of an AT service (Ford, 2012), but the extent of willingness to share small vehicles with strangers may be in doubt, even if there is monitoring of vehicle interiors and other security features. As well, sharing would add to an AT system's logistical challenges.

ATs could be better than today's taxicabs in three ways and worse in one:

- ATs could be better because the vehicles could be more comfortable. Interior space arrangements would match passenger rather than driver needs. ATs could more readily provide passengers with entertainment, communications and other services.
- ATs could be better because the rides would be smoother and speedier. As roads become populated with autonomous vehicles, traffic would become better managed with fewer starts, stops and changes in speed, resulting in briefer trips.
- ATs could be better because the rides would cost less. A comparison of taxicab fares and car-sharing rates suggests that today roughly two-thirds of a taxicab fare covers the cost of the driver. As suggested above, ARVs, when widespread, need not cost fleet operators more than regular automobiles. Fares for ATs could thus be a third or less of present taxicab fares – even lower if users opted to share with strangers.

- ATs would be worse for the user who needs other services that a taxicab driver can provide, for example, assistance with a wheelchair. But an AT fleet operator could provide human assistance for a premium, and could be subsidized for doing so for particular classes of passenger.

19.6 THE STARTLING ADVANTAGE OF ATs WOULD BE THEIR LOW COST

Based on the foregoing, a typical fare structure within an urban area (in today's US dollars) could be a $1.00 hiring charge and then 15 cents a minute and 10 cents a kilometre. A 5 km journey at an average speed of 30 km/hour (i.e., taking ten minutes) would cost $3.00 or 60¢/km. This could be about the same as the adult public transport fare for one traveller (about $3.00 in Toronto) and less than the fare if there were more. A 10 km trip at the same average speed would cost $5 or 50¢/km – less than the public transport fare for two people travelling together. Rates could be higher or lower according to the time of day and the size of the vehicle requested.

The per kilometre rates are instructive when compared with the costs of owning and operating a car, which in Canada average about 55¢/km driven for cars less than four years old (CAA, 2012). For many – younger people in particular (Davis and Dutzik, 2012) – relying on a well-managed and comprehensive AT service could be more appealing than owning a car, or a second or third car, because of its lower overall cost and great convenience and flexibility. ATs will carry people door-to-door, will not have to be parked, will be usable by people who cannot or should not drive, and will allow the use of a wide variety of vehicles according to demand.

The only other comparison of potential AT costs with those of regular automobile ownership and use and of regular taxicabs is that of Burns et al. (2013). These investigators estimated that relative AT costs would be even lower than those suggested above.

ATs need not be only for urban and suburban areas, although that may be where they are first deployed. A Google consultant has suggested that ATs (or individually owned ARVs) could compete on journey time and convenience with high-speed rail for trips other than station to station, at much lower public cost (Templeton, 2012b).

On expressways, ARVs will be able to be platooned at high speed – that is, marshalled automatically into compact, single-file groups – perhaps bringing energy costs down by about a third (Tsugawa, 2011). Because of such energy savings, a volume discount, and possible exploitation of grid connection (discussed below), the total cost of a five-hour, 500 km, door-to-door AT trip from the Toronto to Montreal regions could be less than \$85, if the AT could remain for hire in Montreal until used for a return trip. This cost can be compared with typical station-to-station costs per person of \$50 by bus, \$100 by train and \$200 by air. For longer trips, ATs with beds and washrooms could be available at a premium.

Operators of fleets of ATs may be the only adopters of ARVs. Early deployment by fleet operators will help iron out the legal and technical bugs, making ARVs potentially more available to individual owners. However, fleet owners could meanwhile be establishing AT services that would be convenient and inexpensive enough to reduce car purchase substantially.

Potential purchasers of ARVs may question whether the purchase is advisable when ATs can be summoned on demand, in a range of sizes, at a lower cost than ownership, and used more conveniently because they do not have to be parked, refuelled and cared for in other ways. The arrival of ATs could mark the beginning of the end of individual automobile ownership.

Some people may think they will always want to be able to drive their own car, or that cars must always have human operators. Many decades ago, elevators usually had operators and aircraft were flown only by pilots. A few decades from now, only driverless cars may be allowed on most roads, for safety reasons. Human operators could be a hazard when most vehicles are under automatic control.

19.7 IMPLICATIONS OF ARVs FOR THE AUTOMOBILE INDUSTRY

Individually owned cars are used on average for about an hour a day in the USA (Santos et al., 2011) and probably about the same elsewhere. If ATs were to carry passengers for an average of eight hours a day, other things being equal, only one-eighth of the present number of automobiles per person would be needed.

Other things would not be equal. Because ATs could substitute for much public transport – discussed below – there would be more ATs on the road than the number required to replace today's personal automobiles. Also, because ATs would be used more intensively they could have a shorter life. Nevertheless, the deployment of ARVs could well cause car production to shrink to less than half its present level over the next few decades.

This potential impact of ARVs provides a further reason for automobile manufacturers to counter their development, in addition to the liability issues noted above. Google has already complained that some parts of the auto industry have impeded deployment of driverless cars (DCMW, 2012). Nevertheless, as also noted above, many parts of the industry appear to be contributing strongly to the development of ARVs. To repeat, General Motors has said that 'self-driving cars could be in showrooms by the end of the decade' and that vehicles that 'partially drive themselves' may debut by the middle of the decade (Lienert, 2011).

19.8 ATs AND PUBLIC TRANSPORT

In richer countries, there is usually more travel in large urban regions by motorized personal vehicles than by public transport. For example, data on mode shares in 16 such urban regions showed a preference for travel by personal automobile over public transport in ten of them: Barcelona, Berlin, Chicago, London, Melbourne, New York, Osaka, Rome, Sydney and Toronto. Public transport was used more than personal automobiles in six of them: Hong Kong, Madrid, Paris, Singapore, Tokyo and Vienna (Anon, 2011). Travelling by AT will be more like travelling by car than travelling by public transport. As a consequence, AT services could replace much of the present kinds of public transport.

An AT service could be considered a form of public transport in that it moves people in a manner available to almost all of a population. However, taxicab services are often not considered to be public transport, for example, Walker (2012, pp. 13–14). Nevertheless, some communities provide public transport through taxicab companies, for example, the taxibus services in 11 districts of Montreal (STM, 2012) and the taxibus service that covers much of Rimouski, Quebec (Rimouski, 2012). AT services could thus be considered a type of public transport, but superior to the services usually on offer today.

ATs will be superior because they will travel door-to-door and provide a more comfortable journey than today's services. They will be speedier – chiefly because of uninterrupted travel between origins and destinations – except along highly travelled routes, for which something like present heavy-rail services will still be required.

Consider, for example, the Toronto Dominium Centre in downtown Toronto, a tight cluster of six office towers where 21 000 people work. If a fifth of the people working there were to arrive by AT within 15 minutes in the morning, or leave within 15 minutes in the afternoon, there would be gridlock. ATs can be narrower (the smallest might have only two facing seats), drive more closely together (because of the more precise automatic control), and follow each other at shorter distances (at one-second or less rather than two-second intervals), and they will be more likely to be shared. As a consequence, ATs could eventually carry up to four times as many passengers per lane as human-driven cars (8000 rather than 2000 per hour). Even with this advantage, roads could not cope with the flow from the Toronto Dominium Centre. Moreover, there are several other highly occupied office towers at or close to the intersection of Toronto's Bay and King Streets. There could be even worse congestion at this area's set-down and pick-up points for ATs.

Locations such as Toronto's Bay and King Streets will continue to require heavy-rail transit – subways or regional trains – capable of moving tens of thousands of people per hour per direction. Peripheral stations on the lines serving the dense districts could be served by ATs, as would the dense districts themselves outside of busy periods. Heavy rail lines need extend only from high-density areas to the nearest place where passenger activity would be at a level low enough to allow for ready access by AT during peak periods.

With superior signalling and multi-unit trains, light-rail transport (streetcars or trams on their own rights-of way) can have near the capacity of heavy-rail transport. However, the peak load of light-rail systems is usually within the potential capacity of AT systems. This could make many light-rail systems unnecessary because of the greater convenience of AT systems and their lower cost to operators, users and governments.

Bus systems are almost always well within the capacity of AT systems and would also likely not survive (Grush, 2012). This includes school bus systems, which in Canada are responsible today for much more movement of people than urban transit systems (NRCan, 2011). Thus, driverless cars could bring a major shrinkage in public transport systems as well as in the automotive industry. However, to the extent that AT services would be considered to be a form of public transport, public transport could be due for major expansion, but in a very different form from what we have now.

19.9 ENERGY IMPLICATIONS OF WIDESPREAD DEPLOYMENT OF ATs

With widespread deployment of ARVs – mostly as ATs – there could be more vehicles on the road because ATs will substitute for most, and perhaps eventually all, personal automobile use as well as much use of buses and other conventional public transport. Moreover, ATs will serve users who cannot drive or use public transport, including young people and the elderly. Also, ATs will spend less time parked than today's automobiles, and more of the day on or moving between assignments, contributing to the increase in the number of vehicles on the road. An offsetting factor will be some growth in car sharing by strangers – in the form of sharing of part or all of trips by AT – but likely not enough to compensate completely for the factors contributing to an increase in traffic.

More movement of vehicles will not necessarily result in more fuel use. ATs will be smaller and lighter on average than today's personal vehicles because they will need fewer safety features and driver controls and because the capacity of particular ATs will be matched to the trip requirements. As well as using less energy for these reasons, they will be operated so as to use less energy. This will happen through attainment of more even speeds as a result of better traffic management as well as more even vehicle operation.

The resulting energy savings could be more than enough to offset any growth in traffic. Folsom (2012) has estimated that fuel consumption of ATs propelled by internal combustion engines could be less than that of today's automobiles, that is, in the range of 0.25–0.50 L per 100 km at 50 km/hour vs an average of about 6.2 L/100 km for today's vehicles at that speed. More modest reductions could be sufficient to meet even quite ambitious targets for reductions in consumption of petroleum fuels.

Some of the extraordinary potential reduction in fuel consumption posited by Folsom could be achieved with any motorized vehicle but most would depend on two particular features of ATs. One is what should be ATs' remarkably low mass compared with regular taxicabs, as much as an order less, achievable mainly because of reduced need for safety features and better matching of vehicle size to occupancy. The other would be ATs' more even movement, achievable through the better traffic management and vehicle operation that ATs would allow. This would involve less energy-consuming acceleration and lower maximum speeds.

Reducing oil consumption for transportation remains an imperative, whether for supply or environmental reasons, or both. If petroleum products continue to provide the main fuel for transportation, a major gap between potential demand for and world supply of oil seems likely to emerge within a decade or two (Murray and King, 2012), notwithstanding recent bursts of optimism about supply (Gilbert, 2012) and ongoing heroic efforts to improve the efficiency of transport fuel use (e.g., NHTSA, 2012). A shift from internal combustion engines to electric motors as the source of traction seems the best direction to take, because of the relative ease of producing electrical energy sustainably and then distributing it (Gilbert and Perl, 2010).

Operators of fleets of ATs could be in a better position to switch to electric traction than individual owners of driven or driverless cars, for several reasons:

- Taxicabs travel much more per day than individually owned cars. In New York City, which may be atypical but for which there are good data for 2005, the average taxicab travelled 276 km a day in that year, carrying fare-paying passengers for 61 per cent of the distance (Schaller, 2006). In the USA in 2009, personal automobiles travelled an average of 50 km per day (Davis et al., 2012). For a car less than four years old, operating costs are less than a third of total costs (CAA, 2012). For a taxicab – using the above New York data and excluding driver's remuneration, medallion cost and other taxicab-specific items – operating costs are about two-thirds of vehicle ownership costs. As a consequence, fleet operators have good reason to be more concerned with vehicles' operating characteristics and costs. Electric vehicles can have substantially lower operating costs because they use less fuel, and cheaper fuel, and because the relative simplicity of electric vehicles results in lower maintenance costs (van den Bulk, 2012). Thus, electric vehicles could be relatively more appealing.
- The main challenge in using a battery electric vehicle is accommodating its short range (Deloitte, 2011; Element Energy, 2012; Gerssen-Gondelach and Faaij, 2012). A fleet operator could deploy enough electrically propelled vehicles to ensure that a sufficient number is available to meet demand even though many may be unavailable because their batteries are being charged. An AT with a battery approaching depletion would automatically seek a charging station between hires. Connection, charging and disconnection would be automatic. Fleet operators may choose to invest in fast-charging stations and fewer vehicles, or vice versa, according to circumstances. Individual owners could not make that trade-off.
- Fleet operators could achieve what would in effect be very fast charging through automatic battery exchange (Anon, 2012d). Batteries for battery exchange could be charged during off-peak periods. This would reduce fuel costs overall, but raise outlays on batteries, presenting another trade-off effectively available only to fleet operators.

ATs would have much less mass than today's automobiles and would use much less energy for a given task. Battery-electric ATs could thus have smaller batteries, thereby reducing costs and further reducing energy use. The energy costs of vehicle manufacturing and infrastructure maintenance could be lower for ARVs. Energy costs of vehicle manufacturing could be lower because many fewer vehicles could be produced – if ATs are widely used – and because what is produced will be much lighter. The energy cost of infrastructure maintenance could be lower because lighter vehicles and more even movement will mean less wear and tear on road surfaces – a matter returned to below during the discussion of freight movement.

19.10 PERSONAL RAPID TRANSIT (PRT), ATs ON GUIDEWAYS

If feasible, electric traction should be powered by connection to the grid while in motion – as are electric trolley buses and streetcars – rather than by on-board batteries. This avoids the high financial cost of batteries, the energy cost of moving energy into and out of batteries, which is about 25 per cent (Gerssen-Gondelach and Faaij, 2012), and the energy cost of carrying the weight of batteries (a cost that varies considerably with amount of storage carried, topography, and driving characteristics).

Electrically propelled automobiles could in principle be powered from the grid while on regular roads as trolley buses are so powered: by stringing pairs of wires (catenaries) above one or more lanes. The wires would have to be several metres above the road, to allow space for trucks (lorries) and other large vehicles, and thus the poles or pantographs required to reach such wires from small vehicles could be unwieldy. Connection could be made to roadway-level rails or even inductively to buried wires (Chopra and Bauer, 2013), but these would present additional problems of highway safety and, in the latter case, energy loss. Satisfactory grid connection of small vehicles could require guideways designed for the purpose.

Use of such guideways by ARVs would constitute what is known as personal rapid transit (PRT), defined in the opening section. PRT is usually envisioned as being powered directly from the grid, although in at least one early implementation – at London's Heathrow Airport – the PRT vehicles (often known as pods) are battery powered (ULTra, 2012).

The initial all-in cost of a PRT system including guideways and vehicles appears to be about $15 million per two-way km (Meyer and Morache, 2010). This is low compared, for example, with a light-rail system, which seems to average about $35 per km in the USA (Guerra and Cervero, 2011) and can cost much more (a mostly tunnelled light-rail line in Toronto is costing more than $250 million per km). The PRT cost is nevertheless high enough to require what may be considered to be substantial investment in infrastructure, for example, $300 million for a relatively small 20 km system. Resistance to spending even this amount – low for a transit investment – would be reinforced by the novelty of PRT, which could make for a risky venture.

An AT service could deliver much of the service provided by PRT, at perhaps about the same cost to users, chiefly because passengers would stay in the same low-capacity vehicle during speedy, mostly non-stop trips from origin to destination. An AT service would have the added advantages that travel could be literally door-to-door, and there would be no new public infrastructure cost because existing roads would likely be sufficient.

AT services, requiring less infrastructure, would thus be less disruptive than PRT and, accordingly, could be more successful. Araujo et al. (2012, p. 3) concluded: 'We can glean from our knowledge of innovation that the less disruptive innovations are, the more they can make use of or insert themselves seamlessly into the existing socio-technical infrastructures, the greater their chances of success'.

If the need for a new road is apparent when AT services are established, this could be a guideway allowing powering of electrically propelled ATs from the grid while in motion. To the extent such guideways will be available, ATs' batteries can be smaller. The cost of ATs would be lower as would their energy requirements. Guideways might be constructed to achieve these benefits, as well as to separate vehicles from pedestrians and free present road space for other purposes. Over time, guideways might thus replace many roads as we know them. PRT would evolve from AT services.

Guideways that provided power to ATs and other small ARVs could be of special value for longer journeys by reducing the need to stop for battery charging or replacement. Such guideways might also be constructed where roads are needed but none exist, as in industrializing countries. However, guideway construction, which could require more than two-thirds of the above-noted all-in PRT cost of $15 million per km, may not be a good investment compared with the cost of constructing two-lane paved roads, which in poorer countries is less than $1 million per km (Queiroz, 2012).

19.11 FREIGHT MOVEMENT BY ARVs

Freight-carrying ARVs could allow revolutions in the way goods are moved. There are three main means of goods movement by road: (1) in personal automobiles; (2) by other means in urban areas; and (3) by other means between urban areas.

Much movement of goods occurs in personal automobiles, consuming a surprising share of energy used for freight movement. An analysis of the transport energy involved in moving breakfast cereal from field to table found that 80 per cent was expended in the shopping trip (WBCSD, 2001). In both the USA (NHTS, 2011) and the UK (DfT, 2012), shopping is a major purpose of travel by car, exceeding travelling to and from work in number of trips although not in distance travelled. People who use their cars for business purposes often have additional reasons to value the goods-carrying capacity of personal automobiles. If ATs were to substitute for personal automobiles, goods-carrying arrangements would be essential.

One option has been suggested above: an AT user with a lot of baggage could hire two linked ATs that would travel together to the user's destination. Another possibility would be to have a standardized 'stuff locker' (Templeton, 2012a) that fits in any AT and can be moved by hand or moved automatically to and from stationary lockers. ATs could also move items in this way without carrying passengers, as taxicabs are used today to carry small packages.

Autonomous local delivery vehicles (ALDVs) could do the same thing, carrying many containers. Such vehicles could substitute for mail and courier services if destinations were equipped to receive the standard containers. Larger items and amounts could be so delivered in appropriately sized containers, refrigerated when necessary. However, much business delivery – for example, for construction materials – may require human supervision for many more years. For reasons of energy supply and local and global pollution, ALDVs may well move to electric traction. As with ATs, fleet management of ALDVs could facilitate electrification.

Large vehicles, for example, trucks with trailers, can be automated as readily as smaller vehicles, but the path to electrification of autonomous heavy-duty vehicles (AHDVs) could be different. The primary advantage of automation for heavy-duty vehicles could be facilitation of platooning on expressways, resulting in energy savings of about a third compared with regular operation (Tsugawa, 2011).

Battery powering of heavy-duty vehicles may not be expedient. To match the range provided by the diesel fuel tank of a typical long-distance heavy-duty truck, which weighs about a tonne when full, a heavy-duty battery-powered electric-drive truck would have to carry almost 30 tonnes of battery. This is much more than the average payload of heavy-duty trucks in the USA (FHA, 2009) and Europe (de Ceuster et al., 2009). Put another way, a heavy-duty electric-drive truck would require 1–2 tonnes of battery per hour of operation.

A more feasible way of providing electric propulsion of heavy-duty trucks would be to provide power while in motion, as streetcars and trolley buses receive power. This is not a new concept. Electric trolley trucks were on German roads more than a hundred years ago (Anon, 2009). Today, they are used in mines and for other off-road uses (Adey et al., 2011). Trials of on-road trolley truck operation are underway in Germany and the USA (Siemens, 2012), and in Sweden (Ranch, 2010).

A possible scenario for much freight movement across the 500 km between Toronto and Montreal could involve electrically propelled AHDVs. Such a vehicle could leave a loading bay in Toronto under battery power, travel 10 km to the expressway connecting Toronto and Montreal, and then raise its pantograph to allow direct powering of its electric motors from the pair of wires strung over one lane. As soon as possible during expressway journey, the AHDV is marshalled automatically into a platoon of, say, four vehicles travelling a few metres apart. At Montreal, the AHDV would disengage from the platoon, exit the expressway, and travel the 10 km to its final destination under battery power.

This AHDV's energy consumption for the 500 km trip would be about a quarter of that used by one of today's trucks, chiefly on account of its electric propulsion (Gilbert and Perl, 2010). Moreover, electricity could be generated without use of fossil fuels. Energy consumption would still be higher than if the freight were sent by rail, even counting that used to move the freight the few kilometres before and after the rail trip, and very much higher than if the rail line between Toronto and Montreal were electrified (ibid.). However, with AHDVs, road transports' advantages of reliability, security and overall speed could be achieved at lower financial cost, because of reduced energy and labour costs, and lower environmental and resource costs.

Vehicle weight is an important consideration for infrastructure costs because the impact of a moving vehicle on a road surface is roughly proportional to the cube of the axle load (SDDOT, 2003). Thus, a vehicle with an axle load of 10 tonnes, which could be the case for a loaded large truck, inflicts on average about 1000 times as much damage per km travelled as a vehicle with an axle load of 1 tonne, which could be the case for a medium-sized regular automobile. Trucks are as large as possible primarily to reduce operator costs per tonne carried. If operator costs were not a consideration, there would be an opportunity to reduce truck size and thus infrastructure costs.

19.12 INFRASTRUCTURE IMPLICATIONS OF DEPLOYMENT OF ARVs

The above discussion has touched on several implications for infrastructure planning of the likely widespread deployment of ARVs, including ATs, ALDVs and AHDVs:

- Existing road space could be used much more intensively, making unnecessary the need for additional roads and road expansions, whether minor in nature or major such as the proposed $1 billion bridge between Detroit, Michigan and Windsor, Ontario, which is to supplement an existing road bridge and road tunnel.
- Nevertheless, guideways – often elevated – could be constructed to allow for reduced energy consumption and emissions, to separate road traffic from pedestrians and street activity, and free urban space.
- Continuing roads would require less maintenance because on average ARVs would be lighter and move more evenly; less maintenance would be needed especially if heavy-duty truck sizes were to be reduced by splitting loads among several lighter freight-carrying ARVs.
- There would be fewer vehicles, although more vehicles on the road at any one time; the result would be a much reduced need for parking infrastructure.
- Vehicle manufacturing would decline substantially, thereby reducing the demands of this sector for transport infrastructure.
- Except for heavy rail, whose functions would be limited to serving very high density areas, ATs could replace much public transport, thus obviating, for example, most or all of the recently begun construction of the $5 billion, 19 km Eglinton–Scarborough Crosstown light-rail line in Toronto. Scheduled for completion in 2020, this line seems unlikely – for a further decade or more – to exceed ridership achievable through an AT system on the existing roadway, which is mostly several lanes wide (Munro, 2011; Pace, 2012). A comprehensive AT service providing intercity service could even render unnecessary construction of a better-known transport mega-project: the proposed California High Speed Rail Line, planned to be over 1300 km in length and to cost more than $50 billion (CHSRA, 2012; Templeton, 2012b).
- Energy consumption in respect of vehicles, including their manufacture and use, and for the construction and maintenance of their infrastructure would be much lower, thereby reducing the demands of the energy sector for transport infrastructure.
- Extending the advantages of automation and electrification to heavy-duty long-distance road vehicles would require installation of catenaries above single lanes of expressways.
- Although ARVs will generally have sufficient 'intelligence' to move autonomously, their function would be greatly enhanced by wireless communication – V2V and V2I – which will require secure infrastructure and common standards.

In brief, the likely widespread deployment of ARVs could reduce substantially the transport infrastructure challenges faced by richer and poorer parts of the world, although relatively minor infrastructure requirements will be added.

The primary task of transport infrastructure planners in richer countries could become that of accommodating and even facilitating this coming transformation in transport activity: from the present arrangement whereby most travel is performed as a vehicle operator, to a future in which most travel is performed as a vehicle passenger. Secondary tasks would include preparing for the automation of road freight transport and for the electrification of all road transport.

Such is the promise of ARVs, infrastructure projects, including mega-projects, whose use could be obviated by widespread ARVs could well be delayed or stalled until ARVs' viability, feasibility and utility are better established.

A particular challenge if AT services become widespread could be that of sustaining the use of some rail-based public transport in order to take sufficient advantage of the investment in it. As noted above, this could apply to most light-rail installations and some of the less-used parts of heavy-rail facilities. In many cases this kind of challenge could be addressed by greatly intensifying residential and commercial development at and near stations, thereby creating circumstances where existing rail systems remain necessary.

The chief uncertainties for transport infrastructure planners are whether and – perhaps more important – when ARVs will be deployed. Here are some requirements of a possible path towards widespread use of ARVs in richer countries in the early 2020s:

- Reliability is assured by attainment during 2013 or 2014 of 2 million ARV kilometres without a crash for which the primary reason was the ARV equivalent of a driver error – beyond the present 500000-plus such kilometres – with much of the testing distance being travelled in the demanding circumstances of a Canadian winter.
- Liability issues are resolved during 2013–2014, which seems possible given that already one insurance policy covering ARVs has been issued (AutoNOMOS, 2012); and necessary legislative changes are also made during the same period.
- A company such as Google completes successful trials of AT services during 2015–2017.

The situations in poorer countries are more complex, with much variety among them. In general terms, the transport planners' tasks there could be to help bypass the current practices of richer countries and exploit as soon as possible the opportunities offered by ARVs, subject to the results of the testing regime for richer countries or similar tests. The process could be analogous to poorer countries' bypassing richer countries' telephone practices of the twentieth century and embracing mobile phones with vigour and enterprise (Anon, 2012e; Khan, 2012).

LITERATURE

Accenture (2011), 'Consumers in US and UK frustrated with intelligent devices that frequently crash or freeze, new Accenture survey finds', Accenture News Release, 10 February, accessed 28 June 2013 at http://newsroom.accenture.com/article_display.cfm?article_id=5146.

Adey, E., F. Wall, R. Shail, J. Keech, W. Neal, R. Limprasert, C. Roba and C. Delmore (2011), *Best Practice for Reducing the Carbon Footprint of the Mining Industry*, Budapest: Geonardo Ltd., accessed 30 June 2013 at http://www.impactmin.eu/downloads/impactmin_d33.pdf.

Anon (2009), 'Electric road trains in Germany, 1901–1950', *Low-tech Magazine*, 9 July, accessed 30 June 2013 at http://www.lowtechmagazine.com/2009/07/electric-road-trains-in-germany-1901-1950.html.

Anon (2011), 'Passenger transport mode shares in world cities', *Journeys* (Land Transport Authority Academy, Singapore), **7**, November, 60–70, accessed 28 June 2013 at http://ltaacademy.gov.sg/doc/J11Nov-p60PassengerTransportModeSHares.pdf.

Anon (2012a), 'Look, no hands – automotive technology: driverless cars promise to reduce road accidents, ease congestion and revolutionise transport', *The Economist*, 1 September, accessed 28 June 2013 at http://www.economist.com/news/special-report/21576224-one-day-every-car-may-come-invisible-chauffeur-look-no-hands.

Anon (2012b), 'Motorists not quite ready for driverless technology', Automotive Management Online, 30 November, at http://www.am-online.com/news/2012/11/30/motorists-not-quite-ready-for-driverless-technology/32032/.

Anon (2012c), 'This is your ground pilot speaking: autonomous civil aircraft could be flying before cars go driverless', *The Economist*, 24 November, accessed 28 June 2013 at http://www.economist.com/news/science-and-technology/21567053-autonomous-civil-aircraft-could-be-flying-cars-go-driverless-your.

Anon (2012d), 'Better Place completes battery exchange network', *Globes*, 22 August, at http://www.globes.co.il/serveen/globes/docview.asp?did=1000776245&fid=1725.

Anon (2012e), 'Mobile phone access reaches three quarters of planet's population', press release, Washington, DC: The World Bank, accessed 30 June 2013 at http://www.worldbank.org/en/news/2012/07/17/mobile-phone-access-reaches-three-quarters-planets-population.

Araujo L., K. Mason and M. Spring (2012), *Self-driving Cars: A Case Study in Making New Markets*, London, UK: BIG Innovation Centre, accessed 30 June 2013 at http://www.mbsportal.bl.uk/taster/subjareas/techinnov/bic/143511selfdrivingcars12.pdf.

Ashley, S. (2008), 'Driving towards crashless cars', *Scientific American*, **299**(6), 86–94.

AutoNOMOS (2012), 'Frequently asked questions about the AutoNOMOS project', accessed 30 June 2013 at http://www.autonomos.inf.fu-berlin.de/faq.

Beiker, S.A. (2012), 'Legal aspects of autonomous driving', *Santa Clara Law Review*, **52**(4), 1145–56, accessed 28 June 2013 at http://digitalcommons.law.scu.edu/cgi/viewcontent.cgi?article=2726&context=lawreview.

Benenson, R., S. Petti, T. Franchard and M. Parent (2008), 'Towards urban driverless vehicles', *International Journal of Vehicle Autonomous Systems*, **6**(1), 4–23.

Berger, C. and B. Rumpe (2012), 'Autonomous driving – 5 years after the urban challenge:

the anticipatory vehicle as a cyber-physical system', *Proceedings of the INFORMATIK 2012*, Bonn, Germany: Gesellschaft für Informatik, accessed 28 June 2013 at http://www.se-rwth.de/publications/BR12b.pdf.

Brandom, R. (2012), 'Self-driving cars can navigate the road, but can they navigate the law?', The Verge, 14 December, accessed 30 June 2013 at http://www.theverge.com/2012/12/14/3766218/self-driving-cars-google-volvo-law.

Burns, L.D., W.C. Jordan and B.A. Scarborough (2013), 'Transforming personal mobility', New York: The Earth Institute, Columbia University, 27 January, accessed 29 June 2013 at http://sustainablemobility.ei.columbia.edu/files/2012/12/Transforming-Personal-Mobility-Jan-27-20132.pdf.

CAA (2012), 'Driving costs', Ottawa, Ontario: Canadian Automobile Association, accessed 28 June 2013 at http://www.caa.ca/docs/eng/CAA_Driving_Costs_English.pdf.

Campbell, M., M. Egerstedt, J.P. How and R.M. Murray (2010), 'Autonomous driving in urban environments: approaches, lessons and challenges', *Philosophical Transactions of the Royal Society A*, **368**(1928), 4649–72, accessed 28 June 2013 at http://rsta.royalsocietypublishing.org/content/368/1928/4649.full.pdf+html.

Carnegie, J.A. and P.S. Hoffman (2007), *Viability of Personal Rapid Transit in New Jersey*, report prepared for the New Jersey Department of Transportation and NJ TRANSIT, accessed 28 June 2013 at http://www.njstatelib.org/digit/t764/t7642007z.pdf.

Chopra, S. and P. Bauer (2013), 'Driving range extension of EV with on-road contactless power transfer, a case study', *IEEE Transactions on Industrial Electronics*, **60**(1), 329–38.

CHSRA (2012), 'California High-Speed Rail Program revised 2012 business plan', Sacramento, CA: California High-Speed Rail Authority, accessed 30 June 2013 at http://www.cahighspeedrail.ca.gov/assets/0/152/431/1a6251d7-36ab-4fec-ba8c-00e266dadec7.pdf.

Davis, B. and T. Dutzik (2012), 'Transportation and the new generation', Santa Barbara, CA: Frontier Group, accessed 28 June 2013 at http://www.uspirg.org/reports/usp/transport ation-and-new-generation.

Davis, S.C., S.W. Diegel and R.G. Boundy (2012), *Transport Energy Data Book*, 31st edition, Oak Ridge, TN: Oak Ridge National Laboratory, accessed 30 June 2013 at http://cta.ornl.gov/data/index.shtml.

DCMW (2012), 'Driverless car market watch', website, accessed 28 June 2013 at http://www.driverless-future.com/.

de Ceuster, G., T. Breemersch, B. van Herbruggen, K. Verweij, I. Davydenko, M. Klingender, B. Jacob, H. Arki and M. Bereni (2009), *Effects of Adapting the Rules on Weights and Dimensions of Heavy Commercial Vehicles as Established Within Directive 96/53/EC*, Brussels: EU Directorate-General Energy and Transport, at http://ec.europa.eu/transport/themes/strategies/studies/doc/2009_01_weights_and_dimensions_vehicles.pdf.

Deloitte (2011), 'Unplugged: electric vehicle realities versus consumer expectations', London: Deloitte Touche Tohmatsu Ltd., accessed 30 June 2013 at http://www.deloitte.com/view/en_US/us/Industries/Automotive-Manufacturing/f769ebb8bf4b2310VgnVCM1000001a56f00aRCRD.htm.

DfT (2012), 'Transport statistics Great Britain 2012', London: Department for Transport, accessed 30 June 2013 at https://www.gov.uk/government/uploads/system/uploads/attachment_data/file/36546/TSGB_2012.zip.

Dickmanns, E.D. (2002), 'The development of machine vision for road vehicles in the last decade', *Proceedings of the IEEE Intelligent Vehicle Symposium*, Piscataway, NJ: Institute of Electrical and Electronics Engineers.

Douma, F. and S.A. Palodichuk (2012), 'Criminal liability issues created by autonomous vehicles', *Santa Clara Law Review*, **52**(4), 1157–69, accessed 29 June 2013 at http://digitalcommons.law.scu.edu/cgi/viewcontent.cgi?article=2727&context=lawreview.

Duxbury, C. and J.D. Stoll (2012), 'Volvo plans to roll out self-driving cars in 2014', *Wall Street Journal*, 3 December, accessed 22 June 2013 at http://blogs.wsj.com/drivers-seat/2012/12/03/volvo-plans-to-roll-out-self-driving-cars-in-2014/.

EC (2011), *Roadmap to a Single European Transport Area*, Brussels: European

Commission, accessed 28 June 2013 at http://ec.europa.eu/transport/themes/strategies/2011_white_paper_en.htm.

Element Energy (2012), 'Ground-breaking battery research published', prepared for the Committee on Climate Change (UK), Cambridge, UK: Element Energy Ltd., accessed 30 June 2013 at http://www.element-energy.co.uk/2012/04/ground-breaking-battery-research-published/.

FHA (2009), 'Development of truck payload equivalent factor', Washington, DC: Federal Highway Administration, accessed 30 June 2013 at http://ops.fhwa.dot.gov/freight/freight_analysis/faf/faf2_reports/reports9/s501_2_3_tables.htm.

Folsom, T.C. (2012), 'Energy and autonomous urban land vehicles', *IEEE Technology and Society Magazine*, **31**(2), 28–38.

Ford, H.J. (2012), 'Shared autonomous taxis: implementing an efficient alternative to automobile dependency', Bachelor of Science and Engineering thesis (Alain Kornhauser, supervisor), Princeton University, NJ, accessed 28 June 2013 at http://orfe.princeton.edu/~alaink/Ford,%20Hillary%20Final%20Thesis.pdf.

Fountain, H. (2012), 'Yes, driverless cars know the way to San Jose', *New York Times*, 26 October, accessed 28 June 2013 at http://www.nytimes.com/2012/10/28/automobiles/yes-driverless-cars-know-the-way-to-san-jose.html.

Gelertner, D. (1995), *1939: The Lost World of the Fair*, New York: Free Press.

Gerssen-Gondelach, S.J. and A.P.C. Faaij (2012), 'Performance of batteries for electric vehicles on short and longer term', *Journal of Power Sources*, **212**, 111–29.

Gilbert, R. (2012), 'What we missed in the global energy report', *Globe and Mail*, 21 November, accessed 30 June 2013 at http://www.theglobeandmail.com/report-on-business/economy/economy-lab/what-we-missed-in-the-global-energy-report/article5517963/.

Gilbert, R. and A. Perl (2010), *Transport Revolutions: Moving People and Freight Without Oil*, 2nd edition, Gabriola Island, British Columbia: New Society Publishers.

Google (2012), 'The self-driving car logs more miles on new wheels', Google Official Blog, 7 August, accessed 28 June 2013 at http://googleblog.blogspot.ca/2012/08/the-self-driving-car-logs-more-miles-on.html.

Grush, B. (2012), 'Kiss your bus goodbye!', *Traffic Technology International*, August/September, accessed 28 June 2013 at http://viewer.zmags.com/publication/45672367.

Guerra, E. and R. Cervero (2011), 'Cost of a ride', *Journal of the American Planning Association*, **77**(3), 267–90.

Helft, M. (2012), 'Fortune exclusive: Larry Page on Google', CNNMoney, 11 December, accessed 28 June 2013 at http://tech.fortune.cnn.com/2012/12/11/larry-page/.

Hornyak, T. (2012), 'Japan eyes driverless cars by early 2020s', CNET, 30 June, accessed 28 June 2013 at http://news.cnet.com/8301-17938_105-57464359-1/japan-eyes-driverless-cars-by-early-2020s/.

IEEE (2012), 'Look Ma, no hands!', press release, Piscataway, NJ: Institute of Electrical and Electronics Engineers, 2 September, accessed 28 June 2013 at http://www.ieee.org/about/news/2012/5september_2_2012.html.

ITF (2012), *Transport Outlook 2012: Seamless Transport for Greener Growth*. Paris: International Transport Forum, accessed 28 June 2013 at http://www.internationaltransportforum.org/Pub/pdf/12Outlook.pdf.

Joseph, J. (2012), 'Volvo stepping up to rival Google in autonomous car technology', Digital Trends (website), 7 December, accessed 28 June 2013 at http://www.digitaltrends.com/cars/volvo-stepping-up-to-rival-google-in-autonomous-car-technology/.

Kane, S. (2011), 'Family cars with self-parking technology', The Car Connection, 27 October, accessed 28 June 2013 at http://www.thecarconnection.com/news/1067819_2012-family-cars-with-self-parking-technology.

Khan, Z. (2012), 'Cloud commuting enabling entrepreneurship in Africa', 20 December, accessed 3 July 2013 at http://googleblog.blogspot.ca/2012/12/cloud-computing-enabling.html.

Kornhauser, A.L. (2012), 'The role of automation in revolutionizing public transportation', presentation at a workshop on the 'Future of Road Vehicle Automation' organized by the Transportation Research Board, Irvine, CA, 24–26 July, at http://onlinepubs.trb.org/onlinepubs/conferences/2012/Automation/presentations/Kornhauser.pdf.

Lavrinc, D. (2013), 'Toyota inches oh so cautiously toward autonomous tech', *Wired*, 7 January, accessed 28 June 2013 at http://www.wired.com/autopia/2013/01/ces-2013-toyota-lexus/.

Lienert, A. (2011), 'GM says self-driving vehicles are on horizon', *Edmunds Inside Line*, 17 October, accessed 28 June 2013 at http://www.insideline.com/chevrolet/gm-says-self-driving-vehicles-are-on-horizon.html.

Luettel T., M. Himmelsbach and H-J. Wuensche (2012), 'Autonomous ground vehicles – concepts and a path to the future', *Proceedings of the IEEE*, **100**, 1831–9, accessed 28 June 2013 at http://www.mucar3.de/bib/thlu/luettel2012ieeeproc.pdf.

Marchant, G.E. and R.A. Lindor (2012), 'The coming collision between autonomous vehicles and the liability', *Santa Clara Law Review*, **52**(4), 1321–40, accessed 28 June 2013 at http://digitalcommons.law.scu.edu/cgi/viewcontent.cgi?article=2731&context=lawreview.

Marks, P. (2012), 'Autonomous cars ready to hit our roads', *New Scientist*, **213**(2858), 19–20.

Meyer, A.G. and R. Morache (2010), *Feasibility of Personal Rapid Transit in Ithaca*, report prepared for the New York State Energy Research and Development Authority and the New York State Department of Transportation, accessed 30 June 2013 at https://www.dot.ny.gov/divisions/engineering/technical-services/trans-r-and-d-repository/C-08-25%20Ithaca%20PRT%20Final%20Report%2009-30-10.pdf.

Mitchell, W.J., C.E. Borroni-Bird and L.D. Burns (2010), *Reinventing the Automobile: Personal Urban Mobility for the 21st Century*, Cambridge, MA: The MIT Press.

Mosher, D. (2012), 'Google's Sebastian Thrun: 3 visions in the age of disruption', *Wired*, 1 May, accessed 30 June 2013 at http://www.wired.com/business/2012/05/google-sebastian-thrun-future/.

Munro, S. (2011), 'How many riders will use the Crosstown?', 15 July, accessed 30 June 2013 at http://stevemunro.ca/?p=5461.

Murray, J. and D. King (2012), 'Climate policy: oil's tipping point has passed', *Nature*, **481**(7382), 433–5.

Nashashibi, F., F. Charlot, C. Holguin, M. Parent and L. Bouraoui (2012), 'A cooperative personal automated transport system', *Proceedings of the IEEE International Conference on Control*, Automation, Robotics and Vision (ICARCV), Piscataway, NJ: Institute of Electrical and Electronics Engineers, accessed 28 June 2013 at http://hal.inria.fr/hal-00732860/PDF/P0564.pdf.

NHTS (2011), 'National Household Travel Survey: online analysis tools', Oak Ridge, TN: Oak Ridge National Laboratory, accessed 30 June 2013 at http://nhts.ornl.gov/.

NHTSA (2008), *National Motor Vehicle Crash Causation Survey: Report to Congress*, Washington, DC: National Technical Information Service, accessed 28 June 2013 at http://www-nrd.nhtsa.dot.gov/Pubs/811059.PDF.

NHTSA (2012), 'CAFE – fuel economy', Washington, DC: National Highway Traffic Safety Administration, accessed 30 June 2013 at http://www.nhtsa.gov/fuel-economy.

NRCan (2011), *Energy Efficiency Trends in Canada, 1990 to 2009*, Ottawa, Ontario: Natural Resources Canada, accessed 28 June 2013 at http://oee.nrcan.gc.ca/publications/statistics/trends11/pdf/trends.pdf.

OECD (2012), *Strategic Transport Infrastructure Needs to 2030*, Paris: Organisation for Economic Co-operation and Development, accessed 28 June 2013 at http://www.oecd.org/document/46/0,3746,en_2649_36240452_49830126_1_1_1_1,00.html.

Pace, A. (2012), 'Eglinton–Scarborough Crosstown LRT update', 28 February, accessed 30 June 2013 at http://www.thecrosstown.ca/sites/default/files/Eglinton-Scarborough_Crosstown-LRT-Update_reduced.pdf.

Page, L. (2009), 'Commencement address', University of Michigan, 2 May, accessed 28 June 2013 at http://googlepress.blogspot.ca/2009/05/larry-pages-university-of-michigan.html.

Peden, M., R. Scurfield, D. Sleet, D. Mohan, A.A. Hyder, E. Jarawan and C. Mathers (2004), *World Report on Road Traffic Injury Prevention*, Geneva: World Health Organization, accessed 28 June 2013 at http://www.who.int/violence_injury_prevention/publications/road_traffic/world_report/en/index.html.

Peterson, R.W. (2012), 'New technology – old law: autonomous vehicles and California's insurance framework', *Santa Clara Law Review*, **52**(4), 1341–99, accessed 30 June 2013 at http://digitalcommons.law.scu.edu/cgi/viewcontent.cgi?article=2732&context=lawreview.

PHAC (2012), *Injury in Review, 2012 Edition: Spotlight on Road and Transport Safety*, Ottawa, ON: Public Health Agency of Canada, accessed 28 June 2013 at http://www.phac-aspc.gc.ca/injury-bles/chirpp/injrep-rapbles/ir-eb-2012-eng.php.

Proudfoot, D. (2012), 'BMW working to lead the charge: company looks to new technology to keep drivers engaged', *Globe and Mail*, 6 December, accessed 28 June 2013 at http://www.theglobeandmail.com/globe-drive/green-driving/news-and-notes/bmw-working-to-lead-the-electric-charge/article5997162/.

Queiroz, C. (2012), 'Monitoring road works contracts and unit costs in Sub-Saharan Africa for enhanced governance', presentation at a Construction and Maintenance Unit Costs Workshop, World Bank, Sub-Saharan Africa Transport Policy Program, accessed 30 June 2013 at http://siteresources.worldbank.org/EXTAFRSUBSAHTRA/Resources/1513929-1220884726175/Road-Works-Contracts-Quieros.ppt.

Ranch, P. (2010), *Elektriska vägar – elektrifiering av tunga vägtransporter* [*Electric Roads – The Electrification of Heavy Road Transport*], Stockholm, Sweden: Grontmij AB, accessed 30 June 2013 at http://www.elvag.se/blogg/wp-content/uploads/2010/05/F%C3%B6rstudie.pdf.

Rimouski (2012), 'Traffic and public transportation', Rimouski, QC: Ville de Rimouski, accessed 28 June 2013 athttp://www.ville.rimouski.qc.ca/en/citoyens/nav/circulation/Rimouskibus.html#citebus.

Santos, A., N. McGuckin, H.Y. Nakamoto, D. Gray and S. Liss (2011), *Summary of Travel Trends: 2009 National Household Travel Survey*, Washington, DC: Federal Highway Administration, accessed 30 June 2013 at http://nhts.ornl.gov/2009/pub/stt.pdf.

Schaller (2006), *The New York City Taxicab Fact Book*, Brooklyn, NY: Schaller Consulting, accessed 30 June 2013 at http://www.schallerconsult.com/taxi/taxifb.pdf.

SDDOT (2003), 'Truck weights and highways', Aberdeen, SD: South Dakota Department of Transportation, accessed 30 June 2013 at http://www.sddot.com/resources/Brochures/sddot_truck_briefing_2d.pdf.

Sharma, B.R. (2008), 'Road traffic injuries: a major public health crisis', *Public Health*, **122**(12), 1399–1406.

Siemens (2012), 'Electric-powered road freight traffic', Munich: Siemens AG, accessed 30 June 2013 at http://www.mobility.siemens.com/mobility/global/en/interurban-mobility/road-solutions/electric-powered-hgv-traffic-ehighway/pages/electric-powered-hgv-traffic-ehighway.aspx.

Silberg, G. and R. Wallace (2012), '*Self-driving Cars: The Next Revolution*, Amstelveen, Netherlands: KPMG, and Ann Arbor, MI: Center for Automotive Research, accessed 30 June at https://www.kpmg.com/US/en/IssuesAndInsights/ArticlesPublications/Documents/self-driving-cars-next-revolution.pdf.

Squatriglia, C. (2012), 'California lawmaker wants rules for robo-cars', *Wired*, 29 February, accessed 28 June 2013 at http://www.wired.com/autopia/2012/02/padilla-robo-cars-sb-1298/#more-43198.

STM (2012), '*Taxibus*', Montreal, QC: Société de transport de Montréal, accessed 28 June 2013 at http://www.stm.info/english/info/a-taxi.htm.

Sun, Z., G. Bebis and R. Miller (2006), 'On-road vehicle detection: a review', *IEEE Transactions on Pattern Analysis and Machine Intelligence*, **28**(5), 694–711.

Tam, D. (2012), 'Google's Sergey Brin: you'll ride in robot cars within 5 years', CNET, 25 September, accessed 28 June 2013 at http://news.cnet.com/8301-11386_3-57520188-76/googles-sergey-brin-youll-ride-in-robot-cars-within-5-years/.

Templeton, B. (2012a), 'Where robot cars (robocars) can really take us', accessed 28 June 2013 at http://www.templetons.com/brad/robocars/.

Templeton, B. (2012b), 'Can high speed rail compete with self-driven cars, improved airlines and all the technology of the future?', Forbes/Singularity University, 4 September, accessed 28 June 2013 at http://www.forbes.com/sites/singularity/2012/09/04/can-high-speed-rail-compete-with-self-driven-cars-improved-airlines-and-all-the-technology-of-the-future/.

Transport Canada (2011), 'Canadian motor vehicle traffic collision statistics: 2009', Ottawa, ON: Transport Canada, accessed 28 June 2013 at http://www.tc.gc.ca/eng/roadsafety/tp-tp3322-2009-1173.htm.

Tsugawa, S. (2008), 'A history of automated highway systems in Japan and future issues', *Proceedings of the 2008 IEEE International Conference on Vehicular Electronics and Safety*, Columbus, Ohio, 22–24 September, Piscataway, NJ: Institute of Electrical and Electronics Engineers.

Tsugawa, S. (2011), 'An automated truck platoon for energy saving', *Proceedings of the 2011 IEEE/RSJ International Conference on Intelligent Robots and Systems*, Piscataway, NJ: Institute of Electrical and Electronics Engineers, pp. 4109–14.

ULTra (2012), 'Heathrow announces plans for an additional Personal Rapid Transit (PRT) system', Bristol: ULTra Global accessed 30 June 2013 at http://www.ultraglobalprt.com/heathrow-announces-plans-additional-personal-rapid-transit-prt-system-heathrow/.

Van den Bulk (2012), 'Costs of the electric car; Veldhoven: Olino Labs, accessed 30 June at http://www.olino.org/us/articles/2009/02/17/costs-of-the-electric-car.

Vanderbilt, T. (2012a), 'Let the robot drive: the autonomous car of the future is here', *Wired*, 20 January, accessed 28 June 2013 at http://www.wired.com/magazine/2012/01/ff_autonomouscars/.

Vanderbilt, T. (2012b), 'Autonomous cars through the ages', *Wired*, 6 February, accessed 28 June 2013 at http://www.wired.com/autopia/2012/02/autonomous-vehicle-history/?pid=1577.

Vandycke, N.L. and L. Wright (2012), *Urban Mass Transport Infrastructure in Medium and Large Cities in Developing Countries*, Washington, DC: The World Bank, accessed 28 June 2013 at http://documents.worldbank.org/curated/en/2012/01/16432315/urban-mass-transport-infrastructure-medium-large-cities-developing-countries.

Vijayenthiran, V. (2011), '2013 Mercedes-Benz S-Class to debut autonomous driving system', High Gear Media, 14 November, accessed 28 June 2013 at http://www.motorauthority.com/news/1068584_2013-mercedes-benz-s-class-to-debut-autonomous-driving-system.

Wagner, C. and T. Mendle (2012), 'Große Akzeptanz für selbstfahrende Autos in Deutschland' [Wide acceptance of self-driving cars in Germany], Motorvision, 9 October, accessed 29 June 2013 at http://www.motorvision.de/service-ratgeber/selbstfahrende-autos-deutschland-22-prozent-deutschen-grosse-akzeptanz-roboterfahrzeuge-39281.html.

Walker, J. (2012), *Human Transit: How Clear Thinking About Public Transit can Enrich our Communities and our Lives*, Washington, DC: Island Press.

WBCSD (2001), *Mobility 2001: World Mobility at the End of the 20th Century*, Geneva, Switzerland: World Business Council for Sustainable Development, accessed 30 June 2013 at http://www.wbcsd.org/Pages/EDocument/EDocumentDetails.aspx?ID=105&NoSearchContextKey=true.

WEC (2011), *Global Transport Scenarios*, London: World Energy Council, accessed 28 June 2013 at http://www.worldenergy.org/documents/wec_transport_scenarios_2050.pdf.

Wolford, J. (2012), 'Florida political ad suggests that self-driving cars will be the death of grandma', WebProNews/Technology, 13 August, accessed 28 June 2013 at http://www.webpronews.com/florida-political-ad-suggests-that-self-driving-cars-will-be-the-death-of-grandma-2012-08.

Yvkoff, L. (2012), 'Many car buyers show interest in autonomous car tech', CNET, 27 April, accessed 28 June 2013 at http://reviews.cnet.com/8301-13746_7-57422698-48/many-car-buyers-show-interest-in-autonomous-car-tech/.

Index